FEATURES AND BENEFITS
Core-Plus Mathematics, Course 1 TEACHER'S GUIDE PART B ©2015

Content and Organization

See page(s):

- Introduction and Organization of Course 1 — v–xii
- Access, Equity, and Differentiation — xii
- Implementing the Curriculum — xiii–xix
- CCSS Alignment and Pathway — xxiii–xxviii

Student and Teacher Friendly

- Engaging student-centered applications invite students to read and do more mathematics on their own. Read *Exponential Decay* and *Medicine and Mathematics*. — 322–323, 326
- Lesson development organizes problems for students into easy-to-understand instructions. See *High Punkin' Chunkin* Problems 3 to 7. — 465–467
- Full-color *Student Edition* page presented alongside *Teacher's Guide* page for easy reference. — 428–T428
- Effective *Teacher's Guide* design provides point-of-use support to make it easier for you to focus on formative assessment as students complete investigations. — 297–T297A

Extensive and Varied Practice

- **Applications** tasks help students use and apply ideas from each lesson. — 307–312
- **Connections** tasks connect each lesson's topics with other mathematics students know. — 483–484
- **Reflections** tasks help students recognize the mathematical practices and habits of mind they employed in the lesson, avoid developing misconceptions, and rethink key ideas that were developed in the lesson. — 316
- **Extensions** tasks provide opportunities to explore further or more deeply important ideas developed in the lesson. — 347–348
- **Review** tasks help students maintain important skills and review prerequisite skills needed for subsequent investigation(s). — 422–423

Formative Assessment and Test Preparation

- **Think About This Situation** assesses students' prior knowledge and motivates the lesson. — 323
- **Summarizing the Mathematics** assesses students' ability to correctly articulate the mathematics developed after each investigation in the lesson. — 431
- **Check Your Understanding** assesses students' ability to solve problems based upon the mathematics developed in each investigation in the lesson. — 303
- **Looking Back** lessons help students review and synthesize key ideas that were developed in the unit. — 456–460
- **Practicing for Standardized Tests** helps students prepare for standardized assessments that include multiple-choice items. — T359A, URM 361

Technology

- *CPMP-Tools*® expands student access to technology so that they are able to select and use appropriate tools strategically. — xiv
- ConnectED is an online education resource built with the teacher in mind, and students can instantly access the entire student edition of their textbook anytime, anywhere online! Within ConnectED are:
  - Student eBook making the Core-Plus Mathematics Project available on any web browser
  - Teacher and student resources for printing or digital deployment
  - Student management and collaboration space for online work
  - eAssessment to create custom assessment for print online/ eAssessment will also deploy and grade assessments online

CCSS COMMON CORE EDITION

COURSE
1

CORE-PLUS
MATHEMATICS
Contemporary Mathematics in Context

Christian R. Hirsch • James T. Fey • Eric W. Hart
Harold L. Schoen • Ann E. Watkins

Beth E. Ritsema • Rebecca K. Walker • Brin A. Keller
Robin Marcus • Arthur F. Coxford

McGraw Hill Education

Cover (tl)Pixtal/AGE Fotostock, (tr)Marty Honig/Getty Images, (bl)Image Source/Alamy (br)Stockbyte/Getty Images

mheonline.com

This material is based upon work supported, in part, by the National Science Foundation under grant no. ESI 0137718. Opinions expressed are those of the authors and not necessarily those of the Foundation.

Send all inquiries to:
McGraw-Hill Education
STEM Learning Solutions Center
8787 Orion Place
Columbus, OH 43240

ISBN: 978-0-07-665797-1
MHID: 0-07-665797-3

Core-Plus Mathematics
Contemporary Mathematics in Context
Course 1 Teacher Edition, Part A

ISBN: 978-0-07-665798-8
MHID: 0-07-665798-1

Core-Plus Mathematics
Contemporary Mathematics in Context
Course 1 Teacher Edition, Part B

Printed in the United States of America.

2 3 4 5 6 7 8 9 QVS 17 16 15 14

Common Core State Standards© Copyright 2010.
National Governors Association Center for Best
Practices and Council of Chief State School Officers.
All rights reserved.

McGraw-Hill is committed to providing instructional materials in Science, Technology, Engineering, and Mathematics (STEM) that give all students a solid foundation, one that prepares them for college and careers in the 21st century.

Core-Plus Mathematics Development Team

Senior Curriculum Developers

Christian R. Hirsch (Director)
Western Michigan University

James T. Fey (Emeritus)
University of Maryland

Eric W. Hart
Maharishi University of Management

Harold L. Schoen (Emeritus)
University of Iowa

Ann E. Watkins
California State University, Northridge

Contributing Curriculum Developers

Beth E. Ritsema
Western Michigan University

Rebecca K. Walker
Grand Valley State University

Brin A. Keller
Michigan State University

Robin Marcus
University of Maryland

Arthur F. Coxford (deceased)
University of Michigan

Principal Evaluator

Steven W. Ziebarth
Western Michigan University

Advisory Board

Diane Briars (formerly)
Pittsburgh Public Schools

Jeremy Kilpatrick
University of Georgia

Robert E. Megginson
University of Michigan

Kenneth Ruthven
University of Cambridge

David A. Smith
Duke University

Mathematical Consultants

Deborah Hughes-Hallett
University of Arizona

Stephen B. Maurer
Swarthmore College

William McCallum
University of Arizona

Doris Schattschneider
Moravian College

Richard Scheaffer
University of Florida

Evaluation Consultant

Norman L. Webb
University of Wisconsin-Madison

Collaborating Teachers

Mary Jo Messenger
Howard Country Public Schools, Maryland

Valerie Mills
Oakland County Schools, Michigan

Jacqueline Stewart
Okemos, Michigan

Technical and Production Coordinator

James Laser
Western Michigan University

Support Staff

Angela Reiter
Hope Smith
Matthew Tuley
Teresa Ziebarth
Western Michigan University

Graduate Assistants

Allison BrckaLorenz
Christopher Hlas
University of Iowa

Michael Conklin
University of Maryland

Jodi Edington
AJ Edson
Nicole L. Fonger
Karen Fonkert
Dana Grosser
Anna Kruizenga
Diane Moore
Western Michigan University

Undergraduate Assistants

Cassie Durgin
University of Maryland

Rachael Lund
Jessica Tucker
Ashley Wiersma
Western Michigan University

Core-Plus Mathematics, CCSS Edition
Field-Test Sites

The CCSS Edition of *Core-Plus Mathematics* builds on the strengths of the 1st and 2nd editions, which were shaped by multi-year field tests in 49 schools in Alaska, California, Colorado, Georgia, Idaho, Iowa, Kentucky, Michigan, Missouri, Ohio, South Carolina, Texas, and Wisconsin. Each text is the product of a three-year cycle of research and development, pilot testing and refinement, and field testing and further refinement. Special thanks are extended to the following teachers and their students who participated in the most recent testing and evaluation of Course 1.

Hickman High School
Columbia, Missouri
Peter Doll

Holland Christian High School
Holland, Michigan
Jeff Goorhouse
Tim Laverell
Brian Lemmen
Mike Verkaik

Jefferson Junior High School
Columbia, Missouri
Marla Clowe
Lori Kilfoil
Martha McCabe
Paul Rahmoeller
Evan Schilling

Malcolm Price Lab School
Cedar Falls, Iowa
James Maltas
Josh Wilkinson

North Shore Middle School
Holland, Michigan
Brenda Katerberg
Sheila Schippers

Oakland Junior High School
Columbia, Missouri
Teresa Barry
Erin Little
Christine Sedgwick
Dana Sleeth

Riverside University High School
Milwaukee, Wisconsin
Cheryl Brenner
Alice Lanphier
Ela Kiblawi

Rock Bridge High School
Columbia, Missouri
Nancy Hanson

Sauk Prairie High School
Prairie du Sac, Wisconsin
Joel Amidon
Shane Been
Kent Jensen
Scott Schutt
Dan Tess
Mary Walz

Sauk Prairie Middle School
Sauk City, Wisconsin
Julie Dahlman
Janine Jorgensen

South Shore Middle School
Holland, Michigan
Lynn Schipper

Washington High School
Milwaukee, Wisconsin
Anthony Amoroso
Debbie French

West Junior High School
Columbia, Missouri
Josephus Johnson
Rachel Lowery
Mike Rowson
Amanda Schoenfeld
Patrick Troup

Introduction

The first three courses in *Core-Plus Mathematics* provide a significant common core of broadly useful mathematics aligned with the Common Core State Standards for Mathematics (CCSS) and intended for all students. They were developed to prepare students for success in college, in careers, and in daily life in contemporary society. *Course 4: Preparation for Calculus* continues the preparation of STEM-oriented (science, technology, engineering, and mathematics) students for success in college mathematics, especially calculus.

A separate alternative fourth-year capstone course, *Transition to College Mathematics and Statistics*, is intended for the large number of students planning to major in college programs that do *not* require calculus.

Core-Plus Mathematics is a problem-based, inquiry-oriented program that builds upon the theme of mathematics as reasoning and sense-making. Through investigations of real-life contexts, students develop a rich understanding of important mathematics that makes sense to them and which, in turn, enables them to make sense out of new situations and problems.

Each of the first three courses in *Core-Plus Mathematics* shares the following mathematical and instructional features.

• Integrated Content

Each year the curriculum advances students' understanding of mathematics along interwoven strands of algebra and functions, statistics and probability, geometry and trigonometry, and discrete mathematics. These strands are unified by fundamental themes, by common topics, by mathematical practices, and by mathematical habits of mind. Developing mathematics each year along multiple strands helps students develop a connected understanding of mathematics and nurtures their differing strengths and talents.

• Mathematical Modeling

The problem-based curriculum emphasizes mathematical modeling including the processes of data collection, representation, interpretation, prediction, and simulation. The modeling perspective permits students to experience mathematics as a means of making sense of data and problems that arise in diverse contexts within and across cultures.

• Access and Challenge

The curriculum is designed to make mathematics accessible to more students while at the same time challenging the most able students. Differences in student performance and interest can be accommodated by the depth and level of abstraction to which core topics are pursued, by the nature and degree of difficulty of applications, and by providing opportunities for student choice of homework tasks and projects.

- ## Technology

  Numeric, graphic, and symbolic manipulation capabilities such as those found in *CPMP-Tools®* and on many graphing calculators are assumed and appropriately used throughout the curriculum. *CPMP-Tools* is a suite of software tools that provide powerful aids to learning mathematics and solving mathematical problems. (See pages xiv–xv for further details.) This use of technology permits the curriculum and instruction to emphasize multiple linked representations (verbal, numerical, graphical, and symbolic) and to focus on goals in which mathematical thinking and problem solving are central.

- ## Active Learning

  Instructional materials promote active learning and teaching centered around collaborative investigations of problem situations followed by teacher-led whole-class summarizing activities that lead to analysis, abstraction, and further application of underlying mathematical ideas and principles. Students are actively engaged in exploring, conjecturing, verifying, generalizing, applying, proving, evaluating, and communicating mathematical ideas.

- ## Multi-dimensional Assessment

  Comprehensive assessment of student understanding and progress through both curriculum-embedded formative assessment opportunities and summative assessment tasks support instruction and enable monitoring and evaluation of each student's performance in terms of mathematical processes, content, and dispositions.

Integrated Mathematics

Core-Plus Mathematics is an international-like curriculum. It replaces the traditional Algebra-Geometry-Advanced Algebra/Trigonometry-Precalculus sequence of high school mathematics courses with a sequence of courses that features a coherent and connected development of important mathematics drawn from four strands.

Algebra and Functions

The *Algebra and Functions* strand develops student ability to recognize, represent, and solve problems involving relations among quantitative variables. Central to the development is the use of functions as mathematical models. The key algebraic models in the curriculum are linear, exponential, power, polynomial, logarithmic, rational, and trigonometric functions. Modeling with systems of equations, both linear and nonlinear, is developed. Attention is also given to symbolic reasoning and manipulation.

Geometry and Trigonometry

The primary goal of the *Geometry and Trigonometry* strand is to develop visual thinking and ability to construct, reason with, interpret, and apply mathematical models of patterns in visual and physical contexts. The focus is on describing patterns in shape, size, and location; representing patterns with drawings, coordinates, or vectors; predicting changes and invariants in shapes under transformations; and organizing geometric facts and relationships through deductive reasoning.

Statistics and Probability

The primary goal of the *Statistics and Probability* strand is to develop student ability to analyze data intelligently, to recognize and measure variation, and to understand the patterns that underlie probabilistic situations. The ultimate goal is for students to understand how inferences can be made about a population by looking at a sample from that population. Graphical methods of data analysis, simulations, sampling, and experience with the collection and interpretation of real data are featured.

Discrete Mathematical Modeling

The *Discrete Mathematics* strand develops student ability to solve problems using recursion, matrices, vertex-edge graphs, and systematic counting methods (combinatorics). Key themes are discrete mathematical modeling, optimization, and algorithmic problem-solving.

Connected Strands

Each of these strands of mathematics is developed within focused units connected by fundamental ideas such as functions, matrices, symmetry, data analysis, and curve-fitting. The strands also are connected across units by CCSS mathematical practices and by mathematical habits of mind.

These important mathematical practices include disposition toward, and proficiency in:

- making sense of problems and persevering in solving them
- reasoning both quantitatively and algebraically
- constructing sound arguments and critiquing the reasoning of others
- using mathematics to model problems in everyday life, society, and in careers
- selecting and using appropriate tools, especially technological tools (graphing calculator, spreadsheet, computer algebra system, statistical packages, and dynamic geometry software)
- communicating precisely and expressing calculations with an appropriate precision
- searching for and making use of patterns or structure in mathematical situations
- identifying structure in repeated calculations, algebraic manipulation, and reasoning

Additionally, mathematical habits of mind such as visual thinking, recursive thinking, searching for and explaining patterns, making and checking conjectures, reasoning with multiple representations, inventing mathematics, and providing convincing justifications are integral to each strand.

Important mathematical ideas are frequently revisited through this attention to connections within and across strands, enabling students to develop a robust and connected understanding of, and proficiency with, mathematics.

Instructional Model

The manner in which students encounter mathematical ideas can contribute significantly to the quality of their learning and the depth of their understanding. *Core-Plus Mathematics* is designed so that students engage in the mathematical behaviors identified in the

CCSS Standards for Mathematical Practices as the primary vehicle for learning the mathematics and statistics elaborated in the CCSS content standards. This is evident in the instructional model described below. Each lesson includes 2–5 focused mathematical investigations that engage students in a four-phase cycle of classroom activities, described in the following paragraph—*Launch, Explore, Share and Summarize*, and *Self-Assessment*. This cycle is designed to engage students in investigating and making sense of problem situations, in constructing important mathematical concepts and methods, in generalizing and proving mathematical relationships, and in communicating, both orally and in writing, their thinking and the results of their efforts. Most classroom activities are designed to be completed by students working collaboratively in groups of two to four students.

LAUNCH class discussion

Think About This Situation

The lesson launch promotes a teacher-led discussion of a problem situation and of related questions to think about. This discussion sets the context for the student work to follow and helps to generate student interest. It also provides an opportunity for the teacher to assess student knowledge and to clarify directions for the investigation to follow. The discussion sets the stage for students to make sense of and persevere in solving the investigation problems. The discussion should not be lengthy nor pre-teach the lesson.

EXPLORE group investigation

Investigation

Classroom activity then shifts to investigating focused problems and questions related to the launching situation by gathering data, looking for and explaining patterns, constructing models and meanings, and making and verifying conjectures. As students collaborate in pairs or small groups, the teacher circulates among students providing guidance and support, clarifying or asking questions (such as why students believe their thinking is true), giving hints, providing encouragement, and drawing group members into the discussion to help groups collaborate more effectively. The investigations and related questions posed by students and teachers drive the learning and offer many opportunities to engage in the CCSS mathematical practices.

SHARE AND SUMMARIZE class discussion

Summarize the Mathematics

This investigative work is followed by a teacher-led class discussion (referred to as Summarize the Mathematics) in which students summarize mathematical ideas developed in their groups, providing an opportunity to construct a shared understanding of important concepts, methods, and justifications. This discussion leads to a class summary of important ideas or to further exploration of a topic if competing perspectives remain. Varying points of view and differing conclusions that can be justified should be encouraged. This discussion based on student thinking during the investigation is crucial to building understanding of mathematical ideas for the procedural skill development to follow.

SELF-ASSESSMENT individual tasks

Check Your Understanding

Students are given a task to complete on their own to check and reinforce their initial understanding of concepts and procedures.

Homework

In addition to the classroom investigations, *Core-Plus Mathematics* provides sets of On Your Own tasks, which are designed to engage students in applying, connecting, reflecting on, extending, and reviewing their evolving mathematical knowledge. On Your Own tasks are provided for each lesson in the materials and are central to the learning goals of each lesson. These tasks are intended primarily for individual work outside of class. Selection of homework tasks should be based on student performance and the availability of time and technology access. Also, students should exercise some choice of tasks to pursue, and, at times should be given the opportunity to pose their own problems and questions to investigate. The chart below describes the types of tasks in a typical On Your Own set.

On Your Own: Homework Tasks	
Applications	These tasks provide opportunities for students to use and strengthen their understanding of the ideas they have learned in the lesson.
Connections	These tasks help students to build links between mathematical topics they have studied in the lesson and to connect those topics with other mathematics that they know.
Reflections	These tasks provide opportunities for students to re-examine their thinking about ideas in the lesson.
Extensions	These tasks provide opportunities for students to explore further or more deeply the mathematics they are learning.
Review	These tasks provide opportunities for just-in-time review and distributed practice of mathematical skills to maintain procedural fluency.

Additional Summarizing Activities

In *Core-Plus Mathematics*, students learn mathematics by doing mathematics. However, it is important that students prepare and maintain summaries of important concepts and methods that are developed. Students should create a **Mathematics Toolkit** that organizes important class-generated ideas and selected Summarize the Mathematics responses as they complete investigations. Math Toolkit Prompts are provided in this *Teacher's Guide* to assist in identifying and summarizing key concepts and methods as they are developed by students.

In addition, the final lesson in each unit is a Looking Back lesson that helps students review and synthesize the key mathematical concepts and techniques presented in the unit. The Summarize the Mathematics questions in this lesson are focused on key ideas of the unit. The Check Your Understanding asks students to prepare a summary of the important concepts and skills developed in the unit. Templates to guide preparation of these *Unit Summaries* can be found in the *Unit Resource Masters*. Completed Unit Summaries should become part of students' Math Toolkits.

Students should retain their Math Toolkits as they continue on to Courses 2–4. In some districts, teachers collect these resources at the end of the school year and return them to students in the fall.

Formative and Summative Assessments

Assessing what students know and are able to do is an integral part of *Core-Plus Mathematics*. There are opportunities for formative assessment in each phase of the instructional cycle. Throughout the curriculum, the term "assessment" is meant to include all instances of gathering information about students' levels of understanding and their disposition toward mathematics for purposes of making decisions about instruction. You may want to consult the extended section on assessment in *Implementing Core-Plus Mathematics* available on ConnectED.

The dimensions of student performance that are assessed in this curriculum (see chart below) are consistent with the assessment recommendations of the National Council of Teachers of Mathematics in the *Assessment Standards for School Mathematics* (NCTM, 1995). They are more comprehensive than those of a typical testing program.

Assessment Dimensions		
Process	**Content**	**Disposition**
Problem Solving	Concepts	Beliefs
Reasoning	Applications	Perseverance
Communication	Representational Strategies	Confidence
Connections	Procedures	Enthusiasm

Several kinds of assessment are available to teachers using *Core-Plus Mathematics*. Some of these sources reside within the curriculum itself, some of them are student-generated, and some are supplementary materials designed specifically for assessment. Understanding the nature of these sources is a prerequisite for selecting assessment tools, establishing guidelines on how to score assessments, making judgments about what students know and are able to do, and assigning grades. The front matter for the unit resources provides information related to the quizzes, tests, take-home tasks, and projects, and scoring and grading of these summative assessments.

Two features of the curriculum, questioning and observation by the teacher, provide fundamental and particularly useful ways of gathering *formative assessment* information. The student text uses questions to facilitate student understanding of new concepts, of how these concepts fit with earlier ideas and with one another, and of how they can be applied in problem situations. Whether students are working individually or in groups, the teacher is given a window to watch how the students think about and apply mathematics as they attempt to answer the questions posed by the curriculum materials. In fact, by observing how students respond to the curriculum-embedded questions, the teacher can assess student performance across all process, content, and attitude dimensions described in the chart above.

Specific features in the student material that focus on different ways students respond to questions are the Summarize the Mathematics, Check Your Understanding, and the

On Your Own homework sets. Summarize the Mathematics features are intended to bring students together, usually after they have been working in small groups, so they may share and discuss the progress each group has made during a sequence of related activities. The questions in the Summarize the Mathematics are focused on the mathematical concepts and procedures developed in the investigation. They should help the teacher and the students identify and formalize the key ideas of the investigation. Each Summarize the Mathematics is intended to be a whole-class discussion, so it should provide an opportunity for teachers to assess, informally, the levels of understanding that the various groups of students have reached.

Following each Summarize the Mathematics, the Check Your Understanding tasks (which can be used for self-assessment) are meant to be completed by students working individually. Responses to these tasks provide an opportunity for students and teachers to assess levels of understanding.

The tasks in the On Your Own homework sets serve many purposes, including formative assessment. Each type of task in the On Your Own homework sets has a different instructional purpose. Applications tasks provide opportunities for students to demonstrate how well they understand and can use the ideas they learned in the investigations of the lesson. Work on Connections tasks enables students to demonstrate how well they understand links between mathematical topics they studied in the lesson and their ability to connect those topics with other mathematics that they know. Reflections tasks enable students to re-examine their thinking about ideas in the lesson and their use of mathematical practices and mathematical habits of mind. Extensions tasks provide opportunities for students to explore further, or more deeply, the mathematics they learned in the investigations. The Review tasks allow for pre-assessment of students' understanding of ideas or procedures needed in the upcoming lessons and also provide information on how well students are retaining previously learned mathematics. The performance of students or groups of students in each of these types of tasks provides the teacher with further information to help assess each student's evolving ability to use, connect, and extend the mathematics of the lesson.

Finally, an opportunity for group self-assessment is provided in the last element of each unit, the Looking Back lesson. These tasks help students pull together and demonstrate what they have learned in the unit and at the same time provide helpful review and confidence-building for students.

Formal Assessment Resources: The *Unit Resource Masters* available on McGraw-Hill Education's ConnectED include lesson quizzes and unit assessments in the form of tests, take-home tasks, and unit projects. There are also banks of questions and year-end projects.

Practicing for Standardized Tests

Opportunities for additional review and practice are provided in eight Preparing for Standardized Tests practice sets. Each Practicing for Standardized Tests master presents 10 questions and a test-taking tip. The questions are presented in the form of test items similar to how they often appear in standardized tests such as state assessments tests, the SAT (Scholastic Aptitude Test), or the ACT (American College Testing). By using these practice sets, students can become familiar with the formats of standardized tests and develop effective test-taking strategies for performing well on such tests.

Since the assessment tasks developed for the Smarter Balanced Assessment Consortium (SBAC) and the Partnership for Assessment of Readiness for College and Careers (PARCC) will include open-ended, multi-stage tasks, student completion of investigations and On Your Own tasks will be beneficial for preparation for these assessments. In particular, the more open distributed review tasks will help students automate and maintain the mathematical concepts needed for standardized assessments. By assigning the review tasks, students will need to choose methods to apply to tasks rather than repeat the same method multiple times.

Access, Equity, and Differentiation

Several research studies have provided evidence that introducing activities through class discussion, teaching students to explain and justify, and making real-world contexts accessible to students promote greater access and equity in mathematics classrooms. (Boaler, J. "Learning from Teaching: Exploring the Relationship Between Reform Curriculum and Equity," *Journal for Research in Mathematics Education,* 2002, Vol. 33, No. 4, 239-258, and Brown, C.A., Stein, M.K., and Forman, E. A. "Assisting teachers and students to reform their mathematics classroom," *Education Studies in Mathematics,* 1996, 31–93). These practices that help promote equity are briefly discussed below.

Introducing Investigations Through Class Discussions Group and class discussions of the aim of investigations, the meaning of contexts, the challenging points within problems, and possible problem access points to which students might turn make tasks more evenly accessible to all students.

Teaching Students to Explain and Justify their Thinking Giving explicit attention to explaining thinking and evaluating what makes a good piece of work helps students improve their work.

Making Real-world Contexts Accessible Considering the constraints that real situations involve and connecting these situations with issues and topics in their own lives helps students view mathematics as something that will help them interpret their world.

Other Practices that Promote Equity Mixed-ability classes, a focus on problem solving, high expectations for all students, attention to a broad array of mathematical topics, and allowing students to restate problems in their own words also appear to help students from different racial, ethnic, and linguistic groups be more successful in mathematics.

Core-Plus Mathematics offers many opportunities for teachers to incorporate these practices into daily routines. One such built-in opportunity is the Think About This Situations (TATS) used to introduce lessons through discussions. Although no TATS questions are in the student text for individual investigations, there are often suggestions in the *Teacher's Guide* for class launches of investigations. Since much of the mathematical content is based on real contexts, it is important that all students understand the contexts and draw on their own or a classmate's background knowledge. Opportunities for students to explain and justify their thinking are built into all curriculum features. Look for opportunities to encourage the habit of mind of justifying their thinking, individually and in small group or class discussions, in order to develop understanding of mathematical concepts.

In addition, periodically, in the *Teacher's Guide* notes provide specific ideas for differentiation at point of use. Look for the margin notes.

Implementing the Curriculum

Considering mathematics topics and knowledge presented at each grade level and how that knowledge is built upon in succeeding grades is key to improving student learning. To support building the teacher expertise to effectively implement *Core-Plus Mathematics,* the developers recommend that districts begin adoption with Course 1 and add a course level each year. Encourage teachers to progress from Course 1 to Course 4: *Preparation for Calculus* in stages, so they can develop an understanding of the growth of mathematical ideas in the curriculum. Realize that teachers will need time and support to improve instruction for their students.

Additional advice related to successful implementation is on the Core-Plus Mathematics Project Web site at www.wmich.edu/cpmp/ under Implementation.

Planning for Instruction

The *Core-Plus Mathematics* curriculum is not only changing what mathematics all students have the opportunity to learn, but also changing how that learning occurs and is assessed. Active learning is most effective when accompanied with active teaching. Just as the student text is designed to actively engage students in doing mathematics, the teacher's resource materials are designed to support teachers in planning for instruction; in observing, listening, questioning, and facilitating student work, and orchestrating classroom discussion; and in managing the classroom.

The *Teacher's Guide* provides suggestions, based on the experiences of field-test teachers. The developers highly recommend that teachers who are teaching *Core-Plus Mathematics* for the first time do so at least in pairs who share a common planning period.

A first step toward planning the teaching of a unit is to review the scope and sequence of the unit. This review provides an overall feel for the goals of the unit and how it holds together. Working through the student investigations, with a colleague if possible, provides help in thinking about and understanding mathematical ideas that may be unfamiliar.

In the *Teacher's Guide*, at the beginning of each unit, you will find a Planning Guide to assist in overall planning. This resource gives a quick overview of lessons, suggested assignments, materials needed, and pacing suggestions.

You will also find teaching notes for each lesson, including instructional suggestions and sample student responses to investigations and homework sets. Thinking about the range of possible responses and solutions to problems proves to be very helpful in facilitating student work.

Some teachers choose to post the homework assignment at the beginning of a lesson along with the due date—usually a day or two following planned completion of the lesson. Other teachers prefer to assign particular tasks at appropriate points during the course of the multiday investigation, and then assign the remaining tasks toward the end of the lesson. Review tasks can be assigned before the completion of the investigation. Note that all recommended assignments include provision for student choice of some tasks. This is but one of many ways in which this curriculum is designed to accommodate and support differences in students' interests and performance levels.

It is strongly recommended that student solutions to Connections tasks be discussed in class. These tasks help students organize and formalize the mathematics developed in context and connect it to other mathematics they have studied. Structuring the underlying mathematics and building connections are best accomplished by comparing and discussing student work and synthesizing key ideas within the classroom.

Some recommended assignments include Just-in-Time Review tasks. It is important that these tasks be assigned as indicated in the Planning Guide to help ensure understanding of ideas or procedures need in the next investigation.

Technology in Course 1

In the 21st century, anyone who faces the challenge of learning mathematics or using mathematics to solve problems can draw on the resources of powerful information technology tools. Calculators and computers can help with calculations, drawing, and data analysis in mathematical explorations and solving mathematical problems.

The Role of Technology in the Teaching and Learning of Mathematics:

> **NCTM Position** Technology is an essential tool for learning mathematics in the 21st century, and all schools must ensure that all their students have access to technology. Effective teachers maximize the potential of technology to develop students' understanding, stimulate their interest, and increase their proficiency in mathematics. When technology is used strategically, it can provide access to mathematics for all students.

See the NCTM position paper on technology at: www.nctm.org/about/content.aspx?id=14233

Graphing Calculators: Graphing calculators with iteration capabilities are assumed for class work and homework. Computer algebra system (CAS) capabilities are desirable.

Computers: With the publication of the CCSS Edition, we are increasingly finding that many *Core-Plus Mathematics* classrooms now have multiple options for computer use: in classrooms featuring a single computer and an interactive whiteboard; in classrooms with multiple computers set up as stations where students can work during selected investigations; and in classrooms where small groups, pairs, or individual students each have laptops on their desks. For some homework tasks, school or home computer availability and access to *CPMP-Tools* are also expected.

Computer software: The use of spreadsheet, interactive geometry, data analysis, vertex-edge graph software, and computer algebra systems (CAS) is incorporated into Course 1 units. The curriculum materials include computer software called *CPMP-Tools* specifically designed to support student learning and problem solving. The software can be accessed at www.wmich.edu/cpmp/CPMP-Tools/.

The suite of Java-based mathematical software, includes four families of programs:

Algebra The software for work on algebra problems includes a spreadsheet and a computer algebra system (CAS) that produces tables and graphs of functions, manipulates algebraic expressions, and solves equations and inequalities.

Geometry The software for work on geometry problems includes an interactive drawing program for constructing, measuring, and manipulating geometric figures and a set of custom apps for studying geometric models of mechanical devices, tessellations, and properties of special shapes.

Statistics The software for work on data analysis and probability problems provides tools for graphic display and analysis of data, simulation of probability experiments, and mathematical modeling of quantitative relationships.

Discrete Mathematics The software for discrete mathematical modeling provides tools for constructing, manipulating, and analyzing discrete mathematical models.

In addition to the general purpose tools provided for work on tasks in each strand of the curriculum, *CPMP-Tools* includes files that provide electronic copies of most data sets essential for work on problems in each *Core-Plus Mathematics* course. When the opportunity to use computer tools for work on a particular investigation seems appropriate, students can select the *CPMP-Tools* menu corresponding to the content of, and their planned approach to, the problem. Then they can select the submenu items corresponding to the appropriate mathematical operations and required data set(s). Each unit overview in the *Teacher's Guide* provides general information related to *CPMP-Tools* use in the unit. Technology notes at point of use alert teachers to applicable software and specific data sets included in the software.

The CCSS Standard for Mathematical Practice: Use appropriate tools strategically, indicates that mathematically proficient students are familiar enough with tools to make sound decisions about when particular tools might be helpful. Access to technology as described in this section will allow students to gain that proficiency. Access to technology will also provide students opportunities to explore and deepen their understanding of mathematical concepts. The freely available *CPMP-Tools* software reduces some of the inequities in access to technology for schools, teachers, and students.

Materials Needed for Course 1

The following is a complete list of items used in the eight units of Course 1. Each Unit Planning Guide indicates the items used in that unit.

Necessary

Rubber bands and weights
Meter sticks
Compasses
Protractors
Transparent rulers in metric and
   English scales
Dice
Watch with second hand or stopwatch
Red and black checkers
Various balls that bounce
Coins and unpopped corn or beans

12-foot loop of rope with knots at
   6-inch intervals
Spaghetti or linguini
Linkage strips
Mirror tiles (or plastic sheets) to make
   two- and three-mirror kaleidoscopes
Acrylic plastic mirrors
Coffee stirrers or small-holed straws
Pipe cleaners
Set of tetrahedral, octagonal, decahedral,
   and icosahedral dice
One penny per student

Optional

Identical weights such as small cubes
   or plastic interlocking blocks

Backgammon set
Colored pencils

Online Resources

The *Core-Plus Mathematics* student text, *Teacher's Guide, Unit Resource Masters*, and other resources are included on McGraw-Hill Education's ConnectED. Custom tailoring of assessment items can be accomplished using eAssessment. *CPMP-Tools* is available for download at www.wmich.edu/cpmp/CPMP-Tools/.

Orchestrating Lessons

Core-Plus Mathematics is designed to engage students in the CCSS mathematical practices as the primary vehicle for learning mathematics and statistics. The activities often require both students and teachers to assume roles quite different than those in more traditional mathematics classrooms. Becoming accustomed to these new roles usually takes time, but field-test teachers report that the time and effort required are well worth it in terms of student learning and professional fulfillment. Although realistic problem solving and investigative work by students are the heart of the curriculum, how teachers orchestrate the launching of an investigation and the sharing and summarizing of results is critical to successful implementation.

Students enter the classroom with differing backgrounds, experience, and knowledge. These differences can be viewed as assets. Engaging the class in a free-flowing give-and-take discussion of how students think about the launch situations serves to connect lessons with the informal understandings of data, shape, change, and chance that students bring to the classroom. Try to maximize the participation of students in these discussions by emphasizing that their ideas and possible approaches are valued and important and that definitive answers are not necessarily expected at this time.

Once launched, an investigation may involve students working together collaboratively in small groups for a period of days punctuated occasionally by brief class discussion of questions students have raised. In this setting, the investigation becomes driven primarily by the instructional materials themselves. Rather than orchestrating class discussion, the teacher shifts to circulating among the groups and observing, listening, and interacting with students by asking guiding or probing questions that typically promote students' use of the mathematical practices (page xxiii). These small-group investigations lead to (re)invention of important mathematics that makes sense to students. Sharing, and agreeing as a class, on the mathematical ideas that groups are developing is the purpose of the Summarizing the Mathematics (STM) in the instructional materials.

Class discussions at STMs are orchestrated somewhat differently than during the launch of a lesson. At this stage, mathematical ideas and methods still may be under development and may vary for individual groups. So class discussion should involve groups comparing their methods and results, analyzing their work, and arriving at conclusions agreed upon by the class.

The investigations deepen students' understanding of mathematical ideas and extend their mathematical language. Technical terminology and symbolism are introduced as needed. This sometimes occurs in student materials immediately following an STM and before the corresponding Check Your Understanding task. The technical terminology and symbolism should be introduced by the teacher as a natural way of closing the class discussion summarizing investigation content.

Periodically, you will find samples of class discussions centered around Think About This Situations and Summarize the Mathematics curriculum features at point of use. These sample discussions, called Promoting Mathematical Discourse, may provide some ideas for your class discussions. These sample discussions are indicated by Promoting Mathematical Discourse.

Managing Classroom Activities
Active Learning and Collaborative Work

The *Core-Plus Mathematics* curriculum materials are designed to promote active, collaborative learning and group work for two important reasons. First, a collaborative environment fosters students' ability to make sense of mathematics and develop deep mathematical understandings. Collaborative learning is an effective method for engaging all the students in the learning process, particularly students who have been under represented in mathematics classes. Second, practice in collaborative learning in the classroom is practice for real life: students develop and exercise the same skills in the classroom that they need in their lives at home, in the community, and in the workplace.

Value of Individuals

Perhaps the most fundamental belief underlying the use of collaborative learning is that every student is viewed as a valuable resource and contributor. In other words, every student participates in group work and is given the opportunity and time to voice ideas and opinions. Implementing this concept is not easy nor does it happen automatically. In order to set a tone that will promote respect for individuals and their contributions, classroom norms should be established. Teachers should initiate a discussion and together write all the student-formulated classrooms rules for both individual and group behavior. The positively stated rules of behavior should be posted in the classroom and every member of the learning community should be held responsible for adhering to them.

Need for Teaching Social Skills

Experience has shown that social skills are critical to the successful functioning of any small group. Because there is no guarantee that students of any particular age will have the social skills necessary for effective group work, it often is necessary to teach these skills to build a collaborative learning environment.

These social skills are specific skills, not general goals. Examples of specific social skills that the teacher can teach in the classroom include responding to ideas respectfully, keeping track of time, disagreeing in an agreeable way, involving everyone, and following directions. Though goals such as cooperating and listening are important, they are too general to teach.

One method of teaching social skills is to begin by selecting a specific skill and then having the class brainstorm to develop a script for practicing that skill. Next, the students practice that skill during their group work. Finally, in what is called the processing, the students discuss within their groups how well they performed the assigned social skill. Effective teaching of social skills requires practicing and processing; merely describing a specific social skill is not enough. The *Teacher's Guide* includes specific collaborative skills to practice and processing prompts for student self-assessment.

The culture created within the classroom is crucial to the success of this curriculum. It is important to inculcate in students a sense of inquiry and responsibility for their own learning. Without this commitment, active, collaborative learning by students cannot be effective. Some students seem satisfied with the rationale that collaboration is important in workplace. Others may need to understand that the struggle of verbalizing their thinking, listening to others' thinking, questioning themselves and other group members, and coming to an agreement increases their understanding and retention of the mathematics while contributing to the formation of important thinking skills or habits of mind.

Issues of helping students to work collaboratively will become less pressing as both you and your students experience this type of learning. *Implementing Core-Plus Mathematics* provides additional information related to the challenge of facilitating collaborative work including support to help teachers make decisions about group size, composition, method of selection, the duration of groups and dealing with student absences. This resource also offers a number of practical suggestions from *Core-Plus Mathematics* teachers on effectively pacing instruction in a student-centered classroom.

Additional Resources

Implementing Core-Plus Mathematics contains expanded information on:

- unit descriptions and topics for Courses 1–4,
- managing classroom activities,
- differentiation built into the program,
- the assessment program,
- communication with parents, and
- mathematics program evaluation.

You will find it useful to have the implementation guide available for reference throughout the school year. *Implementing Core-Plus Mathematics* is available on ConnectED.

Articles that are related to *Core-Plus Mathematics* written by developers and teachers are available on the Core-Plus Mathematics Project Web site at www.wmich.edu/cpmp under Publications and on ConnectED. These articles were written based on first edition experiences (from 1998 to 2000), but in many cases are still applicable to this edition.

Topics include:

- selecting and implementing Core-Plus Mathematics,
- effectively using collaborative groups,
- classroom pacing considerations,
- options for acceleration paths to AP Calculus or AP Statistics
- meeting the needs of ELL and LEP students,
- college placement
- the International Baccalaureate Program, and
- achievement in Science.

Annotated Bibliography Available on the CPMP Web site under Publications are references to articles, book chapters, dissertations, papers presented at conferences, and field-test reports based on the program. Some of these resources can be downloaded.

Professional Development Opportunities A variety of professional development opportunities are provided by McGraw-Hill and the Core-Plus Mathematics Project. Workshops are listed on the CPMP Web site www.wmich.edu/cpmp/ under Implementation. Experienced *Core-Plus Mathematics* teacher-consultants can be contracted to provide onsite inservice. Contact your McGraw-Hill sales representative or the CPMP office (cpmp@wmich.edu) for provider names.

Parent Resource Resources for parents including how to help with homework, research supporting *Core-Plus Mathematics*, evidence of success, and frequently asked question are available at www.wmich.edu/cpmp/parentresource.html and on ConnectED.

UNIT 1 Patterns of Change

Patterns of Change develops student ability to recognize and describe important patterns that relate quantitative variables, to use data tables, graphs, words, and symbols to represent the relationships, and to use reasoning and calculating tools to answer questions and solve problems.

Topics include variables and functions, algebraic expressions and recurrence relations, coordinate graphs, data tables and spreadsheets, and equations and inequalities.

Lesson 1 Cause and Effect
Lesson 2 Change Over Time
Lesson 3 Tools for Studying Patterns of Change
Lesson 4 Looking Back

UNIT 2 Patterns in Data

Patterns in Data develops student ability to summarize, represent, and interpret real-world data on a single count or measurement variable through the use of graphical displays of the distribution, measures of center, and measures of spread.

Topics include distributions of data and their shapes, as displayed in dot plots, histograms, and box plots; measures of center (mean and median) and their properties; measures of spread including interquartile range and standard deviation and their properties; and percentiles and outliers.

Lesson 1 Exploring Distributions
Lesson 2 Variability
Lesson 3 Looking Back

UNIT 3 Linear Functions

Linear Functions develops student ability to recognize and represent linear relationships between variables and to use tables, graphs, and algebraic expressions for linear functions to solve problems in situations that involve constant rate of change or slope.

Topics include linear functions, slope of a line, rate of change, modeling linear data patterns, solving linear equations and inequalities, equivalent linear expressions.

Lesson 1 Modeling Linear Relationships
Lesson 2 Linear Equations and Inequalities
Lesson 3 Equivalent Expressions
Lesson 4 Looking Back

UNIT 4 Discrete Mathematical Modeling

Discrete Mathematical Modeling develops student ability in modeling, reasoning, and problem solving as they use vertex-edge graphs to model and solve problems about networks, paths, and relations.

Topics include vertex-edge graphs, mathematical modeling, optimization, algorithmic problem solving, using Euler paths to find efficient routes, using vertex coloring to avoid conflicts, and matrix representations to aid interpretation.

Lesson 1 Euler Circuits: Finding the Best Path

Lesson 2 Vertex Coloring: Avoiding Conflict

Lesson 3 Looking Back

UNIT 5 Exponential Functions

Exponential Functions develops student ability to recognize and represent exponential growth and decay patterns, to express those patterns in symbolic forms, to solve problems that involve exponential change, and to use properties of exponents to write expressions in equivalent forms.

Topics include exponential growth and decay functions, data modeling, growth and decay rates, half-life and doubling time, compound interest, and properties of exponents.

Lesson 1 Exponential Growth

Lesson 2 Exponential Decay

Lesson 3 Looking Back

UNIT 6 Patterns in Shape

Patterns in Shape develops student ability to visualize and describe two- and three-dimensional shapes, to represent them with drawings, to examine shape properties through both experimentation and careful reasoning, and to use those properties to solve problems.

Topics include Triangle Inequality, congruence conditions for triangles, special quadrilaterals and quadrilateral linkages, Pythagorean Theorem, properties of polygons, tilings of the plane, properties of polyhedra, cylinders, cones, and the Platonic solids.

Lesson 1 Triangles, Quadrilaterals, and Their Properties

Lesson 2 Polygons and Their Properties

Lesson 3 Polyhedra and Their Properties

Lesson 4 Looking Back

UNIT 7 — Quadratic Functions

Quadratic Functions develops student ability to recognize and represent quadratic relations between variables using data tables, graphs, and symbolic formulas, to solve problems involving quadratic functions, and to express quadratic polynomials in equivalent factored and expanded forms.

Topics include quadratic functions and their graphs, applications to projectile motion and economic problems, expanding and factoring quadratic expressions, and solving quadratic equations by the quadratic formula and calculator approximation.

Lesson 1 Quadratic Patterns

Lesson 2 Equivalent Quadratic Expressions

Lesson 3 Solving Quadratic Equations

Lesson 4 Looking Back

UNIT 8 — Patterns in Chance

Patterns in Chance develops student ability to solve problems involving chance by constructing sample spaces of equally-likely outcomes or geometric models and to use simulation to decide whether a model is consistent with the data.

Topics include sample spaces, equally-likely outcomes, probability distributions, mutually exclusive (disjoint) events, Addition Rule, union, intersection, two-way frequency tables, simulation, random digits, discrete and continuous random variables, Law of Large Numbers, and geometric probability.

Lesson 1 Calculating Probabilities

Lesson 2 Modeling Chance Situations

Lesson 3 Looking Back

Common Core State Standards and *Core-Plus Mathematics* Course 1

Connecting the Standards for Mathematical Practice to the Standards for Mathematical Content

Core-Plus Mathematics is designed so that students engage in the mathematical behaviors identified in the CCSS Standards for Mathematical Practices (listed below) as the primary vehicle for learning the mathematics and statistics elaborated in the CCSS content standards. "The Standards for Mathematical Practice describe ways in which developing student practitioners of the discipline of mathematics increasingly ought to engage with the subject matter." (CCSS p. 8) The *Core Plus Mathematics* texts regularly provide opportunities for students to develop and reflect on the mathematical dispositions and "habits of mind" described in CCSS's Standards for Mathematical Practices as an integral part of both class work and homework.

CCSS Standards for Mathematical Practices

1. Make sense of problems and persevere in solving them.
2. Reason abstractly and quantitatively.
3. Construct viable arguments and critique the reasoning of others.
4. Model with mathematics.
5. Use appropriate tools strategically.
6. Attend to precision.
7. Look for and make use of structure.
8. Look for and express regularity in repeated reasoning.

A detailed correlation of Courses 1–4 is included in the *CCSS Guide to Core-Plus Mathematics* which can be downloaded from ConnectED.

Curriculum Analysis and Implementation

For the next few years, schools in many states will be transitioning to the Common Core State Standards for Mathematics (CCSS) K–12. If your district is considering adopting *Core-Plus Mathematics,* you may wish to utilize the curriculum analysis tools developed by the Common Core State Standards Mathematics Curriculum Materials Analysis Project: www.mathedleadership.org/ccss/materials.html to assist with curriculum study. Three tools were developed to provide detailed information about the extent to which curriculum materials align with and support the implementation of CCSS. Tool 1 focuses on mathematics content trajectories, Tool 2 focuses on mathematical practices, and Tool 3 focuses on important considerations complementary to the standards like equity, assessment, and technology that can impact implementation of mathematics curricula.

It is advisable to collaborate with middle school mathematics teachers from your feeder school(s) to plan articulation between the Grades 6–8 CCSS and those for high school. Some topics in the CCSS are introduced in middle school and used or extended in high school. For these standards you may find that some material in *Core-Plus Mathematics* will need fewer days to complete than is suggested in each Unit Planning Guide.

Typically, the cognitive demand of the problems in *Core-Plus Mathematics* Course 1 exceeds that of similar content in middle school programs.

To further assist your curriculum study and implementation, the CCSS Standards that apply to each lesson are listed in the Course 1 *Teacher's Guide*. See page T1 for the first instance of this feature. A full listing of CCSS standards by lesson is available for download on ConnectED.

Connecting the CCSS for Mathematics to the English Language Arts

In addition to studying the alignment of *Core-Plus Mathematics* with the CCSS for Mathematics, *Core-Plus Mathematics* assists schools in meeting the CCSS for English Language Arts with respect to the standards for reading informational text, for technical reading, and for writing.

Access and Equity

Downloading the *CPMP Tools* public-domain software, freely available at www.wmich.edu/cpmp/CPMP-Tools/, to school and home computers, or using the software online in libraries and other public Internet access sites enables students to develop the CCSS Standard for Mathematical Practice: Use appropriate tools strategically. This includes selecting and using technology tools to explore and deepen understanding of concepts, to visualize mathematical ideas and view consequences of varying assumptions, to model and solve problems, to compare predictions from data, and to become sufficiently familiar with technology tools to make sound decisions about when various features of the software might be helpful.

CCSS Pathway Through Course 1

It is in students' best interest to complete the CCSS Pathway outlined on the next pages and the suggested assignments in each Unit Planning Guide. If they complete the investigations and tasks listed in the Unit Planning Guides, students will be able to complete subsequent units in *Core-Plus Mathematics* and will learn the topics specified in the CCSS. The CCSS Pathway through Courses 1–3 is included in the *CCSS Guide to Core-Plus Mathematics* which can be downloaded from ConnectED. Also, see the less-detailed CCSS Alignment appendix in each student text for Courses 1–3.

Course 1 Pathway

Unit 1   Patterns of Change

Lesson 1 Cause and Effect

(optional depending on students' middle school background)

Investigation 1 Physics and Business at Five Star Amusement Park

Investigation 2 Taking Chances

Investigation 3 Trying to Get Rich Quick

Lesson 2 Change Over Time

Investigation 1 Predicting Population Change

Investigation 2 Tracking Change with Spreadsheets (Problems 1–4)

Lesson 3 Tools for Studying Patterns of Change

Investigation 1 Communicating with Symbols

Investigation 2 Quick Tables, Graphs, and Solutions

Investigation 3 The Shapes of Algebra (optional depending on students' middle school background)

Lesson 4 Looking Back

Unit 2   Patterns of Data

Lesson 1 Exploring Distributions

Investigation 1 Shapes of Distributions (Problems 1–8)

Investigation 2 Measures of Center

Lesson 2 Measuring Variability

Investigation 1 Measuring Position

Investigation 2 Measuring and Displaying Variability: The Five-Number Summary and Box Plots

Investigation 3 Identifying Outliers

Investigation 4 Measuring Variability: The Standard Deviation

Investigation 5 Transforming Measurements

Lesson 3 Looking Back

Unit 3   Linear Functions

Lesson 1 Modeling Linear Relationships

Investigation 1 Getting Credit

Investigation 2 Symbolize It

Investigation 3 Fitting Lines

TABLE OF CONTENTS

UNIT 5

Exponential Functions

I n everyday conversation, the phrase "growing exponentially" is used to describe any situation where some quantity is increasing rapidly with the passage of time. But in mathematics, the terms *exponential growth* and *exponential decay* refer to particular important patterns of change.

For example, when wildlife biologists estimated the population of gray wolves in Michigan, Wisconsin, and Minnesota, they found it growing exponentially—at an annual rate of about 25% from a base of about 170 wolves in 1990 to about 3,100 wolves in 2003.

In this unit, you will develop understanding and skill required to study patterns of change like growth of the midwestern gray wolf population and decay of medicines in the human body.

The key ideas and strategies for studying those patterns will be developed in two lessons.

LESSONS

1 Exponential Growth

Recognize situations in which variables grow exponentially over time. Write *NOW-NEXT* and "*y = ...*" rules that express those patterns of change. Use tables, graphs, and spreadsheets to solve problems related to exponential growth. Use properties of integer exponents to write exponential expressions in useful equivalent forms.

2 Exponential Decay

Recognize and solve problems in situations where variables decline exponentially over time. Use properties of fractional exponents to write exponential expressions in useful equivalent forms.

Exponential Functions

Unit Overview

In many quantitative problems, key variables are related in patterns that are described well by linear models. But there are many other important situations in which variables are related by nonlinear patterns. Among the most important nonlinear patterns of change are those that can be modeled well by rules of the form $y = a(b^x)$. Since the independent or manipulated variable occurs in such rules as an exponent, those relations are called exponential functions. Exponential functions are useful in solving problems involving change in populations, pollution, temperature, bank savings, drugs in the bloodstream, and radioactive materials. In fact, it is the widespread usefulness of exponential functions that has led us to introduce them ahead of the more familiar quadratic functions.

Another very strong reason for introducing exponential functions at this relatively early stage of the curriculum is the fact that the difference equation for exponential growth, $NEXT = NOW \times b$, is a natural counterpoint to the difference equation for linear change, $NEXT = NOW + b$. Capitalizing on these connections and comparisons as you and your students work through this unit will help students begin to develop a useful intuitive understanding of linearity and exponential change as well as generally useful recursive (or sequential) ways of thinking about and modeling patterns of change.

The material of this unit is organized into two main lessons. Lesson 1 asks students to explore a variety of situations involving exponential growth. The first three investigations involve problem conditions that can be analyzed by reasoning about recursive patterns of change and modeled by the $NEXT = NOW \times b$ form or rules in the closed form $y = a(b^x)$. The fourth investigation deals with the problem of modeling patterns of change in data that are only approximately exponential. Then the fifth investigation builds on student experiences with patterns of exponential change in context to develop several of the most familiar and useful general rules for operating with exponential expressions.

Lesson 2 explores patterns of change that can be represented well by exponential decay models. The first two investigations explore several different exponential decay contexts, leading students to identify the characteristics of *NOW-NEXT* and closed form rules that provide accurate models. Then the third investigation provides further experience in finding models for approximately exponential decay patterns in experimental data. The fourth investigation develops further algebraic rules for operating with exponential expressions, and the fifth investigation develops the concept of radicals and some basic properties for simplifying those expressions.

- Recognize and give examples of growth and decay situations in which exponential functions are likely to match the patterns of change that are observed or expected. This function-recognition skill should apply to information given in data tables, graphs, or verbal descriptions of related changing variables

- Develop ability to use reasoning, estimation, and curve-fitting utilities to find exponential functions to match patterns of change in exponential growth and decay situations. This should include rules in the "$y = ...$" and *NOW-NEXT* forms

- Use exponential rules to produce tables and graphs to answer questions about exponential change of variables

- Interpret an exponential function rule in order to sketch or predict the shape of its graph and the pattern of change in tables of values

- Describe major similarities and differences between linear and exponential patterns of change

- Develop skill in rewriting exponential and radical expressions in equivalent forms

CCSS and CPMP Pathways

The two pathways for this unit are identical and include all of the algebraic concepts and skills in the unit. Your honors or STEM students would be well advised to complete Extensions tasks beyond those listed in the Unit Planning Guide for all students.

CPMP-Tools

In this unit, students may wish to use the exponential and linear regression models in *CPMP-Tools*. Students can save partially completed work and also print or email finished solutions. This saves valuable class or homework time normally needed to copy calculator displays or restart problems at home.

Data sets included in *CPMP-Tools* for this unit are:
Page 310 Dow Jones Averages
Page 311 Voters in U.S. Elections
Page 357 Cold Surgery
Page 358 Surgery Time and Cost

For Lesson 2, Investigation 3, "Modeling Decay," students may wish to enter their experimental data into *CPMP-Tools*, Data Analysis software rather than a calculator to find a function model.

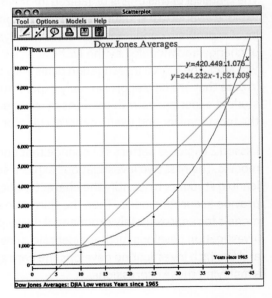

UNIT 5

Lesson Objectives	Pathways: Pacing and OYO Assignments*	Resources
Lesson 1 Exponential Growth • Develop disposition to look for and ability to recognize exponential growth patterns and phenomena • Develop ability to represent exponential functions with rules in the form $y = a(b^x)$ where $a > 0$ and $b > 1$ • Develop ability to write *NOW-NEXT* rules for exponential growth patterns • Develop ability to use tables and graphs to solve problems about exponential growth • Develop ability to use reasoning, estimation, and curve-fitting utilities to model data patterns exhibiting exponential-type trends • Develop skill in use of standard rules for writing exponential expressions in equivalent forms	<u>CCSS Pathway</u> (11 days, includes assessment) **Investigation 1:** OYO—choose two of A1–A3, C17–C19, R25, E30, Rv35, Rv36 **Investigation 2:** OYO—choose two of A4–A6, choose two of C20–C22, E31, Rv37, Rv38 **Investigation 3:** Problem 6 optional OYO—choose two of A7–A9, C23, R26, R27, E32 or E33, Rv39, Rv40 **Investigation 4:** Some students do Problem 1, others do Problem 2. OYO—C23, Rv41–Rv43 **Investigation 5:** OYO—A13–A16, R29, E34, Rv44, Rv45 <u>CPMP Pathway</u> (11 days, includes assessment) Use CCSS Pathway	• Graphing calculators with iteration capabilities • *CPMP-Tools* or graphing calculators with exponential regression capabilities • Unit Resource Masters
Lesson 2 Exponential Decay • Develop ability to recognize patterns of change characterizing exponential decay phenomena • Develop ability to write explicit $y = a(b^x)$ and *NOW-NEXT* rules for exponential decay functions • Develop ability to interpret zero and fractional exponents and to calculate or estimate values of expressions with those exponents • Develop ability to interpret half-life of decay phenomena and to use symbolic rules, tables, and graphs to estimate those values • Develop ability to use reasoning, estimation, and curve-fitting utilities to model exponential decay patterns • Use symbolic rules, tables, and graphs to solve problems involving exponential decay • Develop skill in use of standard rules for writing exponential expressions in equivalent forms • Develop skill in simplifying radicals	<u>CCSS Pathway</u> (11 days, includes assessment) **Investigation 1:** Problem 3 optional OYO—A1, A2, C19, R26, Rv37–Rv39 **Investigation 2:** OYO—choose two of A3–A7, A8, C20, R27, Rv40, Rv41 **Investigation 3:** Some groups do Problem 1, others do Problem 2, and all do Problem 3. CYU is optional. OYO—A11, C21, choose one of E31–E33, Rv42, Rv43 **Investigation 4:** OYO—A12–A16, C22, C23, R28, Rv44, Rv45 **Investigation 5:** OYO—A17, A18, C24, C25, R30, E34 or E36, E35, Rv46, Rv47 <u>CPMP Pathway</u> (11 days, includes assessment) Use CCSS Pathway	• Red and black checkers to demonstrate the TATS pollution cleanup simulation • Golf balls and other bouncing balls • Rulers for experiments • Graphing calculators with iteration capabilities • *CPMP-Tools* or graphing calculators with exponential regression capabilities • 100 coins and unpopped corn or beans for experiments • Unit Resource Masters
Lesson 3 Looking Back • Review and synthesize the major objectives of the unit	(2 days, includes assessment) Some groups do Task 1 and Task 3 Parts b and d. Some groups do Task 2 and Task 3 Parts a and d. All do Tasks 4–6.	• *CPMP-Tools* or graphing calculators with exponential regression capabilities • Unit Resource Masters

* *When choice is indicated, it is important to leave the choice to the student.*

Note: *It is best if Connections tasks are discussed as a whole class after they have been assigned as homework.*

Note: *The Planning Guide assumes students have access to technology for homework.*

Exponential Growth

In the popular book and movie *Pay It Forward*, 12-year-old Trevor McKinney gets a challenging assignment from his social studies teacher.

> *Think of an idea for world change, and put it into practice!*

Trevor came up with an idea that fascinated his mother, his teacher, and his classmates. He suggested that he would do something really good for three people. Then when they ask how they can pay him back for the good deeds, he would tell them to "pay it forward"—each doing something good for three other people.

Trevor figured that those three people would do something good for a total of nine others. Those nine would do something good for 27 others, and so on. He was sure that before long there would be good things happening to billions of people all around the world.

290 UNIT 5 | Exponential Functions

Exponential Growth

L esson 1 asks students to explore a variety of situations involving exponential growth. Students explore exponential growth initially with the "Pay It Forward" scenario made popular by the movie of the same name. Other contexts used to develop the understandings and skills listed in the objectives below are bacteria and population growth and the growth of money invested to earn compound interest. In Investigation 4, students use exponential regression models for less uniform data patterns. Students begin by looking at situations that can be modeled using functions of the form $y = b^x$, where b is an integer greater than 1. As the lesson progresses, students will deal with situations in the form $y = a(b^x)$, where both a and b are greater than 1. When dealing with compound interest situations, students will encounter b values between 1 and 2. Students also have the opportunity to develop several of the familiar and basic "laws of exponents" such as $a^m a^n = a^{m+n}$.

Lesson Objectives

- Develop disposition to look for and ability to recognize exponential growth patterns and phenomena

- Develop ability to represent exponential functions with rules in the form $y = a(b^x)$ where $a > 0$ and $b > 1$

- Develop ability to write *NOW-NEXT* rules for exponential growth patterns

- Develop ability to use tables and graphs to solve problems about exponential growth

- Develop ability to use reasoning, estimation, and curve-fitting utilities to model data patterns exhibiting exponential growth patterns

- Develop skill in use of standard rules for writing exponential expressions in equivalent forms

Common Core CCSS
State Standards
Focused on:
N-RN.1, A-SSE.1, A-SSE.3, A-CED.1, A-CED.2, A-REI.10, F-IF.3, F-IF.7, F-IF.8, F-BF.1, F-BF.2, F-LE.1, F-LE.2, F-LE.3, S-ID.6

Connected to:
N-Q.1, F-IF.4, F-IF.5, F-IF.9, F-BF.3

THINK ABOUT THIS SITUATION

Continue Trevor's kind of Pay It Forward thinking.

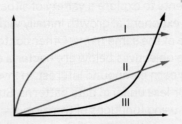

a How many people would receive a Pay It Forward good deed at each of the next several stages of the process?

b What is your best guess about the number of people who would receive Pay It Forward good deeds at the tenth stage of the process?

c Which of the graphs at the right do you think is most likely to represent the pattern by which the number of people receiving Pay It Forward good deeds increases as the process continues over time?

In this lesson, you will discover answers to questions like these and find strategies for analyzing patterns of change called *exponential growth*. You will also discover some basic properties of exponents that allow you to write exponential expressions in useful equivalent forms.

 INVESTIGATION 1

Counting in Tree Graphs

The number of good deeds in the Pay It Forward pattern can be represented by a *tree graph* that starts like this:

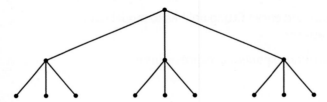

The vertices represent the people who receive and do good deeds. Each edge represents a good deed done by one person for another. As you work on the problems of this investigation, look for answers to these questions:

What are the basic patterns of exponential growth in variations of the Pay It Forward process?

How can those patterns be expressed with symbolic rules?

The point of asking these questions in a Think About This Situation is to get students to make quick intuitive guesses, not to actually do all the calculations. The other thing that this set of questions will reveal is how facile students are at recognizing exponential growth situations and at applying appropriate mathematical reasoning to deal with them. Since exposure to exponential growth patterns is now a part of many middle school curricula, you might find that your students have done quite a bit of prior work with that topic. Their responses here might lead you to adjust teaching plans for the unit, to move more quickly than one might if students have little previous exposure to exponential growth patterns.

You may wish to encourage brainstorming of realistic deeds and try to refer to them later in the investigation to demonstrate the power of exponential growth. See the Pay It Forward Web site (www.pifexperience.org) for more ideas, some clips from the movie, examples of what students around the world have done, and for opportunities to share your own stories.

THINK ABOUT THIS SITUATION

a In the Pay It Forward process described here, the first six stages would yield the following numbers of good deeds: 3, 9, 27, 81, 243, and 729.

b Students should guess the number of good deeds, but they are not expected to have well-practiced strategies for finding the answer. (The tenth stage would yield $3^{10} = 59,049$ good deeds.)

c Graph III represents the good deed pattern best because it shows increase at an increasing rate. Students may suggest the other graphs at this time. The important point is that they should be able to tell a story about the process that matches their graph choice.

PROMOTING MATHEMATICAL DISCOURSE

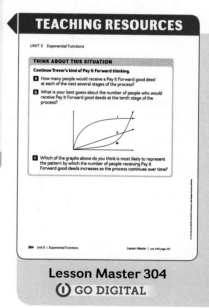

TEACHING RESOURCES

Lesson Master 304
⏻ GO DIGITAL

Think About This Situation, *page 291*

A student volunteer reads the top of page 291.

Teacher: Let's think about this situation. How many people would receive a Pay It Forward good deed in each of the next several stages of the process?

Marie: Starting from 27?

Teacher: Well, let's first hear someone explain how good deeds were done.

James: If Trevor did something good for 3 people, and then each of them did something good for 3 people, that would be 3 times 3 or 9 people that would have something good done for them. Then if each of those 9 people did something good for 3 people, that would be 9 times 3 or 27 good deeds already.

Juan: So, next would be 81 more good things happening.

Teacher: Do you all agree with Juan? *(Students indicate agreement.)* At what stage of the Pay It Forward process do we have 81 good deeds done?

Amy: The fourth stage.

Teacher: Remember that we expect people to explain their thinking in this class without being asked to do so.

Amy: Oh yeah. At the first stage, 3 good deeds were done. So, 9 is stage 2, 27 is stage 3, and 81 is the fourth stage.

Teacher: Okay, now guess the number of good deeds at the tenth stage of the process. *(Pause.)* Miko, what number do you have in mind?

Miko: Maybe about 1,000.

Aravind: No, it would be more than that. Probably like 10,000.

Teacher: Anyone else want to tell the class your guess?

Travis: I was thinking more like 30,000.

Teacher: Okay, everyone write down a guess for now. You will see how close you were when you do Problem 1 of the investigation. Which of the graphs here do you think is most likely to represent the pattern by which the number of Pay It Forward good deeds increases as the process continues over time?

Drew: I think it's the first graph because at first, the number of Pay It Forward good deeds increases rapidly. But then eventually, it will have spread to most people, and the number of new people who receive Pay It Forward good deeds will start to level off.

Chris: I think it's the third one because for the first couple of stages, the number was pretty low, but then the number would get bigger and bigger.

Teacher: Does anyone want to make a case for the second graph?

Tammi: No, it can't be the second one because that graph is increasing at a constant rate, and we know that the numbers aren't increasing at a constant rate.

Teacher: Good thinking. Well, in this lesson you will discover answers to questions like these and find strategies for analyzing patterns of change called exponential growth.

Counting in Tree Graphs

The goal of this investigation is to develop student understanding and skill in recognizing and modeling patterns of exponential growth with rules like $NEXT = b \cdot NOW$ and $y = b^x$. The central problem setting is the Pay It Forward process, varied to present situations for different exponential growth rates. Tree graphs are used to provide a visual image of the multiplicative growth pattern. A second example involving bacteria reproduction is presented in the Check Your Understanding task. Throughout this investigation, stress the pattern of change, not the starting point.

COLLABORATION SKILL

Propose ways to approach a problem.

1 At the start of the Pay It Forward process, only one person does good deeds—for three new people. In the next stage, the three new people each do good things for three more new people. In the next stage, nine people each do good things for three more new people, and so on, with no person receiving more than one good deed.

a. Make a table that shows the number of people who will receive good deeds at each of the next seven stages of the Pay It Forward process. Then plot the (*stage*, *number of good deeds*) data.

Stage of Process	1	2	3	4	5	6	7	8	9	10
Number of Good Deeds	3	9	27							

b. How does the number of good deeds at each stage grow as the tree progresses? How is that pattern of change shown in the plot of the data?

c. How many stages of the Pay It Forward process will be needed before a total of at least 25,000 good deeds will be done?

2 Consider now how the number of good deeds would grow if each person touched by the Pay It Forward process were to do good deeds for only two other new people, instead of three.

a. Make a tree graph for several stages of this Pay It Forward process.

b. Make a table showing the number of good deeds done at each of the first 10 stages of the process and plot those sample (*stage*, *number of good deeds*) values.

c. How does the number of good deeds increase as the Pay It Forward process progresses in stages? How is that pattern of change shown in the plot of the data?

d. How many stages of this process will be needed before a total of 25,000 good deeds will have been done?

3 In the two versions of Pay It Forward that you have studied, you can use the number of good deeds at one stage to calculate the number at the next stage.

a. Use the words *NOW* and *NEXT* to write rules that express the two patterns.

b. How do the numbers and calculations indicated in the rules express the patterns of change in tables of (*stage*, *number of good deeds*) data?

c. Write a rule relating *NOW* and *NEXT* that could be used to model a Pay It Forward process in which each person does good deeds for four other new people. What pattern of change would you expect to see in a table of (*stage*, *number of good deeds*) data for this Pay It Forward process?

4 What are the main steps (not keystrokes) required to use a calculator to produce tables of values like those you made in Problems 1 and 2?

1 a.

Stage of Process	1	2	3	4	5	6	7	8	9	10
Number of Good Deeds	3	9	27	81	243	729	2,187	6,561	19,683	59,049

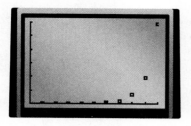

INSTRUCTIONAL NOTE

The vertices represent people who do good deeds and not the good deeds. Good deeds are represented by edges. Students might suggest putting an entry of (0, 1) in the table since the originator of the good deed tree will have done so in response to a good deed done for him or her. If that is done, the answers to the questions about total number of good deeds will be different by 1 in each case.

b. The number of good deeds triples from one stage to the next. This pattern of change is shown in the plot by the increase in the vertical distance from the x-axis and also between data points. Reading along the x-axis, the vertical distance from the x-axis from one point to the next point increases by a multiple of 3. (Students may not recognize the multiplicative change in vertical distance from one point to the next. You may wish to draw a parallel to linear change at the Check Your Understanding following Investigation 2.)

c. **INSTRUCTIONAL NOTE** Students may need prompting to realize that entries in the table of Part a show numbers of good deeds done at each stage, not cumulative totals up to and including that stage. Let them think about this before prompting. It might be helpful to suggest that students add a third row to their table from Part a, showing the cumulative total of good deeds under this scheme. After the ninth stage, a total of 29,523 good deeds will have been done.

2 a.

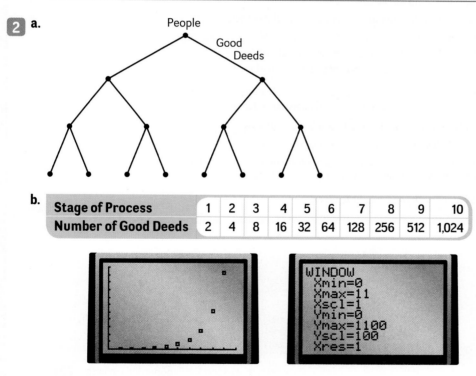

People
Good Deeds

b.

Stage of Process	1	2	3	4	5	6	7	8	9	10
Number of Good Deeds	2	4	8	16	32	64	128	256	512	1,024

(Note that this graph can look almost identical to that for the 3-good-deed table, depending on how the y-axis scale is chosen. This is a very fundamental sense in which graphs can be misleading and students need to attend to the scales being used. The general pattern of the exponential function graphs is characteristic, regardless of scale.)

NOTE The solutions to Problem 2 Parts c and d, 3, and 4 are on page T293.

5 It is also convenient to have rules that will give the number of good deeds N at any stage x of the Pay It Forward process, without finding all the numbers along the way to stage x. When students in one class were given the task of finding such a rule for the process in which each person does three good deeds for others, they came up with four different ideas:

$$N = 3x$$
$$N = x + 3$$
$$N = 3^x$$
$$N = 3x + 1$$

a. Are any of these rules for predicting the number of good deeds N correct? How do you know?

b. How can you be sure that the numbers and calculations expressed in the correct "$N = \ldots$" rule will produce the same results as the *NOW-NEXT* rule you developed in Problem 3?

c. Write an "$N = \ldots$" rule that would show the number of good deeds at stage number x if each person in the process does good deeds for two others.

d. Write an "$N = \ldots$" rule that gives the number of good deeds at stage x if each person in the process does good deeds for four others.

SUMMARIZE THE MATHEMATICS

Look back at the patterns of change in the number of good deeds in the different Pay It Forward schemes—three per person and two per person.

a Compare the processes by noting similarities and differences in:

   i. Patterns of change in the tables of (*stage, number of good deeds*) data;
   ii. Patterns in the graphs of (*stage, number of good deeds*) data;
   iii. The rules relating *NOW* and *NEXT* numbers of good deeds; and
   iv. The rules expressing number of good deeds N as a function of stage number x.

b Compare patterns of change in numbers of good deeds at each stage of the Pay It Forward process to those of linear functions that you have studied in earlier work.

   i. How are the *NOW-NEXT* rules similar, and how are they different?
   ii. How are the "$y = \ldots$" rules similar, and how are they different?
   iii. How are the patterns of change in tables and graphs of linear functions similar to those of the Pay It Forward examples, and how are they different?

Be prepared to share your ideas with the rest of the class.

c. Each new stage yields twice the number of good deeds as the previous stage. This makes for a pattern of growth that increases at an increasing rate and a plot showing points with a vertical distance from the x-axis that doubles from one data point to the next data point.

d. At the 14th stage, a total of 32,766 good deeds will have been done.

3 **a.** The pattern of change for Problem 1 is $NEXT = 3 \cdot NOW$.
The pattern of change for Problem 2 is $NEXT = 2 \cdot NOW$.
(When the problem asks for the pattern of change, a starting value is not necessary. If students report starting values, they will likely choose starting at 3 and starting at 2, respectively, since that is where their tables begin. Note that this is not the y-intercept for the rules $y = 3^x$ and $y = 2^x$.)

b. In the tables, each number of good deeds is either 3 times or 2 times the number at the previous stage.

c. $NEXT = 4 \cdot NOW$, starting at 4. The pattern of change would be increasing at an increasing rate.

4 Enter the first number of good deeds in the calculator. Then use that answer times 3 for each stage. (Some students may recall the rule from middle school work and simply produce a table by entering $y = 3^x$ in the Y= menu.)

5 **a.** Yes, the third choice, $N = 3^x$, is correct. One way to check its correctness is to use the table feature of a calculator and compare a table made using $N = 3^x$ to the table made in Problem 1. Students may also test various values of x in the rule and compare the results with their table entries from Problem 1. Students could also note the meaning of $N = 3^x$ for each value of x. It means use 3 as a factor x times.

b. The first few stages could be compared.

c. $N = 2^x$, where x is the stage number and N is the number of good deeds at stage x.

d. $N = 4^x$, where x is the stage number and N is the number of good deeds at stage x.

UNIT 5 Exponential Functions

SUMMARIZE THE MATHEMATICS

Look back at the patterns of change in the number of good deeds in the different Pay It Forward schemes—three per person and two per person.

a Compare the processes by noting similarities and differences in:

i. Patterns of change in the tables of (stage, *number of good deeds*) data;

ii. Patterns in the graphs of (stage, *number of good deeds*) data;

iii. The rules relating *NOW* and *NEXT* numbers of good deeds; and

iv. The rules expressing number of good deeds *N* as a function of stage number *x*.

b Compare patterns of change in numbers of good deeds at each stage of the Pay It Forward process to those of linear functions that you have studied in earlier work.

i. How are the *NOW-NEXT* rules similar, and how are they different?

ii. How are the "*y* = …" rules similar, and how are they different?

iii. How are the patterns of change in tables and graphs of linear functions similar to those of the Pay It Forward examples, and how are they different?

Be prepared to share your ideas with the rest of the class.

Lesson Master | *use with page 293* Unit 5 | Exponential Functions 305

Lesson Master 305
ⓘ GO DIGITAL

UNIT 5 Exponential Functions   Name _____
                                 Date _____

Comparing Functions

	Linear Functions	Exponential Growth Functions	Exponential Decay Functions
y = … rule			
NOW-NEXT rule			
Table			
Graph			
Context Type			

306 Unit 5 | Exponential Functions   Student Master | *use with pages 293 and 299*

Student Master 306
ⓘ GO DIGITAL

MATH TOOLKIT

Compare linear functions to exponential growth functions, specifically addressing the tables, rules, and graphs. A blackline master is provided for students to organize their thinking.

SUMMARIZE THE MATHEMATICS

a

i. In both tables, *y* values increase at an increasing rate. With the 3-per-person table, each *y*-value entry is three times the previous entry. In the 2-per-person table, each *y*-value entry is twice the previous entry. The entries in the 3-per-person table increase much more rapidly than those in the 2-per-person table.

ii. In the graphs, the vertical distance from the *x*-axis for successive points either triples or doubles. The pattern shows points with *y* values that are increasing at an increasing rate. The 3-per-person graph shows *y* values increasing at a faster rate than the 2-per-person graph. (It is important for students to connect their vocabulary such as "steeper" or "rising faster" to the multiplicative rate of increase in the vertical distance.)

iii. The *NOW-NEXT* rules are set up similarly, but the 3-per-person situation *NOW*s are multiplied by 3, whereas the 2-per-person situation *NOW*s are multiplied by 2. The rules are $NEXT = 3 \cdot NOW$, starting at 3, and $NEXT = 2 \cdot NOW$, starting at 2.

iv. Both are in the form $N = b^x$, but the *b* value for each rule is determined by the number of good deeds done by one person at each stage—three in the first situation and two in the second.

b

i. Both have predetermined starting values, and both involve performing a single operation on the *NOW* value to calculate the *NEXT* value. The *NOW-NEXT* rules for linear functions involve repeatedly *adding* a constant number, while the Pay It Forward exponential *NOW-NEXT* rules involve repeated *multiplication* by a constant number.

ii. Linear functions are of the form $y = a + bx$, where a constant is multiplied by *x* and another constant is added to this expression. The rules for the Pay It Forward process were of the form $y = b^x$. For these cases, the variable was an exponent to represent repeated multiplicative growth.

iii. In the tables of linear functions, there is a constant additive change between successive *y* entries (given a constant rate of change in the *x* entries). With the tables of the Pay It Forward examples, the consecutive *y* values differ by a constant multiplicative factor. As the name would imply, graphs of linear functions are straight lines. When the *x* values increase by a constant amount, successive points are a constant vertical distance apart. Exponential graphs of the type encountered in this investigation begin somewhat flat and then increase at an increasing rate. When the *x* values increase by a constant amount, the vertical distance from the *x*-axis increases by a multiplicative factor.

PROCESSING PROMPT _____ proposed that we do
                        (group number)

_____ on _____ .
(solution strategy)   (problem number)

ELL TIPS In recent years, educational specialists have done significant research to determine the most effective way to teach content to English language learners. Many models focus on teaching content and language simultaneously.

One such model is the Cognitive Academic Language Learning Approach (CALLA). It was developed by Anna Uhl Chamot and J. Michael O'Malley. In the CALLA model, content becomes the means by which language skills are learned, not vice versa. The model assumes that students will master academic language as they need it to understand and process content. Academic language becomes the means by which students communicate major concepts and processes particular to a subject area.

Much of the early research for the CALLA approach involved interview with actual ELLs. Many were high-achievers who had developed specific learning strategies to help them learn material in different content areas. CALLA suggests that ELLs need to be prepared with an arsenal of learning strategies to be successful in a content-based classroom.

The CALLA model focuses on three goals:

1. selecting major topics from a content area

2. developing the academic language skills needed to understand and process the material from that content area

3. using specific learning strategies that can aid in the learning of that content and language

UNIT 5

 CHECK YOUR UNDERSTANDING

The patterns in spread of good deeds by the Pay It Forward process occur in other quite different situations. For example, when bacteria infect some part of your body, they often grow and split into pairs of genetically equivalent cells over and over again.

a. Suppose a single bacterium lands in a cut on your hand. It begins spreading an infection by growing and splitting into two bacteria every 20 minutes.

   i. Complete a table showing the number of bacteria after each 20-minute period in the first three hours. (Assume none of the bacteria are killed by white blood cells.)

Number of 20-min Periods	1	2	3	4	5	6	7	8	9
Bacteria Count	2	4							

   ii. Plot the (*number of time periods, bacteria count*) values.

   iii. Describe the pattern of growth of bacteria causing the infection.

b. Use *NOW* and *NEXT* to write a rule relating the number of bacteria at one time to the number 20 minutes later. Then use the rule to find the number of bacteria after fifteen 20-minute periods.

c. Write a rule showing how the number of bacteria N can be calculated from the number of stages x in the growth and division process.

d. How are the table, graph, and symbolic rules describing bacteria growth similar to and different from the Pay It Forward examples? How are they similar to, and different from, typical patterns of linear functions?

INVESTIGATION 2

Getting Started

The patterns of change that occur in counting the good deeds of a Pay It Forward scheme and the growing number of bacteria in a cut are examples of *exponential growth*. Exponential functions get their name from the fact that in rules like $N = 2^x$ and $N = 3^x$, the independent variable occurs as an exponent. As you work on the problems in this investigation, look for answers to the following questions:

> *What are the forms of NOW-NEXT and "y = …" rules*
> *for basic exponential functions?*

> *How can those rules be modified to model other*
> *similar patterns of change?*

✓ CHECK YOUR UNDERSTANDING

a. i.

Number of 20-minute Periods	1	2	3	4	5	6	7	8	9
Number of Bacteria in Cut	2	4	8	16	32	64	128	256	512

ii.

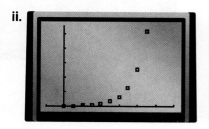 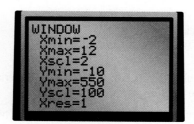

iii. The number of bacteria increases at an increasing rate, doubling from one time period to the next.

b. $NEXT = 2 \cdot NOW$, starting at 1; after fifteen 20-minute periods, there would be 32,768 bacteria.

c. $N = 2^x$, where x is the number of 20-minute periods and N represents the number of bacteria.

d. Students should recognize that the table, graph, and rule for this context are identical to those of the two-person Pay It Forward situation. However, in the bacteria growth table, the y values represent the total number of bacteria at each stage whereas in the Pay It Forward table, the y values represent only the number of good deeds done at that stage, not the cumulative total.

   In the tables of linear functions, there is a constant additive rate of change between successive y entries. With the tables of exponential rules, the consecutive y values differ by a constant multiplicative factor. As the name implies, graphs of linear functions are straight lines, where exponential graphs of the type in this investigation begin somewhat flat and then increase at an increasing rate.

INVESTIGATION 2   **CCSS**   A-SSE.1, A-CED.1, A-CED.2, A-REI.10, F-IF.3, F-IF.7, F-BF.1, F BF.2, F-LE.1, F-LE.2, N-Q.1, F-IF.4, F-IF.9, S-ID.6

Getting Started

The aim of this investigation is to extend student understanding of exponential functions to deal with cases in which the multiplicative growth begins from a starting value other than 1. Students should learn how to model these exponential growth patterns with *NOW-NEXT* and "$y = ...$" rules and to recognize the implications of the different starting values for the y-intercept of the graphs.

   Problems 1–4 deal with the bacteria function and the Pay It Forward situation where the initial value is greater than 1. Have students work these problems and discuss them before moving on to Problems 5–8.

1 Infections seldom start with a single bacterium. Suppose that you cut yourself on a rusty nail that puts 25 bacteria cells into the wound. Suppose also that those bacteria divide in two after every quarter of an hour.

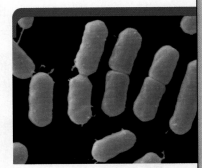

  a. Make and record a guess of how many bacteria you think would be present in the cut after 8 hours (32 quarter-hours) if the infection continues to spread as predicted. (Assume that your body does not fight off the infection and you do not apply medication.) Then answer the following questions to check your ability to estimate the rate of exponential growth.

  b. Complete a table showing the first several numbers in the bacteria growth pattern:

Number of Quarter-Hour Periods	0	1	2	3	4
Number of Bacteria in the Cut	25	50			

  c. Use *NOW* and *NEXT* to write a rule showing how the number of bacteria changes from one quarter-hour to the next, starting from 25 at time 0.

  d. Write a rule showing how to calculate the number of bacteria N in the cut after x quarter-hour time periods.

  e. Use the rules in Parts c and d to calculate the number of bacteria after 8 hours. Then compare the results to each other and to your initial estimate in Part a.

2 Compare the pattern of change in this situation to the simple case that started from a single bacterium by noting similarities and differences in the:

  a. tables of (*number of time periods, bacteria count*) values;

  b. graphs of (*number of time periods, bacteria count*) values; and

  c. *NOW-NEXT* and "$N = ...$" rules.

3 Investigate the number of bacteria expected after 8 hours if the starting number of bacteria is 30, 40, 60, or 100, instead of 25. For each starting number at time 0, complete Parts a–c. (Divide the work among your classmates.)

  a. Make a table of (*number of time periods, bacteria count*) values for 8 quarter-hour time periods.

  b. Write two rules that model the bacteria growth—one relating *NOW* and *NEXT* and the other beginning "$N = ...$."

  c. Use each rule to find the number of bacteria after 8 hours and check that you get the same results.

  d. Now compare results from two of the cases—starting at 30 and starting at 40.

   i. How are the *NOW-NEXT* and "$N = ...$" rules for bacteria counts similar, and how are they different?

   ii. How are patterns in the tables and graphs of (*number of time periods, bacteria count*) data similar, and how are they different?

Custom Medical Stock Photo/Getty Images

1 **a.** Guesses will vary. You may wish to ask students for some quick guesstimates as you launch the problem. The number will actually be more than 100 billion after 8 hours.

b.

Number of Quarter-Hour Periods	0	1	2	3	4
Number of Bacteria in Cut	25	50	100	200	400

c. $NEXT = 2 \cdot NOW$, starting at 25

d. $N = 25(2^x)$, where x is the number of quarter-hour periods and N is the number of bacteria in the cut.

e. Students should compare their guesses from Part a to the actual amount of 107,374,182,400 bacteria.

2 **a.** Both tables have entries for the number of bacteria that are twice the previous entry.

b. Both graphs have similar overall shapes, though the graph with the starting number of 25 bacteria begins and remains "above" the graph starting with one bacterium.

c. The *NOW-NEXT* rules will only differ in their starting values—the simple case at 1 and the new case at 25. Because both cases double every time stage, the "$N = ...$" rules will still involve taking 2 to a power of x, however, the case starting at 25 will now have a constant factor of 25 in the rule.

> **INSTRUCTIONAL NOTE** There doesn't seem to be any standard terminology for that term in exponential expressions. However, students will realize that it tells the y-intercept of the graph and the $x = 0$ or "starting" value, when time is zero, of the exponential growth pattern. Students may see this more clearly after Problem 3. You may choose to use the term "coefficient" for the "a" value in the $y = a(b)^x$ form.

3 | **INSTRUCTIONAL NOTE** In Problem 3 each student should complete Parts a–c for one starting value and compare with other students.

a.

Number of Quarter-Hours	0	1	2	3	4	5	6	7	8
Number of Bacteria in Cut	30	60	120	240	480	960	1,920	3,840	7,680

Number of Quarter-Hours	0	1	2	3	4	5	6	7	8
Number of Bacteria in Cut	40	80	160	320	640	1,280	2,560	5,120	10,240

Number of Quarter-Hours	0	1	2	3	4	5	6	7	8
Number of Bacteria in Cut	60	120	240	480	960	1,920	3,840	7,680	15,360

Number of Quarter-Hours	0	1	2	3	4	5	6	7	8
Number of Bacteria in Cut	100	200	400	800	1,600	3,200	6,400	12,800	25,600

NOTE The solutions to Problem 3 Parts b–d are on page T296.

Just as bacteria growth won't always start with a single cell, other exponential growth processes can start with different initial numbers. Think again about the Pay It Forward scheme in Investigation 1.

4 Suppose that four good friends decide to start their own Pay It Forward tree. To start the tree, they each do good deeds for three different people. Each of those new people in the tree does good deeds for three other new people, and so on.

a. What *NOW-NEXT* rule shows how to calculate the number of good deeds done at each stage of this tree?

b. What "$N = ...$" rule shows how to calculate the number of good deeds done at any stage x of this tree?

c. How would the *NOW-NEXT* and "$N = ...$" rules be different if the group of friends starting the tree had five members instead of four?

d. Which of the Pay It Forward schemes below would most quickly reach a stage in which 1,000 good deeds are done? Why does that make sense?

Scheme 1: Start with a group of four friends and have each person in the tree do good deeds for two different people; or

Scheme 2: Start with only two friends and have each person in the tree do good deeds for three other new people.

In studying exponential growth, it is helpful to know the *initial value* of the growing quantity. For example, the initial value of the growing bacteria population in Problem 1 was 25. You also need to know when the initial value occurs. For example, the bacteria population was 25 after 0 quarter-hour periods.

In Problem 4 on the other hand, 12 good deeds are done at Stage 1. In this context, "Stage 0" does not make much sense, but we can extend the pattern backward to reason that $N = 4$ when $x = 0$.

5 Use your calculator and the ⬛ key to find each of the following values: $2^0, 3^0, 5^0, 23^0$.

a. What seems to be the calculator value for b^0, for any positive value of b?

b. Recall the examples of exponential patterns in bacterial growth. How do the "$N = ...$" rules for those situations make the calculator output for b^0 reasonable?

6 Now use your calculator to make tables of (x, y) values for each of the following functions. Use integer values for x from 0 to 6. Make notes of your observations and discussion of questions in Parts a and b.

i. $y = 5(2^x)$ **ii.** $y = 4(3^x)$

iii. $y = 3(5^x)$ **iv.** $y = 7(2.5^x)$

a. What patterns do you see in the tables? How do the patterns depend on the numbers in the function rule?

b. What differences would you expect to see in tables of values and graphs of the two exponential functions $y = 3(6^x)$ and $y = 6(3^x)$?

b. In the "$y = \ldots$" rules below, x is the number of quarter-hour time periods and N is the number of bacteria in the cut.

$NEXT = 2 \cdot NOW$, starting at 30; $N = 30(2^x)$
$NEXT = 2 \cdot NOW$, starting at 40; $N = 40(2^x)$
$NEXT = 2 \cdot NOW$, starting at 60; $N = 60(2^x)$
$NEXT = 2 \cdot NOW$, starting at 100; $N = 100(2^x)$

c. After 8 hours, the bacteria counts are respectively: 128,849,018,880; 171,798,691,840; 257,698,037,760; and 429,496,729,600.

d. i. The *NOW-NEXT* rules differed only in their starting values, 30 or 40. These starting values became the coefficients of the exponential terms in the "$N = \ldots$" rules.

ii. The graphs have the same general shape but different y-intercepts. The tables have the same pattern of change: the y values double for each increase of 1 in x, but because the functions have different starting values, the values in the tables are different.

> **DIFFERENTIATION**
>
> For students who need a bit more challenge, ask them to write a rule that gives the number of bacteria after t hours. Two such rules are $N = 30(16^t)$ and $N = 30(2^{4t})$.

4 **a.** $NEXT = 3 \cdot NOW$, starting at 12 good deeds done. (Note we are counting the number of deeds, not the number of people.)

b. $N = 4(3^x)$, where x represents integers greater than or equal to 1.

c. The starting value for the *NOW-NEXT* rule would be $3 \times 5 = 15$, rather than $3 \times 4 = 12$. In the "$N = \ldots$" rule, the coefficient multiplied by 3^x would be 5 rather than 4.

d. Scheme 2 will produce 1,458 good deeds in Stage 6, while Scheme 1 will produce 1,024 good deeds in Stage 8.

The results for Scheme 2 are greater than those for Scheme 1 for every stage beyond the first. This is reasonable because the size of the exponential base is much more influential in shaping the pattern of growth than is the starting value.

5 **a.** b^0 has a value of 1, for any positive value of b.

b. At Stage 0, or x values of 0, the bacteria rules give the initial amounts of bacteria since $b^0 = 1$ and is multiplied by the initial amount of bacteria a.

6 **a.** When a table starts with $x = 0$, the first y value is the coefficient in the function rule. The pattern in the y values of the table is that consecutive y values are multiplied by the number to which x is the exponent. That number is the multiplicative growth factor.

b. Assuming the x entries are increasing in integer increments, each y entry in a $y = 3(6^x)$ table would be 6 times that of the previous y entry, as opposed to only 3 times for each entry in a $y = 6(3^x)$ table. The y entry for $x = 0$ would be 3 for $y = 3(6^x)$ and 6 for $y = 6(3^x)$. The graph of $y = 3(6^x)$ has the y value of 3 when $x = 0$ and grows rapidly as x increases. The graph of $y = 6(3^x)$ has the y value of 6 when $x = 0$ and grows less rapidly as x increases.

> **DIFFERENTIATION**
>
> Some students find examining patterns like this helpful in understanding why $n^0 = 1$.
>
> $64 = 2^6$
> $32 = 2^5$
> $16 = 2^4$
> $\underline{} = 2^3$
> $\underline{} = 2^2$
> $\underline{} = 2^1$
> $\underline{} = 2^0$

7 Suppose you are on a team studying the growth of bacteria in a laboratory experiment. At the start of your work shift in the lab, there are 64 bacteria in one petri dish culture, and the population seems to be doubling every hour.

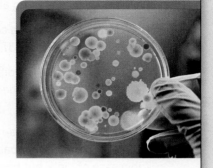

a. What rule should predict the number of bacteria in the culture at a time x hours after the start of your work shift?

b. What would it mean to calculate values of y for negative values of x in this situation?

c. What value of y would you expect for $x = -1$? For $x = -2$? For $x = -3$ and -4?

d. Use your calculator to examine a table of (x, y) values for the function $y = 64(2^x)$ when $x = 0, -1, -2, -3, -4, -5, -6$. Compare results to your expectations in Part c. Then explain how you could think about this problem of bacteria growth in a way so that the calculator results make sense.

8 Study tables and graphs of (x, y) values to estimate solutions for each of the following equations and inequalities. In each case, be prepared to explain what the solution tells about bacteria growth in the experiment of Problem 7.

a. $1,024 = 64(2^x)$

b. $8,192 = 64(2^x)$

c. $64(2^x) > 25,000$

d. $4 = 64(2^x)$

e. $64(2^x) < 5,000$

f. $64(2^x) = 32$

SUMMARIZE THE MATHEMATICS

The exponential functions that you studied in this investigation describe patterns of change in bacteria growth and numbers of people in a Pay It Forward tree. They have some features in common.

a Each *NOW-NEXT* rule fits the pattern *NEXT* = $b \cdot$ *NOW*, starting at a. What do the values of b and a tell about the pattern of change represented by the *NOW-NEXT* rule? How will that pattern be illustrated in a table or a graph of (x, y) values?

b Each "$y = \ldots$" rule fits the pattern $y = a(b^x)$. What do the values of a and b tell about the pattern of change represented by the rule? How will that pattern be illustrated in a table or a graph of (x, y) values?

c What is the value of b^x, when x is 0? What would this result mean in a problem situation where exponential growth is being studied?

d How would you calculate values of b^x when x is a negative number? What would those results mean in a problem situation where exponential growth is being studied?

Be prepared to explain your ideas to the entire class.

7 **a.** $N = 64(2^x)$

b. Using negative values of x would mean the number of hours previous to the starting point of the work shift. The y values would then represent the number of bacteria at previous time periods.

c. For $x = -1, -2, -3, -4, \ldots$, corresponding y values are 32, 16, 8, 4, ...

d.

x	−6	−5	−4	−3	−2	−1	−0
y	1	2	4	8	16	32	64

Since moving forward in time produces doubling of the number of bacteria, moving backward should reasonably involve multiplying the current amount by one-half (or dividing by 2).

8 **INSTRUCTIONAL NOTE** Encourage students to use tables for some parts and graphs for other parts. As you review answers to these questions, be sure to ask students to explain their strategies for producing exact or approximate solutions. At this point, they will have only scanning of tables and graphs or guess-and-test strategies available, since formal solution of exponential equations requires logarithms.

If students are comfortable with their graphing calculators and not intimidated by thinking about bacteria growth occurring almost continuously during any one-hour period, they might come up with more precise estimates for some of the inequalities in this problem. Meaning of fractional exponents is dealt with in Lesson 2, but it would be appropriate to raise the question here too.

a. $x = 4$; The bacteria population is 1,024 after 4 hours.

b. $x = 7$; The bacteria population is 8,192 after 7 hours.

c. $x \geq 9$; The bacteria population will be more than 25,000 after 9 or more hours. (Assuming nearly continuous growth, a more precise estimate would be $x > 8.61$ hours.)

d. $x = -4$; Four hours before the work shift began, the bacteria population was 4.

e. $x \leq 6$; The bacteria population will be less than 5,000 for every time amount less than or equal to 6 hours. (Assuming nearly continuous growth, a more precise estimate would be 6.288 hours.)

f. $x = -1$; The population was 32, 1 hour before the work shift began.

PROMOTING MATHEMATICAL DISCOURSE

TEACHING RESOURCES

UNIT 5 Exponential Functions

SUMMARIZE THE MATHEMATICS

The exponential functions that you studied in this investigation describe patterns of change in bacteria growth and numbers of people in a Pay It Forward tree. They have some features in common.

a Each NOW-NEXT rule fits the pattern NEXT = b · NOW, starting at a. What do the values of b and a tell about the pattern of change represented by the NOW-NEXT rule? How will that pattern be illustrated in a table or a graph of (x, y) values?

b Each "y = ..." rule fits the pattern y = a(bˣ). What do the values of a and b tell about the pattern of change represented by the rule? How will that pattern be illustrated in a table or a graph of (x, y) values?

c What is the value of bˣ, when x is 0? What would this result mean in a problem situation where exponential growth is being studied?

d How would you calculate values of bˣ when x is a negative number? What would those results mean in a problem situation where exponential growth is being studied?

Be prepared to explain your ideas to the entire class.

Lesson Master use with page 297   Unit 5 | Exponential Functions   **307**

Lesson Master 307
ⓘ GO DIGITAL

DIFFERENTIATION

Depending on the level of your students, you may wish to introduce the expression $\frac{1}{b^{|x|}}$ for calculating with negative exponents. You could ask students to examine and extend patterns to help their understanding.

$$81 = 3^4$$
$$27 = 3^3$$
$$9 = 3^2$$
$$\underline{\quad} = 3^1$$
$$\underline{\quad} = 3^0$$
$$\underline{\quad} = 3^{-1}$$
$$\underline{\quad} = 3^{-2}$$

MATH TOOLKIT

• For the rule $y = a(b^x)$, explain how the values of a and b relate to the graph of an exponential function.

• $b^0 = \underline{\quad}$

SUMMARIZE THE MATHEMATICS

a The a values will not tell much about the pattern of change in tables or graphs. They do tell the initial value of the dependent variable y in a table and the y value of the first data point for the graph.

The b values will be quite informative about patterns of change in the tables and graphs. In tables, the b value will determine what each y value entry is multiplied by to establish the next y value (assuming unit increases in x values); in graphs, the b value will determine the multiplicative increase of the vertical distance from the x-axis for consecutive points (i.e., the greater the b value, the greater the rate of increase).

b As in the response to Part a, the a values will not tell much about the pattern of change in tables or graphs. They do tell y values corresponding to x values of 0 in the tables and y-intercepts of the graphs.

The b values will be quite informative about patterns of change. In tables, the b value will determine what each entry is multiplied by to establish the next (again, assuming unit increases in x values); in graphs, the b value will determine the rate of increase of the vertical distance of the graph from the x-axis (i.e., the greater the b value, the greater the rate of increase).

c For any value of b, $b^0 = 1$. This means that in any exponential growth situation modeled by the function $y = ab^x$, at time $x = 0$, the quantity being modeled has value $ab^0 = a(1)$.

d One could calculate b^x values when x is negative by multiplying $\frac{1}{b}$ by itself, $|x|$ times. In terms of a problem situation, this result when multiplied by the initial amount would give values of the dependent variable $|x|$ number of time periods before analysis of the problem situation began.

Summary

INSTRUCTIONAL NOTE You may wish to have students again recognize the parallel between linear and exponential change. See page T297B.

PROCESSING PROMPT I was able to articulate my thinking about _____ .
(mathematical idea)

Linear Change

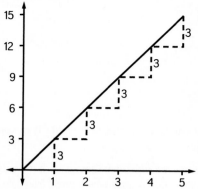

Each unit change in *x* gives an additive change of 3 in *y*.

Exponential Change

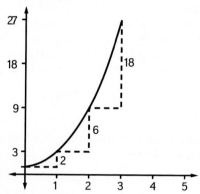

Each unit change in *x* gives a change of 3 times the previous *y* change.

PROMOTING MATHEMATICAL DISCOURSE

Summarize the Mathematics, *page 297*

Teacher: The exponential functions that you studied in this investigation describe patterns of change in bacteria growth and numbers of good deeds in a Pay It Forward tree. They have some features in common. Each *NOW-NEXT* rule fits the pattern *NEXT = b • NOW*, starting at *a*. What do the values of *b* and *a* tell about the pattern of change represented by the *NOW-NEXT* rule?

Yoko: The *a* value tells the starting point.

Teacher: How can you see that in the table or graph of the relation?

Zack: It's the first value in the table on the second row.

Evan: And it's the *y*-intercept of the graph.

Dre: But in the Pay It Forward problem, the first number in the table wasn't the *y*-intercept.

Evan: Oh yeah, you're right. So what can we call it?

Mary: Well, it's still the first point on a plot of the data.

Teacher: Okay. Let's step back a minute. What were we just describing? I don't mean repeat or summarize what we said, but rather what question were we answering?

Isabella: We were talking about what the *a* meant in the tables and graphs.

Teacher: Do the rest of you agree? *(Agreement indicated.)* Okay. But what does *a* tell you about the pattern of change represented by the *NOW-NEXT* rule?

Robert: Well, not much! It tells us where to start but really nothing about the change in values.

Teacher: Do the rest of you agree with that? *(Agreement indicated.)* Then, what is it about the rule that tells you about the pattern of change?

Robert: The *b* value tells about the pattern of change.

Teacher: Please expand on your thinking.

Robert: I mean the *b* value tells how fast the numbers will go up. The *NEXT* values will be *b* times the previous value.

Gina: We could say that the *b* value tells how fast the values are increasing—like two times or three times as much.

Teacher: How will that pattern of change be illustrated in a table or graph of the (*x*, *y*) values?

Claire: In the table, the *b* value is the number that you multiply by to get the next number in the table. And in the graph, the *b* value makes the points go up faster or slower depending on how big of a number *b* is.

Teacher: Does anyone disagree with what Claire said, or have anything to add?

Zack: I don't disagree with what Claire said, but I would have said that the *b* value determines how high up from the *x*-axis the next point is. Can I show what I mean on that grid on the board? *(Goes to grid.)* You look at how far up a point is and then the next point has to be *b* times higher.

Teacher: Okay. Each "*y* = ..." rule fits the pattern $y = a(b^x)$. What do the values of *a* and *b* tell about the pattern of change represented by the rule? And how will that pattern be illustrated in a table or a graph of (*x*, *y*) values? Be sure to talk about the pattern of change as well as about the tables and graphs.

Yoko: That's the same as the last question!

Teacher: Exactly the same?

Yoko: The *a* value is the starting point like I said before. But it doesn't really tell how fast the change is.

Teacher: But how does this *a* value relate to the table and the graph?

Claire: Oh, this *a* value *will be* the *y*-intercept of the graph.

Teacher: Always?

Claire: Yes, it has to be, because in the "*y* = ..." rule, when you use an *x* of 0, b^x is 1 and $a(b^x) = a$.

Najah: That means the *a* value in this rule may not even appear in the table of data that we use. Like in the Pay It Forward problem, we used the rule that had an *a* value of 1 because the *y*-intercept was 1, even though the starting number of good deeds was 3.

Kerry: The *b* value still represents the same thing in the "*y* = ..." rule as it did in the *NOW-NEXT* rule.

Teacher: Which was ...?

Kerry: It determines how fast the *y* values increase. It's the number we multiply in the table to get the next number, and it determines how fast the points on the graph go up away from the *x*-axis.

Teacher: Do you all agree? *(Students nod or say "yes.")* Claire reminded us that the value of b^0 is 1. What would this mean in a problem situation where exponential growth is being studied?

Jamal: That would be like at stage 0, there is one thing—like one person or one bacteria.

Teacher: How would you calculate values of b^x when *x* is a negative number?

Adria: Just type the *b* value raised to the negative power in the calculator.

Delia: Or if you had a table of the numbers for when *x* is positive, you could just keep dividing the *y* values by *b* to go backwards in the table to the negative numbers.

Teacher: Can you be more specific?

Zack: For b^x, the initial value is one. So you would take 1 divided by *b* to get the answer for $x = -1$. Then for when *x* was -2, you would take that answer and divide it by *b* again, and so on.

Teacher: We will learn more about the idea that $b^{-1} = \frac{1}{b}$ and other negative exponents in Investigation 4. For now, what does this repeated dividing by *b* mean in a problem situation where exponential growth is being studied?

Jamal: The *y* values for the negative *x* values would be the amounts of something, like bacteria, that we would have had before we started the problem.

Isabella: The negative *x*s are like negative time periods before we started measuring. But it doesn't seem to make sense to have negative time periods for the Pay It Forward tree or when you start with only 1 bacterium. How can you have a half of a bacterium anyway? *(Students chuckle.)*

Teacher: Okay, for homework you are going to do the Check Your Understanding where you will investigate another problem situation involving exponential growth—the growth of mold.

✔️ CHECK YOUR UNDERSTANDING

The drug penicillin was discovered by observation of mold growing on biology lab dishes. Suppose a mold begins growing on a lab dish. When first observed, the mold covers 7 cm² of the dish surface, but it appears to double in area every day.

a. What rules can be used to predict the area of the mold patch 4 days after the first measurement:

    i. using *NOW-NEXT* form?

    ii. using "*y* = …" form?

b. How would each rule in Part a change if the initial mold area was only 3 cm²?

c. How would each rule in Part a change if the area of the mold patch increased by a factor of 1.5 every day?

d. What mold area would be predicted after 5 days in each set of conditions from Parts a–c?

e. For "*y* = …" rules used in calculating growth of mold area, what would it mean to calculate values of *y* when *x* is a negative number?

f. Write and solve equations or inequalities that help to answer these questions.

    i. If the area of a mold patch is first measured to be 5 cm² and the area doubles each day, how long will it take that mold sample to grow to an area of 40 cm²?

    ii. For how many days will the mold patch in part i have an area less than 330 cm²?

SIR ALEXANDER FLEMING
Scottish bacteriologist who discovered penicillin

INVESTIGATION **3**

Compound Interest

Every now and then you may hear about somebody winning a big payoff in a state lottery. The winnings can be 1, 2, 5, or even 100 million dollars. The big money wins are usually paid off in annual installments for about 20 years. But some smaller prizes are paid at once. How would you react if this news report were actually about you?

Kalamazoo Teen Wins Big Lottery Prize

A Kalamazoo teenager has just won the daily lottery from a Michigan lottery ticket that she got as a birthday gift from her uncle. In a new lottery payoff scheme, the teen has two payoff choices.

One option is to receive a single $10,000 payment now.

In the other plan, the lottery promises a single payment of $20,000 ten years from now.

Mary Evans Picture Library/Alamy

✅ CHECK YOUR UNDERSTANDING

a.   i. $NEXT = 2 \cdot NOW$, starting at 7 or initial value of 7

    ii. $y = 7(2^x)$

b.   i. $NEXT = 2 \cdot NOW$, starting at 3 or initial value of 3

    ii. $y = 3(2^x)$

c.   i. $NEXT = 1.5 \cdot NOW$, starting at 7 or initial value of 7

    ii. $y = 7(1.5^x)$

d. After 5 days for—
   Part a: 224 cm^2
   Part b: 96 cm^2
   Part c: 53.156 cm^2

e. These would be the areas of the mold sample in the days previous to the $x = 0$ day.

f.   i. $5(2^x) = 40$; $x = 3$; It will take 3 days to get an area of 40 cm^2.

    ii. $5(2^x) < 330$; $x \le 6$
    For the first six days, the mold will have an area less than 330 cm^2.

INVESTIGATION 3   A-SSE.1, A-SSE.3, A-CED.1, A-CED.2, A-REI.10, F-IF.3, F-IF.8, F BF.1, F-BF.2, F-LE.1, F-LE.2, N-Q.1, F-IF.4

Compound Interest

The goal of this investigation is to extend your students' understanding and skill in working with exponential functions to cases where the growth rate is a fraction and to apply that work to problems involving compound interest on investments. As you launch this investigation, get students to express their ideas of what would influence their choices between the two options. Then get them to make a guess about which of the two main options highlighted would yield the greater investment return after 10 years. Don't do any calculations to check those ideas in the investigation launch—resolving that question is one of the key points of the problems that follow.

    Student responses will vary. Those with knowledge of or experience with investing may be more apt to receive the $10,000 now and invest it. In fact, after 10 years, the CD would have a value of $21,589.25.

> **TECHNOLOGY NOTE** As students begin this investigation, you may wish to allow them to use the calculator braces to set up recursion that keeps track of the number of stages. For example, enter **{0,10000}** on the home screen as a seed for the sequence. Then define a sequence as **{Ans(1)+1,1.08Ans(2)}**. Repeatedly pressing **ENTER** will produce ordered pairs of numbers. The first number in any pair is the counter; the second number in the pair is the corresponding term in the sequence.

1 Imagine that you had just won that Michigan lottery prize.

   a. Discuss with others your thinking on which of the two payoff methods to choose.

   b. Suppose a local bank called and said you could invest your $10,000 payment in a special 10-year certificate of deposit (CD), earning 8% interest compounded yearly. How would this affect your choice of payoff method?

As you work on the problems of this investigation, look for answers to the question:

How can you represent and reason about functions involved
in investments paying compound interest?

Of the two lottery payoff methods, one has a value of $20,000 at the end of 10 years. The value (in 10 years) of receiving the $10,000 payoff now and putting it in a 10-year certificate of deposit paying 8% interest compounded annually is not so obvious.

- After one year, your balance will be:
  $10,000 + (0.08 \times 10,000) = 1.08 \times 10,000 = \$10,800$.

- After the second year, your balance will be:
  $10,800 + (0.08 \times 10,800) = 1.08 \times 10,800 = \$11,664$.

During the next year, the CD balance will increase in the same way, starting from $11,664, and so on.

2 Write rules that will allow you to calculate the balance of this certificate of deposit:

   a. for the next year, using the balance from the current year.

   b. after any number of years x.

3 Use the rules from Problem 2 to determine the value of the certificate of deposit after 10 years. Then decide which 10-year plan will result in more money and how much more money that plan will provide.

4 Look for an explanation of your conclusion in Problem 3 by answering these questions about the potential value of the CD paying 8% interest compounded yearly.

   a. Describe the pattern of growth in the CD balance as time passes.

   b. Why isn't the change in the CD balance the same each year?

   c. How is the pattern of increase in CD balance shown in the shape of a graph for the function relating CD balance to time?

   d. How could the pattern of increase have been predicted by thinking about the rules (*NOW-NEXT* and "$y = \ldots$") relating CD balance to time?

Lesson 1 | Exponential Growth   **299**

1 **INSTRUCTIONAL NOTE** Do not let students do calculations before recording their guesses for Parts a and b. The aim of this problem is to see what their instincts are as a prelude to the careful investigation of options. As students work on Problems 2–6, they will develop a better sense of how initial amounts and interest affect total investments. You will want to come back to these two payoff options later and ask which option is better—the yearly amount or the lump sum—with the same interest rate compounded annually for 10 years.

INSTRUCTIONAL NOTE

Consider having students post their answers to Problem 1.

a. Responses will vary depending on the students' intuitions.

b. Students may realize that 8% is a good interest rate compared to other savings plans. For those who claim it is unrealistic in the current banking environment, you might suggest that the bank might be using the special rate to attract the deposit and get free publicity for its business.

2 **INSTRUCTIONAL NOTE** Students might need to continue the calculation pattern demonstrated in the text for several more lines before they are confident of the rules that capture it accurately.

a. $NEXT = 1.08 \cdot NOW$, starting at 10,000

b. $y = 10{,}000(1.08^x)$

DIFFERENTIATION If students have trouble realizing that $NEXT = NOW*0.08 + NOW$ can be written equivalently as $NEXT = NOW*1.08$, you might have them find $NEXT \div NOW$ for several successive values to see the constant ratio of 1.08. Then ask, "How could you calculate the $NEXT$ value in one step?" Some students may need to do this through most of the unit before they start going straight to $1 + r$.

3 The certificate of deposit will grow to $21,589.25 at the end of ten years, so it is $1,589.25 more than $20,000 to be paid at the same time.

INSTRUCTIONAL NOTE

You might have a class discussion after students have completed Problem 3. These three problems all focus directly on the initial problem situation.

4 a. The pattern of growth starts out at $800 per year and the annual interest earned increases gradually until in the final year there is an increase of nearly $1,600 from interest earned.

b. The account balance increases at an increasing rate because the interest earned is added to the balance, making a larger balance on which the 8% interest is earned in each succeeding year.

c. A graph of the account balance will be gently curved upward, showing an increase at an increasing rate. If the increase was constant, the graph would be a straight line.

d. Prior experiences with the sort of NOW-$NEXT$ and "$y = ...$" rules that model growth of the certificate of deposit investment suggest the exponential graph that occurs. However, because the growth rate is quite close to 1 (not 2 or 3 or 4 as in the Pay It Forward and bacteria examples), the graphs have more gentle curvature.

5 Suppose that the prize winner decided to leave the money in the CD, earning 8% interest for more than 10 years. Use tables or graphs to estimate solutions for the following equations and inequalities. In each case, be prepared to explain what the solution tells about the growth of a $10,000 investment that earns 8% interest compounded annually.

 a. $10,000(1.08^x) = 25,000$

 b. $10,000(1.08^x) = 37,000$

 c. $10,000(1.08^x) = 50,000$

 d. $10,000(1.08^x) \geq 25,000$

 e. $10,000(1.08^x) \leq 30,000$

 f. $10,000(1.08^x) = 10,000$

6 Compare the pattern of change and the final account balance for the plan that invests $10,000 in a CD that earns 8% interest compounded annually over 10 years to those for the following possible savings plans over 10 years. Write a summary of your findings.

 a. Initial investment of $15,000 earning only 4% annual interest compounded yearly

 b. Initial investment of $5,000 earning 12% annual interest compounded yearly

SUMMARIZE THE MATHEMATICS

Most savings accounts operate in a manner similar to the bank's certificate of deposit offer. However, they may have different starting balances, different interest rates, or different periods of investment.

a Describe two ways to find the value of such a savings account at the end of each year from the start to year 10. Use methods based on:

  i. a rule relating *NOW* and *NEXT*.
  ii. a rule like $y = a(b^x)$.

b What graph patterns would you expect from plots of (*year, account balance*) values?

c How would the function rules change if the interest rate changes? If the initial investment changes?

d Why does the dollar increase in the account balance get larger from each year to the next?

e How are the patterns of change that occur with the bank investment similar to and different from those of other functions that you've used while working on problems of Investigations 1 and 2? On problems of previous units?

Be prepared to explain your methods and ideas to the class.

5 **INSTRUCTIONAL NOTE** Encourage students to alternate use of table and graphs. One is confronted here with the temptation to consider fractional exponents to get exact solutions to the given equations and inequalities. If interest is only compounded annually (the problem statement does not suggest anything different), then one cannot find exact solutions to the given equations. The solutions below provide both close approximations, using fractional exponents, and the nearest integer year.

INSTRUCTIONAL NOTE

Discuss Problem 5 after students have completed it. Solicit student solutions and have students who used fractional exponentials explain their thinking. If none did, ask students whether fractional exponents make sense and have them use them.

a. Nearest whole number $x = 12$, since $10{,}000(1.08)^{12} \approx 25{,}182$. After 12 years, the certificate is worth about \$25,000. Using fractional exponents, $x \approx 11.906$ since $10{,}000(1.08)^{11.906} \approx 25{,}000$. Students could modify the table settings to get these fractional exponents.

b. Nearest whole number $x = 17$, since $10{,}000(1.08)^{17} \approx 37{,}000$. After 17 years, the certificate is worth about \$37,000. This is a very accurate estimate for the solution one would provide if fractional exponents were used.

c. Nearest whole number $x = 21$, since $10{,}000(1.08)^{21} \approx 50{,}338$. After 21 years, the certificate is worth about \$50,000. A more precise fractional value of x would be 20.912, since $10{,}000(1.08)^{20.912} \approx 50{,}000$.

d. $x \geq 12$

The CD is worth more than \$25,000 at 12 years and beyond. A more precise value of x using fractional exponents would be 11.906 years and beyond.

INSTRUCTIONAL NOTE

Some students may mistakenly solve Parts d and e as equalities.

e. $x \leq 14$ or $x < 15$

The CD is worth less than \$30,000 for up to 15 years. More precisely, using fractional exponents, 14.275 years or less.

f. $x = 0$

The CD is worth \$10,000 at the time of the investment.

6 a. \$15,000 invested at 4% annually for 10 years yields \$22,204.

b. \$5,000 invested at 12% annually for 10 years yields \$15,529.

Summary: In Problem 3, \$10,000 invested at 8% annually for 10 years yields \$21,589. Comparing the three plans, you notice that the plan investing \$15,000 at 4% annually results in the most money. But thinking about the pattern of change, in the plan with the highest interest (12%), the initial investment tripled while the initial investments for 8% and 4% only doubled and increased by a factor of about 1.5, respectively.

INSTRUCTIONAL NOTE As a follow up to Problem 6, you might want to ask students whether they think that in general doubling the interest rate will double the return after ten years, given the same \$10,000 investment (it does much better). Then ask them to think about the ultimate effect of doubling the initial investment but keeping the interest rate the same (this will result in doubling of ultimate investment value, a result that can be seen by comparing the exponential function rules).

Lesson Master 308
ⓘ **GO DIGITAL**

MATH TOOLKIT

Explain how you can determine the future value of a given amount of money if you are given:

- the principal.
- the interest rate.
- the number of years the principal is invested.

SUMMARIZE THE MATHEMATICS

a **i.** Using a *NOW-NEXT* rule, one could simply multiply the starting balance by the sum of 1 and the interest rate. This would give the balance at the end of the first year of the account. To find out the balance at the end of each additional year, one would need to continue multiplying the result by the sum of 1 and the interest rate.

ii. To use a rule like $y = a(b^x)$ to find the needed balances, it would be necessary to substitute the starting amount for a and the sum of 1 and the interest rate for b. Then, to find any end-of-year balance, one could substitute the year desired for x and evaluate the rule.

b Graphs of compound interest functions increase at an increasing rate; but often the growth factor is not much more than 1, and it may be difficult to observe this on a graph.

c If the interest rate changes, the b value in $NEXT = b \cdot NOW$, starting at a, and in $y = a(b^x)$ would need to be altered. If the initial investment changed, the first *NOW* value would change in $NEXT = b \cdot NOW$. The a value would need to be changed in $y = a(b^x)$.

d The dollar increase gets larger from year to year because each additional year the account balance that earns interest is itself increasing. The interest earned one year earns interest of its own in succeeding years. The amount of increase is a set percentage being taken of larger and larger amounts; this leads to an increasing rate of change when change is measured in dollars per year.

e The bank investment pattern of change is similar to the good deed and bacteria situations' patterns of change in that they were all nonconstant and all were increasing at an increasing rate (multiplying by a constant value). The bank pattern was not increasing at as rapid a pace as the other exponential situations, but it was similar to the population growth situations studied in the *Patterns of Change* unit involving whales and people. With regard to linear situations studied in previous units, the bank patterns are different in that the linear patterns showed a constant additive rate of change. However, for small numbers of years, the graph of an investment balance growing at compound interest rates that are typical (less than 10%) will appear nearly linear.

PROCESSING PROMPT I changed my thinking about _____ because ... .
                                                                        (mathematical idea)

Teacher Notes

✔️ CHECK YOUR UNDERSTANDING

In solving change-over-time problems in Unit 1, you discovered that the world population and populations of individual countries grow in much the same pattern as money earning interest in a bank. For example, you used data like the following to predict population growth in two countries.

- Brazil is the most populous country in South America. In 2011, its population was about 197 million. It was growing at a rate of about 0.9% per year.

- Nigeria is the most populous country in Africa. Its 2011 population was about 162 million. It was growing at a rate of about 2.5% per year.

a. Assuming that these growth rates continue, write function rules to predict the populations of these countries for any number of years x in the future.

b. Compare the patterns of growth expected in each country for the next 20 years. Use tables and graphs of (*year since 2011, population*) values to illustrate the similarities and differences you notice.

c. Write and solve equations that give estimates when:

   i. Brazil's population might reach 300 million.

   ii. Nigeria's population might reach 200 million.

d. Assuming these growth patterns continue, estimate when the population of Nigeria will be greater than the population of Brazil.

INVESTIGATION 4

Modeling Data Patterns

In the *Patterns of Change* unit, you used data about wildlife populations to make predictions and to explore effects of protection and hunting policies. For example, you used information from studies of Midwest wolf populations to predict growth over time in that species. You used information about Alaskan bowhead whale populations and hunting rates to make similar projections into the future.

In each case, you began the prediction with information about the current populations and the growth rates as percents. It is not hard to imagine how field biologists might count wolves or whales by patient observation. But they cannot observe percent growth rates, and those rates are unlikely to be constant from one year to the next. As you work on the problems of this investigation, look for answers to the following question:

> *What are some useful strategies for finding functions modeling patterns of change that are only approximately exponential?*

✔️ CHECK YOUR UNDERSTANDING

a. Brazil: $Y_1 = 197(1.009^x)$, where Y_1 is population in millions; or
NEXT = 1.009 · *NOW*, starting at 197 million.
Nigeria: $Y_2 = 162(1.025^x)$, where Y_2 is population in millions; or
NEXT = 1.025 · *NOW*, starting at 162 million.

b.

Time Since 2011 (in years)	0	5	10	15	20
Brazilian Population (in millions)	197	206	215	225	236
Nigerian Population (in millions)	162	183	207	235	265

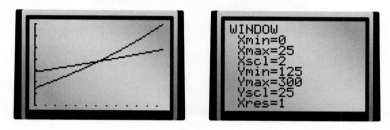

Although the Brazilian population will remain greater than that of Nigeria for many years, the Nigerian population is growing at a greater percentage rate and thus "catches up."

(Note once again how the slow exponential growth does not exhibit the kind of sharp upward bend that students have come to expect from exponential situations with larger growth-rate constants.)

c. > **INSTRUCTIONAL NOTE** Here again we confront the question about whether fractional exponents might have meaning.

> **i.** $300 = 197(1.009^x)$ gives $x \approx 47$. So, the Brazilian population will reach 300 million in about 2058.

> **ii.** $200 = 162(1.025^x)$ gives $x \approx 8.6$. So, the Nigerian population will reach 200 million in about the middle of 2019.

d. In 2023, about 12.4 years after 2011

INVESTIGATION **4** **CCSS** A-SSE.1, A-CED.1, A-CED.2, A-REI.10, F-BF.1, F-BF.2, F-LE.1, F LE.2, F-LE.3, S-ID.6, N-Q.1, F-IF.4, F-IF.5, F-BF.3

Modeling Data Patterns

The first challenge is fitting an appropriate function model to available data. The sensible steps in this modeling process include: consideration of relationships that might be embedded in the context, informal inspection of the pattern of change in the data, experimentation with possible function rules, and, if necessary, the use of a curve-fitting utility to find the "best" model.

The aim of this investigation is to develop student ability in recognizing data patterns likely to be modeled well by exponential growth functions, in using reasoning to support the choice of an exponential model, and in using graphing calculator experimentation and curve-fitting to find a good regression model. Students should think analytically about the data being modeled as well as to use "guess-and-test" and calculator-based, curve-fitting tools.

1 Suppose that census counts of Midwest wolves began in 1990 and produced these estimates for several different years.

Time Since 1990 (in years)	0	2	5	7	10	20
Estimated Wolf Population	100	300	500	900	1,500	4,200

a. Plot the wolf population data and decide whether a linear or exponential function seems likely to match the pattern of growth well. For the function type of your choice, experiment with different rules to see which rule provides a good model of the growth pattern.

b. Use your calculator or computer software to find both linear and exponential regression models for the given data pattern. Compare the fit of each function to the function you developed by experimentation in Part a.

c. What do the numbers in the linear and exponential function rules from Part b suggest about the pattern of change in the wolf population?

d. Use the model for wolf population growth that you believe to be best to calculate population estimates for the missing years 1994 and 2001 and then for the years 2015 and 2020.

2 Suppose that census counts of Alaskan bowhead whales began in 1970 and produced these estimates for several different years.

Time Since 1970 (in years)	0	5	15	20	26	31
Estimated Whale Population	5,040	5,800	7,900	9,000	11,000	12,600

a. Plot the given whale population data and decide which type of function seems likely to match the pattern of growth well. For the function type of your choice, experiment with different rules to see which provides a good model of the growth pattern.

b. Use your calculator or computer software to find both linear and exponential regression models for the data pattern. Compare the fit of each function to that of the function you developed by experimentation in Part a.

c. What do the numbers in the linear and exponential function rules from Part b suggest about patterns of change in the whale population?

d. Use the model for whale population growth that you believe to be best to calculate population estimates for the years 2002, 2005, and 2010.

1 **a.** 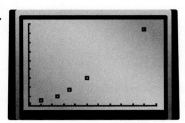 Student rules will vary, but should be exponential in form. (In 2011, wolves were removed from the threatened and endangered species list.
Source: www.fws.gov/midwest/wolf/)

b. Linear regression: $y = 209x - 284$
Exponential regression: $y = 186(1.19^x)$
Students should find the exponential function a better fit than the linear function.

c. For the linear model, the implied starting population would be -284 and the implied growth rate would be 209 wolves per year.
   For the exponential model, 186 would be the implied starting population and 19% would be the implied growth rate.

d. The table below gives approximate populations based on the exponential function in Part b. Each population estimate entry is rounded down to whole wolves.

Time Since 1990 (in years)	4	11	25	30
Year	1994	2001	2015	2020
Estimated Population	372	1,260	14,394	34,349

2 **a.** Student rules will vary. Students may think that both linear and exponential functions could be appropriate, since what is going on is percent growth with a fairly small percent. (Remember from the Whale Tale in the *Patterns of Change* unit that the natural increase was about 3% per year.) A plot of the data will look something like that at the right. But given the context of growth and the distribution of points around the linear regression line (above, below, and then above again), the most appropriate model is exponential. This can be discussed as a whole class during the Summarize the Mathematics discussion.

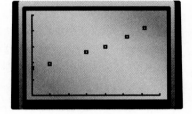

b. Linear regression: $y = 242x + 4,641$
Exponential regression: $y = 5,022(1.03^x)$
Since students are asked to make a comparison between each of these functions and their function in Part a, there should be some explanation given here regarding that comparison.

c. For the linear model, the implied starting (1970) population is around 4,641 with a constant increase of about 242 whales per year.
   For the exponential model, the implied starting population is around 5,022 with the population growing at a compound rate of 3% per year.

TECHNOLOGY NOTE

At this point, you might introduce the following method for entering the regression equation in the Y= menu. Use **ExpReg L1,L2,Y1.** If the default lists are L1 and L2, you can simply use **ExpReg Y1.** Y1 is accessed under Vars, Y-Vars, Function.

d. If students use the full calculator-produced linear and exponential regression formulas (see the Technology Note to the right), they would generate the following table.

Time Since 1970 (in years)	32	35	40
Year	2002	2005	2010
Linear Estimated	12,385	13,111	14,321
Exponential Estimated	12,392	14,131	16,382

SUMMARIZE THE MATHEMATICS

In the problems of this investigation, you studied ways of finding function models for growth patterns that could only be approximated by one of the familiar types of functions.

a How do you decide whether a data pattern is modeled best by a linear or an exponential function?

b What do the numbers a and b in a linear function $y = a + bx$ tell about patterns in:

 i. the graph of the function?
 ii. a table of (x, y) values for the function?

c What do the numbers c and d in an exponential function $y = c(d^x)$ tell about patterns in:

 i. the graph of the function?
 ii. a table of (x, y) values for the function?

d What strategies are available for finding a linear or exponential function that models a linear or exponential data pattern?

Be prepared to share your ideas and reasoning with the class.

 CHECK YOUR UNDERSTANDING

Test your ideas about the connections between functions, problem conditions, and data patterns.

a. What *NOW-NEXT* and "$y = …$" rules will express patterns of change in which a variable quantity is increasing:

 i. at a rate of 20% per year from a starting value of 750?

 ii. at a rate of 4.5% per month from a starting value of 35?

 iii. at a rate of 24 per day from a starting value of 18?

b. Write functions that provide good models for the patterns of change that relate p, q, and r to x in the following tables.

i.

x	−10	−5	0	6	15	20	30
p	1	3	5	8	12	15	18

ii.

x	−10	−5	0	6	15	20	30
p	1	8	60	650	25,000	190,000	11,000,000

iii.

x	−10	−5	0	6	15	20	30
p	1.0	1.3	1.6	2.25	3.4	4.4	7.0

UNIT 5

SUMMARIZE THE MATHEMATICS

a One might look at a plot of the data to see the overall shape of the data and compare those shapes with the various function families studied thus far. If the pattern of change for uniform increases in x values is constant, then a linear model may be best. If the differences in y values for successive data points are increasing by a multiplicative factor, then an exponential model may be best.

b   **i.** In the rule $y = a + bx$, the b value tells the slope of the graph. The greater the absolute value of b, the "steeper" the graph. The sign of b tells whether the graph is increasing (positive b) or decreasing (negative b) from left to right. The a value tells the y-coordinate of the y-intercept of the graph.

   ii. The b value indicates the constant difference between the y values in a table for unit changes in the x values. The a value corresponds to the y value entry for which the x value is 0.

c   **i.** The c value tells the y-coordinate of the y-intercept of the graph. The d value indicates the rate of increase in the graph. The y-coordinate of successive points (one x interval apart) increases by the multiplicative factor d. The higher the value of d, the more rapidly the graph will rise.

   ii. The d value indicates the ratio of a y value and the preceding y value in a table for unit changes in the x values. The c value corresponds to the y value entry for which the x value is 0.

d On many calculators, there are linear regression and exponential regression commands that allow you to find function models based on entered sets of data. If those are not available, you can inspect a data plot and experiment with function rules to see how they match the data pattern. You can also identify the values of parameters in the rules by looking for values of y when $x = 0$ and by looking for a constant difference or constant ratio between successive terms in the table.

MATH TOOLKIT

- For $y = a + bx$, what happens to the graph as b gets closer and closer to 0? What happens when $b = 0$?
- For $y = c(d^x)$, what happens to the graph when d gets closer and closer to 1? What happens when $d = 1$?

✅ CHECK YOUR UNDERSTANDING

a.   **i.** *NEXT* $= 1.20 \cdot$ *NOW*, starting at 750
$y = 750(1.20^x)$, where x is the number of years

  ii. *NEXT* $= 1.045 \cdot$ *NOW*, starting at 35
$y = 35(1.045^x)$, where x is the number of months

 iii. *NEXT* $=$ *NOW* $+ 24$, starting at 18
$y = 18 + 24x$, where x is the number of days

b. Approximate regression equations are given below.

  i. $p = 0.44x + 5.32$

 ii. $q = 58.615(1.498^x)$

 iii. $r = 1.64(1.05^x)$

INVESTIGATION **5**

Properties of Exponents I

In solving the problems in Investigations 1–4, you focused on functions modeling exponential growth. You used what you knew about the problem situations to guide development of the function models, to plan calculations that would answer the given questions, and to interpret information in rules, tables, and graphs. For example, you developed and used the rules $B = 2^x$ and $B = 25(2^x)$ to study the pattern of bacteria growth in a cut.

Since doubling occurs so often in questions about exponential growth, it is helpful to know some basic powers of 2, like $2^2 = 4$, $2^3 = 8$, $2^4 = 16$, ... , $2^9 = 512$, and $2^{10} = 1,024$. When students in one Wisconsin class had memorized those facts, someone suggested reasoning about even higher powers like this:

> Since 2^{10} is about 1,000: the value of 2^{11} should be about 2,000,
> the value of 2^{12} should be about 4,000,
> the value of 2^{13} should be about 8,000,
> $\vdots$
> the value of 2^{20} should be about 1,000,000.

How do you suppose the student was thinking about exponents to come up with that estimation strategy?

To develop and test strategies for working with exponential expressions, it helps to know some basic methods of writing these expressions in useful equivalent forms. Remember that the starting point in work with exponents is an expression like b^n, where b is any real number and n is any non-negative integer. The number b is called the **base** of the exponential expression, and n is called the **exponent** or the **power**.

$$b^n = b \cdot b \cdot b \cdot \cdots \cdot b \ (n \text{ factors}) \quad \text{and} \quad b^0 = 1 \ (\text{for } b \neq 0)$$

As you work on the problems in this investigation, look for answers to this question:

> *How can the above definition of exponent be used to discover*
> *and justify other properties of exponents that make useful*
> *algebraic manipulations possible?*

Products of Powers Work with exponents is often helped by writing products like $b^x \cdot b^y$ in simpler form or by breaking a calculation like b^z into a product of two smaller numbers.

1 Find values for w, x, and y that will make these equations true statements:

a. $2^{10} \cdot 2^3 = 2^y$

b. $5^2 \cdot 5^4 = 5^y$

c. $3 \cdot 3^7 = 3^y$

d. $2^w \cdot 2^4 = 2^7$

e. $b^4 \cdot b^2 = b^y$

f. $9^w \cdot 9^x = 9^5$

2 Examine the results of your work on Problem 1.

a. What pattern seems to relate task and result in every case?

b. How would you use the definition of exponent or other reasoning to convince another student that your answer to Part a is correct?

Properties of Exponents I

This investigation poses a series of problems designed to guide students to discover three basic exponent laws and to develop a rational explanation of those laws based on the definition of exponentiation as repeated multiplication. A parallel investigation in Lesson 2 extends the student repertoire of exponent laws.

The kind of automaticity in use of the various exponent laws that one expects will not develop in this unit. Distributed practice is the key to that kind of learning. Subsequent Review tasks will include practice with the exponent laws. It is important to help students develop a fall-back strategy for use when in doubt—each of the traditionally separate laws can be readily rederived if students keep in mind the fundamental definition on which all are bas ed: $a^n = a \cdot a \cdot \cdots \cdot a$ (n factors of a).

The introduction to this investigation recounts an experience in which students developed some number sense rules of thumb for calculating high powers of 2. You might launch this investigation by posing a question like this:

If you start with 2 and do repeated doubling, you'll discover that 2^{10} is 1,024. Which of the following choices do you think will be closest to the value of 2^{20} and why?

   a. 2,000   b. 10,000   c. 100,000   d. 1,000,000

If students are unable to provide convincing arguments for the right answer ($2^{20} = 1,048,576$), you might simply report that result and tell them that the goal of the investigation ahead is to discover ways to reason about exponential expressions to make such numerical estimates easy. Remind them of the basic definition of b^n and b^0 and set them to work on Problems 1–7.

For each exponent property, students are asked a question like, "How would you use the definition of exponent or other reasoning to convince another student that your ideas are correct?" For students to develop the kind of solid understanding that will help them retain the various laws or be able to correctly derive them again when needed, it is essential that they be pushed to such explanations, rather than simply try to memorize rules in a rote fashion!

You might choose to do an interim summary discussion after each segment of the investigation when all groups have completed work on that segment.

1 **a.** $y = 13$ **b.** $y = 6$ **c.** $y = 8$ **d.** $w = 3$

 e. $y = 6$ **f.** w and x with sum 5; could be 1 and 4, 2 and 3, 4 and 1, etc.

2 **a.** Students might say something like, "When you multiply two exponential expressions with the same base, you add exponents."

 b. In the expression $b^w \cdot b^x$, b^w implies w factors of b, while b^x implies x factors of b. Together there are $w + x$ factors of b.

3 When people work with algebraic expressions that involve exponents, there are some common errors that slip into the calculations. How would you help other students correct their understanding of operations with exponents if their work showed the following errors?

a. $3^5 = 15$

b. $3^4 \cdot 5^2 = 15^8$

c. $3^4 \cdot 5^2 = 15^6$

d. $3^4 + 3^2 = 3^6$

Power of a Power You know that $8 = 2^3$ and $64 = 8^2$, so $64 = (2^3)^2$. As you work on the next problems, look for a pattern suggesting how to write equivalent forms for expressions like $(b^x)^y$ that involve powers of powers.

4 Find values for x and z that will make these equations true statements:

a. $(2^3)^4 = 2^z$

b. $(3^5)^2 = 3^z$

c. $(5^2)^x = 5^6$

d. $(b^2)^5 = b^z$

5 Examine the results of your work on Problem 4.

a. What pattern seems to relate task and result in every case?

b. How would you use the definition of exponent or other reasoning to convince another student that your answer to Part a is correct?

c. What would you expect to see as common errors in evaluating a power of a power like $(4^3)^2$? How would you help someone who made those errors correct their understanding of how exponents work?

Power of a Product The area of a circle can be calculated from its radius r using the formula $A = \pi r^2$. It can be calculated from the diameter using the formula $A = \pi(0.5d)^2$. Next search for a pattern showing how powers of products like $(0.5d)^2$ can be expressed in equivalent forms.

6 Find values for x and y that will make these equations true statements:

a. $(6 \cdot 11)^3 = 6^x \cdot 11^y$

b. $(3\pi)^4 = 3^x \cdot \pi^y$

c. $(2m)^3 = 2^x m^y$

d. $(m^3p)^2 = m^x p^y$

7 Examine the results of your work on Problem 6.

a. What pattern seems to relate task and result in every case?

b. How would you use the definition of exponent or other reasoning to convince another student that your answer to Part a is correct?

c. What would you expect to see as the most common errors in evaluating a power of a product like $(4t)^3$? How would you help someone who made those errors correct their understanding of how exponents work?

UNIT 5

3 | **INSTRUCTIONAL NOTE** Because operations with exponential expressions involve various combinations of multiplication and addition of powers, it is not surprising that students get them confused. It is possible to correct errors by reliance on the meaning of exponential expressions, but at some point students should develop correct habits that don't require returning to first principles for simple calculations. Until that time, it is useful to keep reminding students what exponential expressions mean. This problem is designed to prompt students to develop that habit and not to memorize some flawed or overgeneralized "rules" like "whenever you multiply, you add exponents."

a. Writing $3^5 = 15$ indicates forgetting or misunderstanding of *how* exponents imply multiplication; the exponent 5 means to take 3 as a factor five times, $3 \cdot 3 \cdot 3 \cdot 3 \cdot 3$, to get 243.

b. Writing $3^4 \cdot 5^2 = 15^8$ also indicates misunderstanding of how the exponents imply multiplication. Four factors of 3 and two factors of 5 cannot be combined to get eight factors of 15. Writing out $3 \cdot 3 \cdot 3 \cdot 3 \cdot 5 \cdot 5$, we can rearrange the factors to get $(3 \cdot 3) \cdot (3 \cdot 5) \cdot (3 \cdot 5)$ or $3^2 \cdot 15^2$.

c. Writing $3^4 \cdot 5^2 = 15^6$ indicates that the student knows something about how products lead to addition of powers, but has ignored the requirement that there be a common base. To get 15^6 would require $(3 \cdot 5)$ six times.

d. Writing $3^4 + 3^2 = 3^6$ overlooks the fact that 3^6 means a product with six factors of 3. The student knows that there is something about adding exponents and a common base. But the key that is missing is again the relationship between exponents and repeated factors.

4 **a.** $z = 12$ **b.** $z = 10$ **c.** $x = 3$ **d.** $z = 10$

5 **a.** The general idea in this case can be expressed by saying, "To find a power of a power, multiply the exponents."

b. The expression $(b^x)^y = (b^x) \cdot (b^x) \cdot \cdots \cdot (b^x)$ (y factors) can be interpreted as a product consisting of y groups with x factors of b in each group. By the meaning of multiplication, this means that there will be a total of xy factors of b.

c. The most common errors in evaluating exponential expressions like $(4^3)^2$ will be to evaluate 4^3 as 12 and perhaps to add the exponents to get 4^5. The most basic explanation for someone who makes one of these errors is to return to the meaning of exponents and the expression form in Part b. For example, $(4^3)^2 = 4^3 \cdot 4^3$. From work on Problems 1 and 2, we know that $4^3 \cdot 4^3 = 4^6$.

6 **a.** $x = y = 3$ **b.** $x = y = 4$ **c.** $x = y = 3$ **d.** $x = 6$ and $y = 2$

7 **a.** The general idea can be summarized with words like this, "A power of a product is equal to the product of the same power of each factor."

b. The expression $(ab)^x = (ab) \cdot (ab) \cdot \cdots \cdot (ab)$ (x factors) is an extended product with x factors of a and x factors of b. Thus, its factors can be rearranged to $(a \cdot a \cdot a \cdot \cdots \cdot a)(b \cdot b \cdot b \cdot \cdots \cdot b)$ with x factors each of a and b. The exponential shorthand for this is $a^x \cdot b^x$.

c. In evaluating powers of products like $(4t)^3$, it is always tempting to forget that the exponent applies to both factors, leading to errors like $4t^3$.

SUMMARIZE THE MATHEMATICS

The problems of this investigation asked you to formulate, test, and justify several principles that allow writing of exponential expressions in convenient equivalent forms.

a For each of the properties of exponents you explored in Problems 1–7, how would you explain the property in words that describe the relationship between two equivalent forms of exponential expressions?

b Summarize the properties of exponents you explored in Problems 1–7 by completing these statements to show equivalent forms for exponential expressions:

   i. $b^m \cdot b^n = \ldots$ **ii.** $(b^m)^n = \ldots$ **iii.** $(ab)^n = \ldots$

c What examples would you use to illustrate common errors in use of exponents, and how would you explain the errors in each example?

Be prepared to share your explanations and reasoning with the class.

 CHECK YOUR UNDERSTANDING

Use properties of exponents to write each of the following expressions in another equivalent form. Be prepared to explain how you know your answers are correct.

a. $(y^3)(y^6)$ **b.** $(5x^2y^4)(2xy^3)$

c. $(pq)^3$ **d.** $(p^3)^5$

e. $(7p^3q^2)^2$

SUMMARIZE THE MATHEMATICS

a   **i.** For the rule $a^x a^y = a^{x+y}$, one might say that when two exponential expressions with the same base are multiplied, the result is equal to a single exponential expression with the common base and an exponent equal to the sum of the two original exponents. A simpler explanation is, "When you multiply exponential expressions with the same base, you add exponents."

  ii. For the rule $(a^x)^y = a^{xy}$, one might say that to find the power of a power, you multiply exponents.

  iii. For the rule $(ab)^x = a^x b^x$, one might say that the power of a product is the product of the powers of the factors.

b   **i.** $b^m \cdot b^n = b^{m+n}$

  ii. $(b^m)^n = b^{mn}$

  iii. $(ab)^n = a^n b^n$

c   Students will suggest various common errors in use of exponent law shortcuts. The most common are probably those indicated in Problems 3, 5 Part c, and 7 Part c (answers above). The most effective general type of clarification explanation is probably always to remember the definition of exponent as repeated multiplication of whatever the base is.

MATH TOOLKIT

Summarize the rules of exponents that you have studied in this lesson.

- $b^m \cdot b^n =$
- $(b^m)^n =$
- $(ab)^n =$

✅ CHECK YOUR UNDERSTANDING

a. y^9 because the product indicates 9 factors of y.

b. $10x^3 y^7$ because the product indicates 5 times 2, 3 factors of x, and 7 factors of y.

c. $p^3 q^3$ because the expression indicates 3 factors of pq, which will involve 3 factors of p and 3 factors of q.

d. p^{15} because the expression indicates 5 factors of p^3, which will involve 5 times 3 or 15 factors of p.

e. $49p^6 q^4$ because the expression indicates 2 factors of $7p^3 q^2$ or $(7p^3 q^2)(7p^3 q^2)$.

APPLICATIONS

1 Imagine a tree that each year grows 3 new branches from the end of each existing branch. Assume that your tree is a single stem when it is planted.

   a. How many new branches would you expect to appear in the first year of new growth? How about in the second year of new growth?

   b. Write a rule that relates the number of new branches B to the year of growth R.

   c. In what year will the number of new branches first be greater than 15,000?

2 After seeing the *Pay It Forward* movie, Ethan came up with a similar but simpler idea. He thought it would be good if everyone made a point of paying a compliment to at least one stranger every day. To spread word about his idea, he sent text messages to two friends and asked them to pass the idea on to two others, and so on.

   a. Sketch a tree graph that shows how Ethan's idea might spread to other people in stages from his first text messages. Explain what the vertices and edges on the tree graph represent.

   b. Make a table and a graph showing the number of people contacted at each of the first ten stages of this tree.

   c. Write two rules that can be used to calculate the number of text messages sent at various stages of the tree—one in *NOW-NEXT* form and another in the "$y = \ldots$" form.

   d. How many stages of the texting tree will be needed before 1,000 people have heard about Ethan's idea?

3 The bacteria *E. coli* often cause illness among people who eat infected food. Suppose a single *E. coli* bacterium in a batch of ground beef begins doubling every 10 minutes.

   a. How many bacteria will there be after 10, 20, 30, 40, and 50 minutes have elapsed? Assume no bacteria die.

   b. Write two rules that can be used to calculate the number of bacteria in the food after any number of 10-minute periods—one using *NOW* and *NEXT*, and another beginning "$y = \ldots$."

   c. Use your rules to make a table showing the number of *E. coli* bacteria in the batch of ground beef at the end of each 10-minute period over 2 hours. Then describe the pattern of change in the number of bacteria from each time period to the next.

   d. Find the predicted number of bacteria after 4, 5, and 6 hours.

1 **a.** 3 new branches should appear in the first year.
9 new branches should appear in the second year.

b. $B = 3^R$, where B is the number of new branches each year R.

c. In the 9th year

2 **a.** The vertices in the graph at the right represent the people placing/receiving text messages, and the edges represent the messages.

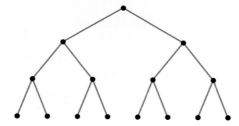

b.

Stage of Texting Tree	1	2	3	4	5	6	7	8	9	10
Number of Texts Made	2	4	8	16	32	64	128	256	512	1,024

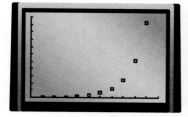 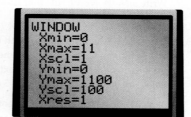

```
WINDOW
 Xmin=0
 Xmax=11
 Xscl=1
 Ymin=0
 Ymax=1100
 Yscl=100
 Xres=1
```

c. $NEXT = 2 \cdot NOW$, starting at 2; $y = 2^x$

d. Nine stages of the texting tree will be needed before 1,000 additional people have heard about Ethan's idea (actually, 1,022 after that stage).

3 **a.** After 10, 20, 30, 40, and 50 minutes, there will be 2, 4, 8, 16, and 32 bacteria, respectively.

b. $NEXT = 2 \cdot NOW$. Students might choose a starting value of 1 or 2. $y = 2^x$, where y is the number of bacteria and x is the number of 10-minute time periods.

c. Students do not need to include $(0, 1)$ in the table since the task indicates at the end of each 10-minute period. The bacteria double from one 10-minute period to the next.

10-min Periods	1	2	3	4	5	6	7	8	9	10	11	12
Bacteria Count	2	4	8	16	32	64	128	256	512	1,024	2,048	4,096

d. After 4 hours (24 time periods), there will be 16,777,216 bacteria.
After 5 hours (30 time periods), there will be 1,073,741,824 bacteria.
After 6 hours (36 time periods), there will be 68,719,476,736 bacteria.

ON YOUR OWN

4 The left figure shown below is called a "chair." It can be subdivided into four congruent, smaller "chairs" as shown at the right. Each of the smaller chairs can be subdivided into four congruent, still smaller chairs, and this process can be continued.

Stage 0

Stage 1

a. Draw a picture of Stage 2 in the process that creates smaller "chairs" and count the number of small chairs at this stage.

b. Make a table that shows the number of small chairs at each stage of the process.

Stage	0	1	2	3	4	5	...	n
Number of "Chairs"	1	4						

c. Write a *NOW-NEXT* rule that shows how the number of chairs increases from each stage to the next.

5 Suppose that Ethan first talked with three friends about his idea for encouraging people to pay compliments to strangers. Then he and the three friends each start a branch of the texting tree by sending messages to 3 other people and asking them to send to 3 others and so on.

a. Sketch a tree graph that shows how the idea would spread to other people in stages from the first text messages sent by the four friends.

b. Make a table and a graph showing the number of people contacted at each of the first four stages of this tree.

c. Write two rules that can be used to calculate the number of text messages sent at various stages of the tree—one in *NOW-NEXT* form and another in the "$y = \ldots$" form.

d. How many stages of the texting tree will be needed before 1,000 people have heard about Ethan's idea?

4 The sequence of nested chairs leads to an exponential function or geometric sequence with growth factor 4.

a. The nest of chairs at Stage 2 will look like the graphic at the right. It consists of 16 small chairs.

b.

Stage	0	1	2	3	4	5	...	n
Number of "Chairs"	1	4	16	64	256	1,024	...	4^n

c. $NEXT = 4 \cdot NOW$, starting at 1

5 **a.**

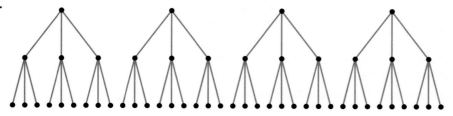

b.

Stage of Texting Tree	1	2	3	4
Number of Texts Made	12	36	108	324

A graph of the first 5 stages will produce a plot like this:

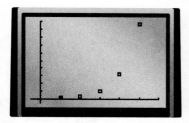 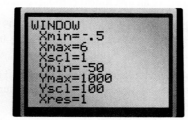

c. $NEXT = 3 \cdot NOW$, starting at 12; $y = 4(3^x)$

d. After 4 stages of the texting tree, 480 people will have gotten Ethan's message; after 5 stages, the number will increase by 972 people to 1,452 people.

6 Suppose 50 *E. coli* bacteria are introduced into some food as it is being processed, and the bacteria begin doubling every 10 minutes.

   a. Make a table and a graph showing the number of bacteria from Stage 0 to Stage 6 of the infection process.

   b. Write two rules that can be used to calculate the number of bacteria infecting the food at various stages of this process—one in *NOW-NEXT* form and another in "$y = \dots$" form.

   c. Predict the number of bacteria present after 3 hours. Explain how you made your prediction.

7 Suppose that a local benefactor wants to offer college scholarships to every child entering first grade at an elementary school in her community. For each student, the benefactor puts $5,000 in a separate savings fund that earns 5% interest compounded annually.

   a. Make a table and a graph to show growth in the value of each account over the 12 years leading up to college entry.

   b. Compare the pattern of growth of the account in Part a to one in which the initial deposit is $10,000. Compare values of each account after 12 years.

   c. Compare the pattern of growth of the account in Part a to one in which the interest rate is 10% and the initial deposit is $5,000. Compare values of each account after 12 years.

   d. Compare values of the accounts in Parts b and c after 12 years. What does this suggest about the relative importance of interest rate and initial balance in producing growth of an investment earning compound interest?

8 In 2009, the number of people worldwide living with HIV/AIDS was estimated at more than 33.3 million. That number was growing at an annual rate of about 8%.

   a. Make a table showing the projected number of people around the world living with HIV/AIDS in each of the ten years after 2009, assuming the growth rate remains 8% per year.

   b. Write two different kinds of rules that could be used to estimate the number of people living with HIV/AIDS at any time in the future.

   c. Use the rules from Part b to estimate the number of people living with HIV/AIDS in 2025.

   d. What factors might make the estimate of Part c an inaccurate forecast?

Lesson 1 | Exponential Growth **309**

6 **a.**

10-min Periods	0	1	2	3	4	5	6
Bacteria Count	50	100	200	400	800	1,600	3,200

b. $NEXT = 2 \cdot NOW$, starting at 50; $y = 50(2^x)$

c. 13,107,200 bacteria

Three hours is 18 10-minute intervals. Students might use a calculator table and scroll down to $x = 18$, or use the "$y = ...$" rule and substitute $x = 18$. They could also trace on their graph to $x = 18$.

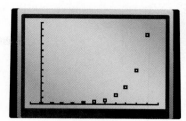

7 **a.**

Year	0	1	2	3	4	5	6
Balance	5,000	5,250	5,513	5,788	6,078	6,381	6,700

Year	7	8	9	10	11	12
Balance	7,036	7,387	7,757	8,144	8,552	8,979

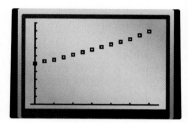

b. Even though the interest rates are the same, the investment of $10,000 grows faster than the $5,000 investment. This can be seen in the graphs of the two plans. With a $5,000 initial amount, the account has a final value of $8,979. With a $10,000 initial amount, an account with $17,959 results. When the investment is doubled, the final balance is, too.

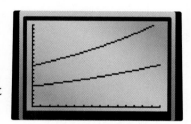

c. Investment at a rate of 10% grows much faster than an investment rate of 5%. After 12 years, the 5% rate account is worth $8,979, while the 10% rate account is worth $15,692.

Doubling the rate amount does *not* double the account's final balance. However, the 10% rate led to a tripling of the initial investment, while the 5% rate increased the investment by a factor of a bit less than 2.

d. Student responses should include thoughts about the importance of the interest rate when looking for accounts and that doubling the initial investment for the same interest rate will double the final balance.

8 **a.**

Years After 2009	0	1	2	3	4	5	6	7	8	9	10
AIDS Cases (in millions)	33.3	36.0	38.8	41.9	45.3	48.9	52.8	57.1	61.6	66.6	71.9

b. $NEXT = 1.08 \cdot NOW$, starting at 33.3; $y = 33.3(1.08^x)$

c. $33.3(1.08^{16}) \approx 114.1$; the model estimates that about 114.1 million will be living with HIV/AIDS in the year 2025.

d. Answers will vary and may include comments about breakthroughs in medicine and prevention measures.

ON YOUR OWN

9 Studies in 2001 gave a low estimate of 7,700 for the population of Arctic bowhead whales. The natural annual growth rate was estimated to be about 3%. The harvest by Inuit people is very small in relation to the total population. Disregard the harvest for this task.

a. If the growth rate continued at 3%, what populations would be predicted for the years 2005, 2010, 2015, and 2020?

b. Which change of assumptions will lead to a greater 2015 whale population estimate

    i. increasing the assumed population annual growth rate to 6%, with the 2001 low population estimate of 7,700, or

    ii. increasing the 2001 population estimate to 14,400, but maintaining the 3% growth rate?

c. Find the time it takes for the whale population to double under each of the three sets of assumptions in Parts a and b.

10 The Dow Jones Industrial Average provides one measure of the "health" of the U.S. economy. It is a weighted average of the stock prices for 30 major American corporations. The following table shows the low point of the Dow Jones Industrial Average in selected years from 1965 to 2010.

Year	DJIA Low
1965	841
1970	631
1975	632
1980	759
1985	1,185
1990	2,365
1995	3,832
2000	9,796
2005	10,012
2010	9,686

Source: finance.yahoo.com/9/hp?s=^DJI+Historical+Prices

a. Find what you believe are the best possible linear and exponential models for the pattern of change in the low value of the Dow Jones Industrial Average over the time period shown in the table (use $t = 0$ to represent 1965). Then decide which you think is the better of the two models and explain your choice.

b. Use your chosen predictive model from Part a to estimate the low value of this stock market average in 2015 and 2020. Explain why you might or might not have confidence in those estimates.

c. Some stockbrokers who encourage people to invest in common stocks claim that one can expect an average return of 10% per year on that investment. Does the rule you chose to model increase in the Dow Jones average support that claim? Why or why not?

Michael Nagle/Getty Images News/Getty Images

9 **a.** If the growth rate continued at 3%, predicted populations would be (2005, 8,666), (2010, 10,047), (2015, 11,647), and (2020, 13,502).

  b. **i.** Increasing the growth rate to 6% yields a 2015 estimate of 17,409 whales.

   ii. Increasing the 2001 number of initial population to 14,400 yields a 2015 estimate of 21,781 whales.

  c. Assuming an initial population of 7,700 and a growth rate of 3%, the population would double after almost 23.5 years.
   Assuming an initial population of 7,700 and a growth rate of 6%, the population would double after almost 12 years.
   Assuming an initial population of 14,400 and a growth rate of 3%, the population would double after almost 23.5 years.
   (Note that the doubling time is independent of the initial amount.)

10 **a.** Linear: $y = 244x - 1,521$
   Exponential: $y = 420(1.076^x)$
   The exponential model seems to be the better fit because the graph fits the data points better.

TECHNOLOGY NOTE

These data are in *CPMP-Tools* under Statistics, Data Analysis, Data, Unit 5.

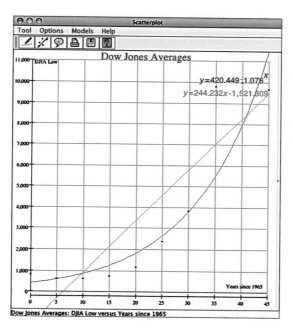

Dow Jones Averages: DJIA Low versus Years since 1965

  b. Using the exponential estimate, the predicted 2015 low is 16,363 and the predicted 2020 low is 23,601. The large increases between 1990 and 2000 probably lead to a model that is misleading over a long period of time. This problem is a good caution against extrapolating too far beyond real data in any model.

  c. The exponential regression model suggests a 7.6% annual increase.

11 The following table shows the number of votes cast in a sample of U.S. Presidential elections between 1840 and 2008.

Year of Election	Major Party Candidates	Total Votes Cast
1840	Harrison vs. Van Buren	2,412,694
1860	Lincoln vs. Douglas	4,681,267
1880	Garfield vs. Hancock	9,217,410
1900	McKinley vs. Bryan	13,997,429
1920	Harding vs. Cox	26,765,180
1940	Roosevelt vs. Willkie	49,902,113
1960	Kennedy vs. Nixon	68,832,482
1980	Reagan vs. Carter	86,509,678
2000	Bush vs. Gore	105,417,475
2004	Bush vs. Kerry	122,293,548
2008	Obama vs. McCain	131,463,122

Source: uselectionatlas.org/RESULTS

a. Find rules for what you think are the best possible linear and exponential models of the trend relating votes cast to time (use $t = 0$ to represent the year 1840).

b. Which type of model—linear or exponential—seems to better fit the data pattern? Why do you think that choice is reasonable?

c. In what ways is neither the linear nor the exponential model a good fit for the data pattern relating presidential election votes to time? Why do you think that modeling problem occurs?

12 In 1958, Walter O'Malley paid about $700,000 to buy the Brooklyn Dodgers baseball team. He moved the team to Los Angeles, and in 1998 his son and daughter sold the team for $350,000,000. Assume that the team's value increased exponentially in annual increments according to a rule like $v = a(b^t)$, where $t = 0$ represents the year 1958.

a. What value of a is suggested by the given information?

b. Experiment to find a value of b that seems to give a rule that matches growth in team value prescribed by the given information.

c. What annual percent growth rate does your answer to Part b suggest for the value of the Dodgers team business?

d. According to the model derived in Parts a and b, when did the value of the Dodgers team first reach $1,000,000? $10,000,000? $100,000,000?

13 Find values for w, x, and y that will make these equations true statements.

a. $5^4 \cdot 5^5 = 5^y$

b. $3^6 \cdot 3^4 = 3^y$

c. $5^3 \cdot 5 = 5^y$

d. $7^w \cdot 7^6 = 7^{11}$

e. $1.5^w \cdot 1.5^x = 1.5^6$

f. $c^3 \cdot c^5 = c^y$

Lesson 1 | Exponential Growth **311**

11 a. Linear model: $y = 0.79t - 19$ (in millions)
Exponential model: $y = 3.37(1.023^t)$ (in millions)

b. Neither seems a good fit to the data, so student answers may vary greatly.

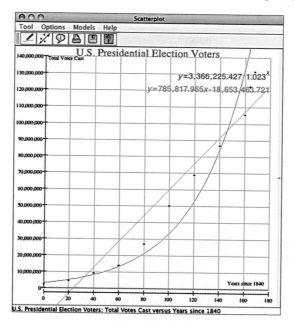

c. From 1840 to 1940, the data appears to have an exponential pattern, while from 1940 to 2000, a linear pattern seems a better fit. This probably mirrors unevenness in the growth of the U.S. population over intervals of several decades. However, there are also some significant sociopolitical events that undoubtedly shaped the numbers of voters. For example, African-Americans were granted suffrage in 1870, but the struggle to have real access to voting rights continued into the later half of the 20th century. Women were not allowed to vote in federal elections until 1920.

12 a. An a value of 700,000 is suggested.

b. A b value of 1.168 gives a reasonable fit, since $700,000(1.168^{40}) \approx 348,989,010$.

c. A growth rate of almost 17% is suggested.

d. According to the model in Part b:
$1,000,000 was first reached in about 1960 or 1961 ($2 < t < 3$).
$10,000,000 was first reached in about 1975 or 1976 ($17 < t < 18$).
$100,000,000 was first reached in about 1989 or 1990 ($31 < t < 32$).

13 a. $y = 9$

b. $y = 10$

c. $y = 4$

d. $w = 5$

e. Any combination of w and x adding to 6

f. $y = 8$

ON YOUR OWN

14 Write each of the following expressions in a simpler equivalent exponential form.

a. $7^4 \cdot 7^9$ b. $4.2^2 \cdot 4.2^5$ c. $x \cdot x^4$

d. $(c^2)(c^5)$ e. $(5x^3y^4)(4x^2y)$ f. $(7a^3bm^5)(b^4m^2)$

g. $(4x^3y^5)(10x)$ h. $(-2c^4d^2)(-cd)$

15 Find values for x, y, and z that will make these equations true statements.

a. $(7^5)^2 = 7^z$ b. $(4.5^2)^3 = x^6$ c. $(9^3)^x = 9^{12}$

d. $(t^3)^7 = t^z$ e. $(7 \cdot 5)^4 = 7^x \cdot 5^y$ f. $(3t)^4 = 3^x t^y$

g. $(5n^3)^2 = 5^x n^y$ h. $(c^5d^3)^2 = c^x d^y$

16 Write each of the following expressions in a simpler equivalent exponential form.

a. $(x^2)^3$ b. $(5a^3c^4)^2$ c. $(3xy^4z^2)^4$ d. $(-5x^3)^2$

CONNECTIONS

17 Partially completed tables for four relations between variables are given below. In each case, decide if the table shows an exponential or a linear pattern of change. Based on that decision, complete a copy of the table as the pattern suggests. Then write rules for the patterns in two ways: using rules relating NOW and NEXT y values and using rules beginning "$y = \ldots$" for any given x value.

a.

x	0	1	2	3	4	5	6	7	8
y				8	16	32			

b.

x	0	1	2	3	4	5	6	7	8
y				40	80	160			

c.

x	0	1	2	3	4	5	6	7	8
y				48	56	64			

d.

x	0	1	2	3	4	5	6	7	8
y				125	625	3,125			

18 The diagram below shows the first stages in the formation of a geometric figure called a Koch curve. This figure is an example of a *fractal*. At each stage in the growth of the figure, the middle third of every segment is replaced by a "tent" formed by two equal-length segments. The new figure is made up of more, but shorter, segments of equal length.

Start

Stage 0   Stage 1   Stage 2

14. a. 7^{13}

   b. 4.2^7

   c. x^5

   d. c^7

   e. $20x^5y^5$

   f. $7a^3b^5m^7$

   g. $40x^4y^5$

   h. $2c^5d^3$

15. a. $z = 10$

   b. $x = 4.5$

   c. $x = 4$

   d. $z = 21$

   e. $x = 4$ and $y = 4$

   f. $x = 4$ and $y = 4$

   g. $x = 2$ and $y = 6$

   h. $x = 10$ and $y = 6$

16. a. x^6

   b. $25a^6c^8$

   c. $81x^4y^{16}z^8$

   d. $25x^6$

CONNECTIONS

17. a.

x	0	1	2	3	4	5	6	7	8
y	1	2	4	8	16	32	64	128	256

NEXT = 2 · *NOW*, starting at 1; $y = 2^x$

b.

x	0	1	2	3	4	5	6	7	8
y	5	10	20	40	80	160	320	640	1,280

NEXT = 2 · *NOW*, starting at 5; $y = 5(2^x)$

c.

x	0	1	2	3	4	5	6	7	8
y	24	32	40	48	56	64	72	80	88

NEXT = *NOW* + 8, starting at 24; $y = 8x + 24$

d.

x	0	1	2	3	4	5	6	7	8
y	1	5	25	125	625	3,125	15,625	78,125	390,625

NEXT = 5 · *NOW*, starting at 1; $y = 5^x$

a. Make a sketch showing at least one more stage in the growth of this fractal. Describe any symmetries that the fractal has at *each* stage.

b. Continue the pattern begun in this table.

Stage of Growth	0	1	2	3	4	5	6	7
Segments in Design	1	4						

c. Write a rule showing how the number of segments at any stage of the fractal can be used to find the number of segments at the next stage.

d. Write a rule that can be used to find the number of segments in the pattern at any stage x, without finding the numbers at each stage along the way. Begin your rule, "$y = \dots$."

e. Use the rule from Part d to produce a table and a graph showing the number of segments in the fractal pattern at each of the first 15 stages of growth. At what stage will the number of segments in the fractal first reach or pass 1 million?

19 News stories spread rapidly in modern society. With broadcasts over television, radio, and the Internet, millions of people hear about important events within hours. The major news providers try hard to report only stories that they know are true. But quite often rumors get started and spread around a community by word of mouth alone.

Suppose that to study the spread of information through rumors, two students started this rumor at 5 P.M. one evening: "Because of the threat of a huge snowstorm, there will be no school tomorrow and probably for the rest of the week." The next day they surveyed students at the school to find out how many heard the rumor and when they heard it.

a. What pattern of rumor spread is suggested by each of the graphs below?

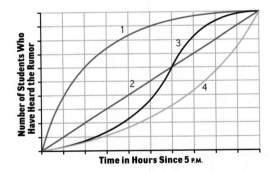

b. Which pattern of change in number of students who have heard the rumor is most likely to match experimental results in case:

   i. the rumor is spread by word of mouth from one student to another?

   ii. the rumor is mentioned on radio and television broadcasts between 5 and 6 P.M.?

18 **a.**

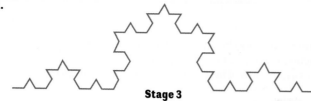

Stage 3

There is one vertical line of symmetry through the center of the whole figure.

b.

Stage of Growth	0	1	2	3	4	5	6	7
Segments in Design	1	4	16	64	256	1,024	4,096	16,384

c. *NEXT* = 4 · *NOW*, starting at 1

d. $y = 4^x$

e. At the 10th stage of growth, there are 1,048,576 segments. (Students should not be expected to write the table below in their assignment.)

Stage of Growth	8	9	10	11	12	13	14	15
Segments in Design	65,536	262,144	1,048,576	4,194,304	16,777,216	67,108,864	268,435,456	1,073,741,824

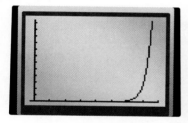 

19 **a.** Graph 1 suggests a pattern in which the rumor spread rapidly and then slowed down. The function increases at a decreasing rate. Graph 2 suggests a pattern in which the rumor was spreading at a constant rate (people per hour). Graph 3 shows a pattern in which the rumor spreads at an increasing rate until around 11:00 P.M. and then continues to spread, but at a decreasing rate. Graph 4 shows the rumor spreading at an increasing rate.

b. **i.** Graph 3 is the most promising model for spread by word of mouth. At first when only a few students have heard the rumor, the "calling tree" will have few branches. However, as more students get in on the rumor, the calling tree will spread the word more rapidly in each time interval. When most students have heard the rumor, there are fewer people left to "get the word," so the spread slows down. (This is a classic logistic or S curve that occurs when a population is growing rather exponentially at first but slows down as it approaches the limits to growth, like food and space resources.)

ii. Because of the quick rate of spread at the beginning (specifically between 5:00 and 6:00 P.M.), Graph 1 seems to be a logical fit for the case in which the rumor is mentioned on radio and television. Use of mass media gives fast initial spread of information and then a slowing rate of spread as the number in on the rumor approaches the limiting value of the available rumor audience.

20 Ethan thought about trying to spread his idea for "paying compliments to strangers" by contacting 100 people himself. He figured that he could address and send a message to each of his friends at a rate of 1 minute per text message.

a. At that rate, how long would it take him to spread the word to 100 people?

b. Look back at your results from work on Applications Task 2 and estimate the time it would take to reach 100 people if he used the texting tree idea instead.

21 Exponential functions, like linear functions, can be expressed by rules relating x and y values and by rules relating *NOW* and *NEXT* y values when x increases in steps of 1. Compare the patterns of (x, y) values produced by these functions: $y = 2(3^x)$ and $y = 2 + 3x$ by completing these tasks.

a. For each function, write another rule using *NOW* and *NEXT* that could be used to produce the same pattern of (x, y) values.

b. How would you describe the similarities and differences in the relationships of x and y in terms of their function graphs, tables, and rules?

22 The population of our world was about 7 billion in 2011. At the present rate of growth, that population will double approximately every 60 years.
(**Source**: *The World Factbook 2011.* CIA.)

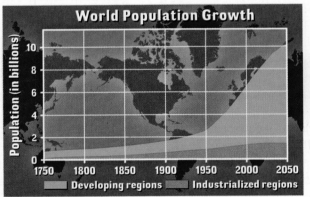

Sources: United Nations Population Division and Population Reference Bureau, 1993.

a. Assuming this rate continues, what will be the population 60, 120, 180, and 240 years from 2011?

b. How would that growth pattern compare to a pattern that simply added 7 billion people every 60 years?

c. Do you think the population is likely to continue growing in the "doubling every 60 years" pattern? Explain your reasoning.

d. How might rapid population growth affect your life in the next 60 years?

23 One way to think about rates of growth is to calculate the time it will take for a quantity to double in value. For example, it is common to ask how long it will take a bank investment or a country's population to double.

20 **a.** At that rate it would take 100 minutes or $1\frac{2}{3}$ hours to spread the word to 100 people.

b. Using the texting tree idea, it would take fewer than 6 full stages of the tree, or less than 6 minutes: $2 + 4 + 8 + 16 + 32 + 64 = 126$.

21 **a.** $y = 2(3^x)$; $NEXT = 3 \cdot NOW$, starting at 2
$y = 2 + 3x$; $NEXT = NOW + 3$, starting at 2
(Other starting values could be appropriate.)

b. The graph of $y = 2 + 3x$ would be a straight line with a constant slope. In the table and on the graph, for unit increases in successive x values, the y values would increase by 3 units. $y = 2(3^x)$ has a graph that increases at an increasing rate, and in both the table and on the graph, successive y values are related by a constant multiplicative factor. The *NOW-NEXT* rules may look similar at first glance in that they both contain a 3 and both start at 2. However, it is important to note that for the linear relationship, the 3 is added to the *NOW* value to obtain the *NEXT* value, while in the exponential relationship, each *NEXT* value is created by the product of 3 and the *NOW* value.

22 **a.** 60, 120, 180, and 240 years from 2011, the population will be 14 billion, 28 billion, 56 billion, and 112 billion, respectively.

b. Adding only 7 billion people every 60 years, 60, 120, 180, and 240 years from 2011, the population will be 14 billion, 21 billion, 28 billion, and 35 billion, respectively— a much slower rate of growth.

c. Student opinions may vary, but may give way to an interesting class discussion. Limits of food and energy resources, crowding of living space, disease due to crowding, and other factors could well limit population growth.

d. Student opinions may vary, though opinions will likely focus on healthcare, food supply, safety, and other community issues.

a. If the U.S. population in 2010 was about 308.7 million and growing exponentially at a rate of about 0.8% per year, how long will it take for the U.S. population to double?

b. One year's growth is 0.8% of 308.7 million, or about 2.5 million. How long would it take the U.S. population to double if it increased *linearly* at the rate of 2.5 million per year?

c. How long does it take a bank deposit of $5,000 to double if it earns interest compounded annually at a rate of 2%? At a 4% rate? At a 6% rate? At an 8% rate? At a 12% rate?

d. Examine your (*rate, time to double*) data in Part c. What pattern suggests a way to predict the doubling time for an investment of $5,000 at an interest rate of 3% compounded annually? Check your conjecture. If your prediction was not close, search for another pattern for predicting doubling time and check it.

24 The sketch below shows a small circle of radius 10 millimeters and the results of four different size transformations—each with scale factor 1.5 applied to the previous circle.

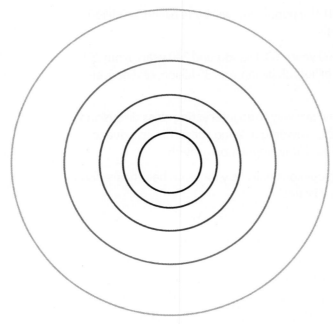

a. Make a table of (*radius, circumference*) values for the five circles and plot a graph of the resulting ordered pairs.

b. Write a *NOW-NEXT* rule showing how the circumference of each circle is related to the next larger circle.

c. If the pattern of expanding circles with the same center were continued, what rule would show how to calculate the circumference of the *n*th circle?

d. Enter the areas of the first five circles in the pattern in a new row of your table for Part a. Then write a rule that would show how to calculate the area enclosed by the *n*th circle in that pattern.

23
   a. Approximately 87 years

   b. Approximately 123 years

   c. (2%, 35 years), (4%, 17.67 years), (6%, 11.9 years), (8%, 9 years), and (12%, 6.12 years)

   d. Predictions may vary, but the actual amount is about 23.45 years. The general rule is that *doubling time* $= 70 \div$ *interest rate in percent*. For example 5% interest will cause doubling in 14 years.

> **NOTE** This rule of thumb is based on the fact (beyond the scope of our work on exponential functions at this stage) that the natural logarithm of 2 is about 0.69. The derivation follows:
>
> Principal after t years is given by $P_0 e^{rt}$, where r is the interest rate as a decimal and P_0 is the initial balance. Doubling time is found by solving the equation $2P_0 = P_0 e^{rt}$ for t.
>
> $$2P_0 = P_0 e^{rt}$$
> $$2 = e^{rt}$$
> $$\ln 2 = rt$$
> $$t \approx \frac{\ln 2}{r}$$

24
   a.

Radius	10	15	22.5	33.75	50.625
Circumference	62.8	94.2	141.4	212.1	318.1
Area	314	707	1,590	3,579	8,052

   b. *NEXT* $= 1.5 \cdot$ *NOW*, starting at 62.8

   c. $C = 20\pi(1.5)^{n-1}$

   d. See the table in Part a. The general formula is $\pi(10 \cdot 1.5^{n-1})^2$.

ON YOUR OWN

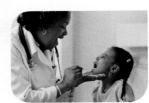

REFLECTIONS

25 One common illness in young people is *strep throat*. This bacterial infection can cause painful sore throats. Have you or anyone you know ever had strep throat? How does what you have learned about exponential growth explain the way strep throat seems to develop very quickly?

26 In using exponential functions to model patterns of change in populations, you frequently have to deal with very large numbers like the 2010 U.S. Census population of 308,745,538.

   a. When and how can you round off such very large (or very small) numbers, without sacrificing precision of results?

   b. The mathematical constant π is equal to 3.141592654... . In what situations might it be acceptable to use approximate values like 3, 3.1, or 3.14 in calculations without sacrificing essential precision of results?

27 Exponential functions, like linear functions, can be expressed by rules relating x and y values.

   a. In exponential functions with rules $y = a(b^x)$:

      i. how does the value of a affect the graph?

      ii. how does the value of b affect the graph?

   b. In linear functions with rules $y = a + bx$:

      i. how does the value of a affect the graph?

      ii. how does the value of b affect the graph?

28 In everyday media reports, the term "exponential growth" is used to describe any pattern of rapid increase of a quantity. Examples from work in this unit could be used to show that this imprecise use of mathematical language can be misleading.

   a. Give an example of exponential growth that really involves fairly slow increase of a quantity.

   b. Give an example of linear growth that involves fairly rapid increase of a quantity.

   c. When is it technically correct to use the term "exponential growth"?

29 Make a table to compare the values of 2^b and b^2 for several different positive integer values of b.

b							
2^b							
b^2							

   a. For what values of b is $2^b = b^2$?

   b. For what values of b is $2^b > b^2$? Explain your reasoning.

25 The apparently sudden onset of strep throat and other similar bacterial illnesses can be explained in part by the way exponential growth tends to occur slowly at first but then simply jumps up very rapidly.

26 a. Rounding off very large (or very small) numbers without sacrificing precision of results is a judgment call in most situations. While there are some specific guidelines about the effects of errors on calculations (errors tend to be exaggerated by multiplication or division in the same way that exponential growth or decay occur at increasing rates), in most practical situations one has only to ask, "How accurate do I need my final answer to be? What is likely to happen if I round off the input data to various numbers of significant digits?" Students will have seen numerous examples in the work of this unit where data were rounded and then analyzed as certain numbers of thousands, millions, or billions, rather than using all significant place-value digits. In general, it is good practice to choose measurement units for a situation that will allow use of arithmetic with small whole numbers, rather than large whole numbers or decimals with many digits to the right of the decimal point.

b. The mathematical constant $\pi = 3.141592654\ldots$ can be rounded to 3, 3.1, or 3.14 in many calculations without sacrificing essential precision of results. For example, if one wants to estimate the volume or surface area of a cylindrical object, using 3 as an approximation of π is often adequate. The same applies to estimating circumference or area of a circle. Better to use a simple approximation and get an estimate that is in the ballpark than to use a more precise value of π and make mistakes in mental or paper-and-pencil arithmetic.

At the same time, there will be occasions in which a precise value of π should be used because errors will lead one astray. Once again, the basic principle is to do what makes sense and to run checks on results to see that no egregious error has been made.

27 a. In exponential functions with rules $y = a(b^x)$:

  i. the value of a indicates the y-intercept of the graph $(0, a)$.

  ii. the value of b affects the rate of increase or curvature of the graph—larger values of b mean graphs that increase more rapidly.

b. In linear functions with rules $y = a + bx$:

  i. the value of a again indicates the y-intercept point of the graph.

  ii. the value of b indicates the constant slope of the straight line graph. Each increase of 1 in the value of x implies a change of b in the value of y.

28 a. One example of exponential growth that really involves fairly slow increase of a quantity is the surprisingly slow rate at which bank savings earning interest of only 1% or 2% grow.

b. The rate of linear growth is impressive or not depending on the units involved. Perhaps the most familiar examples of linear growth are motion at constant speed or payment for work at a constant hourly wage. If an airplane is cruising at 600 miles per hour, the miles traveled increase pretty impressively.

NOTE The solutions to Task 28 Part c and Task 29 are on page T317.

EXTENSIONS

UNIT 5

30 The drawings below show five stages in growth of a design called the *dragon fractal*.

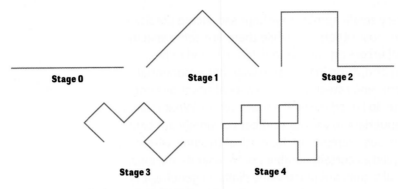

Stage 0   Stage 1   Stage 2

Stage 3   Stage 4

a. Draw Stage 5 of growth in the dragon fractal.

b. What pattern of change do you see in the number of segments of the growing fractal?

c. Make a table and a plot of the data showing that pattern of change.

d. Write a rule relating *NOW* and *NEXT* and a rule beginning "$y = \ldots$" for finding the number of segments in the figure at each stage of growth.

e. How many segments will there be in the fractal design at Stage 16?

f. At what stage will the fractal design have more than 1,000 segments of equal length?

31 In this task, you will examine more closely the Koch curve fractal from Connections Task 18.

Stage 0   Stage 1   Stage 2

Recall that in moving from one stage to the next, each segment is divided into three equal—length parts. A tent is raised over the middle section with sides equal in length to the parts on each side.

a. If the original line segment is 1 inch long, how long is each segment of the pattern in Stage 1? How long is each segment of the pattern in Stage 2?

b. Complete the following table showing the length of segments in the first 10 stages.

Stage	0	1	2	3	4	5	6	7	8	9
Segment Length (in inches)	1	$\frac{1}{3}$								

c. It is technically correct to use the term "exponential growth" only when a dependent variable changes according to an equation of the form $NEXT = k \cdot NOW$ or $y = Ab^x$. That is, when values for y increase at a constant multiplicative rate.

29

b	1	2	3	4	5	6	7
2^b	2	4	8	16	32	64	128
b^2	1	4	9	16	25	36	49

a. $2^b = b^2$ for both $b = 2$ and $b = 4$.

b. For positive integer values of b, $2^b > b^2$ when $b \geq 5$ and when $b = 1$. Values in the table and plots of the graphs of the two functions give evidence in support of the conclusion that $x^2 > 2^x$ only between $x = 2$ and $x = 4$.

EXTENSIONS

30 **a.**

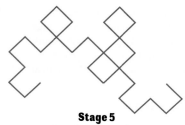

Stage 5

b. The number of segments doubles at each stage.

c.

Stage x	0	1	2	3	4	5	6
Number of Segments y	1	2	4	8	16	32	64

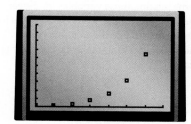

```
WINDOW
 Xmin=0
 Xmax=7
 Xscl=1
 Ymin=0
 Ymax=100
 Yscl=10
 Xres=1
```

d. $NEXT = 2 \cdot NOW$, starting at 1
$y = 2^x$

e. $y = 2^{16} = 65{,}536$ segments

f. The Stage 10 design will have more than 1,000 (1,024) segments.

31 **a.** Segments in Stage 1 are $\frac{1}{3}$ of an inch long. Segments in Stage 2 are $\frac{1}{9}$ of an inch long.

b.

Stage	0	1	2	3	4	5	6	7	8	9
Segment Length (in inches)	1	$\frac{1}{3}$	$\frac{1}{9}$	$\frac{1}{27}$	$\frac{1}{81}$	$\frac{1}{243}$	$\frac{1}{729}$	$\frac{1}{2{,}187}$	$\frac{1}{6{,}561}$	$\frac{1}{19{,}683}$

ON YOUR OWN

c. Look back at Parts c and d of Connections Task 18 where you wrote rules giving the number of short segments at each stage of the pattern. Then use that information and the results of Part b to complete the following table giving the total length of the pattern at each stage.

Stage	0	1	2	3	4	5	6	7	8	9
Pattern Length (in inches)	1	$\frac{4}{3}$								

d. What appears to be happening to the total length of the pattern as the number of segments in the pattern increases?

32 Banks frequently pay interest more often than once each year. Suppose your bank pays interest compounded *quarterly*. If the annual percentage rate is 4%, then the bank adds 4% ÷ 4 = 1% interest to the account balance at the end of each 3-month period.

a. Explore the growth of a $1,000 deposit in such a bank over 5 years.

b. Compare the quarterly compounding with annual compounding at 4%.

c. Repeat the calculations and comparisons if the annual rate is 8%.

33 Many people borrow money from a bank to buy a car, a home, or to pay for a college education. However, they have to pay back the amount borrowed plus interest. To consider a simple case, suppose that for a car loan of $9,000 a bank charges 6% annual rate of interest compounded quarterly and the repayment is done in quarterly installments. One way to figure the balance on this loan at any time is to use the rule:

new balance = 1.015 × old balance − payment.

a. Use this rule to find the balance due on this loan for each quarterly period from 0 to 20, assuming that the quarterly payments are all $250.

b. Experiment with different payment amounts to see what quarterly payment will repay the entire $9,000 loan in 20 payments (5 years).

c. Create a spreadsheet you can use in experiments to find the effects of different quarterly payment amounts, interest rates, and car loan amounts. Use the spreadsheet to look for patterns relating those variables for 5-year loans. Write a brief report of your findings. (You might want to have cells in the spreadsheet for each of the variables, *original loan amount, interest rate,* and *quarterly payment amount,* and then a column that tracks the *outstanding loan balance* over a period of 20 quarters.)

c.

Stage	0	1	2	3	4	5	6	7	8	9
Pattern Length (in inches)	1	$\frac{4}{3}$	$\frac{16}{9}$	$\frac{64}{27}$	$\frac{256}{81}$	$\frac{1{,}024}{243}$	$\frac{4{,}096}{729}$	$\frac{16{,}384}{2{,}187}$	$\frac{65{,}536}{6{,}561}$	$\frac{262{,}144}{19{,}683}$

d. The length appears to be increasing exponentially using the model $y = \left(\frac{4}{3}\right)^x$. This makes sense because the number of segments at Stage x is 4^x and the length of each segment at Stage x is $\left(\frac{1}{3}\right)^x$. (You might connect back to this reasoning in Lesson 2 when the rule for evaluating powers of fractions is developed. $\left(\frac{a}{b}\right)^n = \frac{a^n}{b^n}$.)

32 a. With quarterly compounding of 1%, after 5 years the account will have a value of $1,220.19.

b. With an annual compounding of 4%, after 5 years the account will have a value of $1,216.65.

c. With quarterly compounding of 2%, after 5 years the account will have a value of $1,485.95.
With an annual compounding of 8%, after 5 years the account will have a value of $1,469.33.

33 Students should not be expected to complete a table for 20 payments. You may wish to have them record multiples of 5, as below.

a.

Number of Quarter-Year Periods	0	5	10	15	20
Balance Due (in $)	9,000	8,407	7,769	7,082	6,341

b. A payment of about $525 will repay the loan in 5 years.

c. Student findings will vary. One possible spreadsheet would look like this:

Payments.xlsx

◇	A	B	C	D	
1	Quarter	Balance	rate:	1+0.015	
2	0	D3	payment:	250	
3	A2+1	(D$1)*B2−D$2	loan:	9,000	
4	⋮	⋮			
5					

A fill-down command applied to columns **A** and **B** would give running balance. Changing values of **D1**, **D2**, and **D3** would produce immediate recalculation of the balance values in column **B**.

Students should discover that changes in loan amount and repayment amount will have a greater effect on time to pay off such a loan than will modest changes in the interest rate.

34 The Wheaton Boys and Girls Club has 511 members and a calling tree in which, starting with the president, members are asked to pass on news to two other members.

a. What function rule shows how to calculate the total number T of members informed after x stages of the process have been completed? It might help to begin by finding these sums:

$$1$$
$$1 + 2$$
$$1 + 2 + 4$$
$$1 + 2 + 4 + 8$$
$$1 + 2 + 4 + 8 + 16$$
$$\vdots$$

Use the function rule you came up with to make a table and a graph showing values of T for $x = 0, 1, 2, 3, 4, 5, 6, 7, 8$.

b. What function rule gives the number of people N in the club who have not yet been called after stage x of the calling tree process? Use the function rule you came up with to make a table and graph showing values of N for $x = 0, 1, 2, 3, 4, 5, 6, 7, 8$.

c. Describe the patterns of change shown in tables and graphs of the rules that express T and N as functions of x and compare them to each other and to other functions you've encountered.

REVIEW

35 Write each of the following calculations in more compact form by using exponents.

a. $5 \times 5 \times 5 \times 5$

b. $3 \times 3 \times 3 \times 3 \times 3 \times 3 \times 3 \times 3$

c. $1.5 \times 1.5 \times 1.5 \times 1.5 \times 1.5 \times 1.5$

d. $(-10) \times (-10) \times (-10) \times (-10) \times (-10) \times (-10) \times (-10) \times (-10)$

e. $\underbrace{6 \times 6 \times \cdots \times 6}_{k \text{ factors}}$

f. $\underbrace{a \times a \times \cdots \times a}_{m \text{ factors}}$

36 Do these calculations *without* use of the exponent key (⌃) on your calculator.

a. 5^4 b. $(-7)^2$ c. 10^0

d. $(-8)^3$ e. 2^8 f. 2^{10}

34 **a.** $T = 2^{x+1} - 1$ gives the total number of people who have been informed by stage x.

x	0	1	2	3	4	5	6	7	8
T	1	3	7	15	31	63	127	255	511

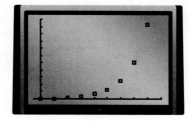

b. $N = 511 - (2^{x+1} - 1)$ gives the number of people yet to be called after stage x. This is equivalent to $N = 512 - 2^{x+1}$.

x	0	1	2	3	4	5	6	7	8
N	510	508	504	496	480	448	384	256	0

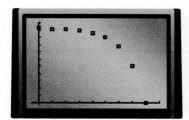 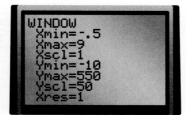

Notice how $y = 512 - 2^{x+1}$ declines very slowly at first (relative to the task required) and then drops sharply at the end as the branching of the tree dramatically increases the number of calls being made at successive stages of the process.

c. The pattern relating total number of calls to calling tree stage is nearly identical to that of exponential growth functions encountered throughout this lesson. It is what one would get if you shifted the graph of $y = 2^x$ one unit to the left (the "$x + 1$ effect") and then translated it down by one unit.

The graph of $y = 512 - 2^{x+1}$ looks like a kind of upside down exponential. The pattern is what one would get by reflecting 2^{x+1} across the x-axis and then translating it 512 units up. The result is a graph that declines slowly at first and then very rapidly as the exponential growth of the subtractive term 2^{x+1} begins to kick in. It's another way of looking at the rate at which the total number of people who have been called grows.

REVIEW

⏱ **JUST IN TIME**

35 **a.** 5^4 **b.** 3^8 **c.** 1.5^6

    d. $(-10)^8$ **e.** 6^k **f.** a^m

⏱ **JUST IN TIME**

36 **a.** $5^4 = 625$ **b.** $(-7)^2 = 49$ **c.** $10^0 = 1$

    d. $(-8)^3 = -512$ **e.** $2^8 = 256$ **f.** $2^{10} = 1{,}024$

37 Draw and label each triangle as accurately as you can. After you draw the triangle, use a ruler to determine the lengths of the remaining sides and a protractor to find the measures of the remaining angles.

	AB	BC	CA	m∠ABC	m∠BCA	m∠CAB
a.	2.5 in.	4 in.		125°		
b.	12 cm			45°		45°

38 Given that $\frac{1}{4}$ of 160 is 40, and that 10% of 160 is 16, find the values of the following without using a calculator. Explain how you obtained your answers.

a. $\frac{3}{4}$ of 160, $\frac{5}{4}$ of 160, and $1\frac{3}{4}$ of 160

b. 5% of 160, 95% of 160, and 105% of 160

39 Anthony took an inventory of the colors of the shirts that he owns and made a table of his findings.

Shirt Color	Green	Blue	Black	Red	Other
Number	5	2	4	3	6

a. Identify two types of graphs that would be appropriate for Anthony to make to display this data. Choose one of them and make it.

b. What percent of Anthony's shirts are red?

c. What percent of Anthony's shirts are not green?

d. If Anthony were to randomly choose a shirt to wear, what is the probability that he would choose a black shirt?

40 A line passes through the points (1, 1) and (5, −7). Determine whether or not each point below is also on the line. Explain your reasoning.

a. (8, −12)　　　b. (0, 3)　　　c. (3, −4)　　　d. (−3, 9)

41 Consider the two solids shown below.

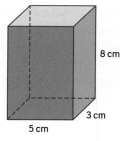
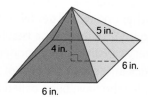

For each solid, complete the following.

a. How many faces does the solid have? For each face, describe the shape and give its dimensions.

b. Identify all faces that appear to be parallel to each other.

37

	AB	BC	CA	m∠ABC	m∠BCA	m∠CAB
a.	2.5 in.	4 in.	$5\frac{13}{16}$ in.	125°	20°	35°
b.	12 cm	8.5 cm	8.5 cm	45°	90°	45°

🕐 **JUST IN TIME**

38 **a.** Since $\frac{1}{4}$ of 160 is 40, students should be able to use mental math to find:

- $\frac{3}{4}$ of 160 is $3(40) = 120$.

- $\frac{5}{4}$ of 160 is $5(40) = 200$.

- $1\frac{3}{4}$ of 160 is either $\frac{7}{4}$ of 160, which is $7(40) = 280$, or 1 and $\frac{3}{4}$ of 160, which is $160 + 3(40) = 280$.

b. Since 10% of 160 is 16, students may think about these problems as:

- 5% of 160 is $\frac{1}{2}(10\%)$ of 160 or $\frac{1}{2}(16) = 8$.

- 95% of 160 is $160 - (5\%$ of 160$) = 160 - 8 = 152$.

- 105% of 160 is $160 + (5\%$ of 160$) = 168$.

39 **a.** The data could be represented in a pie chart or bar graph.

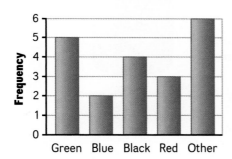

b. 15% are red.

c. 75% are not green.

d. $\frac{4}{20} = \frac{1}{5}$

40 $y = -2x + 3$. Students should verify by substitution whether each point is on the line.

a. Not on line   **b.** On line

c. Not on line   **d.** On line

41 **a.** The prism has six faces. There are two 3 cm by 5 cm rectangles, two 3 cm by 8 cm rectangles, and two 5 cm by 8 cm rectangles. The pyramid has five faces. One square 6 in. on a side and four isosceles triangles with base of 6 in. and height of 5 in.

b. In the prism, each pair of opposite faces are parallel to each other. There are no parallel faces in the pyramid.

c. Identify all faces that appear to be perpendicular to each other.

d. Find the surface area.

e. Find the volume. (Recall that the formula for the volume of a pyramid is $V = \frac{1}{3}Bh$, where B is the area of the base and h is the height of the pyramid.)

42 Evaluate each of these algebraic expressions when $x = 3$ and be prepared to explain why you believe you've produced the correct values.

a. $3x + 7$

b. $7 + 3x$

c. $5 - 4x + 3x^2$

d. $8(4x - 9)^2$

e. $\frac{5x - 2}{5 + 2x}$

f. $-2x^2$

g. $(-2x)^3$

h. $\sqrt{25 - x^2}$

i. $\frac{x + 12}{x + 4}$

43 When you use formulas to find values of dependent variables associated with specific values of independent variables, you need to be careful to "read" the directions of the formula the way they are intended. For example, the formula for surface area of a circular cylinder is $A = 2\pi r^2 + 2\pi rh$.

a. What is the surface area of a cylinder with radius 5 inches and height 8 inches? How do you know your calculation used the formula correctly?

b. Sketch a cylinder for which the height is the same length as the radius r. Show that the surface area of the cylinder is $A = 4\pi r^2$. What algebraic properties did you use in your reasoning?

44 Graph each of the following lines on grid paper. Then, for Parts a and b, write an equation of the line.

a. A line with slope of $\frac{2}{3}$ and y-intercept at $(0, 6)$

b. A line with slope of 0.5 and x-intercept at $(-2, 0)$

c. A line with equation $y = -3x - 5$

45 Algebra can be helpful in solving puzzles that involve relationships between two or more numbers. For each puzzle below, write an equation that represents the situation. Then use the equation to determine what the two numbers are in each case.

a. One number is 15 more than a second number. The sum of the two numbers is 59. What are the two numbers?

b. One number is 3 times a second number. The product of the two numbers is 192. If both numbers are positive, what are the two numbers?

c. One number is 8 less than a second number. The sum of the smaller number and 4 times the larger number is 52. What are the two numbers?

c. In the prism, each face is perpendicular to every face adjacent to it. There are no perpendicular faces in the pyramid.

d. Prism: $SA = 2(15) + 2(24) + 2(40) = 158$ cm^2

Pyramid: $SA = 36 + 4\left(\frac{1}{2}\right)(6)(5) = 96$ in^2

e. Prism: $V = 5(3)(8) = 120$ cm^3

Pyramid: $V = \frac{1}{3}(36)(4) = 48$ in^3

42   **a.** 16   **b.** 16   **c.** 20

d. 72   **e.** $\frac{13}{11}$ **f.** -18

g. -216 **h.** 4   **i.** $\frac{15}{7}$

43   **a.** $2\pi(5)^2 + 2\pi(5)(8) = 130\pi \approx 408$. The calculation requires correct use of order of operations, so the first move is squaring 5, then doing the multiplications in the separate terms, and finally adding the two terms.

b. The surface area of a cylinder for which $r = h$ will be $2\pi r^2 + 2\pi rr$ which is $2\pi r^2 + 2\pi r^2$. This is equivalent to $(2 + 2)\pi r^2$ by the distributive property (or simply combining like terms).

44   **a.**

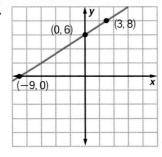

equation: $y = \frac{2}{3}x + 6$

b.

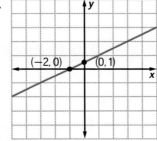

equation: $y = 0.5x + 1$

c.

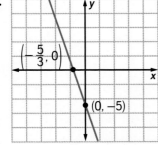

45   **a.** $n + (n + 15) = 59$
The numbers are 22 and 37.

b. $n(3n) = 192$
The numbers are 8 and 24.

c. $(n - 8) + 4n = 52$
The numbers are 12 and 4.

ON YOUR OWN

TEACHING RESOURCES

Assessment Masters 311–320
ⓘ GO DIGITAL

Lesson 1 | Exponential Growth   **T321**

LESSON
2

Exponential Decay

In 2010, there was a serious accident on the Deepwater Horizon drilling rig at the BP Macondo oil well in the Gulf of Mexico. Before the well was capped, nearly 5 million barrels of oil spread over the surface of the water and onto the nearby shores of Louisiana and Mississippi. That oil spill was eventually cleaned up—some of the oil evaporated, some was picked up by specially equipped boats, and some sank to the ocean floor as sludge. But the experience had lasting impact on thinking about environmental protection.

For scientists planning environmental cleanups, it is important to be able to predict the pattern of dispersion in such contaminating spills. Suppose that an accident dropped some pollutant into a large aquarium. It's not practical to remove all water from the aquarium at once, so the cleanup has to take place in smaller steps. A batch of polluted

water is removed and replaced by clean water. Then the process is repeated.

Think about the following experiment that simulates pollution and cleanup of the aquarium.

- Mix 20 black checkers (the pollution) with 80 red checkers (the clean water).

- Remove 20 checkers from the mixture (without looking at the colors) and replace them with 20 red checkers (clean water). Record the number of black checkers remaining. Then shake the new mixture. This simulates draining off some of the polluted water and replacing it with clean water.

USCG

Exponential Decay

Lesson 2 explores patterns of change that can be represented well by exponential decay models. The lesson begins with a series of problems analyzing bouncing balls that lead to discrete exponential decay and progresses to several examples of continuous decay of medications (leading to notions of fractional exponents and half-life). In the third investigation, students are asked to explore various models for experiments—some naturally modeled by exponential functions and some (for contrast) by linear functions. Finally there are two investigations that develop further algebraic rules involving powers of fractions, quotients, negative exponents, and radicals, specifically the simplification of such expressions.

Lesson Objectives

- Develop ability to recognize patterns of change characterizing exponential decay phenomena

- Develop ability to write explicit $y = a(b^x)$ and *NOW-NEXT* rules for exponential decay functions

- Develop ability to interpret zero and fractional exponents and to calculate or estimate values of expressions with those exponents

- Develop ability to interpret half-life of decay phenomena and to use symbolic rules, tables, and graphs to estimate those values

- Develop ability to use reasoning, estimation, and curve-fitting utilities to model exponential decay patterns

- Use symbolic rules, tables, and graphs to solve problems involving exponential decay

- Develop skill in use of standard rules for writing exponential expressions in equivalent forms

- Develop skill in simplifying radicals

Lesson Launch

When a pollutant enters some body of water like a lake or stream, it usually mixes with the clean water. As new water enters the lake or stream and polluted water leaves or is removed, the density of the pollutant gradually decreases. This process is modeled by a series of "remove-and-replace" operations in which some polluted water is replaced by clean water at each stage. The resulting pattern leads to the classic exponential decay graph that does not decrease at a steady rate (linear), but in a curve that is steep at first and gradually becomes less steep and asymptotic to the *x*-axis.

Common Core State Standards CCSS

Focused on:
N-RN.1, N-RN.2, A-SSE.1, A-CED.2, A-REI.10, F-IF.3, F-IF.4, F-IF.5, F-IF.7, F-IF.8, F-BF.1, F-BF.2, F-BF.3, F-LE.1, F-LE.2, F-LE.5, S-ID.6

Connected to:
N-Q.1, A-SSE.3, F-IF.9, F-LE.3

- In the second step, remove 20 checkers from the new mixture (without looking at the colors) and replace them with 20 red checkers (more clean water). Record the number of black checkers remaining. Then stir the new mixture.

- Repeat the remove-replace-record-mix process for several more steps.

THINK ABOUT THIS SITUATION

The graphs below show two possible outcomes of the pollution and cleanup simulation.

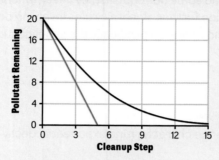

a What pattern of change is shown by each graph?

b Which graph shows the pattern of change that you would expect for this situation? Test your idea by running the experiment and plotting the (*cleanup step, pollutant remaining*) data.

c What sort of function relating pollution *P* and cleanup steps *x* would you expect to match your data plot? Test your idea using a graphing calculator or computer software.

The pollution cleanup experiment gives data in a pattern that occurs in many familiar and important problem situations. That pattern is called *exponential decay*. Your work on problems of this lesson will reveal important properties and uses of exponential decay functions and fractional exponents.

INVESTIGATION 1

More Bounce to the Ounce

Most popular American sports involve balls of some sort. In designing those balls, one of the most important factors is the bounciness or *elasticity* of the ball. For example, if a new golf ball is dropped onto a hard surface, it should rebound to about $\frac{2}{3}$ of its drop height. The pattern of change in successive rebound heights will be similar to that of the data in the pollution cleanup experiment.

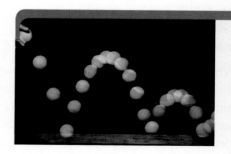

Terry Oakley/Alamy

Lesson 2 | Exponential Decay **323**

THINK ABOUT THIS SITUATION

a The line shows a constant decrease in the pollutant remaining as the time increases. The curve shows large decreases initially, but the rate of decrease slows as time increases.

b One sample experiment is provided:

Cleanup Step	0	1	2	3	4	5	6
Black Checkers Left	20	16	13	10	8	7	6

c Students might connect this to a *NOW-NEXT* pattern, but it seems unlikely at this point that they will be able to write a rule relating *P* and *x*, unless they have worked with exponential decay in prior studies. The rule that models the ideal of the experiment is $P = 20(0.8^x)$. If 20% are removed at each step, 80% remain.

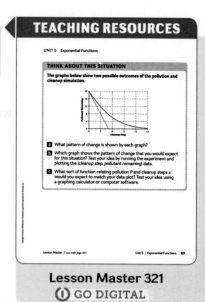

Lesson Master 321
⓪ **GO DIGITAL**

INVESTIGATION **1** **CCSS** A-CED.2, A-REI.10, F-IF.7, F-BF.1, F-BF.2, F-LE.5, S-ID.6, N-Q.1, F-IF.5, F-LE.1

More Bounce to the Ounce

The goal of this investigation is to focus students' attention on a pattern of change in which the dependent variable changes by the same factor (between 0 and 1) as the independent variable increases. The questions engage students first in theoretical analysis and then in experiments to see how well the theory predicts what happens in practice.

In the most recent set of On Your Own tasks, students practiced mental mathematics in Review Task 38. They can use these strategies to help them calculate the values for this table. It will be important for students to leave their responses in fraction form so they can maintain $\frac{2}{3}$ as a factor in each of their table values. They will need the $\frac{2}{3}$ as the base in their exponential function that models the bouncing ball.

> **INSTRUCTIONAL NOTE** It is a good idea to have several students in each group watch for the maximum rebound height. This is difficult to capture and usually takes students a bit of practice. Some teachers have given students small self-stick notes to mark rebound heights on the wall. Measuring can be done when the ball stops bouncing. Hard surfaces, such as tile, work better than carpeting.

> **COLLABORATION SKILL**
>
> Experimentation requires group members to take on to or be assigned different tasks.

As you work on the problems of this investigation, look for answers to this question:

What mathematical patterns in tables, graphs, and symbolic rules are typical of exponential decay relations?

1 Suppose a new golf ball drops downward from a height of 27 feet onto a paved parking lot and keeps bouncing up and down, again and again. Rebound height of the ball should be $\frac{2}{3}$ of its drop height. Make a table and plot of the data showing expected heights of the first ten bounces of the golf ball.

Bounce Number	0	1	2	3	4	5	6	7	8	9	10
Rebound Height (in feet)	27										

  a. How does the rebound height change from one bounce to the next? How is that pattern shown by the shape of the data plot?

  b. What rule relating *NOW* and *NEXT* shows how to calculate the rebound height for any bounce from the height of the preceding bounce?

  c. What rule beginning "*y* = …" shows how to calculate the rebound height after any number of bounces?

  d. How will the data table, plot, and rules for calculating rebound height change if the ball drops first from only 15 feet?

As is the case with all mathematical models, data from actual tests of golf ball bouncing will not match exactly the predictions from rules about ideal bounces. You can simulate the kind of quality control testing that factories do by running some experiments in your classroom. Work with a group of three or four classmates to complete the next problems.

2 Get a golf ball and a tape measure or meter stick for your group. Decide on a method for measuring the height of successive rebounds after the ball is dropped from a height of at least 8 feet. Collect data on the rebound height for successive bounces of the ball.

  a. Compare the pattern of your data to that of the model that predicts rebounds which are $\frac{2}{3}$ of the drop height. Would a rebound height factor other than $\frac{2}{3}$ give a better model for your data? Be prepared to explain your reasoning.

  b. Write a rule using *NOW* and *NEXT* that relates the rebound height of any bounce of your tested ball to the height of the preceding bounce.

  c. Write a rule beginning "*y* = …" to predict the rebound height after any bounce.

3 Repeat the experiment of Problem 2 with some other ball such as a tennis ball or a volleyball.

  a. Study the data to find a reasonable estimate of the rebound height factor for your ball.

  b. Write a rule using *NOW* and *NEXT* and a rule beginning "*y* = …" to model the rebound height of your ball on successive bounces.

Tim Fuller

Bounce Number	0	1	2	3	4	5	6	7	8	9	10
Rebound Height (in feet)	27	18	12	8	$\frac{16}{3}$	$\frac{32}{9}$	$\frac{64}{27}$	$\frac{128}{81}$	$\frac{256}{243}$	$\frac{512}{729}$	$\frac{1{,}024}{2{,}187}$

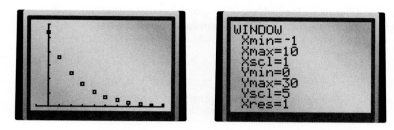

a. Successive rebound heights are $\frac{2}{3}$ of the previous height. The plot shows successive data points lower than those that came before, but in a smooth pattern of $\frac{2}{3}$ of the vertical distance of the previous point to the *x*-axis.

b. $NEXT = \frac{2}{3} \cdot NOW$, starting at 27

c. $y = 27\left(\frac{2}{3}\right)^n$

d. If the ball is dropped from only 15 feet, the 27 will be replaced by 15 in the rules of Parts b and c.

Bounce Number	0	1	2	3	4	5	6	7	8	9	10
Rebound Height (in feet)	15	10	$\frac{20}{3}$	$\frac{40}{9}$	$\frac{80}{27}$	$\frac{160}{81}$	$\frac{320}{243}$	$\frac{640}{729}$	$\frac{1{,}280}{2{,}187}$	$\frac{2{,}560}{6{,}561}$	$\frac{5{,}120}{19{,}683}$

The plot will start lower on the *y*-axis but decrease in much the same curved pattern.

2 a–c. In this problem, students will produce their own data by experiment. The graph of the student data will probably not be as smooth as the theoretical data graph in Problem 1, but their results should reflect a pattern of exponential decay. Students should estimate the rebound factor using their own method. One strategy students might use is to compute a few of the ratios between successive rebound heights and find the average of these values. The rebound factor should be close to 0.67.

TECHNOLOGY NOTE You may wish to use the Texas Instruments CBL or CBR or a similar piece of technology to measure the height and graph the relationship. Give the students plenty of time to practice using the technology.

3 A sample response using a tennis ball follows.

a.

Bounce Number	0	1	2	3
Rebound Height (in inches)	50	30	18	10

b. $NEXT = 0.6 \cdot NOW$, starting at 50
$y = 50(0.6^x)$

SUMMARIZE THE MATHEMATICS

Different groups might have used different balls and dropped the balls from different initial heights. However, the patterns of (*bounce number, rebound height*) data should have some similar features.

a Look back at the data from your experiments.

   i. How do the rebound heights change from one bounce to the next in each case?

   ii. How is the pattern of change in rebound height shown by the shape of the data plots in each case?

b List the *NOW-NEXT* and the "*y* = ..." rules you found for predicting the rebound heights of each ball on successive bounces.

   i. What do the rules relating *NOW* and *NEXT* bounce heights have in common in each case? How, if at all, are those rules different, and what might be causing the differences?

   ii. What do the rules beginning "*y* = ..." have in common in each case? How, if at all, are those rules different, and what might be causing the differences?

c What do the tables, graphs, and rules in these examples have in common with those of the exponential growth examples in Lesson 1? How, if at all, are they different?

d How are the exponential decay data patterns, graphs, and rules similar to and different from those of linear functions and other types of functions you've studied in earlier units?

Be prepared to compare your data, models, and ideas with the rest of the class.

✅ CHECK YOUR UNDERSTANDING

When dropped onto a hard surface, a brand new softball should rebound to about $\frac{2}{5}$ the height from which it is dropped.

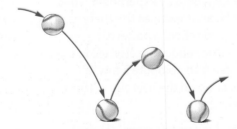

a. If the softball is dropped 25 feet from a window onto concrete, what pattern of rebound heights can be expected?

   i. Make a table and plot of predicted rebound data for 5 bounces.

   ii. What *NOW-NEXT* and "*y* = ..." rules give ways of predicting rebound height after any bounce?

SUMMARIZE THE MATHEMATICS

a   **i.** The (*bounce number, rebound height*) data should approximately fit a pattern in which the rebound height on one bounce is a constant multiple of the rebound height on the previous bounce.

   ii. The rebound factor is a number between 0 and 1 leading to a smooth curve showing the rebound height decreasing at a decreasing rate.

b   **i.** All rules should have the form $NEXT = b \cdot NOW$, starting at a, with different values of b for different balls and different values of a for different initial drop heights. In all rules, b was between 0 and 1.

   ii. All should have the form $y = a(b^x)$, again with different values of a and b $(0 < b < 1)$ for initial drop heights and different balls.

c   The tables should have a declining, rather than growing, trend in the dependent variable. Successive y values will be related by a common factor between 0 and 1, rather than a number greater than 1 for exponential growth.

   The graphs should have similar curvature. However, decay graphs decrease over time while growth graphs increase over time.

   The rules have the same general patterns but you need $b > 1$ for growth and $0 < b < 1$ for decay.

d   Both linear and exponential functions are always increasing or always decreasing, depending on the numerical coefficients. However, exponential decay and growth functions are bounded from below by the x-axis, while linear functions are unbounded (unless constant).

   The rules for linear and exponential functions both involve two significant constants. In both $y = a + bx$ and $y = a(b^x)$, the value of a tells the y-intercept $(0, a)$ of the graph and the value of b tells about change in the dependent variable. In linear functions, the y values change by a constant additive value b for unit changes in the x value. In exponential functions, the y values change by a constant multiplicative factor b for unit changes in the x values.

PROCESSING PROMPT   Describe your tasks/participation in this investigation.

TEACHING RESOURCES

UNIT 5   Exponential Functions

SUMMARIZE THE MATHEMATICS

Different groups might have used different balls and dropped the balls from different initial heights. However, the patterns of (*bounce number, rebound height*) data should have some similar features.

a Look back at the data from your experiments.
  i. How do the rebound heights change from one bounce to the next in each case?
  ii. How is the pattern of change in rebound height shown by the shape of the data plots in each case?

b List the *NOW-NEXT* and the "*y = ...*" rules you found for predicting the rebound heights of each ball on successive bounces.
  i. What do the rules relating *NOW* and *NEXT* bounce heights have in common in each case? How, if at all, are those rules different, and what might be causing the differences?
  ii. What do the rules beginning "*y = ...*" have in common in each case? How, if at all, are those rules different, and what might be causing the differences?

c What do the tables, graphs, and rules in these examples have in common with those of the exponential growth examples in Lesson 1? How, if at all, are they different?

d How are the exponential decay data patterns, graphs, and rules similar to and different from those of linear functions and other types of functions you've studied in earlier units?

Be prepared to compare your data, models, and ideas with the rest of the class.

322   Unit 5 | Exponential Functions   Lesson Master | use with page 325

Lesson Master 322
① GO DIGITAL

MATH TOOLKIT

Students might compare exponential growth and decay models using this prompt: How are rules, tables, and graphs of exponential growth and decay functions similar and how are they different?

NOTE   The solution to the Check Your Understanding is on page T326.

b. Here are some data from bounce tests of a softball dropped from a height of 10 feet.

Bounce Number	1	2	3	4	5
Rebound Height (in feet)	3.8	1.3	0.6	0.2	0.05

   i. What do these data tell you about the quality of the tested softball?

   ii. What bounce heights would you expect from this ball if it were dropped from 20 feet instead of 10 feet?

c. What *NOW-NEXT* and "$y = ...$" rules would model rebound height of an ideal softball if the drop were from 20 feet?

d. What rule beginning "$y = ...$" shows how to calculate the height y of the rebound when a new softball is dropped from any height x? What connections do you see between this rule and the rule predicting rebound height on successive bounces of the ball?

INVESTIGATION 2

Medicine and Mathematics

Prescription drugs are a very important part of the human health equation. Many medications are essential in preventing and curing serious physical and mental illnesses.

Diabetes, a disorder in which the body cannot metabolize glucose properly, affects people of all ages. In 2010, there were about 18.8 million diagnosed cases of diabetes in the United States. It was estimated that another 7.0 million cases remained undiagnosed. (**Source:** diabetes.niddk.nih.gov/dm/pubs/statistics/index.htm)

In 5–10% of the diagnosed cases, the diabetic's body is unable to produce insulin, which is needed to process glucose.

To provide this essential hormone, these diabetics must take injections of a medicine containing insulin. The medications used (called insulin

©Guy Cali/Corbis

delivery systems) are designed to release insulin slowly. The insulin itself breaks down rather quickly. The rate varies greatly among individuals, but the following graph shows a typical pattern of insulin decrease.

✔ CHECK YOUR UNDERSTANDING

a. **i.**

Bounce Number	0	1	2	3	4	5
Rebound Height (in feet)	25	10	4	$\frac{8}{5}$	$\frac{16}{25}$	$\frac{32}{125}$

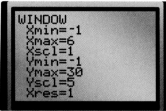

```
WINDOW
 Xmin=-1
 Xmax=6
 Xscl=1
 Ymin=-1
 Ymax=30
 Yscl=5
 Xres=1
```

ii. $NEXT = \frac{2}{5} \cdot NOW$, starting at 25 and $y = 25\left(\frac{2}{5}\right)^x$.

b. **i.** The rebound height of the softball is consistently less than what would be expected from a new softball. Furthermore, the ratio of the rebound height from one drop to the next is not consistent. So, the data may indicate that this softball is used or not top quality.

ii. Responses will depend on choice of height ratio. A reasonable choice is 0.35.

c. $NEXT = \frac{2}{5} \cdot NOW$, starting at 20 and by $y = 20\left(\frac{2}{5}\right)^x$.

d. The rule predicting rebound height for any drop height of a softball is $y = \frac{2}{5}x$. This linear relationship between drop height and rebound height is applied repeatedly to get the succession of rebound heights on a series of bounces.

INVESTIGATION **2** **CCSS** A-SSE.1, A-CED.2, A-REI.10, F-IF.3, F-IF.4, F-IF.5, F-IF.7, F-IF.8, F BF.1, F-BF.2, F-BF.3, F-LE.5, F-IF.9, F-LE.1, F-LE.3

Medicine and Mathematics

The goal of this investigation is to extend student understanding of, and skill in working with, exponential decay relationships and their tables, graphs, and rules. Since decay or metabolism of medicines in the body is a nearly continuous process, the problems here motivate interpretation of fractional exponents.

Breakdown of Insulin in Bloodstream

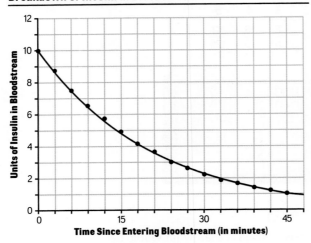

As you work on the problems of this investigation, look for answers to the following questions:

How can you interpret and estimate or calculate values of expressions involving fractional or decimal exponents?

How can you interpret and estimate or calculate the half-life of a substance that decays exponentially?

1 Medical scientists often are interested in the time it takes for a drug to be reduced to one half of the original dose. They call this time the **half-life** of the drug. What appears to be the half-life of insulin in this case?

2 The pattern of decay shown on this graph for insulin can be modeled well by the function $y = 10(0.95^x)$, where x is the number of minutes since the insulin entered the bloodstream.

    a. Use your calculator or computer software to see how well a table of values and graph of this rule matches the pattern in the graph above.

    b. What do the numbers 10 and 0.95 tell about the amount of insulin in the bloodstream?

    c. Based on the function modeling insulin decay, what percent of active insulin is actually used up with each passing minute?

3 What rule relating *NOW* and *NEXT* shows how the amount of insulin in the blood changes from one minute to the next, once 10 units have entered the bloodstream?

4 The insulin decay graph shows data points for three-minute intervals following the original insulin level. But the curve connecting those points reminds us that the insulin breakdown does not occur in sudden bursts at the end of each minute! It occurs *continuously* as time passes.

1 About 15 minutes

2 **a.** A table of values and graph from this rule fit the pattern fairly well. A slightly faster decay than shown in the plotted data is suggested.

b. The number 10 is the initial dosage of insulin. The number 0.95 says that from one minute to the next 95% remains active.

c. The rule suggests that 95% of the insulin is still active. Thus, 5% of the insulin is used up each minute.

3 $NEXT = 0.95 \cdot NOW$, starting at 10

What would each of the following calculations tell about the insulin decay situation? Based on the graph, what would you expect as reasonable values for those calculations?

a. $10(0.95)^{1.5}$ b. $10(0.95)^{4.5}$ c. $10(0.95)^{18.75}$

5 Mathematicians have figured out ways to do calculations with fractional or decimal exponents so that the results fit into the pattern for whole number exponents. One of those methods is built into your graphing calculator or computer software.

a. Enter the function $y = 10(0.95^x)$ in your calculator or computer software. Then complete a copy of the following table of values showing the insulin decay pattern at times other than whole-minute intervals.

Elapsed Time (in minutes)	0	1.5	4.5	7.5	10.5	13.5	16.5	19.5
Units of Insulin in Blood	10							

b. Compare the entries in this table with data shown by points on the graph on the preceding page.

c. Study tables and graphs of your function to estimate, to the nearest tenth of a minute, solutions for the following equations and inequality. In each case, be prepared to explain what the solution tells about decay of insulin.

i. $2 = 10(0.95^x)$

ii. $8 = 10(0.95^x)$

iii. $10(0.95^x) > 1.6$

6 Use the function $y = 10(0.95^x)$ to estimate the half-life of insulin for an initial dose of 10 units. Then estimate the half-life in cases when the initial dose is 15 units. When it is 20 units. When it is 25 units. Explain the pattern in those results.

SUMMARIZE THE MATHEMATICS

In this investigation, you have seen another example of the way that patterns of exponential decay can be expressed by function rules like $y = a(b^x)$.

a What NOW-NEXT rule describes this pattern of change?

b What do the values of a and b tell about the situation being modeled? About the tables and graphs of the (x, y) values?

c How can you estimate or calculate values of b^x when x is not a whole number?

d What does the half-life tell about a substance that decays exponentially? What strategies can be used to estimate or calculate half-life?

Be prepared to compare your responses with those of your classmates.

4 **a.** Amount of insulin remaining after 1.5 minutes is about 9.3 units.

b. Amount of insulin remaining after 4.5 minutes is about 7.9 units.

c. Amount of insulin remaining after 18.75 minutes is about 3.8 units.

5 **a.** A table of sample values for $y = 10(0.95^x)$:

Elapsed Time (in minutes)	0	1.5	4.5	7.5	10.5	13.5	16.5	19.5
Units of Insulin in Blood	10	9.3	7.9	6.8	5.8	5.0	4.3	3.7

b. The values in the table fit "smoothly" between the corresponding values for whole number time units, lying on the graph pattern for the function $y = 10(0.95^x)$.

c. **i.** $x \approx 31.4$

After about 31.4 minutes, the initial 10-unit dose has metabolized to leave only 2 units of insulin still active in the blood.

ii. $x \approx 4.3$

After about 4.3 minutes, the initial 10-unit dose has metabolized to leave 8 units of insulin still active in the blood.

iii. $x < 35.7$; $10(0.95^{35.7}) \approx 1.6023$

For the first 35.7 minutes after the insulin enters the blood, the amount of active insulin remains above 1.6 units.

6 In every case, the half-life turns out to be just about 13.5 minutes. This is because $0.95^{13.5}$ is very close to one-half. When $0.95^x = 0.5$, then $y = a(0.95^x)$ will equal one-half of a.

SUMMARIZE THE MATHEMATICS

a $NEXT = b \cdot NOW$, starting at a, where $0 < b < 1$.

b The value of a is the initial value or amount before the decay begins. The value of b is the decay rate or factor. The y value associated with an x value of 0 on the table is a. The y-intercept on the graph is $(0, a)$. On the table, the ratio of one y value to the previous y value (given that x is increasing by single units) is b. On the graph, b is the factor that reduces the vertical distance from the x-axis for successive points 1 unit apart on the x-axis.

c Values of b^x for values of x that are between whole numbers can be estimated as being between the y values for adjacent integer values of x or as the y value from a graph of $y = b^x$. Another method is to use a calculator to compute b^x.

d Half-life tells the time it takes a decaying substance to be reduced to one-half its initial amount. The half-life can be estimated by scanning a table of values or graph for the decay function $y = a(b^x)$ in search of the value of x for which the y value is half of the initial amount a.

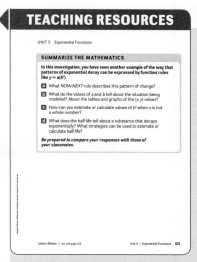

MATH TOOLKIT

- Explain what is meant by half-life.
- If the radioactive decay of a substance is modeled by $y = 100(0.67^x)$, what do the 100 and 0.67 represent?
- What strategies can you use to find the half-life of this substance?

✔️ CHECK YOUR UNDERSTANDING

The most famous antibiotic drug is penicillin. After its discovery in 1929, it became known as the first *miracle drug*, because it was so effective in fighting serious bacterial infections.

Drugs act somewhat differently on each person. But, on average, a dose of penicillin will be broken down in the blood so that one hour after injection only 60% will remain active. Suppose a patient is given an injection of 300 milligrams of penicillin at noon.

a. Write a rule in the form $y = a(b^x)$ that can be used to calculate the amount of penicillin remaining after any number of hours x.

b. Use your rule to graph the amount of penicillin in the blood from 0 to 10 hours. Explain what the pattern of that graph shows about the rate at which active penicillin decays in the blood.

c. Use the rule from Part a to produce a table showing the amount of active penicillin that will remain at *quarter-hour* intervals from noon to 5 P.M.

  i. Estimate the half-life of penicillin.

  ii. Estimate the time it takes for an initial 300-mg dose to decay so that only 10 mg remain active.

d. If 60% of a penicillin dose remains active one hour after an injection, what percent has been broken down in the blood?

INVESTIGATION 3

Modeling Decay

When you study a situation in which data suggest a dependent variable decreasing in value as a related independent variable increases, there are two strategies for finding a good algebraic model of the relationship. In some cases, it is possible to use the problem conditions and reasoning to determine the type of function that will match dependent to independent variable values. In other cases, some trial-and-error exploration or use of calculator or computer curve-fitting software will be necessary before an appropriate model is apparent.

From a scientific point of view, it is always preferable to have some logical explanation for choice of a model. Then the experimental work is supported by understanding of the relationship being studied. As you work on the following problems, look for answers to these questions:

What clues in problem conditions are helpful in deriving function models for experimental data involving decay?

How can logical analysis of an experiment be used as a check of a function model produced by your calculator or computer curve-fitting software?

Lesson 2 | Exponential Decay **329**

a. $y = 300(0.6^x)$

b.

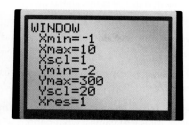

The pattern shows relatively rapid decrease in the amount of active penicillin at first and then a slower decrease in the active amount.

c. The amount remaining at quarter-hour intervals from noon to 5 P.M. will be as in this table.

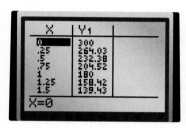 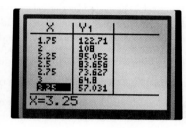 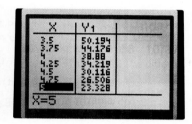

    i. The half-life of penicillin is between 1.25 and 1.5 hours. $300(0.6^{1.357}) \approx 149.99$

    ii. There will be less than 10 milligrams remaining after about 6.65 hours.

d. 60% remaining means 40% has been metabolized or broken down in the blood.

INVESTIGATION **3** **CCSS** A-SSE.1, A-CED.2, A-REI.10, F-IF.5, F-IF.7, F-IF.8, F-BF.1, F-BF.2, F-LE.1, F-LE.2, F-LE.5, S-ID.6, A-SSE.3, F-IF.4

Modeling Decay

The goal of this investigation is to develop student ability to derive exponential models that fit patterns in experimental data and to compare the data patterns to what logical analysis of the experiment suggests might happen. Students are asked to think first, then experiment, and to compare the function models suggested by logic to the models derived from use of calculator or computer tools.

1. Suppose that you were asked to conduct this experiment:

   - Get a collection of 100 coins, shake them well, and drop them on a tabletop.

   - Remove all coins that are lying heads up and record the number of coins left.

   - Repeat the shake-drop-remove-record process until 5 or fewer coins remain.

   a. If you were to record the results of this experiment in a table of (*drop number, coins left*) values, what pattern would you expect in the data? What function rule would probably be the best model relating drop number n to number of coins left c?

   b. Conduct the experiment, record the data, and then use your calculator or curve-fitting software to find a function model that seems to fit the data pattern well.

   c. Compare the model suggested by logical analysis of the experiment to that found by fitting a function to actual data. Decide which you think is the better model of the experiment and be prepared to explain your choice.

2. Suppose that the experiment in Problem 1 is modified in this way:

   - Get a collection of 100 coins and place them on a table top.

   - Roll a six-sided die and remove the number of coins equal to the number on the top face of the die. Record the number of coins remaining. For example, if the first roll shows 4 dots on the top of the die, remove four coins, leaving 96 coins still on the table.

   - Repeat the roll-remove-record process until 10 or fewer coins remain.

   a. If you were to record the results of this experiment in a table of (*roll number, coins left*) values, what pattern would you expect in that data? What function rule would probably be the best model relating roll number n to number of coins left c?

   b. Conduct the experiment, record the data, and then use your calculator or curve-fitting software to find a function model that seems to fit the data pattern well.

   c. Compare the model suggested by logical analysis of the experiment to that found by fitting a function to actual data. Decide which you think is the better model of the experiment and be prepared to explain your choice.

3. How are the data from the experiments in Problems 1 and 2 and the best-fitting function models for those data different? Why are those differences reasonable, in light of differences in the nature of the experiments that were conducted?

330 UNIT 5 | Exponential Functions

1 **a.** Logical analysis of this planned experiment would suggest a model that produces values that are reduced by half each subsequent drop number. The function is $c = 100(0.5^n)$.

b. Results from student replication of the experiment are likely to yield data patterns similar to what would be expected by logical analysis—but not exactly the same data at every stage.

c. Student views about the value of theoretical and experimental models will vary. The general point about such a probability-based situation is that over the long-run the results are likely to average out very close to the logical model. However, on any individual trial, there could be noticeable variation from what theory predicts.

2 **a.** The numbers of coins removed at each stage will vary randomly from 1 to 6, for an average per trial of 3.5 coins. This suggests the formula $c = 100 - 3.5n$.

b. Once again, experimental results will not be nearly as smooth as a linear pattern that logical analysis suggests. However, over many trials, the trend should be modeled well by such a linear function.

c. Once again, student opinions might vary about which model is best. The approximation-derived model reveals the sort of random variation that one has to expect in practice.

3 The logical and experimental model for Problem 1 seemed to fit the conditions that one expects for exponential decay—a constant percent removed at each stage. The second experiment, on the other hand, fits the conditions that one expects from linear change—on average, a fixed amount subtracted at each stage.

SUMMARIZE THE MATHEMATICS

In this investigation, you compared two strategies for developing models of patterns in experimental data where a dependent variable decreases in value as a related independent variable increases.

a What differences did you notice between models suggested by logical analysis of the experiments and by curve-fitting based on real data?

b How were the models for each experiment similar, and how were they different? How are those similarities and differences explained by logical analysis? How are they illustrated by patterns in experimental data plots?

c What kinds of problem conditions suggest situations in which a linear model is likely to be best? Situations in which an exponential model is likely to be best?

Be prepared to compare your responses with those from other groups.

✔ CHECK YOUR UNDERSTANDING

Consider the following experiment:

- Start with a pile of 90 kernels of unpopped popcorn or dry beans.

- Pour the kernels or beans onto the center of a large paper plate with equal-sized sectors marked as in the diagram below.

- Shake the plate so that the kernels or beans scatter into the various sectors in a somewhat random pattern.

- Remove all kernels that land on the sector marked "1" and record the trial number and the number of kernels or beans remaining.

- Repeat the shake-remove-record process several times.

a. If you were to record the results of this experiment in a table of (*trial number*, *kernels left*) values, what pattern would you expect in that data? What function rule would probably be the best model for the relationship between trial number n and kernels left k?

SUMMARIZE THE MATHEMATICS

The key point of this investigation was that both logical and data-based analysis of a problem situation are valuable strategies in reasoning about patterns of change.

a In general, data from actual experiments will exhibit less smooth patterns than what is predicted by logical analysis. As a result, the curve-fitting tools will produce function rules similar to a rule deduced by logical reasoning.

b For one of the experiments, both logical analysis and (in all likelihood) data analysis suggested a pattern of exponential decay; in the other, both logical and data analysis suggested a linear decay pattern. These trends are evident in data plots, since the exponential situation produces a plot that is decreasing at a decreasing rate, while the linear situation gives a straight line trend with negative slope.

c The distinguishing feature of linear change is constant additive (or subtractive) change, while exponential change features constant multiplicative change with a factor greater than 1 for growth and between 0 and 1 for decay.

✔ CHECK YOUR UNDERSTANDING

a. This experiment suggests exponential decay with factor $\frac{2}{3}$; a rule like $k = 90\left(\frac{2}{3}\right)^n$ will probably model experimental results well. Starting from 90 kernels, the theoretical model suggests a data pattern like this:

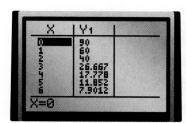 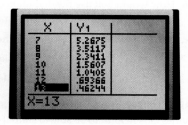

TEACHING RESOURCES

UNIT 5 Exponential Functions

SUMMARIZE THE MATHEMATICS

In this investigation, you compared two strategies for developing models of patterns in experimental data where a dependent variable decreases in value as a related independent variable increases.

a What differences did you notice between models suggested by logical analysis of the experiments and by curve-fitting based on real data?

b How were the models for each experiment similar, and how were they different? How are those similarities and differences explained by logical analysis? How are they illustrated by patterns in experimental data plots?

c What kinds of problem conditions suggest situations in which a linear model is likely to be best? Situations in which an exponential model is likely to be best?

Be prepared to compare your responses with those from other groups.

324 Unit 5 | Exponential Functions   Lesson Master | use with page 331

Lesson Master 324
ⓘ **GO DIGITAL**

MATH TOOLKIT

- Explain the difference between theoretical data and experimental data.
- Describe how you can determine whether a data set is linear or exponential.

TECHNOLOGY NOTE

This experiment can be simulated using **randBin(90,2/3)**. On the second round, start with the number left, which should be close to 60, and repeat the process.

b. Conduct the experiment and record the data. Then use your calculator or curve-fitting software to find the model that seems to fit the data pattern well.

c. Compare the models suggested by logical analysis of the experiment and by fitting of a function to actual data. Decide which is the better model of the experiment and explain your choice.

INVESTIGATION 4

Properties of Exponents II

In studying the rebound height of a bouncing ball, you calculated powers of the fraction $\frac{2}{3}$. You can calculate a power like $\left(\frac{2}{3}\right)^4$ by repeated multiplication $\left(\frac{2}{3}\right)\left(\frac{2}{3}\right)\left(\frac{2}{3}\right)\left(\frac{2}{3}\right)$. But there is a shortcut rule for such calculations with exponents.

As you work on the problems in this investigation, make notes of answers to this question:

What exponent properties provide shortcut rules for calculating powers of fractions, quotients of powers, and negative exponents?

Powers of a Fraction As you work on the next calculations, look for a pattern suggesting ways to write powers of fractions in useful equivalent forms.

1. Find values of x and y that will make these equations true statements:

   a. $\left(\frac{3}{5}\right)^3 = \frac{3^x}{5^y}$

   b. $\left(\frac{c}{5}\right)^2 = \frac{c^x}{5^y}$

   c. $\left(\frac{4}{n}\right)^5 = \frac{4^x}{n^y}$ $(n \neq 0)$

   d. $\left(\frac{c^2}{n}\right)^3 = \frac{c^x}{n^y}$ $(n \neq 0)$

2. Examine the results of your work on Problem 1.

   a. What pattern seems to relate task and result in every case?

   b. How would you use the definition of exponent or other reasoning to convince another student that your answer to Part a is correct?

   c. What would you expect to see as the most common errors in evaluating powers of a fraction like $\left(\frac{3}{5}\right)^4$? Explain how you would help someone who made those errors correct their understanding of how exponents work.

Quotients of Powers Since many useful algebraic functions require division of quantities, it is helpful to be able to simplify expressions involving quotients of powers like $\frac{b^x}{b^y}$ $(b \neq 0)$.

3. Find values for x, y, and z that will make these equations true statements.

   a. $\frac{2^{10}}{2^3} = 2^z$

   b. $\frac{3^6}{3^2} = 3^z$

   c. $\frac{10^9}{10^3} = 10^z$

   d. $\frac{2^x}{2^5} = 2^7$

   e. $\frac{7^x}{7^y} = 7^2$

   f. $\frac{b^5}{b^3} = b^z$

   g. $\frac{3^5}{3^5} = 3^z$

   h. $\frac{b^x}{b^x} = b^z$

Terry Oakley/Alamy

b. Student results will vary, however, they obviously won't have the fractional kernel numbers shown in the preceding tables for the exact function rule.

c. Once again, in the long run, with many repetitions of the experiment, results would average out very close to what the theory predicts. However, it is the nature of probabilistic variation that trends in any single run of the experiment will only approximate the theoretical pattern.

INVESTIGATION **4** N-RN.1, F-IF.8, A-SSE.3

Properties of Exponents II

In this investigation, students will extend their toolkit of exponent properties for calculating powers of fractions, quotients of powers, and negative exponents.

1 **a.** $x = y = 3$ **b.** $x = y = 2$

c. $x = y = 5$ **d.** $x = 6, y = 3$

2 **a.** The general pattern might be described in words as, "A fraction raised to a power is equal to the fraction with both numerator and denominator raised to that power."

b. Explanation of the rule in Part a relies on the fact that the product of two fractions is calculated by multiplying numerators and multiplying denominators. The exponential expression $\left(\frac{a}{b}\right)^x$ is shorthand for a product of x factors, each $\frac{a}{b}$. This will lead to a result looking like $\frac{a \cdot a \cdot a \cdot \cdots \cdot a}{b \cdot b \cdot b \cdot \cdots \cdot b}$ with x factors each in numerator and denominator. The numerator and denominator can then be written in exponential shorthand as $\frac{a^x}{b^x}$.

c. Since the exponent is written adjacent to the numerator of a fraction, it is tempting to apply it only to the numerator to get the error $\frac{3^4}{5}$ as an expression for $\left(\frac{3}{5}\right)^4$. Once again, a reminder of what the exponent implies (repeated factors of $\frac{3}{5}$) should help clear up errors with powers of quotients.

3 **a.** $z = 7$ **b.** $z = 4$ **c.** $z = 6$ **d.** $x = 12$

e. x and y can be any numbers for which $x - y = 2$

f. $z = 2$ **g.** $z = 0$ **h.** $z = 0$ for any x

4 Examine the results of your work on Problem 3.

  a. What pattern seems to relate task and result in every case?

  b. How would you use the definition of exponent or other reasoning to convince another student your answer to Part a is correct?

  c. What would you expect to see as the most common errors in evaluating quotients of powers like $\frac{8^{12}}{8^4}$? Explain how you would help someone who made those errors correct their understanding of how exponents work.

5 Use your answers to Problem 3 Parts g and h and Problem 4 Part a to explain why it is reasonable to define $b^0 = 1$ for any base b ($b \neq 0$).

Negative Exponents Suppose that you were hired as a science lab assistant to monitor an ongoing experiment studying the growth of an insect population. If the population when you took over was 48 and it was expected to double every day, you could estimate the population for any time in the future or the past with the function $p = 48(2^x)$.

Future estimates are easy: One day from now, the population should be about $48(2^1) = 96$; two days from now it should be about $48(2^2) = 48(2)(2) = 192$, and so on.

Estimates of the insect numbers in the population before you took over require division: One day earlier, the population should have been about

$48(2^{-1}) = 48 \div 2 = 48\left(\frac{1}{2}\right) = 24$; two days ago, it should have been about:

$$48(2^{-2}) = (48 \div 2) \div 2$$
$$= 48 \div 2^2$$
$$= 48\left(\frac{1}{2^2}\right)$$
$$= 12$$

This kind of reasoning about exponential growth suggests a general rule that for any nonzero number b and any integer n, $b^{-n} = \frac{1}{b^n}$.

6 The rule for operating with negative integer exponents also follows logically from the property about quotients of powers and the definition $b^0 = 1$. Justify each step in the reasoning below.

$$\frac{1}{b^n} = \frac{b^0}{b^n} \qquad (1)$$
$$= b^{0-n} \qquad (2)$$
$$= b^{-n} \qquad (3)$$

7 Use the relationship between fractions and negative integer exponents to write each of the following expressions in a different but equivalent form. In Parts a–f, write an equivalent fraction that does not use exponents at all.

  a. 5^{-3} **b.** 6^{-1} **c.** 2^{-4} **d.** $\left(\frac{2}{5}\right)^{-1}$

  e. $\left(\frac{1}{2}\right)^{-3}$ **f.** $\left(\frac{2}{5}\right)^{-2}$ **g.** x^{-3} **h.** $\frac{1}{a^4}$

4 **a.** Students will have various ways of summarizing the pattern involving quotients of powers. They might say something like, "When dividing exponential expressions with the same base, subtract exponents." Press students to clarify which exponent is subtracted. Students should indicate that the result of the subtraction is the exponent on the same base.

b. Students might offer a variety of explanations for why this pattern involving quotients of powers works. The basic idea is that factors of b in the denominator can be paired with factors of b in the numerator to create factors of $\frac{b}{b}$ which are equal to 1. When this pairing has used up all possible factors of b in the denominator, there will be $x - y$ factors of b left in the numerator.

c. Students will likely suggest the error $\frac{8^{12}}{8^4} = 8^3$. One way to help people correct this error is to write out the factors. Another way is to recognize that the division involves dividing factors of 8, not factors of 12 and 4.

5 For any nonzero base b and exponent x, $\frac{b^x}{b^x} = 1$. But the rule in Part a implies that $\frac{b^x}{b^x} = b^{x-x} = b^0$. So, b^0 must equal 1.

Students will have encountered a bit of work with negative exponents in early exponential growth and decay problems of this unit. Problems 6 and 7 help students connect with those "sensible" interpretations of negative exponents, and then show that the natural definition also connects with the other reasonable rules for operating with quotients of powers.

6 $\frac{1}{b^n} = \frac{b^0}{b^n}, b^0 = 1$ (1) by definition

$\frac{b^0}{b^n} = b^{0-n}$ (2) by rule for quotient of powers

$b^{0-n} = b^{-n}$ (3) arithmetic property of 0

7 **a.** $\frac{1}{125}$ **b.** $\frac{1}{6}$ **c.** $\frac{1}{16}$ **d.** $\frac{5}{2}$

e. 8   **f.** $\frac{25}{4}$ **g.** $\frac{1}{x^3}$ **h.** a^{-4}

8 Examine the results of your work in Problems 6 and 7.

 a. How would you describe the rule defining negative integer exponents in your own words?

 b. What would you expect to see as the most common errors in evaluating expressions with negative integer exponents like $\left(\frac{4}{3}\right)^{-2}$? How would you help someone who made those errors correct their understanding of how negative integer exponents work?

SUMMARIZE THE MATHEMATICS

In this investigation, you discovered, tested, and justified several principles that allow writing of exponential expressions in convenient equivalent forms.

a How would you describe in words the properties for writing exponential expressions in equivalent forms that you discovered in work on Problems 1–8?

b Summarize the properties of exponents you explored in Problems 1–8 by completing each of these statements with equivalent exponential expressions. In each case, $b \neq 0$.

 i. $\left(\frac{a}{b}\right)^m = \dots$ **ii.** $\frac{b^m}{b^n} = \dots$ **iii.** $b^{-n} = \dots$

c What examples would you use to illustrate common errors in use of exponents in expressions like those of Part b, and how would you explain the errors in each example?

Be prepared to explain your ideas to the class.

 CHECK YOUR UNDERSTANDING

Use properties of exponents to write each of the following expressions in another equivalent form. Be prepared to explain how you know your answers are correct.

 a. $(y^3)(y^6)$ **b.** $(5x^2y^4)(2xy^3)$ **c.** $\frac{a^7}{a^5}$

 d. $\left(\frac{5}{3}\right)^3$ **e.** $(pq)^3$ **f.** $(7p^3q^2)^2$

 g. $(T^3)^2$ **h.** $\frac{2}{p^{-4}}$ **i.** -5^2

 j. $(-5)^2$ **k.** $2a^0$ **l.** $(2a)^0$

 m. $4a^{-2}$ **n.** $(4a)^{-2}$

8 **a.** Students might describe the rule defining negative exponents in a variety of ways. The most common informal language is probably something like this: "When you move an exponential expression from the numerator of a fraction to the denominator, you change the sign of the exponent. The same thing happens when you move an expression from the denominator to the numerator of a fraction."

b. Errors might include losing the negative sign or applying the exponent only to the numerator. Student suggestions for correcting understanding may vary.

Summary

For each of the rules governing manipulation of exponential expressions, the students have already been asked to summarize the rules in their own words. So, they should not write them a second time. They may wish to edit their previous work though. As students share their personal wording of the patterns involved in work with equivalent exponential expressions, it will probably be useful to ask them to give illustrative examples, since concept images are often rooted in memory by specific simple examples.

SUMMARIZE THE MATHEMATICS

a Students' descriptions may be similar to the following:
- When dividing expressions with the same base, subtract the exponent of the denominator from the exponent of the numerator. Then use this result as the exponent to the same base.
- A fraction (or quotient) raised to a power is equal to the fraction with both numerator and denominator raised to that power.
- A number raised to a negative power is equal to the reciprocal of the number raised to the absolute value of the power.

b   **i.** Power of a Fraction: $\left(\dfrac{a}{b}\right)^m = \dfrac{a^m}{b^m}, b \neq 0$

   ii. Quotient of Powers: $\dfrac{b^m}{b^n} = b^{m-n}, b \neq 0$

   iii. Negative Exponents: $b^{-n} = \dfrac{1}{b^n}, b \neq 0$

c Students will probably have a variety of ideas about common error patterns. Here are a few that illustrate "mis-examples."

Error 1: $\dfrac{2^8}{2^2} = 2^4$; forgetting that when dividing expressions with the same base, one should subtract the exponent of the denominator from the exponent of the numerator and apply the result to the same base.

Error 2: $x^{-3} = -\dfrac{1}{x^3}$; thinking that the negative exponent changes the sign of the expression.

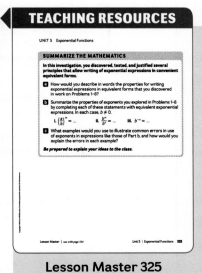
MATH TOOLKIT

Summarize the rules for exponents you studied in this lesson.
- $\left(\dfrac{a}{b}\right)^m =$
- $\dfrac{b^m}{b^n} =$
- $b^{-n} =$

NOTE The solution to the Check Your Understanding is on page T335.

INVESTIGATION **5**

Square Roots and Radicals

In your work on problems of insulin decay, you found that some questions required calculation with exponential expressions involving a fractional base and fractional powers. For example, estimating the amount of insulin active in the bloodstream 1.5 minutes after a 10-unit injection required calculating $10(0.95^{1.5})$.

Among the most useful expressions with fractional exponents are those with power one-half. It turns out that one-half powers are connected to the square roots that are so useful in geometric calculations like those involving the Pythagorean Theorem. For any non-negative number b,

$$b^{\frac{1}{2}} = \sqrt{b}.$$

Expressions like $\sqrt{b}$, $\sqrt{5}$, and $\sqrt{9 - x^2}$ are called *radicals*. As you work on the following problems, keep this question in mind:

How can you use your understanding of properties of exponents to guide your thinking about one-half powers, square roots, radical expressions, and rules for operating with them?

1 For integer exponents m and n, you know that $(a^m)^n = a^{mn}$. That property can be extended to work with fractional exponents.

  a. Write each of these expressions in standard number form without exponents or radicals.

   i. $\left(2^{\frac{1}{2}}\right)^2$ **ii.** $\left(5^{\frac{1}{2}}\right)^2$ **iii.** $\left(12^{\frac{1}{2}}\right)^2$ **iv.** $\left(2.4^{\frac{1}{2}}\right)^2$

  b. How do the results of Part a explain why the definition $b^{\frac{1}{2}} = \sqrt{b}$ makes sense?

2 Write each of the following expressions in an equivalent form using radicals and then in simplest number form (without exponents or radicals).

  a. $(25)^{\frac{1}{2}}$ **b.** $(9)^{\frac{1}{2}}$ **c.** $\left(\frac{9}{4}\right)^{\frac{1}{2}}$ **d.** $(100)^{\frac{1}{2}}$

3 The diagram below shows a series of squares with side lengths increasing in sequence 1, 2, 3, 4, and one diagonal drawn in each square.

1

2

3

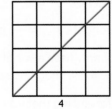
4

  a. Use the Pythagorean Theorem to find the exact length of the diagonal of each square.

  b. How are the lengths of the diagonals in the three larger squares related to the length of the diagonal of the unit square?

Lesson 2 | Exponential Decay   **335**

✅ CHECK YOUR UNDERSTANDING

a. y^9

b. $10x^3y^7$

c. a^2

d. $\dfrac{5^3}{3^3}$

e. p^3q^3

f. $49p^6q^4$

g. T^6

h. $2p^4$

i. -25

j. 25

k. 2

l. 1

m. $\dfrac{4}{a^2}$

n. $\dfrac{1}{16a^2}$

INVESTIGATION **5**   **N-RN.2, F-IF.8**, A-SSE.3, A-CED.2

Square Roots and Radicals

In some sense, work with square roots and radicals doesn't fit smoothly into a unit on exponential functions because, although the function $y = \sqrt{x}$ can be expressed in a form using exponents as $y = x^{\frac{1}{2}}$, the exponent is not the variable as it is with exponential growth and decay functions. The case for inclusion of this investigation on square roots and radicals in this unit and lesson is based in part on the connection through the exponential form for expressing radicals $\left(\sqrt[n]{b^m} = b^{\frac{m}{n}} \text{ and especially } b^{\frac{1}{2}} = \sqrt{b}\right)$ and in part on a desire to introduce some useful algebra involved with radicals. There are, of course, some useful connections of work with radicals in geometry through the Pythagorean Theorem.

The goal of this investigation is to develop student understanding of radical expressions and use of the basic identity $\sqrt{ab} = \sqrt{a}\sqrt{b}$ for positive real numbers. To justify the rule for radicals from a basis of exponent properties, the work begins by connecting square roots to fractional exponents.

1 **a. i.** 2   **ii.** 5   **iii.** 12   **iv.** 2.4

     b. The pattern suggested in Parts a–d is that, whatever the value of $a^{\frac{1}{2}}$ $(a \geq 0)$, when that value is squared, the result should be a because $\left(a^{\frac{1}{2}}\right)^2 = a^{\frac{1}{2} \cdot 2} = a^1 = a$.

2 Applying the thinking of Problem 1 suggests that $25^{\frac{1}{2}}$ is the number that when squared should give 25, so $25^{\frac{1}{2}} = 5$, etc.

     a. $\sqrt{25} = 5$ **b.** $\sqrt{9} = 3$ **c.** $\sqrt{\dfrac{9}{4}} = \dfrac{3}{2}$ **d.** $\sqrt{100} = 10$

3 **a.** The lengths of the diagonals are $\sqrt{2}$, $\sqrt{8}$, $\sqrt{18}$, and $\sqrt{32}$, respectively.

     b. The lengths of the diagonals of the second square, the third square, and the fourth square are respectively 2, 3, and 4 times the length of the diagonal of the unit square.

c. Look for a pattern in the results of Part b to complete the statement beginning:

The length d of each diagonal in a square with sides of length s is given by d = ...

4 The pattern relating side and diagonal lengths in a square illustrates a useful rule for simplifying radical expressions:

For any non-negative numbers a and b: $\sqrt{ab} = \sqrt{a}\sqrt{b}$.

a. What properties of square roots and exponents justify the steps in this argument? For any non-negative numbers a and b:

$$\sqrt{ab} = (ab)^{\frac{1}{2}} \qquad (1)$$
$$= a^{\frac{1}{2}}b^{\frac{1}{2}} \qquad (2)$$
$$= \sqrt{a}\sqrt{b} \qquad (3)$$

b. Modify the argument in Part a to justify this property of radicals:

For any non-negative numbers a and b ($b \neq 0$), $\sqrt{\frac{a}{b}} = \frac{\sqrt{a}}{\sqrt{b}}$.

5 Use the properties of square roots in Problem 4 to write expressions a–h in several equivalent forms. In each case, try to find the simplest equivalent form—one that involves only one radical and the smallest possible whole number inside that radical. Check your ideas with calculator estimates of each form. For example,

$$\sqrt{48} = \sqrt{4}\sqrt{12}$$
$$= 2\sqrt{12}$$
$$= 2\sqrt{4}\sqrt{3}$$
$$= 2 \cdot 2\sqrt{3}$$
$$= 4\sqrt{3}$$

Calculator estimates show that $\sqrt{48} \approx 6.93$ and $4\sqrt{3} \approx 6.93$.

a. $\sqrt{9 \cdot 5}$ **b.** $\sqrt{18}\sqrt{8}$ **c.** $\sqrt{45}$ **d.** $\sqrt{4 \cdot 9}$

e. $\sqrt{4 \cdot \frac{1}{9}}$ **f.** $\sqrt{\frac{9}{4}}$ **g.** $\sqrt{12}$ **h.** $\sqrt{96}$

6 The properties of square roots in Problem 4 are like distributive properties—taking the square root distributes over the product or the quotient of two (or more) numbers. One of the most common errors in working with square roots is distributing the square root sign over addition. However,

$$\sqrt{a + b} \neq \sqrt{a} + \sqrt{b}$$

except in some very special cases. Use several pairs of positive values for a and b to show that taking square roots *does not* distribute over addition (or subtraction).

c. The general formula is $d = s\sqrt{2}$.

4 **a.**

> **NOTE** For positive numbers, it often turns out to be useful (primarily for theoretical reasons) to write radicals in equivalent forms, using the basic property that $\sqrt{ab} = \sqrt{a}\,\sqrt{b}$. As we have developed rules for exponents in this lesson, the familiar simplification rule for radicals can be proven as follows.

$$\sqrt{ab} = (ab)^{\frac{1}{2}} \qquad \text{Definition of } \tfrac{1}{2} \text{ power}$$
$$= a^{\frac{1}{2}}b^{\frac{1}{2}} \qquad \text{Power of Product Property}$$
$$= \sqrt{a}\sqrt{b} \qquad \text{Definition of } \tfrac{1}{2} \text{ power}$$

b. $\sqrt{\dfrac{a}{b}} = \left(\dfrac{a}{b}\right)^{\frac{1}{2}} \qquad \text{Definition of } \tfrac{1}{2} \text{ power}$

$$= \dfrac{a^{\frac{1}{2}}}{b^{\frac{1}{2}}} \qquad \text{Power of Quotient Property}$$

$$= \dfrac{\sqrt{a}}{\sqrt{b}} \qquad \text{Definition of } \tfrac{1}{2} \text{ power}$$

5

> **INSTRUCTIONAL NOTE** There are many mathematically correct equivalent forms for the expressions given in this problem. We give only the "simplest form" results—those in which the number inside the radical sign is as small as possible to obtain by application of the rule in Part a. As students work on the problem given, they should be encouraged to write a variety of equivalent forms and then aim for one that seems to meet the "simplest" criterion.

a. $3\sqrt{5}$ **b.** 12 **c.** $3\sqrt{5}$ **d.** 6

e. $\dfrac{2}{3}$ **f.** $\dfrac{3}{2}$ **g.** $2\sqrt{3}$ **h.** $4\sqrt{6}$

6 It should be easy to find counterexamples because this false distributive property holds only when one or both of a and b is 0. For example,

$$\sqrt{9+4} \neq 3+2, \sqrt{25+9} \neq 5+3, \text{ etc.}$$

SUMMARIZE THE MATHEMATICS

In this investigation, you explored the relationship between fractional exponents and square roots and important properties of radical expressions.

a For $n \geq 0$, what does $\sqrt{n}$ mean, and why does it make sense that $\sqrt{n} = n^{\frac{1}{2}}$?

b What property of square roots can be used to express $\sqrt{n}$ in equivalent, often simpler, forms?

c What formula gives the length of each diagonal in a square with sides of length s?

Be prepared to share your thinking with the entire class.

 CHECK YOUR UNDERSTANDING

Use your understanding of fractional exponents and radical expressions to help complete the following tasks.

a. How could you use a calculator with only $=$, $-$, $\times$, and $\div$ keys to check these claims about values of expressions involving fractional exponents?

   i. $225^{\frac{1}{2}} = 15$ **ii.** $7^{\frac{1}{2}} \approx 2.65$

b. Find the values of these expressions, without use of a calculator.

   i. $36^{\frac{1}{2}}$ **ii.** $\sqrt{81}$

   iii. $\left(\frac{25}{16}\right)^{\frac{1}{2}}$ **iv.** $\sqrt{\frac{49}{81}}$

c. Use the property that for non-negative numbers a and b, $\sqrt{ab} = \sqrt{a}\,\sqrt{b}$ to help write each of these radical expressions in at least two equivalent forms.

   i. $\sqrt{30}$ **ii.** $\sqrt{10}\,\sqrt{40}$

   iii. $\sqrt{\frac{7}{25}}$ **iv.** $\sqrt{\frac{2}{3}}\,\sqrt{\frac{3}{2}}$

d. What is the length of each diagonal in a square with sides of length 7 centimeters?

e. Give a counterexample to show that for nonnegative numbers a and b, $\sqrt{a-b}$ is *not* equal to $\sqrt{a} - \sqrt{b}$.

UNIT 5

SUMMARIZE THE MATHEMATICS

a In general, $\sqrt{n}$ is a number that when squared gives n. It makes sense that $\sqrt{n} = n^{\frac{1}{2}}$ because generalizing the rules for whole number exponents would imply that $\left(n^{\frac{1}{2}}\right)^2 = n^{\frac{1}{2} \cdot 2} = n^1 = n$.

b The most useful property for simplifying square root expressions is $\sqrt{ab} = \sqrt{a}\sqrt{b}$.

c The formula relating the length of the diagonal d of a square with side lengths s is $d = s\sqrt{2}$.

✔ CHECK YOUR UNDERSTANDING

a. **i.** $225^{\frac{1}{2}} = 15$ because $15 \cdot 15 = 225$.

   ii. $7^{\frac{1}{2}} \approx 2.65$ because $2.65 \cdot 2.65 = 7.0225$.

b. **i.** $36^{\frac{1}{2}} = 6$ **ii.** $\sqrt{81} = 9$

   iii. $\left(\frac{25}{16}\right)^{\frac{1}{2}} = \frac{5}{4}$ **iv.** $\sqrt{\frac{49}{81}} = \frac{7}{9}$

c. **i.** $\sqrt{30} = \sqrt{2}\,\sqrt{15} = \sqrt{3}\,\sqrt{10} = \sqrt{5}\,\sqrt{6}$

   Noninteger factors could be used too. For example, $\sqrt{30} = \sqrt{2.5}\,\sqrt{12}$.

   ii. $\sqrt{10}\sqrt{40} = \sqrt{400} = 20 = \sqrt{10}\sqrt{10}\,\sqrt{4} = \ldots$

   iii. $\sqrt{\frac{7}{25}} = \sqrt{7}\,\sqrt{\frac{1}{25}} = \frac{\sqrt{7}}{5}$

   iv. $\sqrt{\frac{2}{3}}\,\sqrt{\frac{3}{2}} = \sqrt{\frac{6}{6}} = \sqrt{1} = 1$

d. The length of the diagonals in a square with sides of length 7 centimeters is $7\sqrt{2}$ centimeters.

e. One counterexample: $\sqrt{9-1} \neq \sqrt{9} - \sqrt{1}$ because $\sqrt{9-1} = \sqrt{8} = 2\sqrt{2}$ and $\sqrt{9} - \sqrt{1} = 3 - 1 = 2$

MATH TOOLKIT

- Explain what is meant by $n^{\frac{1}{2}}$. Give an example.
- Explain what is meant when we say that a radical expression is in simplest form. Give an example.

ON YOUR OWN

APPLICATIONS

1 If a basketball is properly inflated, it should rebound to about $\frac{1}{2}$ the height from which it is dropped.

a. Make a table and plot showing the pattern to be expected in the first 5 bounces after a ball is dropped from a height of 10 feet.

b. At which bounce will the ball first rebound less than 1 foot? Show how the answer to this question can be found in the table and on the graph.

c. Write a rule using *NOW* and *NEXT* and a rule beginning "$y = ...$" that can be used to calculate the rebound height after many bounces.

d. How will the data table, plot, and rules change for predicting rebound height if the ball is dropped from a height of 20 feet?

e. How will the data table, plot, and rules change for predicting rebound height if the ball is somewhat over-inflated and rebounds to $\frac{3}{5}$ of the height from which it is dropped?

2 Records at the Games Galore store show that sales of new electronic games are greatest in the first month after the release date. In the second month, sales are usually only about one-third of sales in the first month. Sales in the third month are usually only about one-third of sales in the second month, and so on.

a. If Games Galore sells 180 copies of one particular game in the first month after its release, how many copies are likely to be sold in the second month? In the third month?

b. What *NOW-NEXT* and "$y = ...$" rules predict the sales in the following months?

c. How many sales are predicted in the 12th month?

d. In what month are sales likely to first be fewer than 5 copies?

e. How would your answers to Parts a–d change for a different game that has first-month sales of 450 copies?

John Gilroy and John Lacko

APPLICATIONS

1 **a.** The theoretical table and plot will look something like this.

x	0	1	2	3	4	5
y	10	5	$\frac{5}{2}$	$\frac{5}{4}$	$\frac{5}{8}$	$\frac{5}{16}$

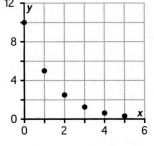

b. The fourth bounce will rebound less than 1 foot (seen in the table). This is the plot point that rises to a y-coordinate less than 1.

c. $NEXT = \frac{1}{2} \cdot NOW$, starting at 10; $y = 10\left(\frac{1}{2}\right)^x$, where x is the number of bounces.

d. If the initial drop is 20, every rebound height will double and the 10 in the rules will be replaced by 20.

e. If the rebound factor changes to $\frac{3}{5}$, that number will replace $\frac{1}{2}$ in the rules and the rebound heights will decay slower. So, the y values in the table for a $\frac{3}{5}$ rebound will be slightly greater than for a rebound factor of $\frac{1}{2}$. In the plot, the points will be slightly higher than the plot in Part a.

2 **a.** 60 copies in second month; 20 copies in third month

b. $NEXT = \frac{1}{3} \cdot NOW$, starting at 180; $y = 180\left(\frac{1}{3}\right)^x$, where x is the number of months after the release date.

c. The model predicts no sales in the 12th month.

d. In month 4, the predicted sales are $\frac{20}{3}$, or about 7. In month 5, the predicted sales are $\frac{20}{9}$, or about 2.25.

e. If the first month sales are 450, then the second month prediction is 150, and the third month prediction is 50. The rules will be $NEXT = \frac{1}{3} \cdot NOW$, starting at 450, and $y = 450\left(\frac{1}{3}\right)^x$. In the 12th month, one can expect no sales. Sales will drop below 5 in month 6 (1.85 in that month and 5.6 in month 5).

3 You may have heard of athletes being disqualified from competitions because they have used anabolic steroid drugs to increase their weight and strength. These steroids can have very damaging side effects for the user. The danger is compounded by the fact that these drugs leave the human body slowly. With an injection of the steroid *cyprionate*, about 90% of the drug and its by-products will remain in the body one day later. Then 90% of that amount will remain after a second day, and so on. Suppose that an athlete tries steroids and injects a dose of 100 milligrams of cyprionate. Analyze the pattern of that drug in the athlete's body by completing the next tasks.

a. Make a table showing the amount of the drug remaining at various times.

Time Since Use (in days)	0	1	2	3	4	5	6	7
Steroid Present (in mg)	100	90	81					

b. Make a plot of the data in Part a and write a short description of the pattern shown in the table and the plot.

c. Write two rules that describe the pattern of amount of steroid in the blood.

   i. Write a *NOW-NEXT* rule showing how the amount of steroid present changes from one day to the next.

   ii. Write a "$y = \ldots$" rule that shows how one could calculate the amount of steroid present after any number of days.

d. Use one of the rules in Part c to estimate the amount of steroid left after 0.5 and 8.5 days.

e. Estimate, to the nearest tenth of a day, the half-life of cyprionate.

f. How long will it take the steroid to be reduced to only 1% of its original level in the body? That is, how many days will it take until 1 milligram of the original dose is left in the body?

4 When people suffer head injuries in accidents, emergency medical personnel sometimes administer a paralytic drug to keep the patient immobile. If the patient is found to need surgery, it's important that the immobilizing drug decay quickly.

For one typical paralytic drug, the standard dose is 50 micrograms. One hour after the injection, half the original dose has decayed into other chemicals. The halving process continues the next hour, and so on.

a. How much of the drug will remain in the patient's system after 1 hour? After 2 hours? After 3 hours?

b. Write a rule that shows how to calculate the amount of drug that will remain x hours after the initial dose.

c. Use your rule to make a table showing the amount of drug left at half-hour intervals from 0 to 5 hours.

d. Make a plot of the data from Part c and a continuous graph of the function on the same axes.

e. How long will it take the 50-microgram dose to decay to less than 0.05 micrograms?

VStock/Alamy

Lesson 2 | Exponential Decay **339**

3 **a.**

Time Since Use (in days)	0	1	2	3	4	5	6	7
Steroid Present (in mg)	100	90	81	72.9	65.6	59.0	53.1	47.8

b.

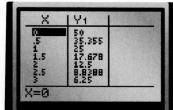

The pattern in the table and graph shows the amount of steroid decreasing at a decreasing rate, but very slowly. It will be many days before the steroid is no longer detectable.

c. **i.** $NEXT = 0.9 \cdot NOW$, starting at 100

   ii. $y = 100(0.9^x)$, where x is the number of days after the steroid is administered.

d. The amount of steroid left after 0.5 days will be about 94.9 milligrams; after 8.5 days, about 40.8 mg.

e. The half-life is approximately 6.6 days.

f. After a bit more than 43 days, the steroid remaining will be 1 milligram or 1% of the initial dose.

4 **a.** 25 micrograms after 1 hour, 12.5 micrograms after 2 hours, 6.25 micrograms after 3 hours

b. $y = 50(0.5^x)$

c.

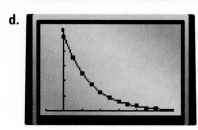
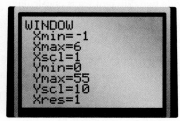

d.

e. The 50 micrograms will decay to 0.05 micrograms in just a bit less than 10 hours.

ON YOUR OWN

5 Radioactive materials have many important uses in the modern world, from fuel for power plants to medical x-rays and cancer treatments. But the radioactivity that produces energy and tools for "seeing" inside our bodies can have some dangerous effects too; for example, it can cause cancer in humans.

The radioactive chemical *strontium-90* is produced in many nuclear reactions. Extreme care must be taken in transport and disposal of this substance. It decays slowly—if an amount is stored at the beginning of a year, 98% of that amount will still be present at the end of the year.

a. If 100 grams (about 0.22 pounds) of strontium-90 are released by accident, how much of that radioactive substance will still be around after 1 year? After 2 years? After 3 years?

b. Write two different rules that can be used to calculate the amount of strontium-90 remaining from an initial amount of 100 grams at any year in the future.

c. Make a table and a graph showing the amount of strontium-90 that will remain from an initial amount of 100 grams at the end of every 10-year period during a century.

Years Elapsed	0	10	20	30	40	50	60	...
Amount Left (in g)	100							

d. Find the amount of strontium-90 left from an initial amount of 100 grams after 15.5 years.

e. Find the number of years that must pass until only 10 grams remain.

f. Estimate, to the nearest tenth of a year, the half-life of strontium-90.

6 The values of expensive products like automobiles *depreciate* from year to year. One common method for calculating the depreciation of automobile values assumes that a car loses 20% of its value every year. For example, suppose a new pickup truck costs $20,000. The value of that truck one year later will be only $20,000 − 0.2(20,000) = $16,000.

a. Why is it true that for any value of x, $x − 20\%x = 80\%x$? How does this fact provide two different ways of calculating depreciated values?

b. Write *NOW-NEXT* and "$y = …$" rules that can be used to calculate the value of the truck in any year.

c. Estimate the time when the truck's value is only $1,000. Show how the answer to this question can be found in a table and on a graph.

d. How would the rules in Part b change if the truck's purchase price was only $15,000? What if the purchase price was $25,000?

David R. Frazier Photolibrary

5 **a.** After 1 year, 98 grams will remain.
After 2 years, 96 grams will remain.
After 3 years, 94.1 grams will remain.

b. $NEXT = 0.98 \cdot NOW$, starting at 100; $y = 100(0.98^x)$, where x is the number of years elapsed.

c.

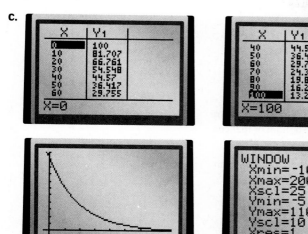

d. After 15.5 years, 73.12 grams will remain.

e. After about 114 years, 9.995 grams will remain.

f. The half-life will be approximately 34.3 years.

6 **a.** The distributive property guarantees the identity:

$$x - 20\%x = x - 0.2x$$
$$= (1 - 0.2)x$$
$$= 0.8x$$
$$= 80\%x$$

You can calculate depreciated values by calculating 80% of the value of the truck, or by calculating 20% of the truck value and subtracting that amount from the truck value.

b. There are two kinds of *NOW-NEXT* rules:

$NEXT = NOW - 0.2 \cdot NOW$ and $NEXT = 0.8 \cdot NOW$, starting at 20,000. In standard exponential form, $y = 20{,}000(0.8^x)$, where x is the number of years after purchase.

c. Truck value will be reduced to only $1,000 in about 13.5 years.

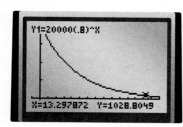
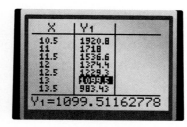

d. The *NOW-NEXT* rules would start at 15,000 and 25,000. The "$y = ...$" rules are $y = 15{,}000(0.8^x)$ and $y = 25{,}000(0.8^x)$.

7 In Applications Task 4 of Lesson 1, you counted the number of "chairs" at each stage in a design process that begins like this:

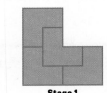

Stage 0   **Stage 1**

The chair at Stage 0 can be made by placing three square tiles in an "L" pattern. Suppose that the tiles used to make the chair design at Stage 0 are each one-centimeter squares. Then the left side and the bottom of that chair are each two centimeters long.

a. Complete a table like this that shows the lengths of those chair sides in smaller chairs used at later stages of the subdivision process.

Subdivision Stage	0	1	2	3	4	5	...	n
Side Length (in cm)	2	...						

b. Write two rules that show how to calculate the side length (in cm) of the smaller chair at any stage—one using *NOW* and *NEXT*, and another beginning "$L = \ldots$."

c. The area of the chair at Stage 0 is 3 square centimeters. What is the area of each small chair at Stage 1? At Stage 2? At Stage 3? At Stage n?

d. Write two rules that show how to calculate the area (in cm²) of the smaller chairs at any stage—one using *NOW* and *NEXT*, and another beginning "$A = \ldots$."

8 Fleas are one of the most common pests for dogs. If your dog has fleas, you can buy many different kinds of treatments, but they wear off over time. Suppose the half-life of one such treatment is 10 days.

a. Make a table showing the fraction of an initial treatment that will be active after 10, 20, 30, and 40 days.

b. Experiment with your calculator or computer software to find a function of the form $y = b^x$ (where x is time in days) that matches the pattern in your table.

Lesson 2 | Exponential Decay **341**

7 **a–c.**

Subdivision Stage	0	1	2	3	4	5	...	n
Side Length (in cm)	2	1	$\frac{1}{2}$	$\frac{1}{4}$	$\frac{1}{8}$	$\frac{1}{16}$	...	$2\left(\frac{1}{2}\right)^n$
Area of Chair (in cm²)	3	$\frac{3}{4}$	$\frac{3}{16}$	$\frac{3}{64}$	$\frac{3}{256}$	$\frac{3}{1,024}$	...	$3\left(\frac{1}{4}\right)^n$

b. $NEXT = NOW \cdot \frac{1}{2}$, starting at 2

$$L = 2\left(\frac{1}{2}\right)^n$$

c. See the table in Part a.

d. $NEXT = NOW \cdot \frac{1}{4}$, starting at 3

$$A = 3\left(\frac{1}{4}\right)^n$$

8 **a.**

Number of Days Since Treatment	10	20	30	40
Fraction of Initial Treatment Still Active	$\frac{1}{2}$	$\frac{1}{4}$	$\frac{1}{8}$	$\frac{1}{16}$

b. $y = (0.933^x)$ is very close but not exact.

ON YOUR OWN

9 Suppose that an experiment to test the bounce of a tennis ball gave the data in the following table.

Bounce Number	1	2	3	4	5	6
Bounce Height (in inches)	35	20	14	9	5	3

a. Find *NOW-NEXT* and "$y = ...$" rules that model the relationship between bounce height and bounce number shown in the experimental data.

b. Use either rule from Part a to estimate the drop height of the ball.

c. Modify the rules from Part a to provide models for the relationship between bounce height and bounce number in case the drop height was 100 inches. Then make a table and plot of estimates for the heights of the first 6 bounces in this case.

d. What percent seems to describe well the relationship between drop height and bounce height of the tennis ball used in the experiment?

10 Consider the following experiment:

- Start with a pile of 100 kernels of popcorn or dry beans.

- Pour the kernels or beans onto the center of a large paper plate with equal-sized sectors marked as in the following diagram. Shake the plate so that the kernels or beans scatter into the various sectors in a somewhat random pattern.

- Remove all kernels that land on the sectors marked "1" *and* "2" and record the trial number and the number of kernels or beans remaining.

- Repeat the shake-remove-count process several times.

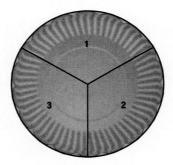

a. If you were to record the results of this experiment in a table of (*trial number, kernels left*) values, what pattern would you expect in that data? What function rule would probably be the best model for the relationship between trial number n and kernels left k?

9 **a.** Using a calculator curve-fitting utility, one rule that fits the data well is
$y = 57(0.62^x)$, where x is the bounce number. This implies $NEXT = 0.62 \cdot NOW$,
starting at 57.

   b. The rules imply the drop height of the ball was about 57 inches.

   c. The rule for an initial drop height of 100 inches would simply replace 57
with 100. In this case, the table and plot would look like this:

 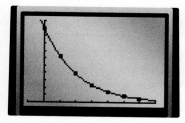

   d. The data suggest a rebound to 62% of drop height on each bounce.

10 **a.** The pattern should show about $\frac{1}{3}$ of the previous number of kernels remaining
after each shake-remove-count process. The rule $k = 100\left(\frac{1}{3}\right)^n$ would best
model the relationship.

b. Which of the following data patterns seems most likely to result from performing the experiment and why?

Table I

Trial Number	1	2	3	4	5
Kernels Left	65	40	25	15	10

Table II

Trial Number	1	2	3	4	5
Kernels Left	80	60	40	20	0

Table III

Trial Number	1	2	3	4	5
Kernels Left	35	15	5	2	0

11 Suppose that you performed the following experiment:

- Roll 100 fair dice and remove all that show 2, 4, or 6 dots on the top face.

- Roll the remaining dice and remove all that show 2, 4, or 6 dots on the top face.

- Repeat the roll-and-remove process, recording the number of dice left at each roll.

a. Complete a table like this showing your prediction of the number of dice remaining after each roll-and-remove stage of the experiment.

Roll Number	1	2	3	4	5	6	7
Estimated Dice Left	100						

b. Write *NOW-NEXT* and "$y = \ldots$" rules that model the relationship between roll number and dice left shown in your table.

c. Suppose that your teacher claimed to have done a similar experiment, starting with only 30 dice, and got the results shown in the next table.

Roll Number	0	1	2	3	4	5	6
Dice Left	30	17	10	4	3	1	1

Is the teacher's claim reasonable? What evidence supports your judgment?

12 Find values of x and y that will make these equations true statements.

a. $\left(\frac{5}{4}\right)^3 = x$

b. $\left(\frac{5}{d}\right)^2 = \frac{5^x}{d^y} \ (d \neq 0)$

c. $\left(\frac{n}{4}\right)^3 = \frac{n^x}{y}$

d. $\left(\frac{t^3}{s}\right)^4 = \frac{t^x}{s^y} \ (s \neq 0)$

13 Write each of the following expressions in a simpler equivalent exponential form.

a. $\left(\frac{4x}{n}\right)^2$

b. $\left(\frac{32x^2y^5}{8x^3y}\right)^2$

c. $\left(\frac{5x}{4y^3}\right)^0$

b. Table III comes closest to what is expected.

11 **a.** The number of dice left (rounded to a whole number) should fit a pattern something like this:

Roll Number	0	1	2	3	4	5	6	7
Estimated Dice Left	100	50	25	13	6	3	2	1

b. $NEXT = 0.5 \cdot NOW$, starting at 100; $y = 100(0.5^x)$, where x is the roll number.

c. The pattern in the teacher's data doesn't exactly fit the theoretical pattern, but it is plausibly close to what one might expect for $y = 30(0.5^x)$. Randomness would influence results from any particular experiment.

12 **a.** $x = \dfrac{125}{64}$

b. $x = y = 2$

c. $x = 3, y = 64$

d. $x = 12, y = 4$

13 **a.** $\dfrac{16x^2}{n^2}$

b. $\dfrac{16y^8}{x^2}$

c. 1

ON YOUR OWN

14 Find values for x and y that will make these equations true statements.

a. $\frac{5^7}{5^5} = 5^y$ b. $\frac{3^x}{3^5} = 3^6$ c. $\frac{t^5}{t^2} = t^y$ d. $\frac{6.4^9}{6.4^9} = 6.4^y$

15 Write each of the following expressions in a simpler equivalent exponential form.

a. $\frac{7^{11}}{7^4}$ b. $\frac{25x^3}{5x}$ c. $\frac{30x^3y^2}{6xy}$ d. $\frac{a^3b^4}{ab^4}$

16 Write each of the following expressions in equivalent exponential form. For those involving negative exponents, write an equivalent form without using negative exponents. For those involving positive exponents, write an equivalent form using negative exponents.

a. 4.5^{-2} b. $(7x)^{-1}$ c. $\left(\frac{2}{5}\right)^{-1}$ d. $\left(\frac{1}{5}\right)^{-4}$

e. $5x^{-3}$ f. $\left(\frac{2}{5}\right)^2$ g. $(4ax)^{-2}$ h. $\frac{5}{t^3}$

17 In Parts a–h below, write the number in integer or common fraction form, where possible. Where not possible, write an expression in simplest form using radicals.

a. $\sqrt{49}$ b. $\sqrt{28}$ c. $98^{\frac{1}{2}}$ d. $\sqrt{\frac{64}{25}}$

e. $\sqrt{6}\,\sqrt{24}$ f. $\sqrt{9+16}$ g. $\sqrt{\frac{12}{49}}$ h. $\left(\sqrt{49}\right)^2$

18 Answer these questions about the side and diagonal lengths of squares.

a. How long is the diagonal of a square if each side is 12 inches long?

b. How long is each side of a square if the diagonal is $5\sqrt{2}$ inches long?

c. How long is each side of a square if the diagonal is 12 inches long?

d. What is the area of a square with a diagonal $5\sqrt{2}$ inches long?

e. What is the area of a square with a diagonal length d units?

CONNECTIONS

19 One of the most interesting and famous fractal patterns is named after the Polish mathematician Waclaw Sierpinski. The start and first two stages in making a triangular *Sierpinski carpet* are shown below. Assume that the area of the original equilateral triangle is 12 square meters.

Stage 0   Stage 1   Stage 2

a. Sketch the next stage in the pattern. Note how, in typical fractal style, small pieces of the design are similar to the design of the whole.

14 **a.** $y = 2$ **b.** $x = 11$ **c.** $y = 3$ **d.** $y = 0$

15 **a.** 7^7 **b.** $5x^2$ **c.** $5x^2y$ **d.** a^2

16 **a.** $\frac{1}{4.5^2}$ **b.** $\frac{1}{7x}$ **c.** $\frac{5}{2}$ **d.** 5^4

   e. $\frac{5}{x^3}$ **f.** $\left(\frac{5}{2}\right)^{-2}$ **g.** $\frac{1}{(4ax)^2}$ **h.** $5t^{-3}$

17 **a.** 7   **b.** $2\sqrt{7}$ **c.** $7\sqrt{2}$ **d.** $\frac{8}{5}$

   e. 12   **f.** 5   **g.** $\frac{2\sqrt{3}}{7}$ **h.** 49

18 **a.** $12\sqrt{2}$

   b. 5

   c. $\frac{12}{\sqrt{2}} \approx 8.5$

   (Note: Rationalizing denominators is not on the agenda right now.)

   d. 25 in^2

   e. $\left(\frac{d}{\sqrt{2}}\right)^2$

CONNECTIONS

19 **a.**

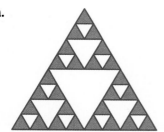

b. Make a table showing (*cutout stage*, *area remaining*) data for cutout stages 0 to 5 of this process.

c. Make a plot of the data in Part b.

d. Write two different rules that can be used to calculate the area of the remaining carpet at different stages. One rule should show change from one stage to the next. The other should be in the form "$y = \ldots$."

e. How many stages are required to reach the point where there is:

  i. more hole than carpet remaining?

  ii. less than 0.1 square meters of carpet remaining?

20 For each of the following rules, decide whether the function represented is an example of:

- An increasing linear function

- A decreasing linear function

- An exponential growth function

- An exponential decay function

- Neither linear nor exponential function

In each case, explain how the form of the rule was used in making your decision.

a. $y = 5(0.4^x)$ **b.** $y = 5 + 0.4x$

c. $y = 0.4(5^x)$ **d.** $y = 0.4 + 5x$

e. $y = \dfrac{5}{x}$ **f.** $y = \dfrac{0.4}{x}$

g. $y = 5 - 0.4x$ **h.** $y = 0.4 - 5x$

i. $NEXT = 0.4 \cdot NOW$ **j.** $NEXT = NOW + 0.4$

k. $NEXT = NOW - 5$ **l.** $NEXT = 5 \cdot NOW$

21 The graphs, tables, and rules below model four exponential growth and decay situations. For each graph, there is a matching table and a matching rule. Use what you know about the patterns of exponential relations to match each graph with its corresponding table and rule. In each case, explain the clues that can be used to match the items without any use of a graphing calculator or computer.

Graphs

Tables

A

x	1	2	3	4
y	40	16	6.4	2.56

B

x	1	2	3	4
y	30	90	270	810

C

x	1	2	3	4
y	60	36	21.6	12.96

D

x	1	2	3	4
y	20	40	80	160

Rules

(1) $y = 100(0.6^x)$

(2) $y = 100(0.4^x)$

(3) $y = 10(2^x)$

(4) $y = 100(3^x)$

Lesson 2 | Exponential Decay **345**

b.

Cutout Number	0	1	2	3	4	5
Area Remaining	12	9	6.75	5.06	3.80	2.85

c.

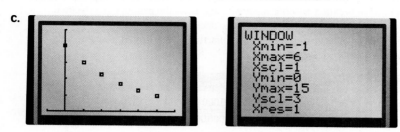

```
WINDOW
 Xmin=-1
 Xmax=6
 Xscl=1
 Ymin=0
 Ymax=15
 Yscl=3
 Xres=1
```

d. $NEXT = 0.75 \cdot NOW$, starting at 12; $y = 12(0.75^x)$

e. **i.** There is more hole than carpet by cutout number 3. (The area of the holes is about 7 cm².)

　　ii. There is less than 0.1 cm² of carpet remaining by cutout number 17.

20 Student explanations should indicate that they have a firm understanding of the relationships between the form of a rule and the type of function—not simply a memorized rule, but an ability to explain why the connections make sense.

a. Exponential decay function

b. Increasing linear function

c. Exponential growth function

d. Increasing linear function

e. Neither linear nor exponential function

f. Neither linear nor exponential function

g. Decreasing linear function

h. Decreasing linear function

i. Exponential decay function

j. Increasing linear function

k. Decreasing linear function

l. Exponential growth function

21

Graph	Table	Rules
I	C	(1)
II	A	(2)
III	B	(4)
IV	D	(3)

One of the most important clues to notice is whether the function is increasing or decreasing. (Does the curve rise or fall? Do the values in the table increase or decrease?) Comparing the bases in the rules will give you good information. Rules (1) and (2) are both decreasing and rule (2) is decreasing faster; rules (3) and (4) are increasing and rule (4) is increasing faster. Finding these similar patterns in the tables and graphs provides the clues to complete this task.

ON YOUR OWN

22 When very large numbers are used in scientific work, they are usually written in what is called *scientific notation*—that is, as the product of a decimal between 1 and 10 (usually rounded to three decimal places) with some power of 10. For example, basic measurements of Earth are often given in scientific notation like this.

Measurement	Standard Form	Scientific Notation
Land Area (in m^2)	148,940,000,000,000	1.489×10^{14}
Volume (in km^3)	1,083,000,000,000,000,000	1.083×10^{18}
Population	6,986,734,000	6.987×10^9
Mass (in kg)	5,974,000,000,000,000,000,000,000	5.974×10^{24}

a. Write each of these large numbers in scientific notation rounded to three decimal places.

   i. 234,567,890   **ii.** 54,987   **iii.** 1,024,456,981,876

b. Use negative exponents to write each of these numbers in scientific notation.

   i. 0.0234   **ii.** 0.00002056   **iii.** 0.000000000008

c. Translate each of these numbers, given in scientific notation, to standard numeral form.

   i. 7.82×10^8 **ii.** 5.032×10^6 **iii.** 8.1×10^{-3}

d. Express the results of these calculations in scientific notation, without using a calculator. Be prepared to explain your reasoning and how you use properties of exponents to reach the results.

   i. $(4 \times 10^{12}) \times (3 \times 10^5)$

   ii. $(40 \times 10^{12}) \div (5 \times 10^5)$

   iii. $(4 \times 10^{12}) \times (3 \times 10^{-5})$

e. Use the Earth measurement data in the table to answer these questions. Express your answers in both scientific and standard notation.

   i. How much land surface is there for each person living today?

   ii. Each kilogram of mass is equal to 1,000 grams. What is the mass of the Earth in grams?

23 In 2010, the U.S. national public debt was 14.0×10^{12} dollars, and the U.S. population was about 3.087×10^8 people. What does this imply in terms of national public debt per person?

24 Every non-negative number x, has a non-negative square root $\sqrt{x}$.

a. Use your calculator or computer software to complete the following table of approximate values for the square root function $y = \sqrt{x}$ for whole numbers from 0 to 10. Then sketch a graph of the function.

x	0	1	2	3	4	5	6	7	8	9	10
$y = \sqrt{x}$											

22 a. **i.** 2.346×10^8

    ii. 5.499×10^4

    iii. 1.024×10^{12}

b. **i.** 2.34×10^{-2}

    ii. 2.056×10^{-5}

    iii. 8.0×10^{-12}

c. **i.** 782,000,000

    ii. 5,032,000

    iii. 0.0081

d. **i.** 1.2×10^{18}

    ii. 8×10^7

    iii. 1.2×10^8

e. **i.** $1.489 \times 10^{14} \div 6.987 \times 10^9 \approx 2.131 \times 10^4$, or about 21,310 m² per person. (Of course, this counts the area of Antarctica and many other essentially uninhabitable land areas.)

    ii. 5.974×10^{24} kg $= 5.974 \times 10^{27}$ g $= 5,974,000,000,000,000,000,000,000,000$ g

23 $14.0 \times 10^{12} \div 3.087 \times 10^8 = (14.0 \div 3.087) \times 10^4$, which is approximately 4.5351×10^4 or about \$45,351 per person. (Note that using estimation strategies, one could round the debt to 15×10^{12} and the population to 3×10^8 and then quickly see that the debt per person is about 5×10^4 or about \$50,000. Scientific notation and fluency with basic whole number arithmetic facts helps with this sort of "order of magnitude" estimation.)

24 a.

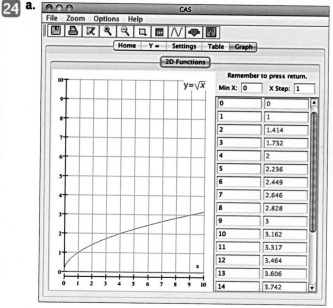

b. How is the pattern of change shown in the table and graph of the *square root function* similar to and different from those of exponential growth and decay functions? How about linear functions?

c. How is the pattern of change shown in the table and graph of the cube root function $y = \sqrt[3]{x}$ similar to and different from those of the functions below?

   i. $y = \sqrt{x}$ **ii.** $y = x^{\frac{1}{3}}$

   iii. $y = x^3$ **iv.** $y = \frac{1}{3}x$

25 The shell of the chambered nautilus is one of the most beautiful designs in nature. The outside image is a spiral, and segments of the spiral match chambers within the shell that increase in size as the spiral unfolds.

    The spiral diagram to the left of the nautilus picture below is similar to the shell. Each outside segment is 1 centimeter long. The individual "chambers" are right triangles.

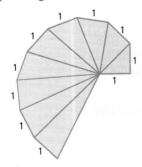 

a. Make a table showing the pattern of lengths for the segments that divide the "shell chambers." Report each segment length in radical form.

b. What rule tells the length of the hypotenuse in the *n*th "chamber"?

REFLECTIONS

26 When some students were discussing the ball bounce experiment, one said that he thought the ball might rebound less on each bounce, but it would never actually stop bouncing just a little bit.

His partners disagreed. They said that because the rebound height decreases on successive bounces, the rebound *time* also decreases. They said that the sum of rebound times would be:

$$\frac{1}{2} + \frac{1}{4} + \frac{1}{8} + \frac{1}{16} + \cdots = 1$$

What do you think?

Lesson 2 | Exponential Decay **347**

b. The pattern of the table and the graph show a steadily increasing function, like exponential growth (not decay) and linear functions with positive slope. However, the rate of increase in y is actually slowing as x increases, the opposite of what happens for exponential growth. Also, linear functions increase at a constant rate while the square root function is increasing, but at a decreasing rate.

c. **i.** The pattern of the table and the graph for $y = \sqrt{x}$ show a slow increase at a decreasing rate very much like $y = \sqrt[3]{x}$. The square root values for an input value are greater than the cube root values for the same input value. Thus, the graph of $y = \sqrt{x}$ is higher than that of the cube root function.

   ii. Since $y = x^{\frac{1}{3}}$ is another representation for the cube root function, the patterns in the tables and graphs are identical.

   iii. The pattern of the table and the graph for $y = x^3$ increases at an increasing rate. The table values and graph are higher than those of the cube root function for $x > 1$.

   iv. The pattern of the table and the graph for $y = \frac{1}{3}x$ shows a constant increase unlike the slow increase at a decreasing rate for the cube root function.

25 **a.** The length of the segment separating chamber 1 from chamber 2 is $\sqrt{2}$, that separating chamber 2 from chamber 3 is $\sqrt{3}$, and so on.

b. The length L of the segment separating chamber $n - 1$ from chamber n is $\sqrt{n}$. So, $L = \sqrt{n}$

   The following kind of algebraic reasoning is not expected from students at this point. However, this can be proven by observing that:

   $L^2 = \left(\sqrt{n-1}\right)^2 + 1^2 = (n - 1) + 1 = n$. So, $L = \sqrt{n}$.

REFLECTIONS

26 This question may generate a lively debate among the students. (Its resolution requires ideas from quadratic functions, which will be developed in Unit 7, and also some work with infinite geometric series that will not occur until Course 3.) Students who believe the ball will stop bouncing in a finite time are on the right track. Since each rebound height is less than the rebound of the preceding bounce, the time the ball takes to rise and fall gets shorter on each succeeding rebound.

   For instance, if the ball is dropped from an initial height of 16 feet, it will take approximately one second to reach the ground ($d = 16t^2$ gives distance traveled by a falling object under the influence of gravity in t seconds). Assuming, for example, that the ball rebounds to only half its drop height, then the time for the next drop back to the ground will take time determined by solving $16t^2 = 8$ or $t = \sqrt{\frac{1}{2}}$. The rebound times will equal the drop times. If you continue solving to find the time required for successive rebound and drop cycles, you will discover that the nth such time period will be $t = 2\left(\sqrt{\frac{1}{2}}\right)^n$ seconds. This pattern defines a geometric (exponential) sequence with finite sum about 6.8.

UNIT 5

27 Suppose a person taking steroid drugs is hospitalized due to a side effect from the drug. Tests taken upon admittance show a steroid concentration of 1.0. The next test one day later shows a concentration of 0.75. Based on these results, the person's family and friends assume that in three more days the drug will be out of the person's system.

   a. What pattern of change are the family and friends assuming?

   b. What might be a more accurate pattern prediction? Why is that pattern more reasonable?

28 In each task of Investigation 4, you were asked to solve several problems involving a common property of exponents, to find a common pattern in the results, and to justify the apparent rule for operating with exponents.

   a. What are the benefits and risks of error in the practice of looking for patterns in repeated calculations?

   b. What are the benefits and risks of relying on specific illustrative examples to justify a claim that a pattern holds "for all values?"

29 The definition $b^0 = 1$ is often hard for people to accept. They argue that if b^5 means "5 factors of b," then b^0 should mean "zero factors of b" and this should be zero. The mathematician's response is that sometimes we make definitions for special cases so that they fit together with patterns covering all other cases. For example, they point out that we define $(-3)(-3) = 9$ because

$$
\begin{aligned}
0 &= (-3)(0) \\
&= (-3)(3 + (-3)) \\
&= (-3)(3) + (-3)(-3) \\
&= -9 + (-3)(-3)
\end{aligned}
$$

   a. What do you think of this argument for $(-3)(-3) = 9$?

   b. What do you think of the general practice of making definitions in special cases so that they fit the rules that apply to all other cases?

30 In various problems in this unit, you developed and applied mathematical models to represent patterns of exponential growth and decay.

   a. How can you assess the probable accuracy of predictions made by those models?

   b. If data on which a model is based do not exactly match the predictions of the model, what is the value of model-based reasoning?

   c. What are the risks and benefits of using calculator or computer tools to develop mathematical models of exponential growth or decay?

EXTENSIONS

31 The African Black Rhinoceros is the second largest of all land mammals. The black rhino has walked the earth for 40 million years, and prior to the 19th century over 1,000,000 of the species roamed the plains of Africa. However, that number has been drastically reduced by hunting and loss of natural habitat.

   The table at the left shows the very sharp decline in black rhino numbers between 1970 and 1993.

Year	Population (in 1,000s)
1970	65
1980	15
1984	9
1986	3.8
1993	2.3

Source: *Mammals of the World,* fifth ed., vol. 2. Johns Hopkins University Press: Baltimore, 1991; www.rhinos-irf.org/information/blackrhino/index.htm

27 a. The family is assuming a linear pattern of change in concentration.

b. An exponential decay with change factor 0.75 is more reasonable. Since some fresh material is added and some diluted taken out, the amount of diluted taken out is less each time. The concentration is decreasing at a decreasing rate.

28 a–b. The benefits of looking for patterns in repeated calculations include the fact that most of us are more comfortable studying patterns of specific numerical results than abstract analysis of problem or situation constraints—seeing numerical patterns is a natural human skill. Furthermore, the inspection of specific numerical examples is a useful check of one's thinking about the problem. The risk of relying on patterns in specific numeric calculations is that one might miss potential counterexamples to a generalization and look instead only for confirming cases. It is a long way from seeing a pattern in a few specific cases to being confident that the pattern will hold for all cases.

29 a. Student responses to the argument will vary.

b. Students will probably have relatively strong opinions about this, which may lead to some rich discussion.

30 a. You can assess the probable accuracy of predictions made by models by comparing predictions of the model (graphically is nice) to the data points on which the model is based.

b. If data on which a model is based do not exactly match the predictions of the model, there is still value in model-based reasoning, because a good model will still give good estimates of actual data.

c. The risks of using calculator or computer tools to develop mathematical models of exponential growth include the possibility that some errant data entry might yield a model that is far from the best. Without doing a check of the match between model and data, one can be led far astray. The benefits include an ability to predict the values of dependent variables from values of independent variables whose outcomes are not known in advance. Furthermore, when one finds that a linear or exponential model is a good fit to data, there are context clues to the underlying processes at work that are reflected in the data.

EXTENSIONS

31 Students may be interested in reading about such a black rhino project online at www.earthwatch.org. The research project is based at Ol Pejeta Conservancy in Nanyuki, Kenya.

a. Experiment with exponential and linear models for the data pattern shown in the table (use 0 for 1970). Decide on a model that seems to be a good fit for the data pattern.

b. Use your model of choice to predict the black rhino population for 2000 and 2005.

c. Since 1996, intense anti-poaching efforts have had encouraging results. Black rhino population estimates for 2000 rose to 2,700 and for 2011 rose to 4,800. Include this additional data and experiment with possible models for future rhino populations. Use your model to predict the black rhino population for 2015 and 2020.

d. Suppose that black rhinos are not poached and their natural habitat is left intact. Assume also that the population would increase at a natural rate of 4% each year after 1993. How would the African population have changed by 2011 under those conditions?

e. As is the case with populations of Alaskan bowhead whales, native Africans might be allowed an annual hunting quota. Suppose that in 1993, the quota was set at 50 per year. What *NOW-NEXT* rule shows how to explore the effect of this hunting and a 4% natural population growth rate? What 2011 population is predicted under those conditions?

f. Construct a spreadsheet to explore the effects of different natural growth rates and hunting quotas and summarize what you learn in a report. In particular, find hunting quotas that would lead to stable black rhino populations if natural population growth rates were 2%, 5%, 7%, and 10% starting with the 2011 population of 4,800.

32 Cigarette smoke contains nicotine, an addictive and harmful chemical that affects the brain, nervous system, and lungs. It leads to very high annual health care costs for our country.

Suppose an individual smokes one cigarette every 40 minutes over a period of 6 hours and that each cigarette introduces 100 units of nicotine into the bloodstream. The half-life of nicotine is 20 minutes.

a. Make a chart that tracks the amount of nicotine in that smoker's body over the 6-hour period, making entries in the chart for every 20-minute period. Describe the pattern of nicotine build-up.

b. Compare the pattern in Part a with the pattern resulting from smoking a cigarette every 20 minutes.

c. Write *NOW-NEXT* rules showing how the amount of nicotine in the body changes over time (in 40-minute intervals for Part a and 20-minute intervals for Part b). Compare these rules to those of simple exponential growth and decay and explain the differences.

d. Because nicotine is strongly addictive, it is difficult for smokers to break the habit. Suppose that a long-time smoker decides to quit "cold turkey." That is, rather than reducing the number of cigarettes smoked, the smoker resolves never to pick up another cigarette. How would the level of nicotine in that smoker's body change over time?

e. How do the results of your analysis in Part d suggest that addiction to nicotine is psychological as well as physical?

a. Calculator-based, best-fitting linear and exponential models for the given data, as well as their tables and graphs, are as follows.

$$y = -2.8x + 54.5 \quad \text{and} \quad y = 63.6(0.86^x)$$

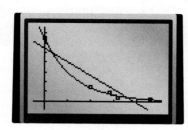

While neither is a perfect model for the rhino census data, our experience with exponential models for population change suggests that it is the better of the two options.

b. The exponential model predicts a population of 0.69 thousand (690) black rhinos in 2000 and 0.32 thousand (320) in 2005. (The linear model predicts negative populations.)

c. Students might use different starting times and starting values for their new models. One strategy that might make sense is to use the original model to predict a 1996 population and then use that as the start of a new model that takes account of the rebounding population data for 2000 and 2011. Doing this, one gets data points (0, 1.43), (4, 2.7), and (15, 4.8) and an exponential model of $y = 1.65(1.078^x)$. This model predicts a 2015 population of 6,874 and a 2020 population of 10,008.

d. The suggested assumptions would be modeled by rules $NEXT = 1.04 \cdot NOW$, starting at 2.3, and $y = 2.3(1.04^x)$, where x is years after 1993. These models predict a 2011 black rhino population of about 4.66 thousand, or 4,660 rhinos.

e. The suggested assumptions would be modeled by the rule $NEXT = 1.04 \cdot NOW - 0.05$, starting at 2.3. This leads to a prediction of a 2011 population of 3.38 thousand, or 3,380 rhinos.

f. A spreadsheet for exploring effects of natural growth and hunting quotas might look something like the one below.

Rhino population.xlsx

	A	B	C	D
1	**Year**	**Population**	**Growth Rate=**	1.02
2	2011	4,800	**Hunting Quota=**	100
3	=A2+1	=D$1*B2−D$2		
4	=A3+1	=D$1*B3−D$2		
5	⋮	⋮		
6				

Finding the stable population hunting quotas for different possible natural growth rates is actually easier than it might seem at first. For example, a 2% natural growth rate will produce an addition of 96 black rhinos in 2012, starting from the base of 4,800 in the year 2011. So, a hunting quota of 96 rhinos would neutralize the natural increase. For 4%, the quota would be 192; for 6%, the quota would be 288, for 8%, the quota would be 384, and for 10%, the quota would be 480. (It could be argued that the situation is a bit more complicated than this, because the hunting might interfere with the natural growth process. However, with hunting relatively small in relation to the total population, this is not likely to be too distorting a factor.)

32 a.

Time (in min)	Nicotine Added (in units)	Accumulated Nicotine (in cm)
0	100	100
20	0	50
40	100	125
60	0	63
80	100	132
100	0	66
120	100	133
140	0	67
160	100	134
180	0	67
⋮	⋮	⋮
340	0	67
360	100	134

(This table has a very interesting stability over time. Notice that in any 40-minute time period there are two half-life decays and an addition of 100 units of nicotine. To get the same amount 40 minutes later, we need a situation in which the current amount x satisfies this equation: $\frac{x}{4} + 100 = x$. The solution to this linear equation is $x = 133\frac{1}{3}$.

Of course, this mathematical analysis assumes that the nicotine of each cigarette is ingested instantaneously at the start of 40-minute intervals. In fact, what is probably a better way to model the situation is to imagine continuous ingestion and decay. That sort of analysis requires more sophisticated mathematics of calculus and differential equations.)

b.

Time (in min)	Nicotine Added (in units)	Accumulated Nicotine (in cm)
0	100	100
20	100	150
40	100	175
60	100	188
80	100	194
100	100	197
120	100	198
140	100	199
160	100	200
180	100	200
⋮	⋮	⋮
340	100	200
360	100	200

The pattern in this table does not go up and down as the table for Part a did. This pattern increases quickly at first and then more slowly stabilizing at 200 units. (The stable value is $x = 200$ because the rule charting accumulation of nicotine is $NEXT = 0.5 \cdot NOW + 100$ and $0.5x + 100 = x$ has solution $x = 200$.)

c. For Part a: $NEXT = 0.25 \cdot NOW + 100$
For Part b: $NEXT = 0.5 \cdot NOW + 100$
These rules are similar to *NOW-NEXT* rules for exponential decay because the *NOW* is multiplied by a value between 0 and 1. They are different because a constant value of 100 is added back in each time a *NEXT* value is calculated.

d. With a half-life of 20 minutes, the level of nicotine would presumably decay very rapidly over time. For example, after ten 20-minute half-life intervals, it would be reduced to $(0.5)^{10} \approx 0.001$ of its amount at the start of the "cold-turkey" abstention.

e. Because the results of Part d suggest rapid physical decay of the body's nicotine content, the lure of cigarette smoking must have a strong psychological appeal.

33 Driving after drinking alcohol is both dangerous and illegal. The National Highway Traffic Safety Administration reported 2,400 youth (15 to 20 years old) alcohol-related traffic fatalities in 2002—an average of about 6 per day. (**Source:** *Traffic Safety Facts 2002: Young Drivers;* www.nhtsa.dot.gov)

Many factors affect a person's Blood Alcohol Concentration (BAC), including body weight, gender, and amount drunk. American Medical Association guidelines suggest that a BAC of 0.05 is the maximum safe level for activities like driving a car.

The following chart gives typical data relating body weight and number of drinks consumed to BAC for people of various weights.

Approximate Blood Alcohol Concentrations					
Weight (in pounds)	1 drink	2 drinks	3 drink	4 drinks	5 drink
100	0.05	0.09	0.14	0.18	0.23
120	0.04	0.08	0.11	0.15	0.19
140	0.03	0.07	0.10	0.13	0.16
160	0.03	0.06	0.09	0.11	0.14
180	0.03	0.05	0.08	0.10	0.13

a. Study the data in the table and decide how BAC for each weight seems to be related to number of drinks consumed. Find *NOW-NEXT* and "$y = \ldots$" rules for the function that seems the best model at each weight. Explain what each rule tells about the effects of additional drinks on BAC.

b. The next table shows how BAC changes over time after drinking stops for a 100-pound person who has had 3 drinks.

Time (in hours)	0	2	4	6	8
BAC	0.14	0.12	0.10	0.08	0.06

   i. What type of function seems to model that pattern of change well?

   ii. Find *NOW-NEXT* and "$y = \ldots$" rules for the function that seems the best model.

   iii. Explain what those rules tell about the way BAC declines over time.

c. Suppose that the pattern in Part b relating BAC to time since last drink applies for the situation in which a 100-pound person has 5 drinks. What is the prediction of time required for the blood alcohol of that 100-pound person to return to a "safe" level of 0.05?

33 **a.** The data relating BAC to number of drinks suggest linear relationships at each weight. Thinking first about the *NOW-NEXT* rules, students may suggest rules different from the ones below. For example, 100 pounds: *NEXT = NOW* + 0.044 starting at 0.05, the first table entry. If students use the data to develop "*y* = ..." rules first, they should have the following responses.

100 pounds: $y = 0.045x + 0.003$ and *NEXT = NOW* + 0.045, starting at 0.003. Rules imply an increase in BAC of 0.045 for each drink with baseline BAC of 0.003.

120 pounds: $y = 0.037x + 0.003$ and *NEXT = NOW* + 0.037, starting at 0.003. Rules imply an increase in BAC of 0.037 for each drink with baseline BAC of 0.003.

140 pounds: $y = 0.032x + 0.002$ and *NEXT = NOW* + 0.032, starting at 0.002. Rules imply an increase in BAC of 0.032 for each drink with baseline BAC of 0.002.

160 pounds: $y = 0.027x + 0.005$ and *NEXT = NOW* + 0.027, starting at 0.005. Rules imply an increase in BAC of 0.027 for each drink with baseline BAC of 0.005.

180 pounds: $y = 0.025x + 0.003$ and *NEXT = NOW* + 0.025, starting at 0.003. Rules imply an increase in BAC of 0.025 for each drink with baseline BAC of 0.003.

b.   **i.** The suggested pattern of change in BAC over time is linear.

ii. Linear rules are given by: *NEXT = NOW* − 0.01, starting at 0.14, and $y = 0.14 - 0.01x$ with time counted in one-hour intervals.

iii. These rules say that BAC declines by approximately 0.01 per hour.

c. If a 100-pound person has 5 drinks, the rules would become $y = 0.23 - 0.01x$ and *NEXT = NOW* − 0.01, starting at 0.23. This means that it would take 18 hours for this drinker to return to a "safe" BAC of 0.05.

34 To study behavior of exponential functions for fractional values of the independent variable, consider several numbers between 0 and 1, like 0.25, 0.5, and 0.75.

  a. How would you expect the values of 5^0, $5^{0.25}$, $5^{0.5}$, $5^{0.75}$, and 5^1 to be related to each other?

  b. What are your best estimates for the values of $5^{0.25}$, $5^{0.5}$, and $5^{0.75}$?

  c. Use a calculator to check your ideas in Parts a and b.

  d. Graph the function $y = 5^x$ for $-1 \le x \le 2$ and explain how it shows the observed pattern of change in values for 5^0, $5^{0.25}$, $5^{0.5}$, $5^{0.75}$, and 5^1.

35 Use what you know about properties of exponents to evaluate these expressions.

$\quad$ **i.** $\left(3^{\frac{1}{4}}\right)^4$ $\qquad\qquad$ **ii.** $\left(5^{\frac{1}{4}}\right)^4$

$\quad$ **iii.** $\left(16^{\frac{1}{4}}\right)^4$ $\qquad\qquad$ **iv.** $16^{\frac{1}{4}}$

$\quad$ **v.** $\left(16^{\frac{1}{4}}\right)^3$ $\qquad\qquad$ **vi.** $(16)^{\frac{3}{4}}$

  a. Look for a pattern to help you explain what $b^{\frac{1}{4}}$ and $b^{\frac{3}{4}}$ must mean for any positive value of b.

  b. Based on your explorations, what meanings are suggested for the expressions $b^{\frac{1}{n}}$ and $b^{\frac{m}{n}}$ when b is a positive number and m and n are positive integers? Use your calculator to check your ideas in the case of some specific examples.

36 Any number that can be expressed as an integer or a common fraction is called a **rational number**. For example, 12, $\frac{3}{5}$, and $\frac{7}{5}$ are rational numbers. If a number cannot be expressed as an integer or common fraction, it is called an **irrational number**.

$\quad$ When you use a computer algebra system for arithmetic and algebraic calculations, it will generally report any numerical results as integers or common fractions whenever that is possible.

  a. Use a computer algebra system to see which of the numbers $\sqrt{2}$, $\sqrt{3}$, $\sqrt{4}$, $\sqrt{5}$, ... , $\sqrt{50}$ are rational numbers and which are irrational.

  b. Based on your work in Part a, what seems to be a way to decide when $\sqrt{n}$ is rational and when it is irrational?

  c. Use a computer algebra system to evaluate $\sqrt{\frac{a}{b}}$ for several different fractions like $\sqrt{\frac{4}{9}}$, $\sqrt{\frac{4}{7}}$, $\sqrt{\frac{5}{9}}$, and $\sqrt{\frac{6}{35}}$.

  d. Based on your work in Part c, what seems to be a way to decide when $\sqrt{\frac{a}{b}}$ is rational and when it is irrational?

34 a–b. Since the given exponent values are evenly distributed between 0 and 1, it is natural to suspect that the function values will also be evenly distributed between 1 and 5. On the other hand, students might have a variety of different ideas. In a series of questions like those of this task, it is tempting to write answers that reflect what the calculator tells, not to think about the problem in the order that is called for. Thus, it will be hard to know whether students really did make a first estimate of what they thought might be true intuitively.

c. The actual values are $5^0 = 1$, $5^{0.25} \approx 1.5$, $5^{0.5} \approx 2.24$, $5^{0.75} \approx 3.34$, and $5^1 = 5$. Thus, far from being evenly distributed, the differences between successive values are 0.5, 0.74, 1.1, and 1.66.

d. Student graphs of $y = 5^x$ should show an upward bend, indicating that the rate of increase is itself increasing as x increases. This is reflected in the data values in Part c.

35

i. $\left(3^{\frac{1}{4}}\right)^4 = 3^1 = 3$ **ii.** $\left(5^{\frac{1}{4}}\right)^4 = 5^1 = 5$

iii. $\left(16^{\frac{1}{4}}\right)^4 = 16^1 = 16$ **iv.** $16^{\frac{1}{4}} = (2^4)^{\frac{1}{4}} = 2^1 = 2$

v. $\left(16^{\frac{1}{4}}\right)^3 = 2^3 = 8$ **vi.** $(16)^{\frac{3}{4}} = \left(16^{\frac{1}{4}}\right)^3 = 2^3 = 8$

a. $b^{\frac{1}{4}}$ is the number multiplied by itself 4 times that results in b. Another way to say this is that $b^{\frac{1}{4}}$ is the number that when it is raised to the fourth power is b, or the fourth root of b; $\left(b^{\frac{1}{4}}\right)^4 = b$.

$b^{\frac{3}{4}}$ will be $\left(b^{\frac{1}{4}}\right)^3$, or the number that when it is raised to the fourth power is b, then raised to the third power, or the fourth root of b then cubed.

b. The pattern, albeit not very extensively developed, suggests that $b^{\frac{1}{n}}$ is the nth root of b and $b^{\frac{m}{n}}$ is the nth root raised to the power m.

36 A computer algebra system (CAS) can generally produce both exact (rational fraction) and approximate (decimal) results for calculations. Settings are optional for what the user would like to get. When a CAS is set in exact mode, it will generally respond to radical expressions like $\sqrt{2}, \sqrt{3}, \sqrt{4}, \sqrt{5}, \ldots, \sqrt{50}$ by simplifying as far as possible the number under the radical sign. Thus, in this exploration, students will discover that only perfect squares will be simplified so that no radical signs remain. This is indicating that only perfect square integers have rational square roots.

a. Only 4, 9, 16, 25, 36, and 49 will have rational square roots.

b. Only perfect square integers will have rational square roots.

c. Only $\frac{4}{9}$ has a rational number square root, $\frac{2}{3}$.

d. In general, when a fraction has been reduced to lowest terms, it will have a rational square root only if both numerator and denominator are perfect square integers.

ASSIGNMENT NOTE

Extensions Task 35 will help students prepare for algebraic expectations on some state end-of-course assessments.

ON YOUR OWN

REVIEW

37 Work on problems that involve exponential growth and decay often requires skill in use of percents to express rates of increase or decrease. Suppose that you are asked to figure new prices for items in a sporting goods store. Show two ways to calculate each of the following price changes—one that involves two operations (either a multiplication and an addition or a multiplication and a subtraction) and another that involves only one operation (multiplication).

a. Reduce the price of a $90 warm-up suit by 20%.

b. Increase the price of a $25 basketball by 30%.

c. Reduce the price of a $75 skateboard by 60%.

d. Increase the price of a $29 sweatshirt by 15%.

e. Reduce the price of a $15 baseball cap by $33\frac{1}{3}$%.

f. Increase the price of a $60 tennis racket by 100%.

38 Sketch and label a diagram for each situation. Then find the measure of the indicated segment or angle.

a. $m\angle XYZ = 140°$ and $\overrightarrow{YB}$ bisects $\angle XYZ$. Find $m\angle BYZ$.

b. $AB = 5$ cm and C is the midpoint of $\overline{AB}$. Find AC.

c. M is the midpoint of $\overline{XY}$, $XM = 3$ cm. Find XY.

d. $\overrightarrow{PQ}$ bisects $\angle RPT$. $m\angle RPQ + m\angle QPT = 82°$. Find $m\angle RPT$ and $m\angle RPQ$.

39 Write *NOW-NEXT* rules that match each of the following *linear decay* functions. Then explain how the "decay" in all three cases is different from exponential decay and how the difference(s) would appear in tables and graphs of (x, y) values for the functions.

a. $y = 5 - 2x$

b. $y = -0.5x + 1$

c. $y = -\frac{x}{3} - 6$

40 Sometimes it is valuable to compare properties of two functions, each represented in a different way.

a. The table below shows a few values for *one* linear function. The graph below represents *another* linear function.

Function I

x	y
1	−1
3	3
5	7

Function II

i. Which function has the greater slope?

ii. How do the *y*-intercepts compare?

Jiri Hubatka/Alamy

UNIT 5

🕐 **JUST IN TIME**

37 **a.** Reduced price: 90 − 0.2(90) or 90(0.8)
Both give a new price of $72.

b. Increased price: 25 + 0.3(25) or 25(1.3)
Both give a new price of $32.50.

c. Reduced price: 75 − 0.6(75) or 75(0.4)
Both give a new price of $30.

d. Increased price: 29 + 0.15(29) or 29(1.15)
Both give a new price of $33.35.

e. Reduced price: $15 - \frac{1}{3}(15)$ or $15\left(\frac{2}{3}\right)$
Both give a new price of $10.

f. Increased price: 60 + 1.00(60) or 60(2)
Both give a new price of $120.

38 **a.**

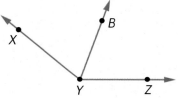

$m\angle BYZ = 70°$

b.

$A \quad\quad\quad\quad C \quad\quad\quad\quad B$

$AC = 2.5$ cm

c.

$X \quad\quad\quad\quad M \quad\quad\quad\quad Y$

$XY = 6$ cm

d.

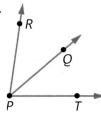

$m\angle RPT = 82°$
$m\angle RPQ = 41°$

39 **a.** *NEXT = NOW* − 2, starting at 5, has a linear graph with slope −2 and *y*-intercept 5.

b. *NEXT = NOW* − 0.5, starting at 1, has a linear graph with slope −0.5 and *y*-intercept 1.

c. *NEXT = NOW* $- \frac{1}{3}$, starting at −6, has a linear graph with slope $-\frac{1}{3}$ and *y*-intercept −6.

In each case, the graph is a line, not a curve. The slope of the line tells the constant subtractive rate of change in *y* as *x* increases in steps of 1. In all three linear decay functions, the *y* values are always decreasing. In this sense, the decay is similar to exponential decay. However, exponential decay has a lower bound of *y* = 0, while linear decay has no lower bound.

> **NOTE** The solution to Task 40 Part a is on page T353.

b. Consider Functions I and II represented by a rule and graph, respectively.

Function I

$y = 3(2^x)$

i. Which function increases the fastest?

ii. How do the y-intercepts compare?

Function II

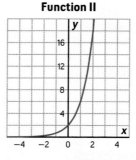

41 Find the missing side lengths in each triangle. Express your answers in both radical and decimal approximation form.

a.

b.

c.

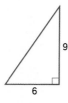

d.

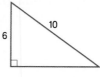

e.

42 Without using a calculator, decide if the following statements are true or false. If the statement is false, explain why.

a. $2 \cdot 2^5 = 4^5$

b. $2 \cdot 2^5 = 2^5$

c. $2 \cdot 2^5 = 2^6$

d. $2 \cdot 3^x + 3^x = (2 + 1)3^x$

e. $3 \cdot 3^x = 3^{x + 1}$

Lesson 2 | Exponential Decay **353**

40 **a.** **i.** The slope for the linear function displayed graphically (3) is larger than that of the linear function in the table (2).

　　ii. The y-intercepts are the same for both functions, $(0, -3)$.

　b. **i.** The exponential function represented by the graph has a growth factor of 3. Thus, it increases faster than $y = 3(2^x)$, which has a growth factor of 2.

　　ii. The y-intercept of the graph is at $(0, 2)$, which is lower than the y-intercept of $y = 3(2^x)$, which is $(0, 3)$.

41 **a.** $c = 5$　　　　　**b.** $c = 13$　　　　　**c.** $c = \sqrt{117} \approx 10.8$

　d. $b = 8$　　　　　**e.** $a = \sqrt{96} = 4\sqrt{6} \approx 9.8$

42 **a.** False; $2 \cdot 2^5 = 2^6$, not 4^5

　b. False; $2 \cdot 2^5 = 2^6$, not 2^5

　c. True

　d. True

　e. True

ON YOUR OWN

43 Make a copy of the diagram at the right. Shade the part of the large square that represents $\frac{1}{2}$ of $\frac{1}{2}$ of $\frac{1}{2}$, and give the answer as a fraction.

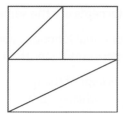

44 Examine each equation below and decide on the method you would use to solve it: use a table, use a graph, or reason with the symbols themselves. Then solve each equation using your preferred method and check your answer.

a. $2^x = 100$

b. $2x + 5 = 100$

c. $100(x + 2) = 800$

d. $100(1.5^x) = 200$

e. $100(b^4) = 200$

45 Write an equation for the line that matches each description.

a. Has slope of -0.5 and y-intercept at $(0, 2)$

b. Contains the points $(0, 5)$ and $(-4, -10)$

c. Is horizontal and contains the point $(7, 12)$

d. Contains the points $(-2, 7.5)$ and $(1, 3)$

46 A basketball team is selling sweatshirts in order to raise money for new uniforms. The rule that gives their profit p in dollars based on the number of sweatshirts they sell n is $p = 5n - 175$.

a. Explain the meaning of the 175 and the 5 in terms of the situation.

b. If they sell 265 sweatshirts, how much profit will they make?

c. How many sweatshirts must they sell in order to make a profit of $2,000?

47 One cell phone plan charges a $40 monthly fee for unlimited calling plus $0.10 per text message t. Another plan charges a $50 monthly fee for unlimited calling and $0.05 per text.

a. Which function rule represents the difference in cost between the two cell phone plans for any number of text messages t?

$$D = 10 + 0.05t$$
$$D = 10 - 0.05t$$
$$D = 0.05 - 10t$$
$$D = 0.05 + 10t$$

b. For what number of texts will the two plans cost the same?

43 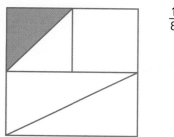 $\frac{1}{8}$

44 **a.** $x \approx 6.644$

b. $x = 47.5$

c. $x = 6$

d. $x \approx 1.710$

e. $b \approx 1.189$

45 **a.** $y = -0.5x + 2$

b. $y = \frac{15}{4}x + 5$

c. $y = 12$

d. $y = -\frac{3}{2}x + \frac{9}{2}$

46 **a.** There is $175 of cost before any sweatshirts are sold. Each shirt will bring in $5 towards the profit.

b. $1,150

c. 435 sweatshirts

47 **a.** $D = 10 - 0.05t$ is the correct equation.

b. 200 texts

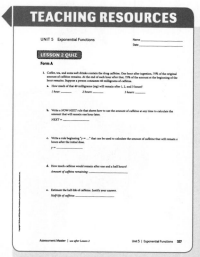

TEACHING RESOURCES

Assessment Masters 327–335

⓪ **GO DIGITAL**

LESSON
3

Looking Back

In this unit, you studied patterns of change in variables that can be modeled well by exponential functions. These functions can all be expressed with rules like

$$NEXT = b \cdot NOW, \text{ starting at } a$$
$$\text{or}$$
$$y = a(b^x).$$

As a result of your work on Lessons 1 and 2, you should be better able to recognize situations in which variables are related by exponential functions, to use data tables and graphs to display patterns in those relationships, to use symbolic rules to describe and reason about the patterns, and to use graphing calculators, spreadsheets, and computer algebra systems to answer questions that involve exponential relationships. You should also be able to write exponential expressions in useful equivalent forms.

The tasks in this final lesson will help you review your understanding of exponential functions and apply that understanding in solving several new problems.

1 Counting Codes
Code numbers are used in hundreds of ways every day—from student and social security numbers to product codes in stores and membership numbers in clubs.

a. How many different 2-digit codes can be created using the digits 0, 1, 2, 3, 4, 5, 6, 7, 8, and 9 (for example, 33, 54, 72, or 02)?

b. How many different 3-digit codes can be created using those digits?

c. How many different 4-digit codes can be created using those digits?

d. Using any patterns you may see, complete a table like the one below showing the relation between number of digits and number of different possible codes.

Number of Digits	1	2	3	4	5	6	7	8	9
Number of Codes									

Looking Back

This lesson includes tasks intended to provide review and practice of key ideas developed throughout the unit and summary questions designed to stimulate student articulation of the key principles and techniques.

It may not be necessary for all students to do all the tasks in this lesson. You might have groups pick one task from Tasks 1, 2, and 3. Groups could make presentations to explain their task to the entire class. Tasks 4, 5, and 6 could then be done by all students and answers checked.

1 **a.** There are $10^2 = 100$ 2-digit codes, from 00 through 99.

   b. There are $10^3 = 1,000$ 3-digit codes.

   c. There are $10^4 = 10,000$ 4-digit codes.

   d.

Number of Digits	1	2	3	4	5	6	7	8	9
Number of Codes	10	10^2	10^3	10^4	10^5	10^6	10^7	10^8	10^9

Common Core State Standards CCSS

This unit focused on the CCSS domains:

The Real Number System, N-RN

Seeing Structure in Expressions, A-SSE

Creating Equations★, A-CED

Reasoning with Equations and Inequalities, A-REI

Interpreting Functions, F-IF

Building Functions, F-BF

Linear, Quadratic, and Exponential Models★, F-LE

Interpreting Categorical and Quantitative Data★, S-ID

Plus the Modeling Conceptual Category

e. Write a rule using *NOW* and *NEXT* to describe the pattern in the table of Part d.

f. Write a rule that shows how to calculate the number of codes *C* for any number of digits *D* used.

g. Music and video stores stock thousands of different items. How many digits would you need in order to have code numbers for up to 8,500 different items?

h. How will your answers to Parts d–f change if the codes were to begin with a single letter of the alphabet (A, B, C, … , or Z) as in A23 or S75?

2 **Eyes on the Prizes** In one women's professional golf tournament, the money a player wins depends on her finishing place in the standings. The first-place finisher wins $\frac{1}{2}$ of the $1,048,576 in total prize money. The second-place finisher wins $\frac{1}{2}$ of what is left; then the third-place finisher wins $\frac{1}{2}$ of what is left, and so on.

a. What fraction of the *total* prize is won

   i. by the second-place finisher?

   ii. by the third-place finisher?

   iii. by the fourth-place finisher?

b. Write a rule showing how to calculate the fraction of the total prize money won by the player finishing in *n*th place, for any positive integer *n*.

c. Make a table showing the actual prize money in dollars (not fraction of the total prize money) won by each of the first five place finishers.

Place	1	2	3	4	5
Prize (in dollars)					

d. Write a rule showing how to calculate the actual prize money in dollars won by the player finishing in place *n*. How much money would be won by the 10th-place finisher?

e. How would your answers to Parts a–d change if

   i. the total prize money were reduced to $500,000?

   ii. the fraction used was $\frac{1}{4}$ instead of $\frac{1}{2}$?

f. When prize monies are awarded using either fraction $\frac{1}{2}$ or $\frac{1}{4}$, could the tournament organizers end up giving away more than the stated total prize amount? Explain your reasoning.

U.S. Women's Open Champion Annika Sorenstam

e. $NEXT = 10 \cdot NOW$, starting at 10

f. $C = 10^D$

g. Four-digit codes will number 10,000 and provide enough for 8,500 different items with 1,500 codes to spare.

h. Each number in the table in Part d will be multiplied by 26 and the rules will be $NEXT = 10 \cdot NOW$, starting at 26, and $C = 26(10^D)$.

2 **a.** **i.** $\frac{1}{4}$ **ii.** $\frac{1}{8}$ **iii.** $\frac{1}{16}$

INSTRUCTIONAL NOTE

Parts a and b are not dollar amounts but parts of the prize.

b. $F = \left(\frac{1}{2}\right)^n$, where n is the place and F is the fraction of the prize money won.

c.

Place	1	2	3	4	5
Prize (in dollars)	524,288	262,144	131,072	65,536	32,768

d. $P = 1{,}048{,}576\left(\frac{1}{2}\right)^n$, where n is the place and P is the prize money won. The tenth-place finisher would receive $1,024.

e. **i.** If total of prizes is reduced to $500,000, the answers to Parts a and b would be the same. However, the answers to Parts c and d would reflect the change in total prize money as follows:

Place	1	2	3	4	5
Prize (in dollars)	250,000	125,000	62,500	31,250	15,625

$P = 500{,}000\left(\frac{1}{2}\right)^n$

When $n = 10$, $P = \$488$.

ii. If the fraction changes to $\frac{1}{4}$ instead of $\frac{1}{2}$, the second-, third-, and fourth-place finishers would receive $\frac{1}{16}$, $\frac{1}{64}$, and $\frac{1}{256}$, respectively. The fraction of the winnings rule is $F = \left(\frac{1}{4}\right)^n$. The answers to Parts c and d would be:

Place	1	2	3	4	5
Prize (in dollars)	262,144	65,536	16,384	4,096	1,024

The prize-money-won rule becomes $P = 1{,}048{,}576\left(\frac{1}{4}\right)^n$. The prize won by the person in tenth place is $1.

f. No. The first-place finisher wins half (or one-fourth) of the total prize money. The second-place finisher wins half (or one-fourth) of the prize money that remains. Each successive finisher wins half (or one-fourth) of what remains, so the tournament organizers cannot give away more than the total prize amount. (Observant students may realize that under the $\frac{1}{4}$ scheme, only a third of the money would be given away.)

3 **Cold Surgery** Hypothermia is a life-threatening condition in which body temperature falls well below the norm of 98.6°F. However, because chilling causes normal body functions to slow down, doctors are exploring ways to use hypothermia as a technique for extending time of delicate operations like brain surgery.

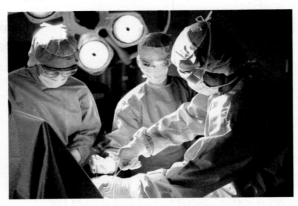

a. The following table gives experimental data illustrating the relationship between body temperature and brain activity.

Body Temperature (in °F)	50	59	68	77	86	98.6
Brain Activity (% Normal)	11	16	24	37	52	100

Source: *USA Today*, August 1, 2001, "Surgery's Chilling Future Will Put Fragile Lives on Ice."

i. Plot the table data and find a "$y = \ldots$" rule that models the pattern in these data relating brain activity level to body temperature. Then express the same relationship with an equivalent *NOW-NEXT* rule.

ii. Use your rules to estimate the level of brain activity at a body temperature of 39°F, the lowest temperature used in surgery experiments on pigs, dogs, and baboons.

iii. Find the range of body temperatures at which brain activity is predicted to be about 75% of normal levels.

b. The next table gives experimental data illustrating the relationship between body temperature and safe operating time for brain surgery.

Body Temperature (in °F)	50	59	68	77	86	98.6
Safe Operating Time (in minutes)	45	31	21	14	9	5

i. Plot the table data and find a "$y = \ldots$" rule that models the pattern in these data relating safe operating time to body temperature. Then express the same relationship with an equivalent *NOW-NEXT* rule.

ii. Use your rules to estimate the safe operating time at a body temperature of 39°F.

iii. Find the body temperature at which safe operating time is predicted to be at least 25 minutes.

Indeed/Digital Vision/Getty Images

Lesson 3 | Looking Back **357**

3 **a.** **i.**

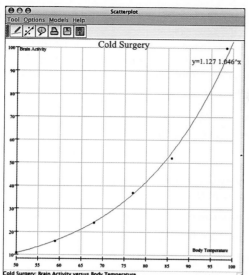

The exponential regression equation rounded to thousandths is $y = 1.127(1.046^x)$ and $NEXT = 1.046 \cdot NOW$, initial value of 1.127.

TECHNOLOGY NOTE

These data are in *CPMP-Tools*.

The rounded-exponential-regression rule is used for parts ii and iii below.

ii. Brain activity is about 6.5% of normal at 39°F.

iii. A temperature of between 92.9 and 93.1°F predicts brain activity 75% of normal.

b. **i.**

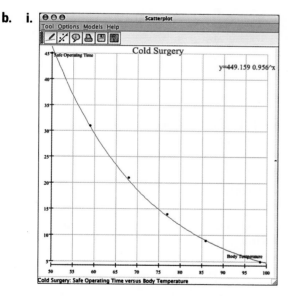

Exponential rules fitting the data pattern would be $y = 449(0.956^x)$ and $NEXT = 0.956 \cdot NOW$, initial value of 449.

ii. Safe operating time at 39°F would be about 78 minutes.

iii. A temperature of less than 64.2°F leads to a predicted safe operating time of at least 25 minutes.

c. Cost is another important variable in medical practice. The next table gives data about charges for a sample of routine surgeries, illustrating the relationship between time required for the operation and hospital charges for use of the operating room.

Time (in minutes)	30	60	90	120	150	180
Cost (in $)	950	1,400	1,850	2,300	2,750	3,200

   i. Plot the table data and find a "$y = \ldots$" rule that models the pattern in these data relating surgery cost to time. Then express the same relationship with an equivalent *NOW-NEXT* rule.

   ii. Use your rules to estimate the cost of an operation that takes 45 minutes.

   iii. Find the time of an operation for which cost is predicted to be $5,000.

d. Compare the "$y = \ldots$" rules for the three functions in Parts a, b, and c. In each case, explain how the rules alone can be used to predict the pattern of change in the dependent variable as the independent variable increases.

4 **Exponent Properties** In Lessons 1 and 2, you discovered and practiced several principles for writing exponential expressions in equivalent (often simpler) forms. Use those principles to find values of x and y that make the following equations true statements.

a. $(2.3^5)(2.3^3) = 2.3^x$ **b.** $2.3^x = 1$

c. $(3.5^x)^y = 3.5^{12}$ **d.** $\dfrac{7^9}{7^4} = 7^x$

e. $\dfrac{7^x}{7^4} = 7^2$ **f.** $(7^3)^x = 7^6$

g. $\left(\dfrac{3}{5}\right)^4 = \dfrac{3^x}{5^y}$ **h.** $(4a)^3 = 4^x a^y$

i. $\dfrac{1}{7^4} = 7^x$

5 **Fractional Powers and Radicals** In Lesson 2, you also discovered and practiced use of expressions in which fractional powers occur. Special attention was paid to square roots, using the exponent one-half. Use what you learned to answer these questions.

a. The value of $3^2 = 9$ and $3^3 = 27$. What does this information tell about the approximate values of $3^{2.4}$ and $3^{2.7}$?

b. For each of these equations, find two different pairs of integer values for a and b that make the equation true.

   i. $\sqrt{48} = a\sqrt{b}$

   ii. $\sqrt{a}\sqrt{b} = \sqrt{36}$

c. i.

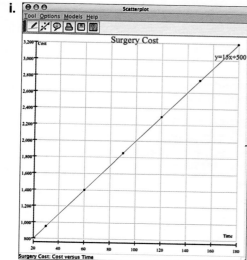

The rules for this linear function would be
$y = 500 + 15x$ and
$NEXT = NOW + 15$,
starting at 500. If you choose to treat time in 30-minute units, the rules would be
$y = 500 + 450x$ and
$NEXT = NOW + 450$,
starting at 500.

ii. An operation that takes 45 minutes will cost $1,175.

iii. An operation with predicted cost of $5,000 will take 300 minutes or 6 hours.

d. The three functions represent examples of exponential growth (base greater than 1), exponential decay (base less than 1), and linear growth (variable is not in an exponent, but as a multiplicative coefficient of the rate of change or slope value).

4 a. $x = 8$

b. $x = 0$

c. Any x and y with product 12

d. $x = 5$

e. $x = 6$

f. $x = 2$

g. x and y both 4

h. x and y both 3

i. $x = -4$

5 a. The values of 3^{24} and 3^{27} are between 9 and 27, with the first of the two having a value closer to 9 and the second having a value closer to 27.

b. i. $\sqrt{48} = 4\sqrt{3} = 2\sqrt{12}$

ii. $\sqrt{36} = \sqrt{6}\sqrt{6} = \sqrt{1}\,\sqrt{36} = \sqrt{2}\,\sqrt{18} = \sqrt{3}\,\sqrt{12} = \sqrt{4}\,\sqrt{9}$.

6 The graphs and tables below model linear and exponential growth or decay situations.

a. Without the use of technology, match each graph with its corresponding table. In each case, describe the clues that you used to match the items.

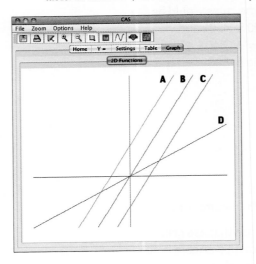

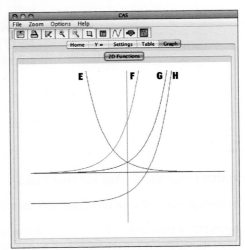

Table 1:

x	−3	−1	1	3
y	−9	−3	3	9

Table 2:

x	−3	−1	1	3
y	−3	−1	1	3

Table 3:

x	−3	−1	1	3
y	27	3	$\frac{1}{3}$	$\frac{1}{27}$

Table 4:

x	−3	−1	1	3
y	$\frac{1}{27}$	$\frac{1}{3}$	3	27

Table 5:

x	−3	−1	1	3
y	−6	0	6	12

Table 6:

x	−3	−1	1	3
y	$\frac{5}{27}$	$\frac{5}{3}$	15	135

Table 7:

x	−3	−1	1	3
y	−12	−6	0	6

Table 8:

x	−3	−1	1	3
y	$-\frac{80}{27}$	$-\frac{8}{3}$	0	24

b. Without using technology, write "$y = \ldots$" rules for each of the graph/table pairs you matched in Part a. For linear function rules of the form $y = a + bx$ and exponential function rules of the form $y = c(d^x) + e$, use your knowledge of what the numbers a, b, c, d, and e tell you about patterns in graphs and table values. Then check using technology.

6 **CCSS** **MATHEMATICAL PRACTICES** You may wish to have students work in pairs on this task. The task requires students to make sense of the task and persevere in solving it, to reason abstractly and quantitatively, and to look for and make use of structure. Some students may formulate the function rules asked for in Part b while thinking about Part a. Those that do not will be asked to formulate the rules in Part b.

a–b.

Graph	Table	Rule
A	5	$y = 3x + 3$
B	1	$y = 3x$
C	7	$y = 3x - 3$
D	2	$y = x$
E	3	$y = \left(\frac{1}{3}\right)^x$
F	6	$y = 5(3^x)$
G	4	$y = 3^x$
H	8	$y = 3^x - 3$

SUMMARIZE THE MATHEMATICS

When two variables are related by an exponential function, that relationship can be recognized from key features of the problem situations, from patterns in tables and graphs of (x, y) data, and from the rules that show how to calculate values of one variable from given values of the other.

a In deciding whether an exponential function describes the relationship between two variables, what hints do you get from

   i. the nature of the situation and the variables involved?
   ii. the patterns in graphs or scatterplots?
   iii. the patterns in data tables?

b Exponential functions, like linear functions, can be expressed by a rule relating x and y values and by a rule relating *NOW* and *NEXT* y values.

   i. Write a general rule for an exponential function, "$y = \dots$"
   ii. Write a general rule relating *NOW* and *NEXT* for an exponential function.
   iii. What do the parts of the rules tell you about the problem situation?
   iv. How do you decide whether a given exponential function rule will describe growth or decay, and why does your decision rule make sense?

c Suppose that you develop or discover a rule (*NOW-NEXT* or "$y = \dots$") that shows how a variable y is an exponential function of another variable x. Describe the different strategies you could use to complete tasks like these:

   i. Find the value of y associated with a specific given value of x.
   ii. Find the value of x that gives a specific target value of y.
   iii. Describe the way that the value of y changes as the value of x increases or decreases.

d Complete each equality to give a useful equivalent form of the first expression.

   i. $a^m a^n = \dots$ **ii.** $(a^m)^n = \dots$ **iii.** $a^0 = \dots$

   iv. $(ab)^n = \dots$ **v.** $\dfrac{1}{a^n} = \dots$ **vi.** $\left(\dfrac{a}{b}\right)^n = \dots$

   vii. $\dfrac{a^m}{a^n} = \dots$ **viii.** $\sqrt{ab} = \dots$ **ix.** $\sqrt{\dfrac{a}{b}} = \dots$

Be prepared to share your responses and thinking with the class.

 CHECK YOUR UNDERSTANDING

Write, in outline form, a summary of the important mathematical concepts and methods developed in this unit. Organize your summary so that it can be used as a quick reference in future units and courses.

SUMMARIZE THE MATHEMATICS

a **i.** Situations that exhibit growth and decay over time are often modeled by exponential functions. But as seen in this "Looking Back" lesson, other situations such as the cold surgery may be best modeled by exponential functions.

ii. The patterns in graphs or scatterplots show curves approaching the x-axis as an asymptote or rising quickly. The vertical distance from the x-axis for unit increases in x should consistently increase or decrease by a multiplicative factor.

iii. The patterns in data tables show that the differences in the function values are not constant. If the differences in the x values are constant, then the y values in the table should have a constant ratio. If the differences in the x values are single units, the constant ratio of a y value divided by the previous y value is the growth or decay factor.

b **i.** $y = a(b^x)$, $b > 0$

ii. $NEXT = b \cdot NOW$, starting at a
The initial or starting value a is determined by the situation or regression equation, and thus may not be the value for $x = 0$ from the "$y = ...$" form.

iii. The b tells you the growth factor and the a locates the y-intercept if the initial value is associated with zero for the dependent variable.

iv. Exponential growth functions are those with base greater than 1 and decay functions are those with base between 0 and 1. This makes sense because multiplication of any positive number by a number greater than 1 always leads to a larger result, and multiplying by a positive fraction less than 1 always leads to a smaller result.

c **i.** To find y for a given x, one needs only substitute the value of x in the rule or trace the graph to the point where x is the given value and read off the corresponding y value. One could also begin with the starting value of the dependent variable and iterate the *NOW-NEXT* rule x times. However, this will work only when x is an integer.

ii. To find x for a specified y, one can scan a table of values or trace a graph until the desired value of y is located and then read off the corresponding value of x. Using the *NOW-NEXT* rule, one could continue iterating until the desired output appears.

iii. Looking at differences in successive y values or at the shape of a graph will give insight into the pattern of change in y values as x increases or decreases.

d **i.** $a^m a^n = a^{m+n}$ **ii.** $(a^m)^n = a^{mn}$ **iii.** $a^0 = 1$

    iv. $(ab)^n = a^n b^n$ **v.** $\dfrac{1}{a^n} = a^{-n}$ **vi.** $\left(\dfrac{a}{b}\right)^n = \dfrac{a^n}{b^n}$

    vii. $\dfrac{a^m}{a^n} = a^{m-n}$ **viii.** $\sqrt{ab} = \sqrt{a}\sqrt{b}$ **ix.** $\sqrt{\dfrac{a}{b}} = \dfrac{\sqrt{a}}{\sqrt{b}}$

UNIT 5 Exponential Functions

SUMMARIZE THE MATHEMATICS

When two variables are related by an exponential function, that relationship can be recognized from key features of the problem situations, from patterns in tables and graphs of (x, y) data, and from the rules that show how to calculate values of one variable from given values of the other.

a In deciding whether an exponential function describes the relationship between two variables, what hints do you get from

  i. the nature of the situation and the variables involved?

  ii. the patterns in graphs or scatterplots?

  iii. the patterns in data tables?

b Exponential functions, like linear functions, can be expressed by a rule relating x and y values and by a rule relating *NOW* and *NEXT* y values.

  i. Write a general rule for an exponential function, "$y = ...$"

  ii. Write a general rule relating *NOW* and *NEXT* for an exponential function.

  iii. What do the parts of the rules tell you about the problem situation?

  iv. How do you decide whether a given exponential function rule will describe growth or decay, and why does your decision rule make sense?

336 Unit 5 | Exponential Functions   Lesson Master | use with page 360

Lesson Masters 336–337
🄌 GO DIGITAL

Student Masters 338–340

GO DIGITAL

Assessment Masters 341–360

GO DIGITAL

CHECK YOUR UNDERSTANDING

You may wish to have students use the Teaching Master, *Exponential Functions* Unit Summary, to help them organize the information. Above all, this should be something that is useful to the individual student.

Practicing for Standardized Tests

Each Practicing for Standardized Tests master presents ten questions that draw on all content strands. The questions are presented in the form of test items similar to how they often appear in standardized tests such as state assessment tests, the Preliminary Scholastic Aptitude Test (PSAT), or the ACT PLAN. We suggest using these practice sets following the unit assessment so students can become familiar with the formats of standardized tests and develop effective test-taking strategies for performing well on such tests. Answers are provided below.

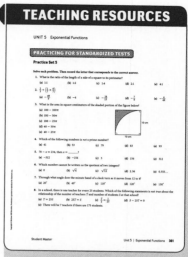

Answers to Practice Set 5

1. (c)   2. (a)   3. (c)   4. (e)   5. (b)

6. (c)   7. (d)   8. (a)   9. (d)   10. (d)

Student Masters 361–362
GO DIGITAL

UNIT 6

Patterns in Shape

Shape is an important and fascinating aspect of the world in which you live. You see shapes in nature, in art and design, in architecture and mechanical devices. Some shapes, like the Rock and Roll Hall of Fame building, are three-dimensional. Others, like the architect's plans for the building, are two-dimensional.

In this unit, your study will focus on describing and classifying two-dimensional and three-dimensional shapes, on visualizing and representing them with drawings, and on analyzing and applying their properties. You will develop understanding and skill in use of the geometry of shape through work on problems in three lessons.

LESSONS

1 Triangles, Quadrilaterals, and Their Properties

Investigate combinations of side lengths and angle measures sufficient to ensure congruence of triangles and of quadrilaterals. Analyze properties of these figures and use those properties to solve design problems.

2 Polygons and Their Properties

Recognize and apply reflection and rotational symmetries of polygons. Investigate additional polygon properties and combinations of polygons that tile a plane.

3 Polyhedra and Their Properties

Recognize, visualize, and develop drawing methods for representing polyhedra and other three-dimensional shapes. Analyze properties of polyhedra.

Patterns in Shape

Unit Overview

The intent of this unit is to review, deepen, and extend students' understanding of two- and three-dimensional shapes, their representations, their properties, and their uses. The fundamental idea of this unit is one of shape—what gives shapes their form and how the shape of an object often influences its function. The unit provides an introduction to mathematical reasoning as a way to discover or establish new facts as consequences of known or assumed facts. As such, the unit lays the groundwork for ideas of mathematical argument and proof that will be developed formally in Courses 2, 3, and 4. *The focus here is on careful visual reasoning, not on formal proof.*

The lessons in this unit are developed and sequenced in a manner consistent with the van Hiele levels of geometric thinking.

Level 0 Visualization (including recognizing, drawing, constructing, manipulating, and describing geometric figures)

Level 1 Analysis (including classifying geometric figures and recognizing how figures and parts of figures are related)

Level 2 Informal Deduction (including reasoning with definitions, analyzing and completing arguments, finding counterexamples, and applying properties of figures and relationships in problem situations)

Level 3 Deduction (including identifying given and to-prove information, understanding the distinction between a statement and its converse, understanding the role of postulates, theorems, and proof and constructing simple deductive arguments)

Level 4 Rigor (involving work in a variety of axiomatic systems, including non-Euclidian geometries)

The primary emphasis is on Levels 0–2 with opportunities for beginning the transition to Level 3. The unit assumes that students have had prior experiences in the middle-school grades with geometric thinking at Levels 0 and 1. The unit also assumes students have a conceptual understanding of measurement ideas, including linear and angle measure, perimeter, area, surface area, and volume, and are familiar with formulas for calculating these measures. We realize that geometric experiences of students in the middle-school grades are often uneven. Review exercises in Units 1–5 have been carefully designed to revisit or build up these geometric understandings.

The unit is designed to be completed in about five weeks. Lessons 1 and 2 focus on two-dimensional shapes, their representations, properties, and applications. Lesson 3 focuses on analogous ideas in three dimensions.

Unit Objectives

- Recognize and classify common two- and three-dimensional shapes

- Visualize and represent two- and three-dimensional shapes

- Analyze and apply properties of polygons and polyhedra

- Use rigid transformations to verify SSS, SAS, ASA conditions for congruence of triangles and use these conditions in solving problems

- Begin to develop ability to establish properties of shapes by careful reasoning from definitions and given or assumed facts

CPMP-Tools

Geometry custom apps have been developed to support student investigation of quadrilateral linkages, triangle congruence, tessellations, and visualizing, generating, slicing, and unfolding three-dimensional figures. Students can download *CPMP-Tools* for use outside of class from www.wmich.edu/cpmp/CPMP-Tools/.

Design a Linkage

The "Design a Linkage" custom app enables students to create quadrilateral linkages by adjusting the lengths of the sides. The motion allowed by the linkage can be dynamically examined and the path of vertex *C* can be tracked. Students can explore design conditions for linkages that involve rotating or rocking motions. This custom app can be used with Lesson 1 Investigation 1 Problem 6 (page 367) and with related homework tasks.

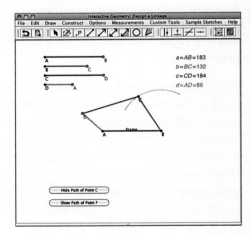

Areas of Quadrilaterals

This custom app provides quick comparisons of the actual area of a quadrilateral with that calculated using an ancient Egyptian formula.

Again the shape can be dynamically changed to note the types of figures for which the two calculations produce the same results and the types of figures for which the formula overestimates the exact area. See Extensions Task 29 (page 394).

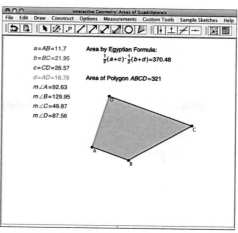

Triangle Congruence

The "Triangle Congruence" custom app allows students to investigate whether three specific side or angle measurements are sufficient information to build a triangle; and if so, whether a second triangle can be formed that is congruent to the triangle formed from the specified sides/angles. Rigid transformations (translations, rotations about a point, and line reflections) are used to verify the congruence of the two triangles. The software tests and records the dimensions of the created triangle(s) to check for congruence. In Lesson 1 Investigation 2 Problem 3 (page 371), students should use this custom app to test for triangle congruence.

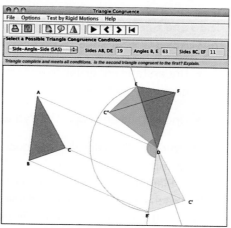

Tiling Custom Apps

Three custom apps have been developed for tilings: "Tilings with Triangles or Quadrilaterals" provides a quick visual investigation of tilings formed by congruent triangles or congruent quadrilaterals by rotating the shapes about the midpoints of their sides. "Tilings with Regular Polygons" enables students to investigate tilings with one or more regular polygons with 3 to 12 sides. This app is particularly useful when considering semiregular tessellations. See Lesson 2 Investigation 3 Problem 6 (page 410) and selected homework tasks. A sample tiling is shown above. "Tilings with Penrose Tiles" enables students to create complex Penrose tilings. This custom app provides a specific kite and dart with color-coded vertices to assist in matching sides of the shapes.

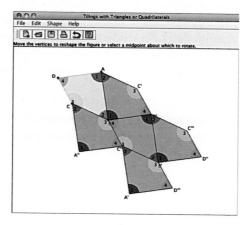

Three-Dimensional (3D) Apps

Three 3D custom apps have been developed for use with this unit. "Slicing or Unfolding Polyhedra" allows students to visualize common polyhedra and manipulate 3D modeling options such as cutting and unfolding (page 427). "Generating Cones and Cylinders" enables students to manipulate 2D shapes to generate these 3D shapes (page 430). The third app, "Slicing Cones and Cylinders," allows students to dynamically manipulate a plane slicing either a cone or a cylinder, and view the corresponding cross section (page 453).

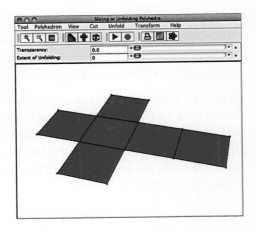

CCSS and CPMP Pathways

The Grade 8 CCSS standards revisited and extended in *Patterns in Shape* are:

- Understand congruence and similarity using physical models, transparencies, or geometry software.

- Understand and apply the Pythagorean Theorem.

If your students have developed a good understanding of the CCSS content above, you may find that some material in this unit will need fewer days to complete than is suggested in the Unit Planning Guide. One approach to assessing students' prior knowledge is to discuss in class each lesson TATS, selected investigation problems (possibly as a think-pair-share activity), and each investigation STM, providing students in-class time to complete the CYUs. Selected OYO tasks can be assigned for homework with special attention to Connections tasks. Typically, the cognitive demand of the problems in *Core-Plus Mathematics* exceeds that of similar content in middle school programs. Thus, it is in students' best interests to at least complete the CCSS Pathway as outlined in the Unit Planning Guide. The curriculum is designed to help students develop the ability to reason in all mathematical strands. Students will be expected to provide reasoning for many statements in this unit. The reasoning and proof expectations are beyond those found in most middle school programs.

Your honors or STEM students would be well advised to complete the richer *Core-Plus Mathematics Project* Pathway described in the Unit Planning Guide. This pathway encompasses the CCSS Pathway and additional material.

Lesson Objectives	Pathways: Pacing and OYO Assignments*	Resources
Lesson 1 Triangles, Quadrilaterals, and Their Properties • Discover and apply the Triangle Inequality and its analog for quadrilaterals • Investigate rigidity of two-dimensional shapes • Discover and apply properties of quadrilateral linkages, including those with rotating bars • Discover and verify using rigid transformations (translation, rotation about a point, and line reflection) combinations of side and angle conditions that are sufficient for testing the congruence of two triangles: Side-Side-Side (SSS), Side-Angle-Side (SAS), Angle-Side-Angle (ASA) • Use congruence conditions to reason about properties of isosceles triangles and select properties of parallelograms • Use area and congruence relationships to justify why the Pythagorean Theorem and its converse are true, and use these results to solve problems involving right triangles • Recall, justify derivations of, and use formulas to find areas of triangles and special quadrilaterals	**CCSS Pathway** (12 days, includes assessment) **Investigation 1:** Problems 1–5 (omit STM Part e and CYU) OYO—A1, A2, C14, C15 or C16, R22, E28 or E29, Rv31–Rv34 **Investigation 2:** OYO—A4–A7, R23, Rv35–Rv38 **Investigation 3:** OYO—A8–A10, C17, C18, R24, R25, Rv39 **Investigation 4:** OYO—A11 or A12, A13, C19–C21, R26, E30, Rv40 **CPMP Pathway** (12 days, includes assessment) Use CCSS Pathway plus **Investigation 1:** Problem 6, Problem 7 (optional) OYO—A3, R23, E27 **Investigation 4:** OYO—E29	• 12-foot knotted loop of rope or cord with knots at 6-inch intervals • Spaghetti • Compasses • Protractors • Rulers • Linkage strips • *CPMP-Tools* custom apps: "Design a Linkage," "Areas of Quadrilaterals," and "Triangle Congruence" • Unit Resource Masters
Lesson 2 Polygons and Their Properties • Discover and apply properties of the interior, exterior, and central angles of polygons • Recognize and describe line and rotational symmetries of polygons and other two-dimensional shapes • (Re)discover which triangles, quadrilaterals, and regular polygons will tile a plane and explore semiregular tessellations • Recognize and describe symmetries of tessellations, including translation symmetry	**CCSS Pathway** (10 days, includes assessment) **Investigation 1:** OYO—A1 or A2, choose one of A3–A5, C10 or C11, C12, choose two of R17–R22, E23 or E24 **Investigation 2:** OYO—A6, A7, C13, C14, Rv28–Rv30 **Investigation 3:** Problems 1–4 and 6 OYO—A8 or A9, C15, C16, Rv31–Rv36 **CPMP Pathway** (10 days, includes assessment) Use CCSS Pathway plus **Investigation 3:** Problem 5 (optional)	• Two-mirror kaleidoscopes • Acrylic plastic mirrors • Protractors • Compasses • Rulers • Three-mirror kaleidoscope(s) • Posterboard • *CPMP-Tools* custom apps: "Tilings with Triangles or Quadrilaterals," "Tilings with Regular Polygons," and "Tilings with Penrose Tiles" • Unit Resource Masters

* *When choice is indicated, it is important to leave the choice to the student.*

Note: *It is best if Connections tasks are discussed as a whole class after they have been assigned as homework.*

Note: *The Planning Guide assumes students have access to technology for homework.*

Lesson Objectives	Pathways: Pacing and OYO Assignments*	Resources
Lesson 3 Polyhedra and Their Properties • Identify and describe important characteristics of common three-dimensional shapes including prisms, pyramids, cones, and cylinders • Construct three-dimensional models of these shapes and describe their two-dimensional components • Sketch three-dimensional shapes using different methods and recognize the advantages and disadvantages of each method • Recognize and describe the plane and rotational symmetries of polyhedra • Recognize whether a polyhedron is rigid and how to reinforce a polyhedron to produce one that is rigid • Explore consequences of the Euler relationship involving the numbers of vertices, faces, and edges and of Descartes' Theorem concerning the face angles in any convex polyhedron • Recall, justify derivations of, and use formulas for finding surface area and volume of common three-dimensional shapes	**CCSS Pathway** <u>(9 days, includes assessment)</u> **Investigation 1:** OYO—choose two of A1–A3, C10, C11, R17, E20, Rv27–Rv29 **Investigation 2:** OYO—A4, A5, C12, C13, R18, choose one of E21–E23, Rv30–Rv32 **Investigation 3:** Problems 1–5 (omit STM Part d and CYU Part d) OYO—A6–A8, C14, R19, E24 or E25, Rv33–Rv36 **Investigation 4:** Omit **CPMP Pathway** <u>(9 days, includes assessment)</u> Use CCSS Pathway plus **Investigation 3:** Problem 6 (optional) **Investigation 4:** optional	• *Optional:* paper triangular prism, square prism, and cylinder • 5-cm and 8-cm small holed straws or coffee stirrers • Long coffee stirrers for braces • Small pipe cleaner pieces • Rulers • *Optional:* Set of regular polyhedra • *Optional:* Interlocking cubes • CPMP-Tools custom apps "Slicing or Unfolding Polyhedra," "Generating Cones and Cylinders," and "Slicing Cones and Cylinders" • Unit Resource Masters
Lesson 4 Looking Back • Review and synthesize the major objectives of the unit	(3 days, includes unit assessment)	• Unit Resource Masters

* *When choice is indicated, it is important to leave the choice to the student.*
Note: *It is best if Connections tasks are discussed as a whole class after they have been assigned as homework.*
Note: *The Planning Guide assumes students have access to technology for homework.*

Patterns in Shape is the beginning of the geometry story. The development of geometry, along with trigonometry, is continued in two units in Course 2, three units in Course 3, and three units in Course 4. Geometry and algebra become increasingly intertwined in later courses. Descriptions of the mathematical topics in these units are in *Implementing Core-Plus Mathematics* and the front matter of each text.

Course 2

Coordinate Methods develops student understanding of coordinate methods for representing and analyzing properties of geometric shapes, for describing geometric change, and for producing animations.

Trigonometric Methods develops student understanding of trigonometric functions and the ability to use trigonometric methods to solve triangulation and indirect measurement problems.

Course 3

Reasoning and Proof develops student understanding of formal reasoning in geometric, algebraic, and statistical contexts and of basic principles that underlie those reasoning strategies.

Similarity and Congruence extends student understanding of similarity and congruence and their ability to use those relations to solve problems and to prove geometric assertions with and without use of coordinates.

Circles and Circular Functions develops student understanding of relationships among special lines, segments, and angles in circles and the ability to use properties of circles to solve problems; develops student understanding of circular functions and the ability to use these functions to model periodic change; and extends student ability to reason deductively in geometric settings.

Course 4

Vectors and Motion develops student understanding of two-dimensional vectors and their use in modeling linear, circular, and other nonlinear motion.

Trigonometric Functions and Equations extends student understanding of, and ability to reason with, trigonometric functions to prove or disprove two trigonometric expressions are identical and to solve trigonometric equations; to geometrically represent complex numbers and complex number operations and to find roots of complex numbers.

Surfaces and Cross Sections extends student ability to visualize and represent three-dimensional shapes using contours, cross sections, and reliefs, and to visualize and represent surfaces and conic sections defined by algebraic equations.

LESSON

1

Triangles, Quadrilaterals, and Their Properties

In previous units, you used the shape of graphs to aid in understanding patterns of linear and nonlinear change. In this unit, you will study properties of some special geometric shapes in the plane and in space. In particular, you will study some of the geometry of two-dimensional figures called *polygons* and three-dimensional figures called *polyhedra*, formed by them.

The geometry of shape is among some of the earliest mathematics. It was used in ancient Egypt to construct the pyramids and to measure land. For example, when the yearly floods of the Nile River receded, the river often followed a different path. As a result,

the shape and size of fields along the river changed from year to year. It is believed that the Egyptians used ropes tied with equally-spaced knots to re-establish land boundaries. To see how a knotted rope might be used in building design and measuring, think about how you could use a piece of rope tied into a 24-meter loop with knots at one-meter intervals.

©Royalty-Free/Corbis

362 UNIT 6 | Patterns in Shape

Triangles, Quadrilaterals, and Their Properties

This first lesson introduces students to the major theme of shape, along with consideration of how the shape and function of an object are often related. For example, a triangle is completely determined by the lengths of its three sides—it is a rigid figure. A unique quadrilateral (or any polygon of more than four sides) is not determined solely by the lengths of its sides—it is not rigid. The flexibility of quadrilaterals makes them useful in the design of mechanical devices involving cranks and rocker motions. Students should be attentive to the similarities and differences in the properties of triangles and quadrilaterals and how knowledge of properties of triangles can be used to reason to properties of special quadrilaterals.

The lesson also develops two of the most important results in elementary geometry—the Triangle Inequality and the Pythagorean Theorem. Applications of the Triangle Inequality provide a way of solving some minimization problems without the use of calculus or calculators. (See on Your Own Task 2 on page 383 and Task 4 on page 457.) The Pythagorean Theorem is the foundation of much further work in mathematics and its applications.

This lesson may be students' first introduction to mathematical reasoning of the form "*If* I know this, *then* I can conclude that." They should be encouraged to view this type of reasoning as a natural extension of the explanations that they often gave in earlier units to support their conclusions. The evidence here is often based on definitions and assumed or given facts rather than patterns in experimental data.

Custom apps in the *CPMP-Tools* interactive geometry software can be used to enhance the study of congruence of triangles via rigid motions, quadrilateral linkages, and areas of quadrilateral shapes.

Teachers and students who have familiarity with other dynamic geometry software such as *The Geometer's Sketchpad* or *Cabri Jr.* may elect to use that instead.

CCSS MATHEMATICAL PRACTICE By having access to technology at school and at home, students will become familiar with technology tools so that they will be able to use tools strategically as recommended in the CCSS.

Common Core State Standards CCSS

Focused on:
G-CO.1, G-CO.2, G-CO.6, G-CO.8, G-CO.9, G-CO.10, G-CO.11, G-CO.12, G-SRT.5, G-GMD.1, G-MG.1, G-MG.3

Connected to:
A-CED.1, A-REI.1, F-IF.4, S-ID.6

- Discover and apply the Triangle Inequality and its analog for quadrilaterals

- Investigate rigidity of two-dimensional shapes

- Discover and apply properties of quadrilateral linkages, including those with rotating bars

- Discover and verify using rigid transformations (translations, rotations about a point, and line reflections) combinations of side and angle conditions that are sufficient for testing the congruence of two triangles: Side-Side-Side (SSS), Side-Angle-Side (SAS), Angle-Side-Angle (ASA)

- Use congruence conditions to reason about properties of isosceles triangles and select properties of parallelograms

- Use area and congruence relationships to justify why the Pythagorean Theorem and its converse are true, and use these results to solve problems involving right triangles

- Recall, justify derivations of, and use formulas to find areas of triangles and special quadrilaterals

UNIT 6

There is considerable variation in students' background experiences with geometry in middle schools. This is an opportunity to informally assess your students' background knowledge of basic geometric shapes and their properties, including perimeter and area, and an opportunity for students to think about shapes regardless of their prior experiences.

Have a group of 3 or 4 students use a rope tied in a loop with 24 marked units (6 inches or 1 foot) to demonstrate each of the situations by using instructions provided by other students in the class. Each group of students could take turns instructing the group with the rope.

Giving students an opportunity to create several different triangles and quadrilaterals should help them conjecture about perimeter and area relationships.

It is important for students to note that triangles (or quadrilaterals) with the same perimeter can have different areas. Parts c and d are special cases of a more general question: "Of all *n*-gons with fixed perimeter (and fixed *n*), which one has the greatest area?" (Answer: regular *n*-gon) This question, in turn, is a special case of a famous problem called the *Isoperimetric Problem*. "Of all two-dimensional shapes with fixed perimeter, which one has the greatest area?" (Answer: the circle.)

THINK ABOUT THIS SITUATION

Suppose that you and two or three classmates each grabbed the rope at a different knot and pulled outward until the loop formed a particular shape.

a How could you position yourselves so that the resulting shape was an equilateral triangle? An isosceles triangle? A right triangle?

b How are the perimeters of the three triangles related? How do you think the areas are related?

c How could you position yourselves so that the resulting shape was a square? A rectangle? A parallelogram that is not a rectangle?

d How are the perimeters of the three quadrilaterals related? How do you think the areas are related?

As you complete the investigations in the following three lessons, you will discover why some shapes are used so frequently in building and in design. You will also discover how knowledge of a few basic properties of geometric figures can be used to reason about many additional properties of those shapes.

INVESTIGATION 1

Form and Function

Buildings and bridges, like most objects around you, are three-dimensional. They have length, height, and depth (or width). To better understand the design of these objects, it is often helpful to examine the two-dimensional shapes of their components. Triangles and special quadrilaterals such as rectangles are among the most commonly occurring two-dimensional shapes in structural designs.

Design Pics/Don Hammond

Lesson 1 | Triangles, Quadrilaterals, and Their Properties **363**

THINK ABOUT THIS SITUATION

a An equilateral triangle is formed when each student holds a knot 8 knots away from each of the other two students. The three students should pull the rope taut.

An isosceles triangle can be formed, for example, by one student holding any knot and the other two students both moving 10 knots along the rope. Moving any other equal number of knots will also determine an isosceles triangle.

In order to form a right triangle, students should position themselves 6, 8, and 10 knots away from each other. They might begin by positioning one student at the right angle of an object in the classroom such as a desk or the corner where the floor and walls meet.

b The perimeter of each of the three triangles will be 24 units. Students may observe that the area of the equilateral triangle is larger than the area of each of the other two triangles.

c A square is formed when four students hold a knot six knots away from each other and create a right angle (see Part a) at one of the corners.

Many rectangles can be formed. Students must position themselves so that opposite sides are of equal length and a right angle (see Part a) is created at each corner.

A parallelogram that is not a rectangle can be formed in the same way as the rectangle, but without a right angle.

d All of the quadrilaterals will have a perimeter of 24 units. The areas of the quadrilaterals will vary depending on the base and height of each shape. The square will have the largest area.

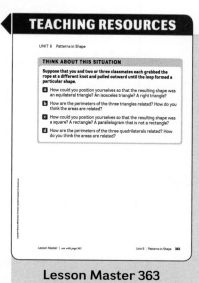
INVESTIGATION 1 CCSS G-GMD.1, G-MG.1, G-MG.3

Form and Function

In this investigation, students investigate conditions on side lengths necessary to build triangles and quadrilaterals. They determine that triangles are rigid and that quadrilaterals are not. These properties lead to important physical applications using the shapes. Students (re)discover the Triangle Inequality and its analogue for quadrilaterals. The Triangle Inequality is an important result in elementary geometry that is widely used in solving minimization problems. They also investigate Grashof's Theorem. Grashof's Theorem provides conditions for four-bar linkage mechanisms to rotate and/or rock, making them useful in mechanical devices. See Extensions Task 27 on page 393.

COLLABORATION SKILL

Help the group move toward consensus.

Think About This Situation, *page 363*

Teacher: Let's think about the Egyptian method for determining shapes by using this 24-foot loop of rope with knots at one-foot intervals. I will call up different groups to make the various figures that are requested. First, how could you position yourselves so that the resulting shape is an equilateral triangle? *(Pause)* Group 1, come on up here in front of the class; talk about your thinking as you make the triangle.

Pamela: Okay, an equilateral triangle has three equal sides.

Eaton: Yeah, so with 24 feet, each side would have to be 8 feet long.

Hope: Pamela, you hold this knot; Talbot, you hold this knot *(counting eight knots down from the first one)*; and, Eaton, you hold this knot *(counting eight more knots down from the second one)*. Now, pull your knot outward away from each other. There, we have it!

Teacher: Okay class, what do you think? Has Group 1 formed an equilateral triangle?

Chang: Yes, because all three sides of the triangle are 8 feet long and that's an equilateral triangle—a triangle with three equal sides.

Teacher: Next, how could you position yourselves so that the resulting shape is an isosceles triangle?

Eaton: What is an isosceles triangle?

Pamela: It's a triangle with two sides that are equal length.

Talbot: So, could we use two sides that are 7 feet long?

Pamela: Let's try it.

Hope: Okay, Talbot, you hold this knot; Eaton, you hold this knot *(counting seven knots down from the first knot)*; and, Pamela, you hold this knot *(counting seven knots down from the second knot)*.

Teacher: Class, do you agree that Group 1 has formed an isosceles triangle? *(Agreement is indicated.)* Is this the only way to form an isosceles triangle using this rope?

Mac: No. I was thinking of having two sides that were 10 feet each, then the third side would only be 4 feet long. All 24 feet of the rope is still used. The perimeter is 24 feet.

Blair: What about other possible isosceles triangles, like one with sides of length 1, 1, and 22 feet? Or of length 2, 2, and 20 feet? You can just pick a length for the two equal sides and use what is left for the third side.

Connie: So, you're saying we could have sides of 3, 3, and 18 feet or 4, 4, and 16 feet?

Blair: Sure, as long as the perimeter is 24 feet and we have two sides the same length.

Teacher: All right. Now how could you position yourselves so that the resulting shape is a right triangle? *(Pause)* Group 2, come on up and show us.

Baker: Well, a right triangle has to have a right angle, so why don't we form a right angle first.

Jasmin: Okay, I'll hold on to this knot and make this the vertex of the right angle. We can use the floor since it's horizontal, and the wall since it's vertical, to make the right angle.

Sandra: Then, I'll hold on to this knot *(pointing to one that was 5 feet down from Jasmin's knot)* and hold it tight against the floor.

Noah: But, which knot should I hold *(trying to hold different knots against the wall, but the rope isn't staying taut on both the hypotenuse and the other leg at the same time)*?

Teacher: We could form a right triangle with a leg that has a length of five, but then it looks like Noah would have to hold on to the rope in between knots. Can you try using different lengths that would allow each of you to hold on to the rope at a knot?

Sandra: I'll try holding this knot *(holding one that is 6 feet down from Jasmin's knot)*.

Noah: Then I'll hold on to this knot *(holding a knot that is 8 feet away from Jasmin's knot)*. I think I can hold this knot and keep the rope taut on both sides.

Teacher: Have they done it? *(Several students clap.)* Good! Briefly discuss with your group how you think the perimeter and area of the three triangles are related. *(Pauses until students are ready.)* What do you think?

Pamela: All the triangles have the same perimeter because they are formed by the same rope. We said the perimeter would be 24 feet.

Teacher: Anyone disagree with Pamela's group? *(Pause)* Who would like to share what your group discussed regarding the area of the triangles? *(Pause)*

Eaton: We said that the area would be the same.

Teacher: Can someone else in your group tell us more about that idea?

Hope: It seemed to us that as the base of the triangle gets smaller, the height of the triangle gets bigger, so the area will stay the same.

Eaton: Well, there are lots of different triangles that could be made with a perimeter of 24 feet. It doesn't seem like all their areas would be the same.

Margi: Yeah, like if you have three of those ropes, you could build three different triangles, and then you could see that the areas are different.

Teacher: Hmm, I wonder which is true? *(The teacher allows this common misconception that figures with equal perimeter have equal areas to go unsettled for a few a while. The class will revisit this idea with rectangles where counterexamples will provide contrary evidence.)* We'll come back to this idea in a few minutes.

Teacher: Okay, let's consider building quadrilaterals then. How could you position yourselves so the shape is a square? Group 4, can you show us?

Dane: Sure. *(Group 4 comes up.)* Dominic, you stand at that desk so you can make a right angle using the corner, and Carolyn, you stand 6 feet away and use that other desk to make a right angle. I will stand by this desk holding on to the rope 6 feet from you and then Madeleine, you use that fourth desk to complete our square. *(Students arrange themselves.)*

Teacher: What do you think? Do they have a square?

Many students: Yes.

Teacher: How might we get a rectangle?

Juanita: We could just take 1 foot from each corner and add length to two sides. So, our 8' by 8' square would be a 10' by 6' rectangle.

Teacher: Is that a rectangle? *(Students indicate agreement.)*

Teacher: How might Group 4 build a parallelogram that is not a rectangle?

Talbot: They can just make angles that aren't square.

Dane: We'll try it. Let's start with a rectangle. *(Students hold the rope creating a rectangle.)*

Juanita: We just have to shift one side over. So you two *(points to two students holding consecutive vertices of the rectangle)* just take one step to the left.

Dane: Let's make sure we move the same distance. *(Students take one step left.)* There, that should be a parallelogram.

Teacher: Is everyone okay with this as a parallelogram that is not a rectangle? Give me a thumbs up if you agree. *(Teacher receives a visual verification of agreement.)* Thank you, Group 4.

Teacher: We need to think about the perimeter and area for each of these quadrilaterals. How are the perimeters related?

Pamela: It's just like the triangles. The perimeter must be 24 feet since we used up all the rope.

Teacher: What about the areas of the quadrilaterals; how are they related?

Eaton: I think there are many different areas—just like I thought was true with the triangles.

Hope: Me too.

Teacher: Hope, can you tell us more about why you agree with Eaton?

Hope: If we had more rope, I could show you, but I guess I can explain it to you. We could build many different quadrilaterals using the rope, and they might have different areas. Like a rectangle with side lengths of 2 feet and 10 feet has an area of 20 square feet, but a rectangle with side lengths of 4 feet and 8 feet has an area of 32 square feet. We could build both of those rectangles with our rope but their areas are different.

Talbot: *(Speaking to the class)* Remember in elementary school when we built arrays of dots? If we have 24 feet of rope, then the rectangles we could make would be 1 by 11, 2 by 10, 3 by 9, 4 by 8, 5 by 7, and 6 by 6. All of those rectangles have different areas but the same perimeters.

Teacher: Do some of you remember doing arrays like Talbot? *(The teacher gets a mixed response.)* Talbot, can you show us an example on the board?

Talbot: *(Draws a 4 × 8 dot array.)*

So, we have a rectangle with a perimeter of 24 and an area of 32. Now, if we make a 3 × 9 array on top of this one, we can see how their areas are different. *(Talbot creates one atop the other.)*

See, I still have a perimeter of 24, but I lost 8 squares and only gained 3, so my new area is 5 less than the area of my first rectangle. The new area is only 27 squares.

(The ideas surfaced by this student allow the teacher some insight into students' prior experiences with perimeter and area. It will be important for him to connect to understandings that students have as they study triangles and quadrilaterals in this lesson.)

Teacher: Thank you, Talbot. We had better return to thinking about how the areas of the 24-foot-perimeter triangles are related. Are all those areas the same? Let's go back to the knotted rope. I need three students to help.

(The teacher has the three students create two triangles with the knotted rope so all students can visually compare the areas. He asks students to create an 8 × 8 × 8 triangle and then an 11 × 11 × 2 triangle—two somewhat extreme cases—hoping that the difference in area will be visible to most students. A discussion ensues. He congratulates them on their "good" thinking and starts them on the lesson.)

Lesson 1 | Triangles, Quadrilaterals, and Their Properties   **T363B**

In this first investigation, you will explore conditions on the sides of triangles and quadrilaterals that affect their shape. In the process, you will discover some physical properties of these shapes that have important applications. As you work on the following problems, look for answers to these questions:

What conditions on side lengths are needed to build triangles and quadrilaterals? What additional constraints are needed to build special quadrilaterals?

Why and how are triangles used in the design of structures like bridge trusses?

Why and how are quadrilaterals used in the design of devices like windshield wipers?

1 Building Triangles Using strands of uncooked thin spaghetti, conduct the following experiment at least three times. Keep a record of your findings, including sketches of the shapes you make.

- Mark any two points along the length of a strand of spaghetti and break the spaghetti at those two points.

- Try to build a triangle with the pieces end-to-end.

- If a triangle can be built, try to build a differently shaped triangle with the same side lengths.

a. Was it possible to build a triangle in each case? If a triangle could be built, could you build a differently shaped triangle using the same three segments? Compare your findings with those of others.

b. If a triangle can be built from three segments, how do the segment lengths appear to be related? Use a ruler and compass to test your conjecture for segments of length 3 cm, 4 cm, and 5 cm. For segments of length 5 cm, 6 cm, and 12 cm. Revise your conjecture if needed.

c. Suppose a, b, and c are side lengths of *any* triangle. Write an equation or inequality relating a, b, and c. How many different equations or inequalities can you write relating a, b, and c?

d. Write in words the relationship that must be satisfied by the side lengths of any triangle (do not use letters to name the side lengths). This relationship is called the **Triangle Inequality**.

2 Special Triangles You may recall from your prior mathematical study that triangles can be classified in terms of their sides as *scalene*, *isosceles*, or *equilateral*.

a. What type of triangle were most of the triangles that you built in your experiment? Explain as carefully as you can why you might expect that result.

b. Draw an isosceles triangle that is not equilateral. Suppose a is the length of two of the sides and b is the length of the base of your triangle. How must a and b be related? Explain your reasoning using the Triangle Inequality.

c. Can you build an equilateral triangle of any side length a? Explain your reasoning using the Triangle Inequality.

Jim Laser

UNIT 6

In keeping with the focus on side lengths, special triangles and special quadrilaterals are characterized in terms of relationships among their side lengths. In particular, here a parallelogram is defined as a quadrilateral with opposite sides the same length. In Connections Task 18 on page 391, students explain why it is also the case that in a parallelogram opposite sides are parallel. In the Course 2 unit *Coordinate Methods*, students use coordinates to prove that if opposite sides of a quadrilateral are parallel, then opposite sides are the same length, thereby establishing the equivalence of the two characterizations (definitions) of a parallelogram.

Computer Access—You may wish to have multiple (laptop) computers available in your classroom or access to a computer lab as students work on problems on pages 367 and 368.

1 | **INSTRUCTIONAL NOTE** Be sure that students are focusing on the visual aspect of the Triangle Inequality in Part a. The numerical aspect is introduced in Part b. If students' first couple of experimental trials do not yield triangles, encourage them to try again. When students compare their results, ask them to describe what they noticed about the three lengths when they could and could not form a triangle.

INSTRUCTIONAL NOTE

This problem may provide an opportunity to confront the tendency of students to make generalizations too quickly.

a. It is not possible to build triangles with any three lengths.

All triangles built with an initial set of three lengths will be the same shape as the initial triangle. Students may notice that the new triangles are reflections, translations, or rotations of the initial triangle.

b. The sum of the lengths of any two sides is greater than the length of the third side. Students should use a ruler and compass to recognize that a triangle can be built using lengths 3 cm, 4 cm, and 5 cm, and a triangle cannot be built using lengths of 5 cm, 6 cm, and 12 cm.

This can be done by drawing one side of the triangle, such as 12 cm, adjusting the compass to measure 5 cm, making an arc at one endpoint of the 12-cm segment, and then making a 6-cm arc at the other endpoint.

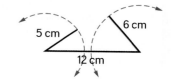

c. Three different inequalities can be written: $a + b > c$, $b + c > a$, and $a + c > b$.

d. *The Triangle Inequality:* The sum of the lengths of any two sides of a triangle is always greater than the length of the third side.

INSTRUCTIONAL NOTE

It is important to check that all students have correctly represented the Triangle Inequality for use in Problems 2 and 3.

2 **a.** Most triangles built were probably scalene because the spaghetti was broken at random spots. The probability of two pieces matching in length is much less than the probability of two pieces being different lengths. Even if you try to break the spaghetti in equal pieces, you may not have exactly equal lengths.

b. $a + a > b$, or $2a > b$, or $a > 0.5b$, where a and b are side lengths of an isosceles triangle as shown at the right. This is true because the Triangle Inequality says that the sum of any two side lengths is greater than the third length.

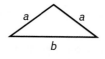

c. An equilateral triangle can be built with any side length a (given $a > 0$). This is true because $2a$ is always greater than the third side a; $2a > a$, for $a > 0$.

3 **Building Quadrilaterals** Now use strands of spaghetti to conduct this quadrilateral-building experiment at least three times. Keep a record of your findings, including sketches of the shapes you make.

- Mark any three points along the length of a strand of spaghetti and break the spaghetti at those three points.

- Try to build a quadrilateral with the pieces end-to-end.

- If a quadrilateral can be built, try to build another, differently shaped quadrilateral with the same side lengths.

a. Was it possible to build a quadrilateral in each case? If a quadrilateral could be built, could you build a differently shaped quadrilateral using the same four segments? Compare your findings with those of others.

b. If a quadrilateral can be built from four side lengths, how are the side lengths related? Use a ruler and compass to test your conjecture for segments of length 3 cm, 5 cm, 8 cm, and 10 cm. For segments of length 4 cm, 4 cm, 7 cm, and 15 cm. For segments of length 2 cm, 4 cm, 8 cm, and 16 cm.

c. Suppose a, b, c, and d are consecutive side lengths of any quadrilateral. Write an equation or inequality relating a, b, c, and d. How many different equations or inequalities can you write relating a, b, c, and d?

d. Write in words the relationship that must be satisfied by the four side lengths of any quadrilateral (do not use letters to name side lengths).

Special Quadrilaterals Quadrilaterals are more complicated than triangles. They have more sides and more angles. In Problem 3, you discovered that using the same four side lengths of a quadrilateral, you could build quite different shapes. Quadrilaterals are classified as *convex*—as in the case of the quadrilateral below on the left—or *nonconvex*—as in the case of the quadrilateral on the right.

Convex   **Nonconvex**

4 Some special convex quadrilaterals can be characterized in terms of side lengths. For example, in completing Part c of the Think About This Situation, you likely created a **parallelogram** by forming a quadrilateral with opposite sides the same length.

a. Show how you can build a parallelogram using four segments cut from a strand of spaghetti and placed end-to-end.

i. How many differently shaped parallelograms can you build with those four segments?

ii. What additional constraint(s) would you have to build into the definition of a parallelogram for it to be a **rectangle**?

Lesson 1 | Triangles, Quadrilaterals, and Their Properties **365**

3 **a.** It is not possible to build a quadrilateral in every case.

Once a quadrilateral is built, angle sizes can be changed to make other shapes. In addition, ordering the lengths of sides differently can result in a new shape as shown in the diagrams.

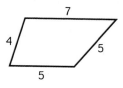 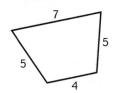

b. Conjecture: The sum of the lengths of any three sides of a quadrilateral is *greater* than the length of its fourth side. Students should check these sets of numbers by drawing one side length on their paper. Then using

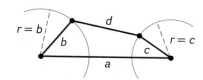

the compass set at the two other lengths, make arcs with centers that are the endpoints of the drawn segment. If the fourth length can be positioned to connect the arcs, then a quadrilateral can be formed. (Students should recognize that more than one quadrilateral shape might be formed.)

A quadrilateral with side lengths of 3, 5, 8, and 10 units can be formed.
$3 + 5 + 8 > 10$

A quadrilateral with side lengths of 4, 4, 7, and 15 units cannot be formed.
$4 + 4 + 7 = 15$

A quadrilateral with side lengths of 2, 4, 8, and 16 units cannot be formed.
$2 + 4 + 8 < 16$

c. Four different inequalities can be written relating a, b, c, and d, the side lengths of a quadrilateral.
$a + b + c > d$
$a + b + d > c$
$a + c + d > b$
$b + c + d > a$

d. The sum of the lengths of any three sides of a quadrilateral is *greater* than the length of its fourth side.

4 **a.** Students should demonstrate using two pairs of spaghetti pieces that are the same length.

i. An infinite number of different parallelograms can be built with these four segments.

ii. To build a **rectangle**, you would have to require that one angle of the parallelogram be a right angle. (This, in turn, would require that all the angles be right angles.)

b. A **kite** is a convex quadrilateral with two distinct pairs of consecutive sides the same length.

   i. Build a kite using the same four segments of spaghetti, in Part a, placed end-to-end.

   ii. How many differently shaped kites can you build with those four pieces?

c. A **rhombus** is a quadrilateral with all four sides the same length.

   i. Build a rhombus using four segments from a strand of spaghetti placed end-to-end.

   ii. How many differently shaped rhombi can you build with those four pieces?

   iii. Explain why a rhombus is a kite.

   iv. Explain why a rhombus is a parallelogram.

   v. What additional constraint(s) would you have to build into the definition of a rhombus for it to be a **square**?

Design Characteristics of Triangles and Quadrilaterals The results of your experiments in building triangles and quadrilaterals lead to important physical applications.

5 Working with a partner, use plastic or cardboard strips and paper fasteners to make each of the models shown below.

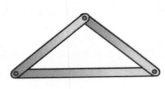 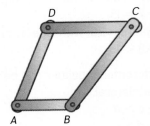

a. Can you change the shape of the triangle model? Can you change any of the features of the model? Explain.

b. What features of the quadrilateral model can you change? What features of the model cannot change?

c. Now add a *diagonal* strip $\overline{BD}$ to your quadrilateral model. What features of this model can change?

d. Triangles are **rigid**. They retain their shape when pressure is applied. Quadrilaterals are rigid when *triangulated* with a diagonal. The process of triangulating is often called *bracing*. How are these facts utilized in the design of the bridge truss shown on page 363?

e. Describe two structures or objects in your community or home that employ the rigidity of triangles in their design.

The nonrigidity of quadrilaterals has important physical applications. For example, mechanical engineers use the flexibility of quadrilaterals in the design of *linkages*.

b. **i.** Students will build a kite using the same spaghetti segments as in Part a, but pairs of equal length pieces will be positioned with a common vertex.

    ii. Students should indicate that an infinite number of kites could be built.

c. **i.** Students will build a rhombus using four equal length spaghetti segments.

    ii. An infinite number of differently-shaped rhombi can be built.

    iii. A rhombus is a kite because it meets the condition "two distinct pairs of consecutive sides the same length." In fact, for a rhombus, any two pairs of distinct consecutive sides are the same length. See the diagram at the right.

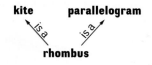

    iv. A rhombus is a parallelogram because opposite sides are the same length.

    v. To build a **square**, you would need to have the additional constraint that one angle be a right angle. (This, in turn, would require that all the angles be right angles.)

5 **a.** You cannot change the shape of the triangle nor any features of the shape. There is only one triangle determined by 3 given side lengths.

b. The angle measures can change, and thus the shape can change. The lengths of the sides remain the same.

c. Once $\overline{BD}$ is added to the model, all features of the quadrilateral are unchangeable.

d. Triangular bracing is seen on the sides, top, and cross spans of the bridge.

e. Students' answers will vary.

NOTE An explanation of the principle behind Grashof's Theorem in Problem 6 is given below.

A four-bar mechanism has at least one revolving link if $s + \ell \le p + q$, where s represents the shortest side in the linkage, ℓ represents the longest side, and p and q represent the remaining two sides. (This condition is necessary but not sufficient.)

Principle 1: When the shortest link is a crank (as in Part a), the mechanism is a crank-rocker mechanism; that is, the shortest crank will rotate 360° while the longer crank will rock back and forth.

Principle 2: When the shortest link is the frame of the mechanism, the mechanism is a double-crank mechanism. (Both cranks will rotate 360°.)

Principle 3: When the shortest link is the coupler, the mechanism is a double-rocker mechanism. (Both cranks will rock.)

In Part a, students consider Principle 1; in Part c, students consider Principle 2. Principle 3 is not considered and is included here to complete Grashof's Theorem. (**Source:** www.cs.cmu.edu/~rapidproto/mechanisms/chpt5.html#HDR69a)

DEFINITION

This definition of **kite** means that a rhombus is a special kite. Some textbooks define a kite in ways that exclude this hierarchy.

CCSS CCSS MATHEMATICAL PRACTICE

In Problem 4, students attend to precision by making explicit use of the definitions of kite and rhombus to think about rigidity of shapes and whether or not a kite is a rhombus and a rhombus is a parallelogram.

DEFINITION

The student-constructed definition of a square in Part cv is a rhombus with a right angle.

6 An important feature of a quadrilateral or 4-bar linkage is that if any side is held fixed so it does not move and another side is moved, then the movement of the remaining sides is completely determined. The side that is fixed is called the *frame*. The two sides attached to the frame are called *cranks*. The crank most directly affected by the user is called the *driver* crank; the other is called the *follower* crank. The side opposite the frame is called the *coupler*.

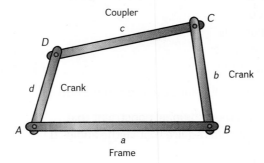

Quadrilateral linkages have different characteristics depending on the lengths *a*, *b*, *c*, *d* of the sides and which side is used as a crank. Explore some of those characteristics using linkage strips or computer software like the "Design a Linkage" custom app.

a. Working with a partner, make several different quadrilateral linkages so that $\overline{AB}$ is the longest side and fixed; $\overline{AD}$ is the shortest side and acts as one of the cranks. Investigate how lengths *a* and *d* are related to lengths *b* and *c* when $\overline{AD}$ can rotate completely. In this case, how does the follower crank move? The coupler? Write a summary of your findings.

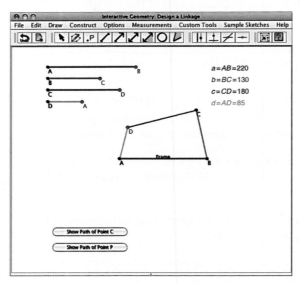

b. The principle you discovered in Part a is called **Grashof's Principle**. How could you use a mechanism satisfying Grashof's Principle to drive the agitator in a washing machine or an automotive windshield wiper?

Lesson 1 | Triangles, Quadrilaterals, and Their Properties **367**

6 | **NOTE** Two parts of Grashof's Theorem are developed in this problem. See page T366 for more information on this theorem.

a. In this case, crank $\overline{AD}$ rotates completely, the follower crank rocks back-and-forth in an arc, and one endpoint of the coupler moves with the rotating crank and one endpoint with the follower crank in an arc. This means that during the motion, part of the coupler goes below the frame and part remains above the frame.

b. An agitator in a washing machine moves back and forth like a rocker, so a rotating crank could be making this motion occur. A windshield wiper goes back and forth in a similar manner.

c. When the shortest side is the frame, both cranks rotate completely.

7 **a.**

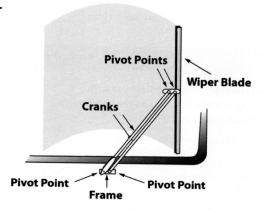

b. It is a parallelogram linkage because both pairs of opposite sides are congruent.

c. The ends of the wiper blade form arcs.

d. When the wiper blade is one-quarter of the way through its cycle, the blade will be vertical and the bottom end of the wiper will be lower than the starting position. When the wiper blade is halfway through its cycle, the blade will still be vertical, and the bottom end will be at a low point of its arc.

e. See the shaded area on the sketch in Part a.

c. Use a quadrilateral linkage satisfying Grashof's Principle to investigate the mechanics of the linkage if the shortest side is used as the frame. Summarize your findings.

7 Examine the bus windshield wiper mechanism shown at the left. The wiper blade is attached to the mechanism in a fixed position.

a. Make a sketch of this mechanism. Label the frame, cranks, and coupler.

b. Explain why this is a parallelogram linkage.

c. As the linkage moves, what paths do the ends of the wiper blade follow?

d. If the wiper blade is vertical (as shown) when the mechanism is at the beginning of a cycle, describe the positions of the blade when the mechanism is one quarter of the way through its cycle and when the mechanism is halfway through its cycle.

e. Sketch the region of the windshield that the blade can keep clean.

SUMMARIZE THE MATHEMATICS

In this investigation, you experimented with building triangles and quadrilaterals with different side lengths. You also investigated how the rigidity of triangles and the nonrigidity of quadrilaterals influence their uses in the design of structures and devices.

a Describe the similarities and differences in what you discovered in your triangle-building and quadrilateral-building experiments.

b Suppose you are told that a triangular garden plot is to have sides of length 5 m, 12 m, and 13 m.

   i. Explain why it is possible to have a triangular plot with these dimensions.

   ii. Explain how you and a partner could lay out such a plot using only a 15-meter tape measure.

   iii. How many differently shaped triangular plots could be laid out with these dimensions? Why?

c What constraints are needed on the lengths of the sides of a quadrilateral for it to be a parallelogram? What additional constraint(s) is (are) needed for it to be a rectangle?

d What does it mean to say that a shape is rigid? How can you make a quadrilateral rigid?

e What must be true about the sides of a quadrilateral linkage if one of the cranks can make a complete revolution? If both cranks can make complete revolutions?

Be prepared to share your ideas and reasoning with the class.

Diane Moore

SUMMARIZE THE MATHEMATICS

a In building the triangles and quadrilaterals, some combinations of side lengths were usable and some were not. When a shape could be found, side lengths satisfied certain inequalities. Side lengths satisfying the Triangle Inequality determined exactly one triangle. A quadrilateral could be built if the sum of the lengths of any three sides is greater than the length of the fourth side. But unlike triangles, differently-shaped quadrilaterals could be formed from identical sets of side lengths, due to angle size differences or a different ordering of side lengths.

b
   i. Such a triangular plot is possible since $5 + 12 > 13, 5 + 13 > 12$, and $12 + 13 > 5$.

   ii. We could measure out a side 13 meters and mark that off. Then we could use 5 meters of the tape to swing an arc of that length from one end of the 13-meter side and then use 12 meters of the 15-meter tape to swing an arc of that length from the other end of the marked segment. The point where the two arcs cross could be connected to both ends of the 13-meter segment to create a garden plot with sides of lengths 5 m, 12 m, and 13 m.

   iii. Only one such plot could be laid out since three sides determine exactly one triangle.

c For a quadrilateral to be a parallelogram, opposite sides must be the same length. For a quadrilateral to be a rectangle, it must first be a parallelogram and then additionally have one right angle which forces all four angles to be right angles. (Some students may refer to a definition of parallelogram as having opposite sides parallel, but hopefully others will remind the class that we are using the side-length definition.)

d A shape is rigid if it remains unchanged when a force or pressure is applied. A quadrilateral can be made rigid by adding a diagonal segment (brace) so that the shape is composed of two triangular pieces.

e If one of the cranks can make a complete revolution, then (1) the sum of the lengths of the shortest and longest sides of the quadrilateral linkage must be less than or equal to the sum of the lengths of the remaining two sides, and (2) the crank that makes a complete revolution must be the shortest side of the quadrilateral linkage.

   In order for both the driver and follower cranks to make complete revolutions, the shortest side must be the frame and the sum of the lengths of the shortest and longest sides must be less than or equal to the sum of the lengths of the other two sides.

PROCESSING PROMPT I helped my group move toward consensus by _____.

NOTE The solutions to Problem 6 Part c and Problem 7 are on page T367.

PROMOTING MATHEMATICAL DISCOURSE

TEACHING RESOURCES

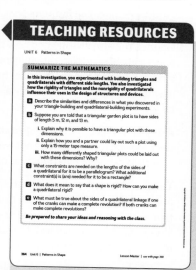

Lesson Master 364
ⓘ **GO DIGITAL**

MATH TOOLKIT

Record your findings related to the Triangle Inequality, its analogue for quadrilaterals, the constraints for parallelogram- and quadrilateral-building, and conditions for 4-bar linkages to have rotating cranks in your math toolkits.

Summarize the Mathematics, *page 368*

Teacher: *(Reading from the book)* In this investigation, you experimented with building quadrilaterals with different side lengths. You also investigated how the rigidity of triangles and the nonrigidity of quadrilaterals influence their use in the design of structures and devices. Describe the similarities and differences in what you discovered in your triangle-building and quadrilateral-building experiments.

Anaya: With both the triangles and quadrilaterals, we were looking for whether or not we could make triangles or quadrilaterals with different sizes of sides.

Teru: Yeah, if we picked any three lengths we couldn't always make a triangle. The sum of any two lengths has to be greater than the third length. And using any four lengths, we couldn't always make a quadrilateral. The sum of any three side lengths of a quadrilateral has to be greater than the fourth side length.

Teacher: Did Teru describe similarities or differences?

Inga: Well, it is the same because one side length must be smaller than all the other side lengths added up in order to make the triangle or quadrilateral. The only difference is in the number of sides.

Jamal: There was another difference too. With triangles, once we made a triangle from three lengths, it was the only triangle shape we could make. Many different quadrilaterals could be made from the same four lengths.

Teacher: Say more about that idea, Jamal.

Jamal: Well, the quadrilateral isn't rigid like the triangle, so you can slide it back and forth. The sides stay the same but the angles change.

Susan: There are really an infinite number of possible quadrilaterals.

Jamal: Exactly. Plus you can rearrange the sides and get a totally different set of quadrilaterals.

Teacher: Good thinking. Now, suppose you are told that a triangular garden plot is to have sides of length 5 m, 12 m, and 13 m. Explain why it is possible to have a triangular plot with these dimensions.

Ivy: Because if you add up the lengths of any two sides it has to be greater than the length of the third side. It's the Triangle Inequality that we found out about when we used spaghetti to build triangles.

Teacher: How could you and a partner lay out such a plot using only a 15-meter tape measure? *(Pause)* No ideas? Take a minute to brainstorm with the person next to you. *(Pause)* Okay, who has a method to propose?

Lance: We could just mark a spot on the ground and use the tape measure to measure off one side of length, say 13 meters. Then we could set the tape measure at 5 meters and make an arc on the ground from one end of the 13-meter side that shows where the 5-meter side could go. Then set the tape measure at 12 meters and make an arc from the other end of the 13-meter side to show where the 12-meter side would go. Wherever the arcs cross would be the third vertex of the triangular plot.

Neil: It is just like what we did with our compasses.

Teacher: Is that the only triangular plot that could be laid out with those dimensions? How many differently-shaped plots could be made?

Logan: There is only one shape that can be made with any three sides.

Teacher: What constraints are needed on the sides of a quadrilateral for it to be a parallelogram? What about the constraints for a rectangle? Share your ideas with the person next to you first, then we will talk about your ideas together.

Teacher: *(After giving students a brief time to share their ideas with a partner)* Okay, how about the constraints needed for a quadrilateral to be a parallelogram?

Anaya: You have to have opposite sides the same length. This is what we did with the rope at the beginning of the lesson.

Teacher: What additional constraints would we need for the parallelogram to be a rectangle?

Teru: We would have to have right angles, too.

Teacher: *(To the class)* What do you think? *(Students indicate verbal and nonverbal agreement.)*

Teacher: Okay, let's think about rigidity. Let's see if we can summarize our ideas from the investigation. What does it mean for a shape to be rigid? How can you make a shape rigid?

Inga: To be rigid just means that the shape can't change. Like if you make a triangle out of linkage strips, it doesn't move. It's rigid.

Jamal: Yeah, we can make the parallelogram rigid by making a rectangle.

Ivy: I don't think so. Remember, if you make a quadrilateral out of linkage strips, you have to make it rigid by adding a diagonal strip. Then you have two triangles, so it's rigid.

Teacher: Earlier, when I observed your groups using the linkage strips, I noticed that each group came to the same conclusion. Are there any questions regarding rigidity that you still have? *(No one offers any questions.)* I wonder if we will be able to use those ideas to make other figures rigid? Let's keep that question in mind while we work on Lessons 2 and 3.

Teacher: To summarize Part e, let's use the "Design a Linkage" custom app. What must be true about the sides of a quadrilateral linkage if one of the cranks can make a complete revolution? What did you find out in your groups?

Bentley: I can come up and demonstrate on the computer.

Teacher: That would be great!

Bentley: Okay. Let's make the frame the longest side and the left crank the shortest side. Then make sure that when we add their lengths together that the total length is shorter than the sum of the other two sides.

Carrie: Or it can be equal to.

Bentley: Right. Thanks, Carrie. Okay, so what we have on the screen now will work because the frame and crank lengths add up to 304.75, and the other two side lengths add up to 316.25. Then, this is the cool part, to see that the crank makes a complete circle, we clicked on the "Show Path of P" button and moved point P to the vertex D. *(As Bentley moves P toward the vertex, the path of P becomes more circular until the point P coincides with the point D and the path of D is revealed as circular.)* There you go. We see that the path is a circle, so the crank makes a complete revolution.

Teacher: Very nice. Did other groups use that feature of the applet? *(Some students indicate they did others indicate they "physically" moved the vertex, thus moving the crank in a circular path.)* Who would like to demonstrate what must be true about the quadrilateral linkage for both cranks to make a complete revolution? *(Many students volunteer; the Teacher selects one.)*

Darla: *(Darla comes up to the computer demo station.)* Okay. We made the frame the shortest side. Actually, this will be easy with the "Show the path of P" feature that Bentley showed us. We also need to click on the "Show the Path of C" button. There, now we have the path of each crank showing up on the screen. We didn't do it this way in our group, but I think what we found out will be more obvious with both paths showing. Let me just make the top segment shorter.

Teacher: Are you referring to the coupler?

Darla: Oh yeah. The coupler. So, just shorten the coupler until we get two circular paths. There. Both paths are circles. So if what we found out in our group is correct, we should have the frame as the shortest side and the total length of the shortest side plus the longest side shorter than or the same as the length of the other two sides added together. Just like Bentley said but with the frame as the shortest side, too. *(Someone from the class indicates that they have checked the lengths and that Darla's conjecture is correct.)*

Teacher: Very nice. *(Then, directed to the whole class)* Did you find the applet helpful? *(Students indicate that they did.)* Were any of you able to access the applet at home? *(The Teacher sees that only a few students accessed the technology at home and makes a mental note to encourage home use and to find other ways to support students' use of applets in future units.)*

✅ CHECK YOUR UNDERSTANDING

Four-bar linkages illustrate how geometric shape and function are related.

a. Examine the adjustable lamp in the diagram. The pivots at the labeled points are snug, but they will allow pivoting to adjust the lamp.

   i. Explain why the parallelogram linkages used in this lamp remain parallelograms as the position of the lamp is adjusted.

   ii. Visualize and describe how the position of the lamp should change as you make parallelogram *AFGC* vertical.

b. Suppose you are given segments of the following lengths: 7, 8, 24, 25.

   i. If possible, sketch and label several different quadrilaterals that can be formed with these side lengths.

   ii. Suppose you build a quadrilateral linkage with consecutive sides of lengths 7, 24, 8, and 25. What can you say about the length of the shortest possible brace that will make the quadrilateral rigid?

   iii. Can a quadrilateral linkage with a rotating crank be constructed from strips of these lengths? Explain your reasoning.

   iv. Can a quadrilateral linkage be made from these strips with two rotating cranks? Explain.

INVESTIGATION 2

Congruent Shapes

Roof trusses are manufactured in different shapes and sizes but they are most often triangular in shape. The "W" or Fink truss shown below is the most widely-used design in building today. The locations of the truss components provide for the most uniform distribution of stresses and forces. The rigidity of triangles is a key element in the design of these trusses. An equally important element is that all trusses for a particular roof are identical or *congruent*.

Lesson 1 | Triangles, Quadrilaterals, and Their Properties **369**

✅ CHECK YOUR UNDERSTANDING

a. **i.** As the position of the lamp changes, the sides of parallelograms *BDEC* and *ACGF* do not change. Hence they will remain parallelograms since both pairs of opposite sides remain equal in length.

   ii. Assuming $\overline{AC}$ and $\overline{FG}$ are parallel to the table, the lamp will move up and to the left.

b. **i.**

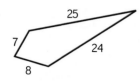
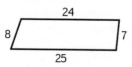

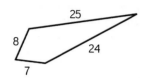
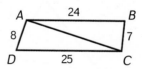

   ii. By the Triangle Inequality, the length of the diagonal plus the length of the shorter of the two sides it connects must be greater than the length of the longer side. For quadrilateral *ABCD*, students may visually recognize that $\overline{AC}$ is the shorter diagonal and reason as follows: $AC + 7 > 24$ and $AC + 8 > 25$, so $AC > 17$.

     (Some students may rule out $\overline{BD}$ as the shortest diagonal by reasoning as follows: $BD + 7 > 25$ and $BD + 8 > 24$, so $BD > 18$ and $BD > 16$. Therefore, $BD > 18$.)

   iii. Yes. A quadrilateral linkage can be made from 7, 8, 24, and 25 lengths, because the sum of the shortest and longest side lengths is equal to the sum of the other two side lengths. Using the shortest side as a crank would result in a mechanism with one rotating crank.

   iv. Yes. Using the shortest side as the frame would result in a mechanism with two rotating cranks.

As you work on the problems of this investigation, look for answers to the following questions:

How can you test whether two shapes are congruent?

What combination of side or angle measures is sufficient to determine if two trusses or other triangular shapes are congruent?

1 As a builder at the home site pictured on page 369, how could you test whether the two trusses standing against the garage wall are congruent? Could you use the same method to test if those two trusses are congruent to the ones already placed in position on the double-car garage?

Congruence of Figures **Congruent figures** have the same shape and size, regardless of *position* or *orientation*. In congruent figures, corresponding segments have the same length and corresponding angles have the same measure. The marks in the diagrams below indicate corresponding side lengths and angle measures that are identical.

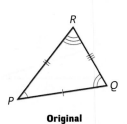

Original

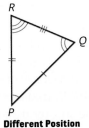

Different Position

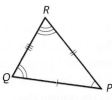

Different Position and Orientation (flipped over)

One way to test for congruence of two figures is to see if one figure can be made to coincide with the other by using a **rigid motion**—slide (*translation*), turn (*rotation about a point*), or flip (*mirror reflection*)—or a sequence of rigid motions. This is, of course, very impractical for large trusses. Your work in the previous investigation suggests an easier method.

2 In Investigation 1, you found that given three side lengths that satisfy the Triangle Inequality, you could build only one triangle.

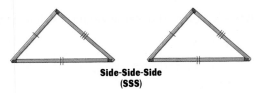

**Side-Side-Side
(SSS)**

a. Explain as carefully as you can why simply measuring the lengths of the three corresponding sides of two triangular roof trusses is sufficient to determine if the trusses are congruent.

b. Could you test if the two trusses are congruent by measuring the lengths of just two corresponding sides? Explain.

c. Could you test if two trusses are congruent by some other method? Explain.

Congruent Shapes

The approach to congruence taken in this investigation is that two figures are congruent provided they have the same shape and size regardless of position or orientation. Students experiment with minimal sets of conditions for triangle congruence. They build two triangles with a set of specified side lengths and/or angle measures (e.g., SAS condition). They then test for congruence using a rigid motion or a sequence of rigid motions to determine whether or not the two triangles coincide (the principle of superposition). Once the conditions for triangle congruence are discovered and verified through additional examples, the conditions are used to reason about properties of triangles and special quadrilaterals and to solve applied problems.

After students discover and verify the SSS, SAS, and ASA congruence conditions for triangles, they revisit the idea that the sum of the measures of the three angles of a triangle is 180° and observe that there is not an AAA congruence condition for triangles. They are introduced to the form of "If ... then" reasoning in the context of using congruent triangles to show that the base angles of an isosceles triangle are congruent.

Congruence of two-dimensional shapes is revisited in Course 2 in terms of coordinate representations of rigid motions. In Course 3, congruence is formally developed as a special case of similarity.

1 Measure to make certain that corresponding sides of the trusses have the same length and corresponding angles have the same measure. The same method could be used to test the congruence of those two trusses with the ones above the double-car garage. For the ones against the wall, place one directly in front of or on top of the other and see if they match perfectly.

2 **a.** Students should recognize that when they had 3 spaghetti segments, they could only make one triangle shape. They might explain by saying something like the following. Once you choose any one length to construct the triangle, the remaining lengths must be attached to that side. The other ends of these two sides will meet at a point to form the triangle. If instead you place the two sides on opposite ends of the first segment, you get a triangle of the same shape but with a different orientation. Since only one triangle can be formed with 3 given lengths, all triangles built with those same segments are congruent (as the trusses are in this example).

b. No. Two corresponding sides could be the same length but the angle between them quite different, which would then require the third side of the two triangles to be different in length.

c. If students are looking at the diagram in the student text, they may suggest only sliding one triangle onto the other to check congruence. If so, ask them if they can sketch two congruent triangles in positions that would require other rigid motions or more than one rigid motion. Although, in some cases, the SSS congruence condition can be verified with 1 or 2 rigid motions, in general, it can be tested using the 3 motions described in Problem 3 Part a.

Conditions for Congruence of Triangles In the following problems, you will explore other combinations of side lengths and angle measures that would provide a simple test of whether two triangular roof trusses are congruent.

3 Use the "Triangle Congruence" custom app to conduct the following triangle-building experiments. For each condition in Parts a–c:

- Try to build a triangle satisfying the given condition. You choose segment lengths and angle measures.

- If a triangle can be built, try to build another with the same three conditions.

- Use rigid motions to test if your two triangles are congruent. If the triangles are congruent, describe the rigid motions(s) that were involved in your test.

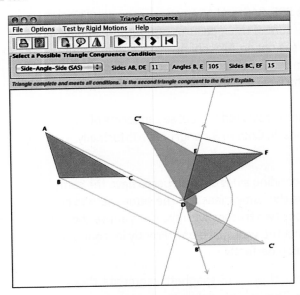

- Make a note if the condition could be used to test for congruence of two triangles.

For each experiment, compare your findings with your classmates and resolve any differences. Keep a record of your agreed-upon findings. Include sketches of the shapes you make.

a. *Side-Angle-Side (SAS) Condition*: You know the lengths of two sides and the measure of the angle between the two sides.

b. *Side-Side-Angle (SSA) Condition*: You know the lengths of two sides and the measure of an angle not between the two sides.

c. *Angle-Side-Angle (ASA) Condition*: You know the measures of two angles and the length of the side between the two angles.

3 **a.** The Side-Angle-Side (SAS) congruence condition determines exactly one triangle. The rigid motions that map the first triangle *ABC* into the second triangle *DEF* are shown below.

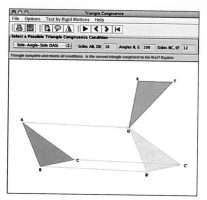

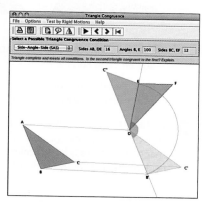

A slide of vertex *A* of the first triangle to corresponding vertex *D* of the second triangle

A turn of vertex *B'* or side $\overline{DB'}$ to the corresponding side $\overline{DE}$ of the second triangle

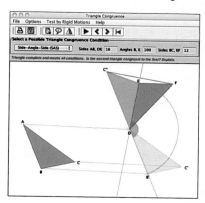

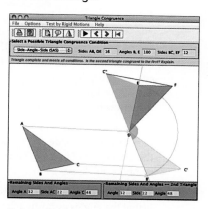

A flip of the first triangle over the line $\overleftrightarrow{DE}$

Select "Show Measurements" under the Option menu for more details.

b. The Side-Side-Angle (SSA) congruence condition does not always determine exactly one triangle. See the example at the right.

c. The same rigid motions described in Part a verify the ASA congruence conditions.

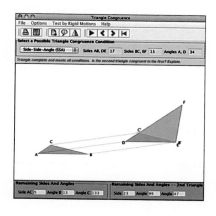

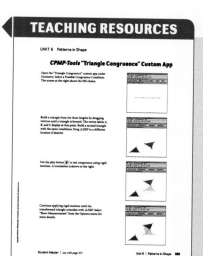

4 You may recall from your prior mathematics study that the sum of the measures of the angles of a triangle is 180°.

   a. How is this **Triangle Angle Sum Property** demonstrated by folding a paper model of a triangle as shown below?

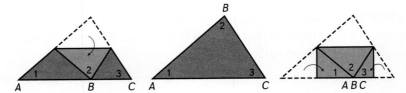

   b. Using a protractor and ruler, carefully draw a triangle with angle measures 40°, 60°, and 80°.

   c. Could a building contractor test whether two triangular roof trusses are congruent by measuring only the corresponding angles? Explain.

5 **Triangles at Work** The Kingpost truss shown below is used primarily for support of single-car garages or short spans of residential construction. The shape of the truss is an isosceles triangle. The support brace $\overline{BD}$ connects the peak of the truss to the midpoint of the opposite side.

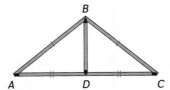

   a. How are the specifications (given info) for this truss shown in the diagram?

   b. Based on the specifications for this truss and the results of your experiments, explain as carefully as you can why △ABD is congruent to △CBD, written △ABD ≅ △CBD. (The congruence notation always lists the letters for corresponding vertices in the same order.)

   c. To properly support the roof, it is important that the brace $\overline{BD}$ is perpendicular to side $\overline{AC}$. Based on your work in Part b, explain why the placement of brace $\overline{BD}$ guarantees that $\overline{BD}$ is perpendicular to $\overline{AC}$ (in symbols, $\overline{BD} \perp \overline{AC}$).

   d. An important property of the Kingpost truss, and *any* isosceles triangle, is that the angles opposite the congruent sides (called **base angles**) are congruent. How does your work in Part b guarantee that ∠A ≅ ∠C?

6 Study the diagram below of a "W" truss. △ABC is an isosceles triangle. Points D, E, F, and G are marked on the truss so that $\overline{CG} \cong \overline{BF}$ and $\overline{CD} \cong \overline{BE}$.

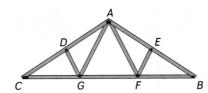

4 **a.** The three angles in the triangle are positioned at the same vertex so that their sum creates a straight angle (180°).

b. Students will have carefully drawn a triangle with angle measures of 40°, 60°, and 80°.

c. No. Triangles with different corresponding side lengths can be constructed given the measures of three angles.

5 **a.** The single tick marks show the two congruent sides of the isosceles triangle. The double tick marks show the two congruent segments, AD and DC, formed by the support brace located at the midpoint of $\overline{AC}$.

b. Since the truss has two corresponding sides the same length and one side in common, $\triangle ABD \cong \triangle CBD$ by the SSS condition.

c. From Part b, the two angles at point D are congruent because they are corresponding angles in the congruent triangles ABD and CBD. These angles also sum to 180°; therefore, both angles must measure 90°, making $\overline{BD} \perp \overline{AC}$.

d. $\angle A$ and $\angle C$ are corresponding angles of the congruent triangles ABD and CBD and are, therefore, congruent.

6 **a.**

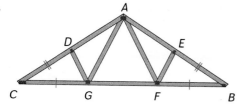

INSTRUCTIONAL NOTE

Students are building careful reasoning skills. Not all students need to master these reasoning skills at this point.

b. Since the angles at B and C are base angles of isosceles triangle ABC, they are congruent. So, $\triangle DCG \cong \triangle EBF$ by SAS. This means that the braces of the truss $\overline{DG}$ and $\overline{EF}$ must be cut equal in length.

a. On a copy of the truss, use tick marks to show the given information.

b. When building the truss, explain as carefully as you can why braces $\overline{DG}$ and $\overline{EF}$ should be cut the same length.

c. Should braces $\overline{AG}$ and $\overline{AF}$ be cut the same length? Explain your reasoning.

SUMMARIZE THE MATHEMATICS

In this investigation, you used rigid motions to help discover combinations of side lengths or angle measures that were sufficient to determine if two triangles were congruent. You also explored how you could use congruent triangles to reason about properties of an isosceles triangle.

a Which sets of conditions—SSS, SAS, SSA, ASA, and AAA—can be used to test if two triangles are congruent?

b For each triangle congruence condition, what rigid motion or sequence of rigid motions was used to verify the condition?

c Write each *Triangle Congruence Condition* in words and illustrate with a diagram.

d If $\triangle PQR \cong \triangle XYZ$, what segments are congruent? What angles are congruent?

e Describe properties of an isosceles triangle that you know by definition or by reasoning.

Be prepared to share your ideas and reasoning with the class.

✅ CHECK YOUR UNDERSTANDING

Wood trusses commonly employ two or more triangular components in their construction. For each truss below, examine the two labeled triangular components. Is enough information provided for you to conclude that the triangles are congruent? Explain your reasoning.

a.
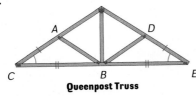
Queenpost Truss

b.
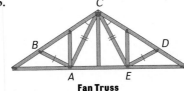
Fan Truss

c.
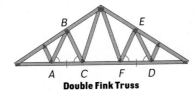
Double Fink Truss

d.
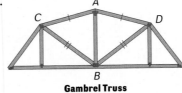
Gambrel Truss

c. Yes. $\overline{AC} \cong \overline{AB}$, $\angle B \cong \angle C$, and $\overline{CG} \cong \overline{BF}$. So, $\triangle ACG \cong \triangle ABF$ by SAS. This means that the braces $\overline{AG}$ and $\overline{AF}$ must be cut equal in length.

NOTE The solutions to Problem 6 Parts a and b are on page T372.

SUMMARIZE THE MATHEMATICS

a SSS, SAS, ASA

b The same three rigid transformations as described in Problem 3 Part a (page T371) will verify the SSS, SAS, and ASA congruence conditions. In some cases, all three motions are not required for two congruent triangles to coincide.

c If three sides of a triangle are congruent to the corresponding sides of another triangle, then the two triangles are congruent. For example, $\triangle ABC \cong \triangle DEF$.

    If two sides and the angle between the sides of one triangle are congruent to the corresponding parts of another triangle, then the two triangles are congruent. For example, $\triangle ABC \cong \triangle DEF$.

    If two angles and the side between the angles of one triangle are congruent to the corresponding parts of another triangle, then the two triangles are congruent. For example, $\triangle ABC \cong \triangle DEF$.

d 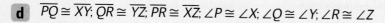 $\overline{PQ} \cong \overline{XY}$; $\overline{QR} \cong \overline{YZ}$; $\overline{PR} \cong \overline{XZ}$; $\angle P \cong \angle X$; $\angle Q \cong \angle Y$; $\angle R \cong \angle Z$

e By definition, at least two sides of an isosceles triangle are equal in length. The two base angles of an isosceles triangle are congruent. (Some students might note that the line from the midpoint of the base to the opposite vertex is perpendicular to the base (i.e., the median to the base is an altitude). This is developed in Investigation 3 so you need not mention it here.)

Lesson Master 366
GO DIGITAL

MATH TOOLKIT

Summarize the three sets of Triangle Congruence Conditions and properties of isosceles triangles. Use diagrams to clarify your summaries.

✔️ CHECK YOUR UNDERSTANDING

a. Yes. $\triangle ACB \cong \triangle DEB$ by the SAS congruence condition.

b. No. SSA is not a congruence condition.

c. Yes. $\triangle ABC \cong \triangle FED$ by the ASA congruence condition.

d. Yes. $\triangle ABC \cong \triangle ABD$ by the SSS congruence condition.

INVESTIGATION 3

Reasoning with Shapes

In your work with the Kingpost truss, you discovered some important properties of isosceles triangles—not by conducting experiments and looking for patterns but by careful reasoning from statements of facts that you and your classmates already understand and agree on. As you work on problems of this investigation, look for answers to the following questions:

What strategies are useful in reasoning about properties of shapes?

What are some additional properties of triangles and quadrilaterals that have important applications?

1 As you may recall, the support brace $\overline{BD}$ of a Kingpost truss as shown below on the left connects the peak of the truss to the midpoint of the opposite side. You used congruent triangles to show that $\overline{BD} \perp \overline{AC}$. In this case, $\overline{BD}$ is said to be a **perpendicular bisector** of $\overline{AC}$, that is $\overline{BD} \perp \overline{AC}$ at the midpoint D of $\overline{AC}$.

To design a Kingpost truss that has the same *span* $\overline{AC}$, but less *pitch* (slope), Beth located point E on the perpendicular bisector of $\overline{AC}$ as shown below on the right.

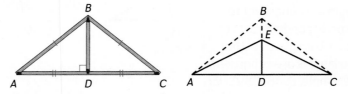

She was confident that the new truss would still be an isosceles triangle. She reasoned as follows:

> I need to show that $\overline{EA} \cong \overline{EC}$. Consider $\triangle ADE$ and $\triangle CDE$.
> Since $\overline{ED}$ is the $\perp$ bisector of $\overline{AC}$, $\angle ADE$ and $\angle CDE$ are right angles and $\overline{AD} \cong \overline{CD}$. The triangles share $\overline{ED}$.
> So, $\triangle ADE \cong \triangle CDE$.
> Since corresponding parts of congruent triangles are congruent, $\overline{EA} \cong \overline{EC}$.

a. Is Beth's reasoning correct? How does she know that $\triangle ADE \cong \triangle CDE$?

b. On a copy of the diagram above on the left, design a new truss that has the same span but greater pitch by locating a point F on the line $\overleftrightarrow{BD}$. Explain carefully why your truss is an isosceles triangle.

c. Explain why *any* point on the perpendicular bisector of a segment will be equally distant from the endpoints of the segment.

Reasoning with Shapes

In this investigation, students are provided further opportunities to use congruent triangles in reasoning about geometric properties. They establish an important property of the perpendicular bisector of a segment. They also provide arguments for select properties of parallelograms, rectangles, and kites. In keeping with the earlier focus on segment lengths determining shapes, students explore how information about diagonals can be used to test whether a quadrilateral is a parallelogram and a rectangle.

A key idea for students to develop is that one very useful way of showing that two segments are the same length or that two angles have the same measure is to identify triangles that have these segments or angles as corresponding parts and then establish that the two triangles are congruent. The result follows from the fact that corresponding parts of congruent triangles are congruent.

Students should *not* be expected to have mastery of reasoning with congruent triangles at this point. However, they should begin to understand and appreciate this kind of reasoning and be able to apply the geometric properties that are established. A more formal development of mathematical reasoning and proof, including the role of postulates and logical inference patterns, is the focus of the first unit of Course 3, *Reasoning and Proof.* Congruence and similarity of triangles will be examined in much more depth in the *Similarity and Congruence* unit in *Core-Plus Mathematics,* Course 3.

1 **a.** Yes, Beth's reasoning is correct. Beth knows $\triangle ADE \cong \triangle CDE$ by the SAS congruence condition.

b.

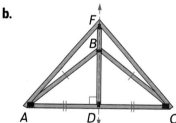

$\overline{FD}$ (or $\overline{BD}$) is a perpendicular bisector of $\overline{AC}$, so m$\angle ADF =$ m$\angle CDF = 90°$. The triangles share $\overline{FD}$ and $\overline{AD} \cong \overline{CD}$. So, $\triangle ADF \cong \triangle CDF$ by the SAS congruence condition. Since corresponding parts of congruent triangles are congruent, $\overline{FA} \cong \overline{FC}$. This means that $\triangle AFC$ is an isosceles triangle.

c. The distance from the endpoints to any point on the perpendicular bisector is the length of the corresponding sides of the two congruent triangles. The reasoning in Parts a and b is valid for any point on the perpendicular bisector of $\overline{AC}$. Therefore, any point on the perpendicular bisector of $\overline{AC}$ will be equally distant from the endpoints of the segment.

2 The truss shown at the right is often used for portions of a house in which a sloped interior ceiling is desired. It is designed so that $\overline{AB} \cong \overline{CB}$ and $\overline{AD} \cong \overline{CD}$.

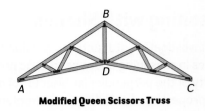

Modified Queen Scissors Truss

    a. How could you reason with congruent triangles to explain why $\angle ABD \cong \angle CBD$?

    b. What other pairs of angles in the truss must also be congruent? Why?

Connecting Quadrilaterals and Triangles In Investigation 1, you found that you could make a quadrilateral linkage rigid by adding a diagonal brace. Diagonals are also helpful in reasoning about properties of quadrilaterals.

3 Recall that by definition of a parallelogram, opposite sides are the same length, or congruent.

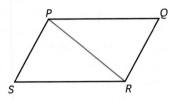

    a. On a copy of parallelogram *PQRS*, use tick marks to indicate segments that are congruent.

    b. Provide an argument to justify the statement:

> *A diagonal of a parallelogram divides the*
> *parallelogram into two congruent triangles.*

    c. Angles in a parallelogram like $\angle Q$ and $\angle S$ are called **opposite angles**.

        i. Explain why $\angle Q \cong \angle S$.

        ii. What reasoning would you use to show that the other pair of opposite angles, $\angle P$ and $\angle R$, are congruent? Compare your argument with others.

    d. What is the sum of the measures of the angles of $\square PQRS$? Give reasons that support your answer.

    e. Would your answer and reasons in Part d change if the figure were a quadrilateral but *not* a parallelogram? Explain your reasoning.

4 Information on diagonal lengths can be used to test whether a quadrilateral is a special quadrilateral. The diagram below shows results of three trials of an experiment with two linkage strips fastened at their midpoints.

    a. In each case, what appears to be true about the quadrilateral that has the given strips as its diagonals? Do you think the same conclusion would hold if you conducted additional trials of the experiment?

2 **a.** Triangles *ABD* and *CBD* share side $\overline{BD}$. So, $\triangle ABD \cong \triangle CBD$ by the SSS congruence condition. Then $\angle ABD \cong \angle CBD$ because they are corresponding angles of congruent triangles.

    b. $\angle A \cong \angle C$; $\angle ADB \cong \angle CDB$. These angles are also corresponding angles of $\triangle ABD$ and $\triangle CBD$.

3 **a.**

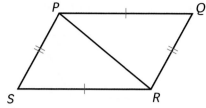

    b. $\triangle PRS \cong \triangle RPQ$ by the SSS congruence condition since $\overline{RS} \cong \overline{PQ}$, $\overline{PS} \cong \overline{RQ}$, and the triangles share side $\overline{PR}$.

    c.   **i.** $\angle Q \cong \angle S$ because they are corresponding angles of congruent triangles.

        ii. Some students might reason that they could use similar logic to find $\triangle QRS \cong \triangle SPQ$ if they were to draw in diagonal $\overline{QS}$ instead of $\overline{PR}$. Others might use corresponding angles of congruent triangles to reason that $m\angle SPR = m\angle QRP$ and $m\angle PRS = m\angle RPQ$, so their sums must be equal. Hence $m\angle SPR + m\angle RPQ = m\angle QRP + m\angle PRS$. So, $\angle P \cong \angle R$.

    d. 360°. Since a diagonal of a parallelogram divides the parallelogram into two triangles (each with an angle sum of 180°), the sum of the angles of the parallelogram must be 2(180°) = 360°.

    e. No. Any diagonal of a (convex) quadrilateral will divide the quadrilateral into two triangles. Therefore, the sum of the angles will be 360°.

4 **a.** All three quadrilaterals appear to be parallelograms.

Parts b–e will provide you a guide to preparing a supporting argument for the statement:

If the diagonals of a quadrilateral bisect each other,
then the quadrilateral is a parallelogram.

b. Study this diagram of a quadrilateral with diagonals that bisect each other.

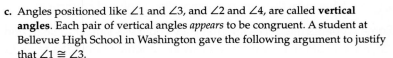

   i. Are pairs of segments given as congruent properly marked? Explain.

   ii. To show quadrilateral *ABCD* is a parallelogram, you must show that opposite sides are the same length. To show that opposite sides $\overline{AB}$ and $\overline{CD}$ are congruent, what triangles would you try to show are congruent? What additional information would you need?

c. Angles positioned like ∠1 and ∠3, and ∠2 and ∠4, are called **vertical angles**. Each pair of vertical angles *appears* to be congruent. A student at Bellevue High School in Washington gave the following argument to justify that ∠1 ≅ ∠3.

   i. Give a reason to support each statement.

m∠1 + m∠2 = 180° (m∠1 is read "measure of ∠1")	**(1)**
m∠2 + m∠3 = 180°	**(2)**
m∠1 + m∠2 = m∠2 + m∠3	**(3)**
m∠1 = m∠3	**(4)**
So, ∠1 ≅ ∠3.	**(5)**

   ii. Use similar reasoning to write an argument justifying that ∠2 ≅ ∠4.

d. Explain why it follows that △*AEB* ≅ △*CED* and △*AED* ≅ △*CEB*.

e. Why can you conclude that $\overline{AB}$ ≅ $\overline{CD}$ and $\overline{AD}$ ≅ $\overline{CB}$? That quadrilateral *ABCD* must be a parallelogram?

5 Diagonal lengths are frequently used in "squaring" building foundations and setting walls in the construction of homes. To square a wall, the bottom plate is held secure and the top of the wall is adjusted until both diagonal measures are the same.

(l r) Matt Meadows

b. **i.** Yes. The diagonals bisect each other, so $\overline{AE} \cong \overline{CE}$ and $\overline{DE} \cong \overline{BE}$.

  ii. Show $\triangle AEB \cong \triangle CED$. You would need $\angle 1 \cong \angle 3$ to use the SAS congruence condition.

c. **i.** (1) Since $\angle 1$ and $\angle 2$ are linear pairs, their angle measures must sum to 180°.
  (2) Since $\angle 2$ and $\angle 3$ are linear pairs, their angle measures must sum to 180°.
  (3) Both expressions are equal to 180°, so they are equal to each other.
  (4) Subtraction Property of Equality
  (5) Definition of congruent angles

  ii. To show that $\angle 2 \cong \angle 4$:
  $$m\angle 2 + m\angle 1 = 180°$$
  $$m\angle 1 + m\angle 4 = 180°$$
  $$m\angle 2 + m\angle 1 = m\angle 1 + m\angle 4$$
  $$m\angle 2 = m\angle 4$$
  $$\angle 2 \cong \angle 4$$

d. $\triangle AEB \cong \triangle CED$ by the SAS congruence condition.
  $\triangle AED \cong \triangle CEB$ by the SAS congruence condition.

e. $\overline{AB}$ and $\overline{CD}$, and $\overline{AD}$ and $\overline{CB}$ are corresponding parts of congruent triangles, so they are congruent. If both pairs of opposite sides of a quadrilateral are congruent, the quadrilateral is a parallelogram.

INSTRUCTIONAL NOTE One of the challenges for students in preparing deductive arguments is deciding where to begin. After students have completed Problem 4, discuss with the class the value of planning an argument *before* trying to write it. A useful strategy of "working backward from the desired conclusion" is illustrated in Part bii. To work backward from a conclusion, students should ask themselves:

(1) What definition or fact do I know that would allow me to conclude what I'm asked to show? (In this case, that quadrilateral *ABCD* is a parallelogram.) State that answer in terms of a labeled diagram.

(2) What definition or fact do I know that would allow me to establish the condition(s) identified in (1)? (In this case, that $\overline{AB} \cong \overline{CD}$ and $\overline{AD} \cong \overline{BC}$.)

(3) Continue working backward by repeating Step 2 as needed. When students arrive at the given facts (in this case, that $\overline{AE} \cong \overline{CE}$ and $\overline{BE} \cong \overline{DE}$), they can then reason with the conditions in reverse order.

After planning an argument, "working forward from given information" is a useful strategy. For example, the argument in Part c justifying that vertical angles are congruent depended on recognizing that the given angles ($\angle 1$ and $\angle 3$) each form a line when paired with $\angle 2$ and reasoning from there. Encourage students to think about a plan for proof before starting to write an argument to justify a conjecture or claim.

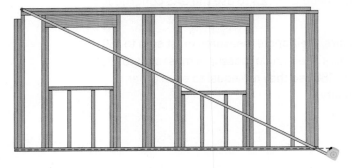

a. Assuming the top and bottom plates are the same length and the two wall studs at the ends are the same length, explain as carefully as you can why the statement, "If the diagonals are the same length, then the wall frame is a rectangle," is true. Your explanation should include a labeled diagram, a statement of what information is given in terms of the diagram, and supporting reasons for your statements.

b. Compare your argument with others. Correct any errors in reasoning.

SUMMARIZE THE MATHEMATICS

In this investigation, you used Triangle Congruence Conditions to support your reasoning about properties of figures.

a What is true about any point on the perpendicular bisector of a segment? How is this related to congruence of triangles?

b What is the sum of the measures of the interior angles of any quadrilateral? How could you convince others of this property?

c What are some special properties of parallelograms? Of rectangles? How are these properties related to congruence of triangles?

d What are some general strategies to consider when trying to establish properties of figures by reasoning?

Be prepared to share your ideas with the class.

✔ CHECK YOUR UNDERSTANDING

Refer to kite *ABCD* with diagonal $\overline{AC}$ shown at the right.

a. Use careful reasoning to explain why ∠1 ≅ ∠2 and ∠3 ≅ ∠4.

b. What must be true about the shorter diagonal $\overline{DB}$? Why?

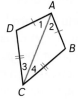

5 **a.**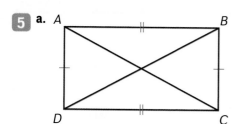

Since $\overline{AB} \cong \overline{CD}$ and $\overline{AD} \cong \overline{CB}$, $ABCD$ is a parallelogram. Since $\overline{AC} \cong \overline{BD}$, $\triangle ABC \cong \triangle BAD$ by the SSS congruence condition. $\angle CBA \cong \angle DAB$ since corresponding parts of congruent triangles are congruent.

$\angle CBA \cong \angle ADC$ and $\angle DAB \cong \angle BCD$ because they are opposite angles of a parallelogram. This means that all four angles are congruent. Since they sum to 360°, each angle is 90°. So, $ABCD$ is a rectangle.

b. Students should compare their reasoning.

SUMMARIZE THE MATHEMATICS

a Any point on the perpendicular bisector of a segment is an equal distance from the endpoints of the segment. If a point on the perpendicular bisector is joined to the endpoints of the segment, two congruent triangles are formed (SAS). So the corresponding sides are congruent.

b The sum of the measures of the interior angles of any quadrilateral is 360°. A convincing argument can be made by drawing one of the diagonals of the quadrilateral. Two triangles are formed, each with an angle sum of 180°, and 2(180°) = 360°.

c Special properties of parallelograms:

- Opposite sides are congruent.
- Each diagonal divides the parallelogram into 2 congruent triangles.
- Opposite angles are congruent.

Special properties of rectangles:

- Rectangles have all of the properties of parallelograms.
- All angles are right angles.

Many of these properties are justified using congruent triangles.

d General strategies are to make a diagram, label information you know on the diagram, and think about other related facts you know that might help to show the property is true. Often it is helpful to try to identify triangles that can be shown to be congruent and reason with corresponding sides or angles.

INSTRUCTIONAL NOTE

This problem could be used as an opportunity for individual students or small groups of students to present their planning strategy and prepared argument to the whole class.

CCSS MATHEMATICAL PRACTICE

Problem 5 is one example of when students attend to precision, construct an argument, and critique the reasoning of others. See Lesson 3 Reflections Task 18 on page 451.

TEACHING RESOURCES

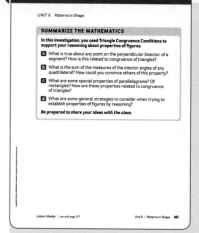

Lesson Master 367
⏻ GO DIGITAL

MATH TOOLKIT

Summarize the properties of parallelograms and rectangles. (Suggest that students leave some space to add other properties they might deduce in the On Your Own tasks.)

NOTE The solution to the Check Your Understanding is on page T378.

INVESTIGATION 4

Getting the Right Angle

Your work on problems in the previous investigations illustrated three important aspects of doing mathematics—experimenting, reasoning from accepted facts to new information, and applying those ideas to practical problems. In your triangle-building experiments, you discovered patterns that suggested the reasonableness of the Triangle Inequality and the Triangle Congruence Conditions. Using various congruence conditions, you were able to carefully reason to properties of special triangles and quadrilaterals. You then applied those properties to a variety of problems. Keep these aspects of doing mathematics in mind as you complete this investigation.

1 Bridging, shown in the diagram below, provides stability between adjacent floor joists. It is generally used when floor spans are greater than 8 feet. If the floor joists are set approximately 16 inches apart, to what length should the bridging be cut? Why should all pieces be cut the same length?

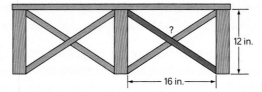

In working on Problem 1, you likely used a special property of right triangles—the *Pythagorean Theorem*. Your work on the remaining problems of this investigation will help you answer these questions:

> *Why is the Pythagorean Theorem true for all right triangles?*
> *Is the converse of the Pythagorean Theorem true and, if so, why?*

The Pythagorean Theorem is often used to calculate the length of the hypotenuse of a right triangle. You can also think of the **Pythagorean Theorem** as a statement of a relationship among areas of three squares.

For any right triangle, the area of the square built on the hypotenuse is equal to the sum of the areas of the squares built on the two legs.

$$a^2 + b^2 = c^2$$

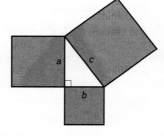

The Greek philosopher Pythagoras (572–497 B.C.) is sometimes credited with first providing a general argument for why this relationship is true for all right triangles. However, the oldest recorded justification is found in an ancient Chinese manuscript written more than 500 years before Pythagoras. The ancient Babylonians and Egyptians also discovered special cases of the relationship.

Matt Meadows

UNIT 6

a. $\overline{AD} \cong \overline{AB}$ and $\overline{BC} \cong \overline{DC}$. $\overline{AC}$ is shared by $\triangle ABC$ and $\triangle ADC$. Thus, $\triangle ABC \cong \triangle ADC$ by the SSS congruence condition. So, $\angle 1 \cong \angle 2$ and $\angle 3 \cong \angle 4$ because they are corresponding parts of congruent triangles.

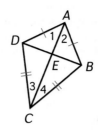

b. $\overline{AD} \cong \overline{AB}$ and $\angle 1 \cong \angle 2$. $\triangle AED$ and $\triangle AEB$ share side $\overline{AE}$. So, $\triangle AED \cong \triangle AEB$ by the SAS congruence condition. From this, students might recognize:

(1) $\overline{DB}$ is perpendicular to $\overline{AC}$. ($\angle AED \cong \angle AEB$ and sum to 180°.)

(2) $\overline{DB}$ is bisected by $\overline{AC}$. ($\overline{DE} \cong \overline{BE}$)

(3) Alternatively, without using the congruent triangles, but using the Triangle Inequality, students might indicate that $DB < DA + AB$.

INSTRUCTIONAL NOTE

The property that one diagonal of a kite is a perpendicular bisector of the other diagonal is justified in Part b. Be sure students recognize this property. In Connections Task 12, they will consider the converse of this property.

INVESTIGATION 4 CCSS G-CO.10, G-SRT.5, A-CED.1, F-IF.4, G-MG.3, S-ID.6

Getting the Right Angle

The Pythagorean Theorem and its converse are the most frequently used theorems from elementary geometry. This investigation assumes students are familiar with the Pythagorean Theorem from their prior study of mathematics in middle school. Here, students examine why the Pythagorean Theorem and its converse are true. Students provide an argument that justifies the Pythagorean Theorem by finding the area of a square in two different ways. They construct triangles and use careful reasoning to verify the converse of the Pythagorean Theorem in a specific case and then use similar reasoning to establish the general case.

1 The bridging should be cut to 20 inches because it is the length of the hypotenuse of a right triangle with legs of length 12 in. and 16 in. and $\sqrt{12^2 + 16^2} = 20$. Each piece should be cut the same length because each of the segments are corresponding parts of congruent right triangles. (This is a specific example of the result that the diagonals of a rectangle are congruent.)

Since there are infinitely many right triangles, it would be impossible to check that $a^2 + b^2 = c^2$ for all of them. Pythagoras's argument, like that outlined in Problem 2, involves reasoning from known facts rather than relying on patterns in specific right triangles. In Problem 2, the argument involves finding the area of the same square *PQRS* in two different ways.

2 Study the diagrams below of a right triangle, a square built on the hypotenuse of the triangle, and an arrangement of congruent copies of the triangle around the square.

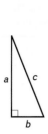 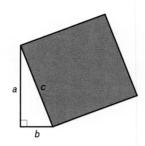 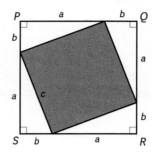

a. Explain as carefully as you can why quadrilateral *PQRS* is a square. Your explanation should include how you know that the sides are straight line segments.

b. Describe two ways to calculate the area of square *PQRS*.

c. Now study the following diagram, which shows another way of thinking about the area of square *PQRS*.

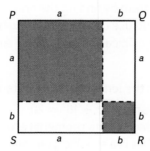

On a copy of this diagram, add two line segments to create four right triangles congruent to the original right triangle. Explain how you know that the triangles are congruent.

d. Place a copy of the right-most diagram above Part a side-by-side with your modification of the diagram in Part c.

  i. How do the areas of the two large squares compare?

  ii. Suppose you remove the four congruent triangles from each of the diagrams. What can you say about the areas of the remaining pieces?

  iii. Explain as precisely as you can what you have shown.

Lesson 1 | Triangles, Quadrilaterals, and Their Properties **379**

2 **a.** $m\angle 1 + m\angle 2 = 90°$ because these angles are the acute angles of a right triangle. This means that all three angle measures add to 180° and $\overline{PS}$ is a straight line segment. The same is true for the other three sides. *PQRS* is a square because all angles are right angles and all sides are of equal length, $a + b$.

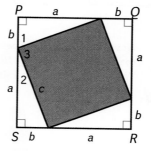

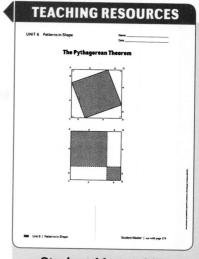
b. The area of square *PQRS* can be found by:

- adding the areas of the 5 polygons that form the larger square.

- multiplying the length of a side of the square by itself.

(Students will use these ideas in Connections Task 19 on page 391 as another way to develop the Pythagorean Theorem.)

c. The four triangles are congruent because each triangle has a right angle and legs of length a and b (SAS condition).

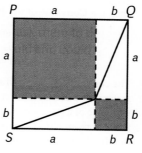

INSTRUCTIONAL NOTE

Students should recall the formulas for, and processes to find, the area of a square and the area of a right triangle. It is highly likely that at least one person in each group will know how to find these areas.

d. **i.** The areas of the two larger squares are the same.

ii. The remaining areas must be the same. (Some students may need to physically remove the congruent triangles by cutting up the larger squares. It is important, however, that they not lose sight of the "bigger picture." They need to keep in mind what they know from part i and reason that starting with equal areas and removing equal areas will result in equal areas left over.)

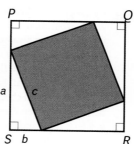

INSTRUCTIONAL NOTE It may be helpful for students to look back at the sketch on page 378 and connect what they find here to the triangle representation of the Pythagorean Theorem.

iii. The area of the largest square with side c is c^2. The areas of the smaller two squares with sides a and b are a^2 and b^2, respectively. The area of the square with side c must be equal to the sum of the areas of the smaller two squares. Hence, $c^2 = a^2 + b^2$.

Now look back at the rope-stretching problem at the beginning of this lesson (page 363). In an attempt to form a right triangle, one group of students at Washington High School stretched the knotted rope as shown below.

They claimed the triangle was a right triangle since $8^2 + 6^2 = 10^2$. These students used the **Converse of the Pythagorean Theorem** in their reasoning:

If the sum of the squares of the lengths of two sides of a triangle equals the square of the length of the third side, then the triangle is a right triangle.

The **converse** of an *if-then* statement reverses the order of the two parts of the statement. Although the converse of the Pythagorean Theorem *is* true, the converse of a true statement may not necessarily be true. For example, consider the statement, "If I'm in math class, then I'm in school," and the converse, "If I'm in school, then I'm in math class." Is the converse necessarily true?

3 **Pythagoras at Work** To lay out a wall perpendicular to an existing wall, a builder measures 3 feet along the base of the existing wall and 4 feet along the floor line where the new wall is to be placed. The builder then checks if the distance between these two points is 5 feet. If so, she knows that the angle between the existing wall and the wall to be constructed is 90°.

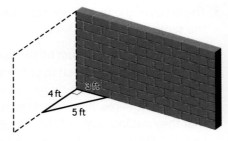

a. Is the builder using the Pythagorean Theorem or the converse of the Pythagorean Theorem? Explain.

b. You can use your understanding of triangle congruence to explain why this "3-4-5 triangle" method guarantees a right angle.

   i. Draw segments of length 3 cm, 4 cm, 5 cm. Then, using a ruler and compass, construct a triangle with these side lengths.

   ii. Use a ruler and protractor to draw a separate 90° angle. From the vertex of the angle, mark off a segment of length 3 cm on a side and of 4 cm on the other side. Connect the two sides to form a right triangle. What should be the length of the hypotenuse?

   iii. Why is the 3-4-5 triangle in part i congruent to the triangle in part ii?

   iv. Why must the 3-4-5 triangle have a right angle? Where is it located?

3 **a.** The builder is using the converse of the Pythagorean Theorem: If $3^2 + 4^2 = 5^2$, then the angle is a right angle.

  b. **i.** Students should use one drawn length and the compass to make intersecting arcs with the other two lengths to form the right triangle.

   ii. 5 cm

   iii. By the SSS congruence condition, the two triangles are congruent.

   iv. The triangle in part i is congruent to the one in part ii which we know has a right angle. The right angle is formed by the sides of lengths 3 and 4. It is opposite the longest side.

c. You can use similar reasoning to show, in general, that if you start with a △ABC where the lengths of its sides *a*, *b*, and *c* satisfy $a^2 + b^2 = c^2$, then you can conclude that △ABC is a right triangle with right angle at C.

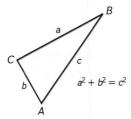

To prove that △ABC is a right triangle, you can reason like you did in Part b.

   i. On a separate sheet of paper, draw and label a *right* triangle with sides (other than the hypotenuse) of the given lengths *a* and *b*.

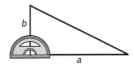

   ii. Write an expression for the length of the hypotenuse of this triangle.

   iii. Why is the triangle you created congruent to the given triangle, △ABC?

   iv. Why must the given triangle, △ABC, be a right triangle? Why is ∠C the right angle?

4 In preparing an architectural drawing of right triangular components of a building, is it possible to draw a triangle congruent to a given *right* triangle under each of the following conditions? In each case, explain your reasoning.

a. You measure the lengths of the two legs of the given right triangle.

b. You measure the lengths of a leg and the hypotenuse of the given right triangle.

Lesson 1 | Triangles, Quadrilaterals, and Their Properties **381**

c. **i.** See student-drawn triangles.

   ii. The length of the hypotenuse is $\sqrt{a^2 + b^2}$ by applying the Pythagorean relation on sides a and b of the student-created right triangle.

   iii. Since the hypotenuse is $\sqrt{a^2 + b^2}$ for $\triangle ABC$ and for the drawn triangle, the two triangles are congruent by use of the SSS condition.

   iv. Since the two triangles are congruent, the corresponding parts are congruent, and $\triangle ABC$ also has a right angle. This right angle is at C because it is formed by the sides of lengths a and b.

4 **a.** Given the lengths of the two legs of a right triangle, it is possible to draw a congruent triangle because a right angle is between the two legs of a right triangle. The triangles would be congruent by the SAS condition. Alternatively, the SSS condition could be used as in Part b. (This is sometimes known as the LL congruence condition for right triangles. LL congruence condition: If the legs of one right triangle are congruent to the corresponding legs of another right triangle, then the triangles are congruent.)

> **NOTE** Problem 4 provides an opportunity to discuss the LL Congruence Conditions for right triangles.

b. Given the lengths of a leg and the hypotenuse of a right triangle, it is possible to draw a congruent triangle. This is true because you can apply the Pythagorean relation to obtain the length of the third side of the right triangle, then use the SSS congruence condition. (HL Congruence condition: If the hypotenuse and a leg of one right triangle are congruent to the hypotenuse and corresponding leg of another right triangle, then the triangles are congruent. HL is not a variant of the previous congruence conditions. If it was given a name, it would be SSA, and earlier we found that this was not a general congruence condition for all triangles.)

SUMMARIZE THE MATHEMATICS

In this investigation, you examined applications of the Pythagorean Theorem and its converse. You also used careful reasoning to provide arguments for why these statements are true.

a Describe the general idea behind your argument that the Pythagorean Theorem is true for all right triangles.

b Describe the general idea behind your argument that the converse of the Pythagorean Theorem is true.

c Give two examples, one mathematical and one not involving mathematics, to illustrate that if a statement is true, its converse may not be true.

d What is the smallest number of side lengths you need to compare in order to test if two right triangles are congruent? Does it make a difference which side lengths you use? Explain.

Be prepared to share ideas and examples with the class.

 CHECK YOUR UNDERSTANDING

In the Think About This Situation at the beginning of this lesson (page 363), you were asked to consider whether four students could form various shapes using a 24-meter loop of knotted rope with knots one meter apart. Reconsider some of those questions using the mathematics you learned in this investigation.

a. Explain how you could use the 24-meter knotted rope to form a right triangle and how you know the shape is a right triangle.

b. Now explain how you could use the 24-meter knotted rope to form a rectangle and how you know that the shape is a rectangle.

c. Look back at your work in Part b. Could you form a second differently shaped rectangle? Explain.

d. Suppose you and two classmates were given a 30-meter loop of rope with knots tied one meter apart. Could you position yourselves so that the resulting triangle is a right triangle? Explain your reasoning.

SUMMARIZE THE MATHEMATICS

a The general idea behind the justification of the Pythagorean Theorem is that you can dissect a square with sides of length $a + b$ two different ways, as shown below at the right. Then you can compare the areas of the pieces of the $(a + b) \times (a + b)$ squares. Comparing, you note that removing four congruent right triangles from each diagram leaves a large $c \times c$ square in one diagram and two smaller $a \times a$ and $b \times b$ squares in the other diagram, so $c^2 = a^2 + b^2$.

b The general idea behind the justification of the converse of the Pythagorean Theorem involves recognizing that if you have a triangle with side lengths a, b, and c that satisfy $a^2 + b^2 = c^2$, then any right triangle that you would make with sides of length a and b would have a hypotenuse of length c (Pythagorean Theorem) and so would be congruent to the triangle with side lengths a, b, and c. Thus, the original triangle must also be a right triangle.

c Possibilities include:

- If you can see, then you have eyes. (true)
  If you have eyes, then you can see. (false)
- If you are in Denver, then you are at an elevation of 1 mile. (true)
  If you are at an elevation of 1 mile, then you are in Denver. (false)
- If a polygon is a square, then it has four sides. (true)
  If a polygon has four sides, then it is a square. (false)
- If $x = -2$, then $x^2 = 4$. (true)
  If $x^2 = 4$, then $x = -2$. (false, could be $x = 2$)
- If two lines are perpendicular, then they intersect at one point. (true)
  If two lines intersect at one point, then they are perpendicular. (false)

d Right triangles can be shown to be congruent by comparing any two corresponding side lengths. Students will likely mention combinations of two legs or a leg and hypotenuse because of their work in Problem 4. These cases are true because knowing you have a right triangle automatically allows you to determine the length of the third side. So, you will know the lengths of all three sides.

It may be necessary to ask students if it is possible to have only one pair of corresponding side lengths of two right triangles to test for congruence. This may prompt them to think about the leg and acute angle case and the hypotenuse and acute angle case. These cases are true because knowing the measure of an acute angle of a right triangle means you know the measures of all three angles. You can then use the ASA condition for congruence.

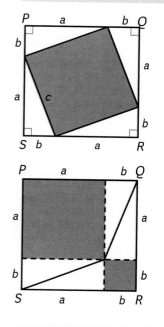

NOTE The solution to the Check Your Understanding is on page T382A.

✅ CHECK YOUR UNDERSTANDING

a. Right triangles with side lengths a, b, and c have to satisfy the conditions $a + b + c = 24$ and $a^2 + b^2 = c^2$. Students may think about this by beginning with a 3-4-5 right triangle and increasing the lengths of the sides that form the right angle. By successively applying the Pythagorean Theorem and checking to see if the sum of the lengths of the three sides is 24, students should identify a 6-8-10 right triangle.

b–c. Students may reason that they could maintain a right angle using a 3-4-5 or 6-8-10 triangle and move farther away or closer to the right angle to lose or gain rope to construct a rectangle. They also may need to check that they maintain the right angle as they move.

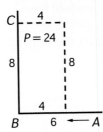

For example, student A moves 2 knots closer to $\angle B$, creating a side of 4 m. Since the opposite side of the rectangle must also be 4 m long, the remaining two sides must have lengths $(24 - 2(4)) \div 2 = 8$ that already exist. Using a fourth student to create the fourth vertex of the rectangle by stretching the additional rope out, students create a 4 m × 8 m rectangle.

Following the same reasoning, student A could move in 1, 3, 4, or 5 knots toward the right angle, forcing student C to move in the necessary amount of knots to use up the 24-meter rope and create a rectangle. Alternatively, the side of length 6 could remain fixed and the sides of length 8 could be reduced to 6 to form a square with perimeter 24.

Other student strategies are possible.

d. $5 + 12 + 13 = 30$ units and $5^2 + 12^2 = 13^2$. By the converse of the Pythagorean Theorem, the triangle formed by positioning so that the three people are 5, 12, and 13 knots apart produces a right triangle.

NOTE Compass and straightedge constructions are provided in the On Your Own assignment set for this lesson. See Applications Tasks 8 and 9.

Constructions provide examples of the creation, analysis, and use of algorithms in geometry. You might have students compare their work with algorithms here with the previous work with algorithms in Unit 4, *Discrete Mathematical Modeling*.

This initial work with constructions will be extended in Course 3.

APPLICATIONS

1 Suppose you are given four segments with lengths 5 cm, 5 cm, 12 cm, 12 cm. Think about building shapes using three or four of these lengths.

a. How many different triangles can you build? Identify any special triangles.

b. Can you build a parallelogram? If so, how many different ones can you build?

c. Can you build a kite? If so, how many different kites can you build?

d. How many different quadrilaterals can you build that are not parallelograms?

2 Four large oil fields are located at the vertices of a quadrilateral *ABCD* as shown. Oil from each of the four fields is to be pumped to a central refinery. To minimize costs, the refinery is to be located so that the amount of piping required is as small as possible.

a. If the refinery is located at position *R*, write an algebraic expression that shows the amount of piping required.

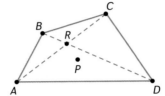

b. For oil fields *A* and *C*, explain why position *R* is a better location for the refinery than position *P*.

c. Explain why position *R* is a better location for the refinery than position *P* in terms of all four oil fields.

d. Is there a better location for the refinery than position *R*? Explain your reasoning.

3 Understanding the body mechanics involved in various physical activities is important to sports physicians and trainers. The diagram at the right shows a person pedaling a bicycle. Key points in the pedaling motion are labeled.

a. What kind of linkage is represented by *ABCD*?

b. Identify the frame, the coupler, the drive crank, and the follower crank.

c. What modifications to the situation would allow it to be modeled by a parallelogram linkage? Should a sports trainer recommend these modifications? Explain your reasoning.

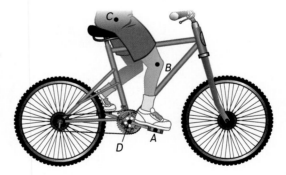

1 **a.** One isosceles triangle can be built with sides 12 cm, 12 cm, and 5 cm.

b. An infinite number of parallelograms can be built.

c. An infinite number of kites can be built.

d. The kite is the only *convex* quadrilateral that is not a parallelogram that can be built. Therefore, from Part c, an infinite number of quadrilaterals that are not parallelograms can be built. (An infinite number of nonconvex quadrilaterals, called darts, can also be built.)

2 **a.** $AR + BR + CR + DR$

b. By the Triangle Inequality, $AP + PC > AC = AR + RC$. So, position R requires less piping than position P.

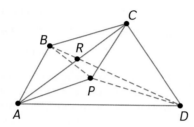

c. $BP + PD > BD = BR + RD$. So, $AP + PC + BP + PD > AR + RC + BR + RD$. Locating the refinery at point R will require less piping.

d. For any other point, the same argument as in Part a would show that R is better. If the point is on one of the diagonals, but not at the intersection of the diagonals, then it is not on the other diagonal. So, one application of the Triangle Inequality shows that the distance has now increased.

3 **a.** Quadrilateral linkage

b. Side CD is the frame, side AB is the coupler, side AD is the driver crank, and CB is the follower crank.

c. CD could be shortened to equal AB and the pedal DA extended to equal CB. A sports trainer would not recommend this adjustment. The pedal would not completely rotate since a person's thigh cannot completely rotate. As is, a person's thigh only needs to make a small arc to continue the pedaling.

ON YOUR OWN

4 A Double Pitch truss, with side lengths and angle measures, is shown below.

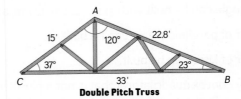

Double Pitch Truss

Which sets of measurements below would be sufficient to test whether a truss *PQR* is congruent to the given truss *ABC*? Explain your reasoning in each case.

a. $PQ = 22.8'$, $PR = 15'$, and $m\angle P = 120°$

b. $PQ = 22.8'$, $PR = 15'$, and $m\angle R = 23°$

c. $RQ = 33'$, $m\angle Q = 23°$, and $m\angle R = 37°$

d. $m\angle P = 120°$, $m\angle R = 37°$, and $m\angle Q = 23°$

e. $PQ = 22.8'$, $RQ = 33'$, and $PR = 15'$

5 Examine each of the following pairs of triangles and the markings that indicate congruence of corresponding angles and sides. In each case, decide whether the information given by the markings ensures that the triangles are congruent. If the triangles are congruent, write the congruence relation and cite an appropriate congruence condition to support your conclusion.

a.

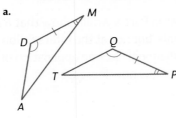

b.

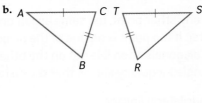

c.

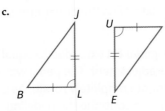

d.

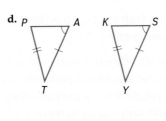

e.

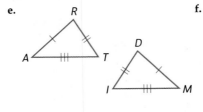

f.

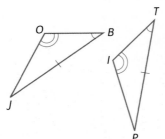

4 **a.** Sufficient by the SAS congruence condition

b. Not sufficient

c. Sufficient by the ASA congruence condition

d. Not sufficient

e. Sufficient by the SSS congruence condition

5 **a.** $\triangle DMA \cong \triangle QPT$ by the ASA congruence condition.

b. The triangles are not necessarily congruent.

c. $\triangle BLJ \cong \triangle SUE$ by the SAS congruence condition.

d. Not necessarily congruent

e. $\triangle ART \cong \triangle MDI$ by the SSS congruence condition.

f. Since $\angle J \cong \angle P$, $\triangle OBJ \cong \triangle ITP$ by the ASA congruence condition.

6 Modified Queenpost trusses are often used for roofs that have wide spans and low pitch.

In manufacturing this particular isosceles triangular truss, the bracing is positioned according to specifications in the diagram below.

a. Explain carefully why braces $\overline{DJ}$ and $\overline{GH}$ should be cut the same length.

b. Explain why braces $\overline{EJ}$ and $\overline{FH}$ should be cut the same length.

c. Give reasons why $\overline{EI}$ and $\overline{FI}$ should be cut the same length.

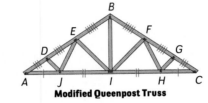

Modified Queenpost Truss

d. Is quadrilateral *EBFI* a special quadrilateral? If so, name it and explain how you know.

7 The diagram below illustrates how a carpenter's square is often used to bisect an angle. (A **bisector of an angle** is a ray that begins at the vertex of the angle and divides the angle into two angles of equal measure.) The square is positioned as shown so that $PQ = RQ$ and $PS = RS$.

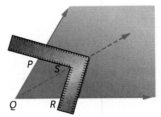

a. Explain why this information is sufficient to conclude that $\triangle PQS \cong \triangle RQS$.

b. Why does ray QS (written $\overrightarrow{QS}$) bisect $\angle PQR$?

UNIT 6

6 **a.** $\triangle ADJ \cong \triangle CGH$ by the SAS congruence condition. So, $\overline{DJ}$ and $\overline{GH}$ must be the same length since they are corresponding parts of congruent triangles. ($\angle A \cong \angle C$ since the truss is isosceles.)

b. $\overline{AE} \cong \overline{CF}$ (since $AD + DE = CG + GF$). So, $\triangle EAJ \cong \triangle FCH$ by the SAS congruence condition. Braces $\overline{EJ}$ and $\overline{FH}$ must be cut the same length because they are corresponding parts of congruent triangles.

c. $\triangle IAE \cong \triangle ICF$ by the SAS congruence condition. So, $\overline{EI}$ and $\overline{FI}$ must be the same length.

d. $EBFI$ is a kite since $\overline{BE} \cong \overline{BF}$ and $\overline{EI} \cong \overline{FI}$.

7 **a.** When you position the carpenter's square so that $PQ = RQ$ and $PS = RS$, you have $\triangle PQS \cong \triangle RQS$ by the SSS congruence condition (since $QS = QS$).

b. Since $\triangle PQS \cong \triangle RQS$, corresponding angles $\angle PQS$ and $\angle RQS$ are congruent.

ON YOUR OWN

8 Draftsmen and industrial designers use a variety of tools in their work. Depending on the nature of the task, these tools vary from sophisticated CAD (computer-assisted design) software to compasses and *straightedges* (rulers with no marks for measuring).

a. Draw an acute angle, ∠ABC. Using a compass, a straightedge, and the algorithm below, construct the bisector of ∠ABC.

Angle Bisector Algorithm: To bisect ∠ABC, do the following.

Step 1: With the compass point at B, draw an arc that intersects $\overrightarrow{BA}$ and $\overrightarrow{BC}$; call the intersection points X and Y, respectively.

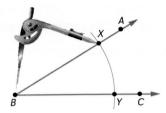

Step 2: With the compass point at point X and using a radius greater than $\frac{1}{2}XY$, draw an arc in the interior of ∠ABC. Then, keeping the same radius, place the compass point at Y and draw a second arc that intersects the first. Label the point of intersection D.

Step 3: Draw the ray $\overrightarrow{BD}$. $\overrightarrow{BD}$ bisects ∠ABC.

b. Explain why this algorithm produces the bisector of ∠ABC. That is, explain how you know that $\overrightarrow{BD}$ bisects ∠ABC. In what way(s) is this algorithm similar to the technique in Applications Task 7?

c. Can this algorithm be used to construct the bisector of a right angle and an *obtuse angle* (an angle with measure greater than 90°)? Explain your reasoning.

d. Think of a line as a "straight" angle. Add steps to the Angle Bisector Algorithm to produce an algorithm for constructing a perpendicular to a given point P on a line.

  i. Draw a line $\overleftrightarrow{AB}$ containing point P. Use your algorithm and a compass and straightedge to construct a perpendicular to $\overleftrightarrow{AB}$ at P.

  ii. Explain how you know that the line you constructed is perpendicular to $\overleftrightarrow{AB}$ at P.

e. How would you modify your algorithm to construct a perpendicular bisector of a segment? Explain as carefully as you can why your method works.

UNIT 6

8 **a.** See the diagram at the right.

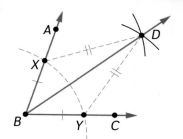

b. Step 1 of the algorithm assures that $BX = BY$. Step 2 of the algorithm assures that $XD = YD$. Of course, $BD = BD$. So by the SSS congruence condition, $\triangle BXD \cong \triangle BYD$. Thus, $\angle XBD \cong \angle YBD$, and so $\overrightarrow{BD}$ bisects $\angle XBY$. Another name for $\angle XBY$ is $\angle ABC$, so $\overrightarrow{BD}$ bisects $\angle ABC$.

    The algorithms here and using the carpenter's square are essentially the same. You position the carpenter's square so that $BX = BY$ and $XD = YD$. Then connect the vertex B to the vertex of the carpenter's square to find the angle bisector.

c. Yes, there is nothing about the algorithm that limits its use to acute angles.

d. **i. Step 1:** With the compass point at P, draw an arc that intersects $\overrightarrow{PA}$ and $\overrightarrow{PB}$. Call the intersection points X and Y, respectively.

    Step 2: With the compass point at point X (and then at point Y) and using a radius greater than $\frac{1}{2}XY$, draw two arcs of the same radius that intersect above (or below) line AB. Label the point of intersection D.

    Step 3: Draw the line PD. $\overleftrightarrow{PD}$ is perpendicular to $\overleftrightarrow{AB}$.

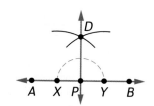

ii. Step 1 assures that $\overline{XP} \cong \overline{YP}$. Step 2 assures that $\overline{XD} \cong \overline{YD}$. Of course, $\overline{PD} \cong \overline{PD}$. So BY the SSS congruence condition, $\triangle PXD \cong \triangle PYD$. Thus, the two angles at P are congruent. Their measures sum to 180° because they form a straight angle. So, each angle is a right angle.

e. **i. Step 1:** With the compass at point A (and then at point B) and using a radius greater than $\frac{1}{2}AB$, draw two large arcs that intersect $\overline{AB}$ and each other on both sides of $\overline{AB}$.

    Step 2: Draw a line that connects the two intersection points C and D of the arcs. $\overleftrightarrow{CD}$ is the perpendicular bisector of $\overline{AB}$.

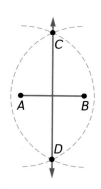

ii. Step 1 of the algorithm assures that $AC = BC = AD = BD$. $\overline{CD}$ is a side of $\triangle ACD$ and $\triangle BCD$, so $\triangle ACD \cong \triangle BCD$ (SSS). $\angle ACE \cong \angle BCE$ because the angles are corresponding angles of these triangles. Since $\overline{CE}$ is a common side for $\triangle ACE$ and $\triangle BCE$, these triangles are congruent (SAS). Thus, $\overline{AE} \cong \overline{EB}$ and $\angle AEC \cong \angle BEC$ because they are corresponding parts of congruent triangles. Since $\angle AEC$ and $\angle BEC$ form a straight line, their measures sum to 180°. Since the two angles have equal measures, each angle is a right angle. Therefore, $\overleftrightarrow{CD}$ is the perpendicular bisector of $\overline{AB}$.

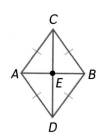

9 Use a ruler to carefully draw a triangle, △*XYZ*. Design and test an algorithm for using a compass and a straightedge to construct △*ABC* so that △*ABC* ≅ △*XYZ*. Provide an argument that your algorithm will always work.

10 In Investigation 3, you were able to provide an argument for why opposite angles of any parallelogram are congruent. Experimenting with a parallelogram linkage should convince you that **consecutive angles** of a parallelogram like ∠1 and ∠2 may not always be congruent.

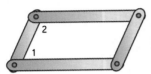 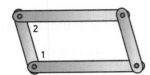 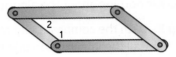

In the first diagram, m∠1 < m∠2. In the next two diagrams, as m∠1 increases, m∠2 decreases. Thinking that there might be some relationship between the angles, students in a class at Columbia-Hickman High School measured the angles and in each case found that m∠1 + m∠2 was about 180°. They tried to find reasons that might explain this relationship.

Examine the reasoning of each student below.

- Give a reason that would support each statement made by the students.

- Then decide if the conclusion follows logically from knowing that quadrilateral *ABCD* is a parallelogram.

a. Anna drew ▱*ABCD* at the right and set out to show that m∠*A* + m∠*B* = 180°. She reasoned as follows.

> Since *ABCD* is a quadrilateral, I know that
> m∠*A* + m∠*B* + m∠*C* + m∠*D* = 360°.
> Since *ABCD* is a parallelogram, I know that
> ∠*A* ≅ ∠*C* and ∠*B* ≅ ∠*D*.
> It follows that m∠*A* + m∠*B* + m∠*A* + m∠*B* = 360°.
> So, 2m∠*A* + 2m∠*B* = 360°.
> Therefore, m∠*A* + m∠*B* = 180°.

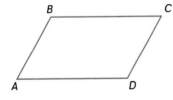

b. Andy drew ▱*ABCD* with diagonal $\overline{BD}$ and then reasoned to show that m∠*A* + m∠*B* = 180°.

> I know that △*ABD* ≅ △*CDB*.
> So, ∠*BDA* ≅ ∠*DBC*.
> I know that m∠*A* + m∠*ABD* + m∠*BDA* = 180°.
> So, m∠*A* + m∠*ABD* + m∠*DBC* = 180°.
> Therefore, m∠*A* + m∠*B* = 180°.

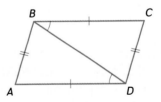

9 Responses will vary. The algorithms should be based on one of the triangle congruence conditions. (You may wish to have students discuss their algorithms with each other in order to see that more than one algorithm is possible.)

One way to construct the triangle would be to:

Step 1: Draw a segment with a straight edge and mark off $\overline{AB}$ using the compass. Label the new segment $\overline{XY}$.

Step 2: Set the compass to the length of $\overline{BC}$. Place the compass point at Y and draw an arc above $\overline{XY}$.

Step 3: Repeat Step 2 with $\overline{AC}$ by placing the compass point at X.

Step 4: Label the intersection of the arcs Z and draw $\overline{XZ}$ and $\overline{YZ}$.

$\triangle ABC \cong \triangle XYZ$ because $\triangle XYZ$ was formed using the same three side lengths as $\triangle ABC$. Thus, we used the SSS triangle congruence condition.

10 **a.** Anna's conclusion follows logically from knowing that $ABCD$ is a parallelogram.

b. Andy's conclusion also follows logically from knowing that $ABCD$ is a parallelogram.

INSTRUCTIONAL NOTE

This is an opportunity to share with students the construction for copying an angle. With that additional construction, students could write congruent triangle construction algorithms based on the SAS and ASA congruence conditions.

TOOLKIT NOTE

You may wish to have students add this property of parallelograms to their lists.

ON YOUR OWN

11 Materials tend to expand when heated. This expansion needs to be considered carefully when building roads and railroad tracks.

In the case of a railroad track, each 220-foot-long rail is anchored solidly at both ends. Suppose that on a very hot day a rail's length expands by 1.2 inches, causing it to buckle as shown below.

— 220 ft —

a. At what point along the rail do you think the buckling will occur?

b. Do you think you could slide a gym bag between the raised rail and the track bed?

c. Approximate this situation using right triangles, and then calculate an estimate of the height of the buckle.

d. Would you expect your estimate of the height of the buckle to be more or less than the actual value? Explain your reasoning.

e. Research *expansion joints*. How does the use of these joints in railroad tracks and concrete highways minimize the problem you modeled in Part c?

12 You can represent the diagonals of a quadrilateral with two linkage strips attached at a point.

a. What must be true about the diagonal strips, and how should you attach them so that the quadrilateral is a parallelogram?

b. What must be true about the diagonal strips, and how should you attach them so that the quadrilateral is a rectangle?

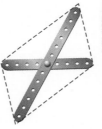

c. What constraint(s) must be placed on the diagonal strips and their placement if the quadrilateral is to be a kite? Give reasons to justify that the shape with your arrangement of diagonals is a kite.

d. What constraints must be placed on the diagonal strips and how they are attached in Part a if the quadrilateral is to be a square? Give reasons to justify that the shape with your arrangement of diagonals is a square.

©John Nakata/Corbis

11 | **INSTRUCTIONAL NOTE** This task is counterintuitive for students and many adults. They are often surprised by the mathematical conclusion. You may wish to use this task to reinforce the idea that mathematics can provide reasoning to support or give a counterexample to initial intuition.

a. The buckling will occur so that the highest point of the buckle is in the middle of the 220-foot-long rail.

b. Responses will vary. After answering Part c, students should see that a gym bag definitely would fit under the rail.

c. Using the Pythagorean Theorem:

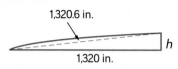

$$(1{,}320.6)^2 = 1{,}320^2 + h^2$$
$$1{,}584.36 = h^2$$
$$39.8 \approx h$$

The height of the triangle is approximately 39.8 inches.

d. Since the railing is curved, the straight line from end to middle actually would be less than 1,320.6 inches. Our estimate of the height of the buckle is more than the actual value. Even if it were only half our estimate, a gym bag would easily fit under it!

e. Expansion points allow the rails to expand without buckling.

12 a. The diagonal strips must bisect each other, that is, they must be attached at their midpoints.

b. The diagonal strips must be equal in length and attached at their midpoints.

c. One diagonal strip must be the perpendicular bisector of the other strip.

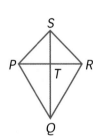

In the diagram, $\overline{SQ}$ is a perpendicular bisector of $\overline{PR}$. To show quadrilateral $PQRS$ is a kite, note that $\overline{PT} \cong \overline{TR}$. $\angle PTS \cong \angle RTS$ (since both angles are 90°), and $\overline{ST} \cong \overline{ST}$. By the SAS congruence condition, $\triangle PTS \cong \triangle RTS$. So, $\overline{PS} \cong \overline{RS}$ since they are corresponding parts of congruent triangles. Similarly, because $\overline{PT} \cong \overline{TR}$, $\angle PTQ \cong \angle RTQ$, and $\overline{TQ} \cong \overline{TQ}$, $\triangle PTQ \cong \triangle RTQ$ by the SAS congruence condition. So, $\overline{PQ} \cong \overline{RQ}$. Quadrilateral $PQRS$ has two distinct pairs of consecutive sides the same length. So, it is a kite.

> **NOTE** Task 12 Part c is the converse of the property of the diagonals of a kite examined in the Check Your Understanding on page 377 in the Student Edition.

d. The diagonal strips must be equal in length and perpendicular bisectors of each other.

In the diagram, since $SQ = PR$ and T is the midpoint of $\overline{SQ}$ and $\overline{PR}$, quadrilateral $PQRS$ is a rectangle by Part b. Since it is the case that $\overline{SQ} \perp \overline{PR}$, students should reason that $\triangle PTQ \cong \triangle RTQ \cong \triangle RTS \cong \triangle STP$ and thus $PQ = QR = RS = SP$. So, quadrilateral $PQRS$ is a square.

13 When a ball with no spin and medium speed is banked off a flat surface, the angles at which it strikes and leaves the cushion are congruent. You can use this fact and knowledge of congruent triangles to your advantage in games of miniature golf and pool.

To make a hole-in-one on the miniature golf green to the right, visualize a point H' so that the side ℓ is the perpendicular bisector of H and H'. Aim for the point P where $\overline{BH}$ intersects ℓ. If you aim for point P, give reasons to justify that the ball will follow the indicated path to the hole. That is, show that $\angle 3 \cong \angle 1$.

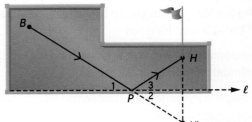

CONNECTIONS

14 Examine the 5-bar linkage at the right.

a. Explain why this linkage is not rigid.

b. Make a sketch of the linkage showing how you could make it rigid. How many braces did you use? Is that the fewest number possible?

c. What is the fewest number of braces required to make a 6-bar linkage rigid? To make an 8-bar linkage rigid? Draw a sketch illustrating your answers.

d. Try to generalize your reasoning. What is the fewest number of braces required to make an n-bar linkage rigid? How many triangles are formed?

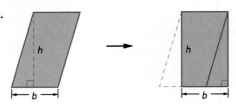

15 *Perimeter* and *area* are important characteristics of two-dimensional shapes. By recalling the formula for the area of a rectangle $A = base \times height$ and using visual thinking, you can develop and easily recall formulas for the areas of parallelograms and triangles. Study each pair of diagrams below in which b is the length of a *base* and h is the corresponding *height* of the shape. Write a formula for the area A of the shape and then explain how the diagrams helped you reason to the formula.

a.

$A = \underline{\ ?\ }$

b.

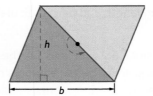

$A = \underline{\ ?\ }$

13 ∠1 ≅ ∠2 because they are vertical angles. △PH'A ≅ △PHA by the SAS congruence condition as marked in the diagram below. So, ∠2 ≅ ∠3 and ∠1 ≅ ∠3 by substitution.

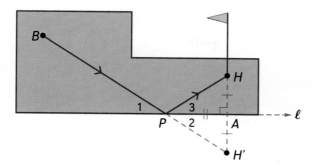

CONNECTIONS

14 a. The linkage is not rigid since the angles can change.

b. Using 2 braces is the fewest number needed to make the linkage rigid.

c. 3 braces; 5 braces. There are many different choices for the placement of the braces; in every case, the linkage is triangulated.

d. $n - 3$ braces will be required and $n - 2$ triangles will be formed.

15 a. $A = b \times h$. The diagrams show that the triangle in the left side of the first figure can be shifted over to the right side as shown in the second figure. This forms a rectangle with base b and height h.

b. $A = \frac{1}{2}(b \times h)$. The diagram shows that if a triangle is rotated about a midpoint of a side, the triangle and its congruent image form a parallelogram with base b and height h. Since the area of a parallelogram is $b \times h$, the area of one triangle is half that of the parallelogram.

ON YOUR OWN

16 The circle below has been dissected into eight sections. These sections can be reassembled to form an "approximate" parallelogram.

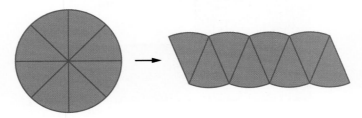

a. How is the base of this "approximate" parallelogram related to the circle?

b. What is the height of the "approximate" parallelogram?

c. How could you dissect the circle into sections to get a better approximation to a parallelogram?

d. Use the above information to produce the formula for the area of a circle.

17 In Applications Task 10, you gave reasons why the sum of the measures of two consecutive angles of a parallelogram is 180°. In the case of □PQRS, this means that m∠P + m∠Q = 180° and m∠P + m∠S = 180°.

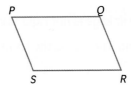

a. Write two similar statements involving other pairs of angles of □PQRS.

b. The Dockland office building on the Elbe River in Hamburg, Germany presents a striking use of parallelograms in architectural design. Suppose in drawing plans for the building, an architect was working from the information shown in the diagram below at the left.

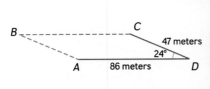

i. Is this enough information to build the outer frame of the front face of the building? Explain your reasoning.

ii. Do you think there is an SAS condition for congruence of parallelograms? Explain.

16 **a.** The base length is half the circle's circumference.

b. The height is equal to the length of the radius of the circle.

c. Cut the circle into smaller congruent wedges; there will be more wedges with shorter arcs.

d. $Area = b \times h$
$$= \frac{1}{2}C \times r$$
$$= \frac{1}{2}(\pi \times d) \times r$$
$$= \frac{1}{2}(\pi \times 2r) \times r$$
$$= \pi r^2$$

17 **a.** $m\angle Q + m\angle R = 180°$; $m\angle R + m\angle S = 180°$

b. **i.** This is enough information. The angle at A must be 156° since the two consecutive angles sum to 180°. $AD = 86$ meters, $DC = 47$ meters, and $AB = 47$ meters (by the definition of a parallelogram). So, the parallelogram is determined and can be built.

ii. Students should recognize that knowing the three parts SAS for a parallelogram meant that a unique parallelogram was built. So, if two parallelograms had these same dimensions, they would be congruent.

18 The sum of the measures of consecutive angles of a parallelogram is 180°. (See Applications Task 10.) That property helps to explain the use of the term "parallel" in parallelogram.

In a parallelogram, opposite sides are parallel.

That is, if opposite sides of a parallelogram are extended, the lines will not intersect. Parts a–c provide an outline of why, in □*ABCD*, $\overline{BC}$ must be parallel to $\overline{AD}$. The reasoning depends on you.

a. What is true about m∠*A* and m∠*B*? Why?

b. Now either $\overline{BC}$ is parallel to $\overline{AD}$, or $\overline{BC}$ is *not* parallel to $\overline{AD}$. If $\overline{BC}$ is *not* parallel to $\overline{AD}$, then the situation would look something like that in the diagram above on the right. What must be true about m∠*A* + m∠*B* + m∠*F*? Why?

c. Explain why the situation in Part b is impossible. What does this tell you about the assumption that $\overline{BC}$ was not parallel to $\overline{AD}$? What can you conclude?

d. How could you use similar reasoning to show that $\overline{AB}$ must be parallel to $\overline{CD}$?

19 Two diagrams used in your reasoning about the Pythagorean Theorem (page 379) are shown below.

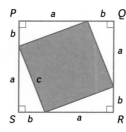 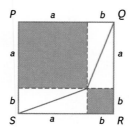

a. Write an expression for the area of square *PQRS* that involves *a*, *b*, and *c* using the diagram above at the left.

b. Write an algebraic expression for the area of square *PQRS* that involves only *a* and *b*, using the diagram above at the right.

c. Use your results from Parts a and b and algebra to show that $a^2 + b^2 = c^2$.

UNIT 6

INSTRUCTIONAL NOTE In this unit, a parallelogram has been defined as a quadrilateral with opposite sides the same length. In this task, students will show that opposite sides of a parallelogram must also be parallel. This task provides an example of indirect reasoning that is often employed by lawyers. This particular kind of argument involves proof by "elimination." Here there are only two possibilities: either $\overline{BC}$ *is parallel* to $\overline{AD}$, or $\overline{BC}$ *is not parallel* to $\overline{AD}$. The case that $\overline{BC}$ is not parallel to $\overline{AD}$ leads to a contradiction and so can be eliminated. The remaining case, $\overline{BC}$ is parallel to $\overline{AD}$, must be true.

18 **a.** $m\angle A + m\angle B = 180°$ because consecutive angles in a parallelogram sum to 180° (Applications Task 10).

  b. $m\angle A + m\angle B + m\angle F = 180°$ because the angles in a triangle sum to 180°.

  c. The three angle measures cannot sum to 180° because $m\angle A$ plus $m\angle B$ already is 180°. So, we must rule out that $\overline{BC}$ is not parallel to $\overline{AD}$ and accept that $\overline{BC}$ is parallel to $\overline{AD}$.

  d. $m\angle B + m\angle C = 180°$. If $\overline{AB}$ is not parallel to $\overline{CD}$, the two lines would intersect (at point F). That would mean that $m\angle B + m\angle C + m\angle F = 180°$. This is not possible since $m\angle F > 0$. So, $\overline{AB}$ must be parallel to $\overline{CD}$.

19 **a.** $A = 4\left(\frac{1}{2}ab\right) + c^2 = 2ab + c^2$

  b. $A = 2ab + a^2 + b^2$

  c. $2ab + c^2 = 2ab + a^2 + b^2$
  $c^2 = a^2 + b^2$

ON YOUR OWN

20 Draw squares of side lengths 2, 4, 7, 8, 10, and 11 centimeters on centimeter grid paper.

a. Measure the diagonals to the nearest 0.1 cm. Record your data in a table.

b. Make a plot of your (*side length, diagonal length*) data. Find a linear model that fits the trend in the data.

  i. What is the slope of the line? What does it mean?

  ii. What is the *y*-intercept? Does it make sense in this context? Explain.

c. Use your model to predict the length of the diagonal of a square with side length of 55 cm.

d. Compare your predicted length to that computed by using the Pythagorean Theorem. Explain any differences.

e. Write a rule that would express *exact* diagonal length D in terms of side length s for any square.

21 The diagram below shows an equilateral triangle, $\triangle ABC$, with an altitude from A to M that forms two smaller triangles.

a. What is the measure of $\angle MAC$?

b. Explain as precisely as you can why $\triangle AMC \cong \triangle AMB$.

c. Find the exact length of the altitude $\overline{AM}$ when the sides of the equilateral triangle have length:

  i. 5 cm   ii. 8 cm

  iii. 10 cm   iv. 1 cm

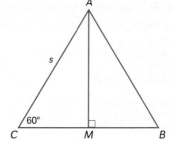

d. Now consider the general problem of finding side lengths of a 30°-60°-90° triangle in which the hypotenuse is of length s.

  i. What expression gives the length of the side opposite the 30° angle?

  ii. What expression gives the length of the side opposite the 60° angle?

e. Write in words how the lengths of the sides of a 30°-60°-90° triangle are related.

REFLECTIONS

22 Why will any parallelogram linkage have two rotating cranks?

23 Explain why there is no Side-Side-Side-Side (SSSS) congruence condition for quadrilaterals.

20 **a.**

Side Length (in cm)	Diagonal Length (in cm)
2	2.8
4	5.7
7	9.9
8	11.3
10	14.1
11	15.6

> **ASSIGNMENT NOTE**
>
> Task 20 should be reviewed in class. Students will use these ideas again in Applications Task 3 on page 413.

b. The linear model shown at the right should be approximately $y = 1.4x$.

   i. The slope (1.4) gives the approximate ratio of diagonal to side length. It also means that for every 1-cm increase in side length, the diagonal length increases by 1.4 cm.

   ii. The y-intercept is (0, 0). Side length of a square must be a positive number.

c. The length of the diagonal is approximately 1.4(55), or 77 cm.

d. Using the Pythagorean Theorem, the diagonal is found to be $\sqrt{2 \times 55^2} \approx 55\sqrt{2} \approx 77.78$ cm. The differences are because the linear model is an approximation of the relationship and because the numbers are rounded.

e. If s is the side length of any square and d is the length of the diagonal, then by the Pythagorean Theorem, $s^2 + s^2 = d^2$, so, $d = s\sqrt{2}$.

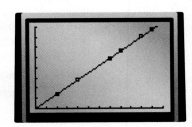

21 **a.** The measure of $\angle MAC = 30°$ since the sum of the angles of a triangle are 180° and the other two angles of $\triangle AMC$ are 90° and 60°.

b. Students may find a variety of correct ways to show $\triangle AMC \cong \triangle AMB$. One way follows.
$\overline{AC} \cong \overline{AB}$ because the sides of an equilateral triangle are congruent. $\overline{AM} \cong \overline{AM}$ because they are the same side. $\angle MAB = 30°$, so $\triangle AMC \cong \triangle AMB$ by the SAS triangle congruence property.

c.   **i.** $AM = \sqrt{5^2 - \left(\frac{5}{2}\right)^2} = \sqrt{\frac{75}{4}} = \frac{5}{2}\sqrt{3}$ cm

   ii. When $s = 8$ cm, $AM = \frac{8}{2}\sqrt{3} = 4\sqrt{3}$ cm

   iii. When $s = 10$ cm, $AM = \frac{10}{2}\sqrt{3} = 5\sqrt{3}$ cm.

   iv. When $s = 1$ cm, $AM = \frac{1}{2}\sqrt{3}$ cm.

d.   **i.** The side opposite the 30° angle is $\frac{s}{2}$.

   ii. The side opposite the 60° angle is $\frac{s}{2}\sqrt{3}$.

e. The shortest side is across from the 30° angle and is half the length of the hypotenuse. The side across from the 60° angle will be $\sqrt{3}$ times the length of the shortest side. One way to express the lengths in increasing order is:
$\frac{1}{2}s, \sqrt{\frac{3}{2}}s, s$.

> **NOTE** You may wish to have students recognize that if the smallest side is the reference length s, then the expressions in ascending order would be s, $3s$, and $2s$.

> **NOTE** The solutions to Tasks 22 and 23 are on page T393.

24 In Investigation 3, you were able to provide reasons justifying that the base angles of an isosceles triangle are congruent. Why does it follow logically that an equilateral triangle is *equiangular*; that is, the three angles of an equilateral triangle are congruent? What is the measure of each angle?

25 Explain why opposite angles of a rhombus are congruent. Are both pairs of opposite angles of a kite congruent? Explain.

26 Look back at Problem 3 of Investigation 4. Could a builder also lay out a wall perpendicular to an existing wall by measuring the existing wall at 6 feet, the location of the new wall at 8 feet, and then check if the distance between the two points is 10 feet? Explain your reasoning. Which method would likely give greater accuracy? Why?

EXTENSIONS

27 The diagram at the right shows a quadrilateral linkage with frame $\overline{AB}$ satisfying Grashof's Principle that you discovered in Problem 6 of Investigation 1 (page 367). When the shortest crank $\overline{AD}$ makes a complete revolution, the other crank $\overline{BC}$ oscillates between two positions moving back and forth in an arc as indicated in the diagram.

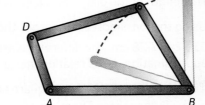

  a. Use software like the "Design a Linkage" custom app to investigate the possible paths of point *C* under the following two conditions.

   i. Quadrilateral *ABCD* is a kite.

   ii. Quadrilateral *ABCD* is a parallelogram, including special types.

   Consider the two cases where the frame is the longest or the shortest side. Write a paragraph summarizing your findings.

  b. Repeat Part a for the case of a point $P \neq C$ on the coupler.

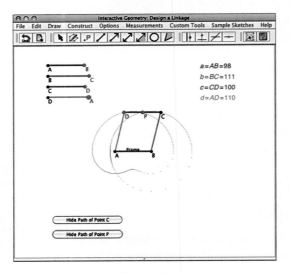

22 In a parallelogram linkage, the sum of the lengths of the shortest side and longest side will always be equal to the sum of the other two sides. By Grashof's Principle, if the frame is the shortest side, both cranks will rotate 360°. Consequently, choosing the frame as one of the shorter sides will allow both cranks of a parallelogram linkage to rotate.

23 Quadrilaterals are not rigid, so knowing four sides still allows the quadrilateral to change shape. This means many differently-shaped quadrilaterals can have corresponding sides congruent.

24 Since all three sides are congruent (and any side may be the base), you can think of each pair of consecutive sides making the base angles congruent. Since the sum of the three angles is 180°, each angle will be 60°.

25 Since a rhombus is a parallelogram, it has the properties of a parallelogram, one of which is that opposite angles are congruent.

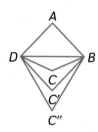

In a kite, only one pair of opposite angles must be congruent. Students might observe that many different kites $ABCD$ can be formed using $\triangle ABD$ as one part; simply choose C as any point on the perpendicular bisector of $\overline{DB}$, below $\overline{DB}$. (See Check Your Understanding page 377.)

26 Yes, the builder could use 6 ft, 8 ft, and 10 ft to check for a right angle since $6^2 + 8^2 = 10^2$. The 6-8-10 triangle would likely give more accuracy. For instance, if the corner angle is measured using a 3-4-5 triangle and the actual measurement of the hypotenuse is $5 + x$, where x is some negligible length, then if that corner angle is measured using a 6-8-10 triangle, the actual measurement of the hypotenuse would be $10 + 2x$, where $2x$ may no longer be considered to be negligible. You can immediately see that by using a larger right triangle to check the corner angle, any error in the corner angle is easier to see (and measure). In fact, it is twice as easy to see the error with a 6-8-10 triangle than with a 3-4-5 triangle.

27 **INSTRUCTIONAL NOTE** This task provides students an opportunity to continue their exploration of quadrilateral linkages and extend their thinking about the relationship between the lengths of sides of a quadrilateral linkage and the resulting movement of the linkage. Since students have a choice of Extensions Task 27 or 28, some students may choose to access the "Design a Linkage" custom app from home. Using a class computer, various students could show their findings. The parenthetical comments in the solution below might be framed as questions you could ask to help students to both make sense of the path of a particular point by reflecting on their experience with the quadrilateral linkages in the lesson, and anticipate the path of a point given a particular type of mechanism (double-crank, crank-rocker, or double-rocker). For example, you might ask, "Why do you think the path of *P* is a circle in a double-crank mechanism?" or "What path might *P* follow, given that this quadrilateral linkage is a crank-rocker mechanism?"

a. **i.** If *ABCD* is a kite and the frame is a longest side, then the path of *C* is an arc. (Recall that in this case, if the driver crank is a longest side, then the quadrilateral is a double-rocker mechanism; if the driver crank is a shortest side, then the quadrilateral is a crank-rocker mechanism.)

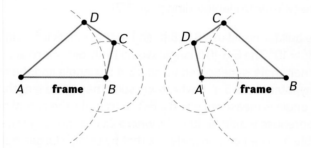

If the frame is a shortest side, then the path of *C* is a circle. (Recall that in this case the quadrilateral linkage is a double-crank mechanism regardless of whether the driver is a shortest or a longest side.)

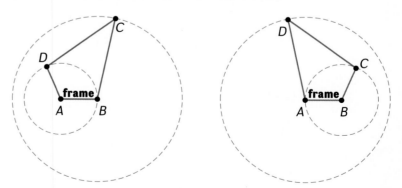

ii. If *ABCD* is a parallelogram (including all special parallelograms), then the path of *C* is a circle for both short and long frames. (Recall that in this case the quadrilateral linkage is a double-crank mechanism.)

b. **i.** If *ABCD* is a kite and the frame is a longest side, then there are two possible paths for *P*. If the driver crank is a longest side, then the path of *P* is an arc. (Recall that in this case the quadrilateral is a double-rocker mechanism.) If the driver crank is a shortest side, then the path of *P* changes as *P* moves between *C* and *D*. As *P* moves closer to *C*, its path becomes more like the path at *C* (an arc); as *P* moves closer to *D*, its path becomes more like the path of *D* (a circle). If *P* is positioned between *C* and *D*, then its path is sort of kidney-shaped (see the figure below). (Recall that in this case the quadrilateral is a crank-rocker mechanism.)

ON YOUR OWN

INSTRUCTIONAL NOTE

Observing the change in the path of *P* as *P* moves toward *D* provides students an informal introduction to the idea of a limit.

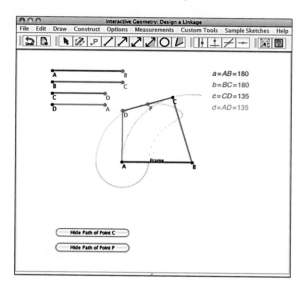

If the frame is a shortest side then there are two possibilities. If the driver crank is a longest side, then the path of *P* is an arc. (Recall in this case that the quadrilateral is a double-rocker mechanism.) If the driver crank is a shortest side, then the path of *P* changes as *P* moves between *C* and *D*. As *P* moves closer to *C* its path becomes more arc-like, and as it moves closer to *D* its path becomes more circular. (Recall in this case that the quadrilateral is a crank-rocker mechanism.)

ii. If *ABCD* is a parallelogram (including a rhombus), then the path of *P* is a circle for both short and long frames.

ON YOUR OWN

28 In order for kites to fly well, they need to have a high ratio of *lift area* to weight. For two-dimensional kites, the lift area is just the area of the kite.

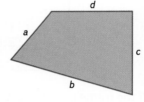

a. On a copy of the kite shown, label its vertices and use markings to show which segments are congruent by definition of a kite.

b. Use congruent triangles to help you find the lift area of the traditional kite shown with cross pieces of lengths 0.8 m and 1.0 m.

c. Suppose the lengths of the diagonals of the kite are *a* and *b* where $a < b$. Use the diagram to help develop a formula for the area of a kite.

d. Can you also use your formula to find the area of a rhombus? Explain your reasoning.

e. Could this formula be used to find the area of any other quadrilaterals? Explain.

29 As noted at the beginning of this lesson, ancient Egyptians had to deal with changes in shape and size of fields caused by the annual flooding of the Nile River. Historians have evidence that the Egyptians calculated the areas of quadrilateral-shaped fields using the formula shown below.

$$A = \tfrac{1}{2}(a + c) \cdot \tfrac{1}{2}(b + d)$$

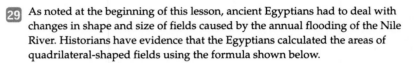

where *a*, *b*, *c*, *d* are the lengths of consecutive sides of the quadrilateral.

a. State this formula in words (without using the labels *a*, *b*, *c*, *d*) using the idea of "average."

b. Describe quadrilaterals for which the formula gives an exact calculation of the area.

c. Use software like the "Areas of Quadrilaterals" custom app to explore cases of other quadrilaterals. For which quadrilateral shapes does the formula overestimate the area? Underestimate the area?

d. Explain why your findings in Part c make sense in terms of area formulas for parallelograms, trapezoids, and kites.

28 **a.** See kite *ABCD* below.

b. The lift area is $\frac{0.8 \cdot 1.0}{2} = 0.4$ m². Since the diagonals are perpendicular, the area of the kite can be found based on the area of the two large congruent triangles. $\frac{1}{2}(0.4)(1.0) + \frac{1}{2}(0.4)(1.0) = 0.2 + 0.2 = 0.4$ m².

c. $\triangle ABD \cong \triangle CBD$ by the SSS congruence condition. Since the diagonals are perpendicular, $\overline{AE}$ and $\overline{CE}$ are altitudes to the base $\overline{BD}$. The kite is made up of two congruent triangles. So, the area can be computed as follows:

$$A = \frac{1}{2}\left(\frac{a}{2}\right)(b) + \frac{1}{2}\left(\frac{a}{2}\right)(b) = \frac{1}{4}ab + \frac{1}{4}ab = \frac{1}{2}ab.$$

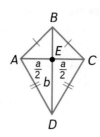

d. Yes, a rhombus is a special kite that has the two distinct pairs of sides the same length. Thus, the properties of a kite will also hold for a rhombus.

e. No. Diagonals will not always divide a given quadrilateral into smaller congruent triangles.

29 **a.** The area of the quadrilateral equals the product of the two averages of the lengths of the opposite sides.

TECHNOLOGY NOTE

Students can use the "Areas of Quadrilaterals" custom app for Task 29.

b. The formula gives an exact calculation of the area of rectangles and squares because opposite sides have the same length and all angles are 90°.

$$A = \frac{1}{2}(a + c)\frac{1}{2}(b + d) = \frac{1}{2}(a + a)\frac{1}{2}(b + b) = ab$$

c. The formula does not underestimate the area of any quadrilateral. (This has not been proven here; it is a result of examples the students will try.)

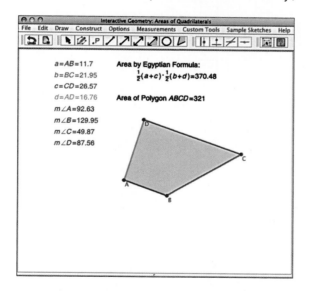

NOTE The solution to Task 29 Part d is on page T395.

30 The television industry has set standards for the sizing of television screens. The ratio of height h to width w is called the *aspect ratio*. The aspect ratio for a conventional television screen is 3:4. That is $\frac{h}{w} = \frac{3}{4}$.

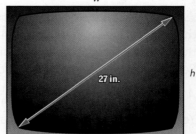

a. Write a rule expressing h as a function of w.

b. Use the Pythagorean Theorem to write a rule relating h, w, and the diagonal length 27.

c. Use your rules in Parts a and b to find the standard dimensions of a 27-inch diagonal TV screen.

d. Check the dimensions you obtained against actual measurements of a 27-inch TV screen.

REVIEW

31 Write an equation that matches each graph. The scale on both axes is 1.

a.

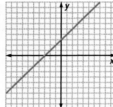

b.

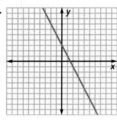

c.

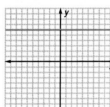

d.

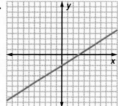

e.

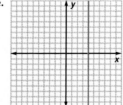

d. The formula overestimates area for parallelograms (that are not rectangles or squares). The area of a parallelogram is the length of the base times the height of the parallelogram. However, half the sum of the lengths of one pair of sides will be greater than the height of the parallelogram, because those sides are each the hypotenuse of right triangles formed by drawing the perpendicular height on each side of the parallelogram.

The formula overestimates area for kites. The area of a kite is half the product of the lengths of the diagonals. Using half the sum of the lengths of the opposite sides results in using lengths that are longer than the lengths of the diagonals, because the sides of the kite are the hypotenuses of the four right triangles formed when drawing the diagonals.

The formula also overestimates area for trapezoids. Half the sum of the lengths of the bases gives a correct number, but half the sum of the lengths of the nonparallel sides will give a number greater than the height of the trapezoid, because those sides are each the hypotenuse of the right triangle that is formed by drawing perpendicular lines (the height) from the ends of the shorter base to the longer base.

INSTRUCTIONAL NOTE

You may wish to remind students of the formula for finding the area of a trapezoid.

30 **a.** $h = \dfrac{3w}{4}$

b. $h^2 + w^2 = 27^2$

c. $\left(\dfrac{3w}{4}\right)^2 + w^2 = 27^2$ or $(0.75w)^2 + w^2 = 27^2$

$\qquad \dfrac{9w^2}{16} + w^2 = 729 \qquad\qquad\qquad 0.5625w^2 + w^2 = 729$

$\qquad\quad \dfrac{25w^2}{16} = 729 \qquad\qquad\qquad\quad 1.5625w^2 = 729$

$\qquad\quad 25w^2 = 11{,}664 \qquad\qquad\qquad\qquad w = \sqrt{\dfrac{729}{1.5625}}$

$\qquad\qquad w^2 = 466.56 \qquad\qquad\qquad\qquad\quad w = 21.6$

$\qquad\qquad\quad w = 21.6$

Now, $h = \dfrac{3w}{4} = \dfrac{3(21.6)}{4} = 16.2$ inches.

The television screen measures 16.2 inches $\times$ 21.6 inches.

d. Students should check their dimensions against the actual dimensions of a 27-inch TV screen.

INSTRUCTIONAL NOTE

Task 30 connects to the previous unit on linear functions.

REVIEW

31 **a.** $y = x + 3$ **b.** $y = -2x + 3$

     c. $y = 6$ **d.** $y = \dfrac{2}{3}x - 2$

     e. $x = 4$

ON YOUR OWN

32 You have a number cube with the numbers 2, 3, 4, 5, 6, and 7 on the faces. You roll the cube and look at the number showing on the top face.

a. What is the probability of rolling an even number?

b. What is the probability of rolling a prime number?

c. What is the probability of rolling a number less than 3?

d. What is the probability of rolling an odd number that is greater than 4?

33 Use the fact that $36 \times 15 = 540$ and mental computation to evaluate the following.

a. $\dfrac{5{,}400}{36}$ b. 3.6×15 c. 72×15 d. $\dfrac{45 \cdot 36}{3}$

34 Without measuring, find the measure of each indicated angle.

a. m∠ABC   b. m∠CBD

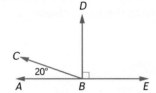

c. m∠CBE

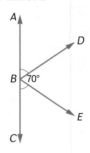

35 Algebraic models can often help you analyze a situation. In this task, you will write algebraic rules for several different situations. Before you write each rule, think about whether a linear or an exponential rule would be better for the situation.

a. Alena's telephone credit card charges $0.50 just to make a call and then charges $0.04 for each minute.

  i. Write a rule that gives the charge for a call based upon the length of the call in minutes.

  ii. Alena wants to be able to make a 40-minute call to her friend. How much will this call cost her?

b. Randy owns a car that is currently worth $8,750. The value of his car decreases by 15% each year.

  i. Write a rule that gives the value of Randy's car t years from now.

  ii. In how many years will Randy's car first be worth less than $2,000?

32 **a.** $\dfrac{3}{6} = \dfrac{1}{2}$

    b. $\dfrac{4}{6} = \dfrac{2}{3}$

    c. $\dfrac{1}{6}$

    d. $\dfrac{2}{6} = \dfrac{1}{3}$

33 **a.** $\dfrac{36 \times 15 \times 10}{36} = 15 \times 10 = 150$

    b. $\dfrac{36 \times 15}{10} = \dfrac{540}{10} = 54$

    c. $2 \times 36 \times 15 = 2 \times 540 = 1{,}080$

    d. $\dfrac{3 \times 15 \times 36}{3} = 540$

🕐 **JUST IN TIME**

34 **a.** 120°

    b. 70°

    c. 55°

35 **a.**   **i.** $c = 0.50 + 0.04m$

        ii. $c = 0.50 + 0.04(40) = \$2.10$

    b.   **i.** $v = 8{,}750(0.85^t)$

        ii. By using graphs or tables of values, students can determine that $8{,}750(0.85^t) < 2{,}000$ after 9.1 years.

36 Solve the following equations by reasoning with the symbols themselves.

    a. $3x - 5 = 9x + 4$ **b.** $9 + \frac{1}{2}x = 14$

    c. $3.2 = 5x + 0.7$ **d.** $2(4x - 8) = 8x + 14$

    e. $2(5^x) = 250$ **f.** $(-2)(-2)^x = 16$

37 Find the value of each expression without using a calculator.

    a. -5^2 **b.** $(-3)^2 - 4(2) + 21$

    c. $148 - 3(-5)$ **d.** $\dfrac{-15 + 8(-3)}{2}$

    e. $-6 + (3 - 5)^3$

38 Rewrite each expression in an equivalent form as an integer or radical expression in simplest form.

    a. $\sqrt{\dfrac{16}{49}}$ **b.** $\sqrt{44}$

    c. $\sqrt{3}\sqrt{15}$ **d.** $2\sqrt{63}$

    e. $81^{\frac{1}{2}}$ **f.** $\dfrac{\sqrt{8}}{2}$

    g. $\sqrt[3]{27}$ **h.** $\sqrt[3]{-1}$

39 The table below gives the number of words spelled correctly (out of ten) by a group of students preparing for a spelling competition.

Number of Words Spelled Correctly	6	7	8	9	10
Number of Students	5	4	10	8	3

    a. Calculate the mean and standard deviation of the number of words spelled correctly.

    b. Colin and Lindsey tried to spell these ten words, and they both spelled all ten of the words correctly. Lindsey then added her score of 10, Colin's score of 10, and the average of the other 30 students and then divided that sum by 3 to get a new mean of 9.33. Is Lindsey's mean the correct mean of all 32 students? If not, explain the problem with her reasoning.

40 Often you will need to convert measures from one unit to another. Use what you know about seconds, minutes, hours, and days to complete each statement.

    a. 80 minutes = _____ seconds = _____ hours

    b. 3 days = _____ hours = _____ minutes

    c. 300,000 seconds = _____ days = _____ years

36 **a.** $x = -\dfrac{3}{2}$ **b.** $x = 10$ **c.** $x = 0.5$

    d. no solution   **e.** $x = 3$ **f.** $x = 3$

37 **a.** -25

    b. 22

    c. 163

    d. $-\dfrac{39}{2} = -19.5$

    e. -14

38 **a.** $\dfrac{4}{7}$

    b. $2\sqrt{11}$

    c. $3\sqrt{5}$

    d. $6\sqrt{7}$

    e. 9

    f. $\sqrt{2}$

    g. 3

    h. -1

39 **a.** $\overline{x} = 8$ words

       $s \approx 1.23$ words

    b. No, it is not the correct mean. Lindsey needed to weight the average of the 30 students. The actual mean of the 32 scores should be

$$\dfrac{830 + 10 + 10}{32} = \dfrac{260}{32} = 8.125 \text{ words.}$$

40 **a.** 80 minutes = <u>4,800</u> seconds = $1\dfrac{1}{3}$ hours

    b. 3 days = <u>72</u> hours = <u>4,320</u> minutes

    c. 300,000 seconds $\approx$ <u>3.472</u> days $\approx$ <u>0.0095</u> years

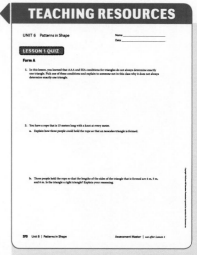

TEACHING RESOURCES

Assessment Masters 370–375

 GO DIGITAL

LESSON
2

Polygons and
Their Properties

Triangles and quadrilaterals are special classes of **polygons**—closed figures in a plane, formed by connecting line segments endpoint-to-endpoint with each segment meeting exactly two other segments. The segments are the *sides* of the polygons, and the points that they join are the *vertices*. Some other polygonal shapes that can be seen in daily life and with which you may be familiar are shown below.

Polygons and Their Properties

This lesson extends the study of triangles and quadrilaterals to polygons and other two-dimensional shapes and designs. In Investigation 1, students explore reflection and rotational symmetries of regular polygons and other shapes. The rotational symmetry of regular polygons is used to develop a method for accurately drawing regular polygons. In Investigation 2, students use their understanding of angle sums of triangles to develop strategies and rules for determining the sum of the measures of the interior (and exterior) angles of any convex polygon and the measures of an interior angle of a regular polygon. They also discover a surprising geometric invariant—the sum of the measures of the exterior angles of any convex polygon is 360°. In Investigation 3, properties of polygons are then used to investigate tiling patterns, particularly patterns comprised of congruent copies of one or more regular polygons. The investigation provides opportunities for informal visual experiences with rigid transformations—line reflections, rotations, and translations.

Lesson Objectives

- Discover and apply properties of the interior and exterior angles of convex polygons and central angles of regular polygons

- Recognize and describe line and rotational symmetries of polygons and other two-dimensional figures

- (Re)discover which triangles, quadrilaterals, and regular polygons will tile a plane and explore semiregular tessellations

- Recognize and describe symmetries of tessellations, including translation symmetry

Lesson Launch

In discussing the Think About This Situation questions, you might consider displaying on the overhead projector some examples of nuts for bolts that are in common use. After discussing the questions, ask students if they can draw an example of a shape that is *not* a polygon. Then have several students show their shapes. If students seem to have difficulty coming up with examples, you might ask them to look around the classroom for examples. Students' earrings will likely provide some examples. Or ask, "What diagrams/figures have you used in your study of mathematics this year that are not polygons?" Students should recall some vertex-edge graphs with arcs or edge-crossings or tree graphs.

Common Core State Standards CCSS
Focused on:
G-CO.3, G-MG.1, G-MG.2
Connected to:
A-CED.2, G-CO.9, G-MG.3

THINK ABOUT THIS SITUATION

As you examine the photos on the previous page, try to identify the polygon in each case and think about some of its features.

a How would you describe the shape of each polygon?

b What features do each of these polygons appear to have in common?

c The designs of most bolts and nuts are based on polygons with an even number of sides. Why do you think this is the case? Why do you think the nuts on many public water mains and fire hydrants have the shape shown?

d Why do you think a stop sign has the shape it has? Would a square or rectangle work just as well?

e Why do you think the cells of a honeycomb are shaped as they are? Would other polygons work just as well?

f Based on your previous work with triangles and quadrilaterals, what are some natural questions you might ask about other polygons?

In this lesson, you will investigate properties of polygons, including relationships among their sides, angles, and diagonals. You also will explore the symmetry of polygons and patterns formed by combinations of polygons. These properties and patterns have important applications in art, design, and manufacturing.

INVESTIGATION 1

Patterns in Polygons

As the thin metal sheets that form the aperture of a camera move together or apart, they determine the amount of light that passes through a camera lens. The closing apertures on various cameras also determine polygons that differ in their number of sides.

Lesson 2 | Polygons and Their Properties **399**

a The photos display five-sided, six-sided, and eight-sided polygons. Students may recall that these polygons are called pentagons, hexagons, and octagons, respectively.

b Each polygon is formed by congruent segments joined at equal angles. Visually, each polygon could be placed inside a circle so that the vertices would be on the circle. (Students may be familiar with the terms "regular" and "convex," but, if not, they will learn them in this lesson.)

c Polygons like those in the student text with an even number of sides will have pairs of parallel sides. This allows the use of common wrenches with parallel "grips." Equipment that should have restricted access have an odd number of sides on the nuts. This means that a special tool is required to loosen and tighten the nut.

d Students' ideas may vary, but they will likely note that octagons have a large area (visual field) as compared, for instance, to a triangle or rectangle that would frame the word "STOP." (You might ask students for the shapes of other traffic control signs indicating that shape-recognition is often part of driver's license exams. Round signs are used at railroad crossings. See www.trafficsign.us.)

e The honeycomb cells formed from hexagons fit together without wasting space. There are other polygons that fit together without wasting space, such as triangles and squares or rectangles. (In this lesson and On Your Own Applications Task 7, students will examine a likely explanation for the bees' choice of hexagons for their honeycombs.)

f Students might ask: Can you always build an *n*-sided polygon given *n* side lengths? Are polygons rigid? Is the sum of the interior angles of a polygon a constant no matter what shape it is? How can you test if two polygons are congruent?

TEACHING RESOURCES

UNIT 6   Patterns in Shape

THINK ABOUT THIS SITUATION

As you examine the photos on page 398 of the *Student Edition*, try to identify the polygon in each case and think about some of its features.

a How would you describe the shape of each polygon?

b What features do each of these polygons appear to have in common?

c The designs of most bolts and nuts are based on polygons with an even number of sides. Why do you think this is the case? Why do you think the nuts on many public water mains and fire hydrants have the shape shown?

d Why do you think a stop sign has the shape it has? Would a square or rectangle work just as well?

e Why do you think the cells of a honeycomb are shaped as they are? Would other polygons work just as well?

f Based on your previous work with triangles and quadrilaterals, what are some natural questions you might ask about other polygons?

376   Unit 6 | Patterns in Shape   Lesson Master | *see with page 399*

Lesson Master 376
(!) GO DIGITAL

INVESTIGATION **1**   **CCSS**   G-CO.3, G-MG.1, A-CED2, G-CO.9, G-MG.3

Patterns in Polygons

In this investigation, an experiment with a two-mirror kaleidoscope leads to the relationship between the number of sides of a regular polygon and the measure of its central angles and to a method for accurately drawing regular polygons. Extensions Task 24 provides an opportunity for students to experiment with a three-mirror kaleidoscope.

The creation of regular polygons using a two-mirror kaleidoscope ensures symmetry. Most students should have a basic understanding of line and rotational symmetry. This investigation is intended to deepen their understanding to be able to enumerate and generalize symmetries of particular polygons. In Problem 5, students should connect characteristics of special quadrilaterals with their symmetries. For example, the symmetry line ℓ for kite $ABCD$ is connected to the fact that $\overline{AB} \cong \overline{AD}$ and $\overline{BC} \cong \overline{DC}$. But the line symmetry also explains why $\angle B \cong \angle D$ and why the longer diagonal bisects the shorter diagonal.

COLLABORATION SKILL

A *skeptic* respectfully challenges group consensus and checks for alternative ideas or possibilities.

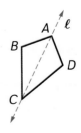

Polygons can be classified in several different ways. One of the most commonly used classifications is in terms of the number of sides they have.

Number of Sides	Name	Number of Sides	Name
3	Triangle	9	Nonagon
4	Quadrilateral	10	Decagon
5	Pentagon	11	11-gon
6	Hexagon	12	Dodecagon
7	Septagon	15	15-gon
8	Octagon	n	n-gon

1 Name the polygons pictured on pages 398 and 399.

The polygonal shapes in the photos are examples of **regular polygons**. In regular polygons, all sides are congruent and all angles are congruent. These shapes also have a certain balance or regularity of form that can be explained in terms of their *symmetry*. As you work on the following problems, look for answers to these questions:

> *How can you accurately draw or build a regular polygon?*
>
> *How can you describe the symmetry of a regular polygon and other shapes?*

2 **Symmetry Patterns** You can discover a method for accurately drawing a regular polygon by conducting the following experiment with a two-mirror kaleidoscope.

Hinge two mirrors together with tape so that you can adjust the angle between them. Draw a line segment on a sheet of paper and place a dot on the segment. Position the mirrors as shown in the photo. Adjust the mirrors so that they make an isosceles triangle with the segment and you can see a regular pentagon. Carefully trace the angle formed by the mirrors. Measure the angle.

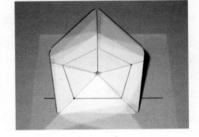

Jim Laser

a. Complete a table like the one below by adjusting the mirrors to form a regular polygon with the given number of sides.

Regular Polygon	3	4	5	6	7	8
Angle Between Mirrors	?	?	72°	?	?	?

b. Predict the angle between the mirrors necessary to form a decagon. Check your prediction.

c. Write a rule that gives the measure M of the angle between the mirrors as a function of the number of sides of the regular n-gon produced by the two-mirror kaleidoscope.

DIFFERENTIATION If some or all of your students have not previously studied polygons, you may wish to provide the student master for completion and inclusion in their notes.

The polygons on page 398 are octagon, pentagon, and hexagon. The polygons from left to right on page 399 are pentagon, hexagon, and septagon. (A seven-sided polygon can be referred to as either a septagon or a heptagon.)

2 **INSTRUCTIONAL NOTE** If students have difficulty positioning the mirror, have them place a marking on the edges of the mirror so that distance from the hinge to the markings is the same in both mirrors. Then align the markings on the line.

a. Students' experiments should produce values close to the following:

Regular Polygon	3	4	5	6	7	8
Angle Between Mirrors	120°	90°	72°	60°	51°	45°

b. The mirror angle for a decagon should be 36°, but students will likely suggest 35°.

c. $M = \dfrac{360°}{n}$

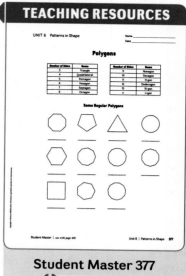

TEACHING RESOURCES

Student Master 377
⊘ GO DIGITAL

The angle you traced in each case is called a **central angle** of the regular polygon.

d. To draw a regular pentagon, first draw a circle with a compass. Next draw a radius and then use a protractor to draw a central angle of 72°. The points where the sides of the angle intersect the circle are two of the vertices of the pentagon How can you find the remaining three vertices using only a compass? Draw the pentagon.

e. Make an accurate drawing of a regular octagon.

f. Write a step-by-step description of a general method for drawing a regular *n*-gon.

3 If you rotate a tracing of a regular pentagon 72° about the center of the pentagon, the tracing will *coincide* (match) with the original figure. Try it. The regular pentagon has 72° **rotational symmetry**.

a. Explain why a regular pentagon also has 144° rotational symmetry. What other rotational symmetries does a regular pentagon have that are less than 360°? We do not consider a 360° rotation since a tracing of any figure will coincide with the original figure after a rotation of 360°.

b. What are the rotational symmetries of an equilateral triangle? Do other triangles have rotational symmetry? Explain.

c. What are the rotational symmetries of a square? Of a regular hexagon?

d. Make a conjecture about the number of rotational symmetries of a regular *n*-gon. What angle measures will these symmetries have? Test your conjecture for the case of a regular octagon.

4 A regular pentagon also has **reflection** or **line symmetry**; sometimes called **mirror symmetry**.

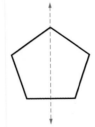

When a mirror or piece of dark-colored Plexiglas is placed on a *line of symmetry*, half of the figure and its reflected image form the entire figure.

When a tracing of the figure is folded along the *line of symmetry*, one-half of the figure exactly coincides with the other half.

a. On a tracing of the regular pentagon above, draw each line of symmetry.

b. Draw an equilateral triangle and then draw each of its symmetry lines. What other triangles have lines of symmetry? What property or properties do these triangles have in common?

Lesson 2 | Polygons and Their Properties   **401**

Jim Laser

d. To find the remaining vertices, you could use the compass to measure the distance between the two vertices and mark off additional vertices along the circumference of the circle. If done accurately, students should end back at the first vertex.

e. Students will need to begin with a central angle of 45° to form a regular octagon.

f. (1) Draw a circle.

(2) Draw a central angle of $\frac{360°}{n}$, where n is the number of sides of the n-gon.

(3) Extend the sides of the angle to intersect the circle.

(4) Use a compass to mark off points on the circle that are the same distance apart as the two points formed by the central angle and the circle.

(5) Draw segments connecting consecutive vertices.

3 **a.** A rotation of 144° will move the pentagon so that it coincides with the original pentagon again. Each vertex will move two vertices over. Thinking about the central angle construction from Problem 2, students should recognize that pentagons also have rotational symmetries of 216° and 288°.

b. Equilateral triangles have rotational symmetries of 120° and 240°. Other triangles would not have rotational symmetry. You need to have congruent sides so that when you rotate the triangle, a side will coincide with the next side.

c. A square will have rotational symmetries of 90°, 180°, and 270°. A regular hexagon will have rotational symmetries of 60°, 120°, 180°, 240°, and 300°.

d. A regular n-gon will have $n - 1$ rotational symmetries. The angles of these rotational symmetries will be the multiples of $\frac{360°}{n}$ less than 360°. A regular octagon has 7 rotational symmetries of 45°, 90°, 135°, 180°, 225°, 270°, and 315°.

4 **INSTRUCTIONAL NOTE** To have approximately regular figures to draw lines of symmetry, students could trace the pentagon in Problem 4 Part d, the stop sign on page 398, and the octagon they drew in Problem 2 Part e. Alternatively, you could provide Student Master 378 for this task.

a.

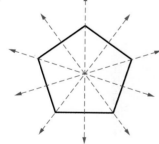

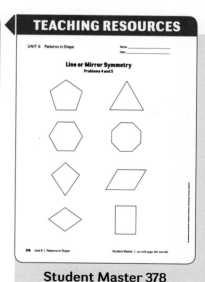
b.

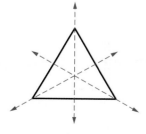

Isosceles triangles will have one line of symmetry. There must be at least two congruent sides to have line symmetry.

c. Describe the lines of symmetry of a square.

d. Draw a regular hexagon and then draw its lines of symmetry.

e. Make and test a conjecture about the number of symmetry lines of a regular octagon.

f. Make a conjecture about the number of symmetry lines of a regular *n*-gon.

    i. Describe where the symmetry lines cut a regular *n*-gon when *n* is an even number.

    ii. Describe where the symmetry lines cut a regular *n*-gon when *n* is an odd number.

g. How is the line of symmetry of a figure related to the segment connecting a point on the figure with its reflection (mirror) image?

5 Now consider the symmetries of special quadrilaterals that are not regular polygons—kites, general parallelograms, rhombuses, and rectangles.

a. Which of these other special quadrilaterals have line symmetry?

    i. In each case, sketch the shape and each of its symmetry lines.

    ii. Which of the quadrilaterals have symmetry lines that join vertices? What do these quadrilaterals have in common?

    iii. Which of the quadrilaterals have symmetry lines that do not join vertices? Where are the symmetry lines located? How do such quadrilaterals differ from those in part ii?

b. Which of these other special quadrilaterals have rotational symmetry?

    i. In each case, what are the angles of the rotational symmetries?

    ii. What property or properties do the quadrilaterals with rotational symmetry have in common?

6 Symmetry is perhaps the most observable characteristic of shapes found in nature. Symmetry is also often an integral part of the art forms created by people throughout history and across many cultures of the world. Examine carefully each of the figures shown below.

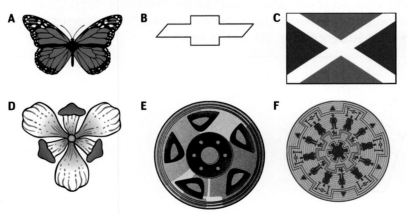

A   B   C

D   E   F

c. A square will have 4 lines of symmetry. Two are the diagonals and the other 2 are the lines connecting the midpoints of opposite sides.

d.

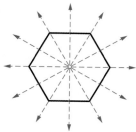

e. A regular octagon will have 8 lines of symmetry.

f. A regular *n*-gon will have *n* lines of symmetry.

   i. If there is an even number of sides, the symmetry lines will either join two midpoints of opposite sides or two opposite vertices.

   ii. If there is an odd number of sides, the lines of symmetry will connect a vertex to the midpoint of the opposite side.

g. The line of symmetry of a shape is the perpendicular bisector of the segment connecting a point on the shape with its image point.

5 **a.** Kites, rhombuses, and rectangles have line symmetry, but not general parallelograms.

   i.

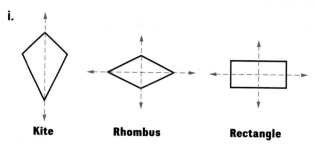

   Kite   Rhombus   Rectangle

   ii. Rhombuses and kites have symmetry lines that join vertices. These quadrilaterals have two pairs of consecutive sides that are congruent.

   iii. A rectangle has symmetry lines that do not join vertices. It has two pairs of opposite sides congruent. But general parallelograms also have opposite sides congruent, and do not have symmetry lines. Thinking about the symmetry lines that connect the midpoints of opposite sides, you can deduce that along with opposite sides congruent, two pairs of consecutive angles must be congruent in order to have symmetry lines that do not join vertices. (A second example of a special quadrilateral with symmetry lines not joining vertices is an isosceles trapezoid.)

b. Parallelograms, rectangles, and rhombuses have rotational symmetry.

   i. They have 180° rotational symmetry.

   ii. They have two pairs of opposite sides congruent.

NOTE The solution to Problem 6 is on page T403.

INSTRUCTIONAL NOTE

Have students test with a mirror or by folding in half along the mirror line. A common misconception is that the rectangle has diagonal lines of symmetry since they "cut the rectangle in half."

a. Which of these figures have reflection symmetry? Using a copy of these figures, for each figure with reflection symmetry, draw its line(s) of symmetry.

b. Which of the shapes have rotational symmetry? For each shape with rotational symmetry, give the angle(s) through which it can be rotated to coincide with itself.

c. If a figure has reflection symmetry, must it have rotational symmetry? Explain your reasoning.

d. If a figure has rotational symmetry, must it have reflection symmetry? Explain.

SUMMARIZE THE MATHEMATICS

In this investigation, you learned how to draw regular polygons and discovered special patterns relating the number of sides to the measure of a central angle and to the number and nature of rotational and reflection symmetries.

a Explain how you would accurately draw a regular *n*-gon.

b Explain how you can test to see if a figure has line symmetry. Describe the number and positions of the lines of symmetry of a regular *n*-gon.

c Explain how you can test if a figure has rotational symmetry. Describe the number of rotational symmetries of a regular *n*-gon, and the measure of the angles of rotation.

Be prepared to share your ideas and thinking with the class.

✔ CHECK YOUR UNDERSTANDING

Make an accurate drawing of a regular nonagon.

a. What is the measure of a central angle?

b. Describe all the rotational symmetries.

c. Sketch all the lines of symmetry. Where do the symmetry lines cut the sides of the nonagon?

d. Consider a regular nonagon drawn by you and one by a classmate. What is the minimum information you need in order to conclude the two nonagons are congruent? Explain your reasoning.

6 **a.** Reflection symmetry is evident in figures A, C, D, and F. (Some students may erroneously think that figure B has line symmetry.)

b. Figures B and C have 180° rotational symmetry.
Figure D has 120° and 240° rotational symmetry.
Figure E has 72°, 144°, 216°, and 288° rotational symmetry.
Figure F has 60°, 120°, 180°, 240°, and 300° rotational symmetry.

c. Just because a figure has reflection symmetry does not mean it must have rotational symmetry. Students will likely explain by noting that the butterfly (figure A) has reflection symmetry but not rotational symmetry. If so, you may wish to help them recognize that they are reasoning by counterexample.

d. Figures can have rotational symmetry without reflection symmetry also. Figures B and E have rotational symmetry but no reflection symmetry.

TEACHING RESOURCES

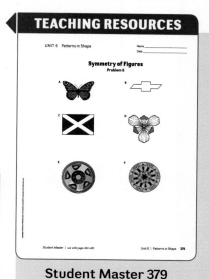

Student Master 379
ⓘ GO DIGITAL

SUMMARIZE THE MATHEMATICS

a Draw a circle. Draw a central angle of $\frac{360°}{n}$, where n is the number of sides of the n-gon. Extend the sides of the angle to intersect the circle. Use a compass to mark off points on the circle that are the same distance apart as the two points formed by the central angle and the circle.

b A figure will have line symmetry if you can place a line on the figure so the shape and its mirror image coincide. Such figures can (theoretically) be folded along the line so that the two halves exactly match. Regular n-gons with an odd number of sides have lines of symmetry that connect a vertex and the midpoint of the opposite side. Regular n-gons that have an even number of sides have some lines of symmetry that connect two opposite vertices and others that connect midpoints of opposite sides. In both cases, there are n lines of symmetry.

c You can test for rotational symmetry by visualizing the shape turning around a point at the center of the shape and checking to see if the shape coincides with itself. For complex shapes, it may be helpful to trace them, cut them out, and physically rotate them to fit in their outline. Regular n-gons have $n - 1$ rotational symmetries about their center. The angles of rotation will be the multiples of $\frac{360°}{n}$ that are less than 360°.

TEACHING RESOURCES

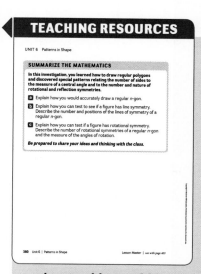

Lesson Master 380
ⓘ GO DIGITAL

PROCESSING PROMPT Today I acted as a skeptic by respectfully challenging

_____ .
(mathematical idea)

NOTE The solution to the Check Your Understanding is on page T404.

INVESTIGATION **2**

The Triangle Connection

Polygons with the same corresponding side lengths can have quite different shapes. As in the special case of quadrilaterals, polygons can be convex or nonconvex. In a **convex polygon**, no segment connecting two vertices is outside the polygon. Unless otherwise stated, in the remainder of this unit and in future units, polygons will be assumed to be convex.

Convex

Convex

Nonconvex

The shape and symmetry of a polygon depend on both side lengths and angle measures. As you work on Problems 1–4, look for answers to the following question:

How are the measures of the angles of any polygon related to the number of sides?

1 **Polygon Angle Sum Property** In Lesson 1, you learned that polygon shapes of four or more sides are not rigid. They can be made rigid by adding diagonal braces.

a. How could you use this idea of *triangulation* to find the sum of the measures of the interior angles of a pentagon? Compare your method and angle sum with others.

b. Use similar reasoning to find the sum of the measures of the interior angles of a hexagon. Why is it not necessary that the hexagon be a regular hexagon?

c. Complete a table like the one below for polygons having up to 9 sides. Examine your table for patterns relating sides, triangles, and angle sums.

Number of Sides	Number of Triangles	Sum of Interior Angles
4		
5	3	540°
6		
⋮		

d. Predict the sum of the measures of the interior angles of a decagon (10 sides). Check your prediction with a sketch.

e. Suppose a polygon has n sides. Write a rule that gives the sum of the measures of its interior angles S as a function of the number of its sides n.

f. Test your rule for $n = 3$ (a triangle) and $n = 4$ (a quadrilateral).

✓ CHECK YOUR UNDERSTANDING

a. 40°

b. There are 8 rotational symmetries, and each is a multiple of 40°: 40°, 80°, 120°, 160°, 200°, 240°, 280°, and 320°.

c. The nine symmetry lines cut the sides of the nonagon at their midpoint and connect to the opposite vertex.

d. Since both nonagons are regular, you need only know that one side of each nonagon is congruent to conclude the regular nonagons are congruent. All interior angles of both nonagons are 140°.

INVESTIGATION **2** **CCSS** **G-MG.1,** A-CED2

The Triangle Connection

In this investigation, students explore relationships involving the measures of the interior angles and exterior angles of convex polygons. Students may find it surprising that while the sum of the measures of the interior angles of a polygon is a function of the number of sides, the sum of the measures of the exterior angles of any convex polygon is a constant, 360°. Deliberate connections between algebra and geometry are achieved through the development and analysis of function rules relating angle measures to the number of sides of an n-gon.

Students may have been introduced in middle school to the terminology "concave" polygon. Since "convex" is the more important idea, these materials use "convex" and "nonconvex" as indicated to characterize polygons and, in Lesson 3, polyhedra.

> **NOTE** Unless otherwise stated, polygons in this unit and future units will be assumed to be convex.

1 **a.** Using the ideas of triangulation, divide the pentagon into three triangles by connecting nonconsecutive vertices. The sum of the measures of the interior angles of a pentagon is then 3(180°) = 540°.

b. 4(180°) = 720°; Any convex hexagon can be triangulated.

c.

Number of Sides	Number of Triangles	Sum of Interior Angles
4	2	360°
5	3	540°
6	4	720°
7	5	900°
8	6	1,080°
9	7	1,260°

d. The sum of the measures of the interior angles of a decagon is 1,440°.

e. $S = (n - 2)180°$

f. For $n = 3$, $S = 180°(3 - 2) = 180°$. For $n = 4$, $S = 180°(4 - 2) = 360°$.

g. Why is your function in Part e a linear function?

    i. What is the slope of the graph of your function?

    ii. What does the slope mean in terms of the variables? Does the
       y-intercept make sense? Why or why not?

2 **A Surprising Property of Polygons** By extending each side of a polygon,
you create an *exterior angle* at each vertex.

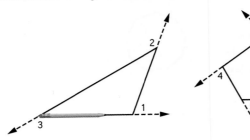

    a. Conduct the following exploration.

    For each shape shown above:

      (1) Place your pencil along the horizontal side of the shape with the tip
          pointing to the right as shown.

      (2) Slide your pencil to the right until the eraser end is at the vertex
          of $\angle 1$.

      (3) Turn your pencil about the vertex so that it aligns with the second
          side.

      (4) Repeat Steps 2 and 3 for each vertex until your pencil has made a
          complete trip around the polygon and is in its original position.

    When the trip is completed, by how much has the pencil turned? What
    does this suggest about the sum of the measures of the exterior angles of
    the shape?

    b. Repeat the exploration by drawing a different polygon of your choice. Did
       you find supporting evidence for your conjecture? What do you think is
       true about the sum of the measures of the exterior angles of any convex
       polygon?

3 Exterior angles can be created by extending sides in either direction.
Suppose a, b, c, and d represent the measures of the exterior angles of
quadrilateral $ABCD$.

    a. Use the diagram and careful reasoning
       to write a general argument for why
       your conjecture in Problem 2 is true
       for any quadrilateral. Compare your
       reasoning with others and resolve
       any differences.

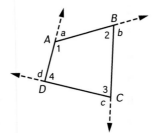

    b. Explain how you might use a similar
       argument in the case of an octagon.

g. The function $S = 180°(n - 2)$ can be written as $S = 180°n - 360°$, which is in linear form $y = ax + b$.

    i. $180°$

    ii. As the number of sides of polygons increases by one, the sum of the measures of the interior angles increases by $180°$. The y-intercept of $-360°$ does not make sense because there is no polygon with zero sides.

INSTRUCTIONAL NOTE

As you listen to groups working on Problem 1 Part g, listen for the connection of the slope of $180°$ to one additional triangle needed to subdivide the polygon. You might ask students for the *NOW-NEXT* relationship and why it exists to prompt the connection.

2 **a.** The pencil will have made a complete ($360°$) rotation. This suggests that the sum of the measures of the exterior angles of the triangle and the pentagon is $360°$.

b. Each person in the group should experiment with a different type of polygon in order to have more instances to support the conjecture that the sum of the measures of the exterior angles for any polygon is $360°$.

3 **a.** At each vertex of the quadrilateral, the interior angle and the exterior angle sum to $180°$. So, $4 \times 180° = 720°$ is the total number of degrees for the 4 straight angles at vertices A, B, C, and D. Now subtracting the sum of the interior angles, which is $360°$, results in $360°$ for the sum of a, b, c, and d.

DIFFERENTIATION

Some students could be encouraged to respond to Problem 3 symbolically.

b. There would be 8 vertices for an octagon. $8 \times 180° = 1{,}440°$. Since the sum of the interior angles is $(8 - 2)180° = 6 \times 180°$, the exterior angles would sum to $1{,}440° - 6 \times 180° = 360°$.

4 **Predicting Angle Measures of Regular Polygons** If a polygon is a regular polygon, then you can find a relationship between the number of its sides and the measure of *each* interior angle.

a. What is the measure of an interior angle of a regular hexagon?

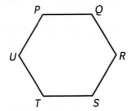

b. Write a rule that gives the measure A of an interior angle of a regular polygon as a function of its number of sides n.

c. What is the measure of an exterior angle of a regular hexagon? Of a regular 15-gon?

d. Write a rule that gives the measure E of an exterior angle of a regular polygon as a function of its number of sides n.

e. Visualize an example of a regular n-gon with an exterior angle drawn. If you added the expressions for your rules in Parts b and d, what should you get? Try it.

f. Are your functions in Parts b and d linear functions? If so, what is the constant rate of change in each case?

SUMMARIZE THE MATHEMATICS

In this investigation, you used reasoning with triangles to help discover a pattern relating the number of sides of a polygon to the sum of the measures of its interior angles. You also discovered a surprising pattern involving the sum of the measures of the exterior angles of a polygon.

a Explain how you can find the sum of the measures of the interior angles of a polygon. What is the measure of one interior angle of a regular n-gon?

b What is true about the sum of the measures of the exterior angles of a polygon? What is the measure of one exterior angle of a regular n-gon?

Be prepared to share your ideas and reasoning with the class.

4 **a.** 120°

b. $A = \dfrac{(n-2)180°}{n}$

c. $\dfrac{360°}{6} = 60°; \dfrac{360°}{15} = 24°$

d. $E = \dfrac{360°}{n}$

e. Adding the measure of an interior angle A with the measure of the exterior angle E should result in 180° since a straight angle is formed by the two angles.

$$\dfrac{(n-2)180°}{n} + \dfrac{360°}{n} = \dfrac{180°n - 360° + 360°}{n} = 180°$$

f. Neither function is linear since the rules are not in the form $y = a + bx$.

Summary

After discussing Part b of the Summarize the Mathematics, you might ask students where they have seen the expression $\dfrac{360°}{n}$ before. What is the connection here? Some students might be encouraged to think about the geometry behind why the exterior angle measure of a regular polygon is the same as the measure of its central angle. Students who accept the challenge could present their thinking in the next class period.

SUMMARIZE THE MATHEMATICS

a You can subdivide the polygon into triangles by drawing all diagonals from one vertex. Then count the triangles (which is always 2 less than the number of sides) and multiply that number by 180° to get the sum of the measures of the interior angles of the polygon. The measure of one interior angle of a regular n-gon is the sum of the measures, as computed above, divided by n.

b The sum of the measures of the exterior angles of a polygon is always 360°. The measure of one exterior angle of a regular n-gon is $\dfrac{360°}{n}$.

MATH TOOLKIT Summarize what you know about the angle measures for regular polygons. Include sketches in your summary.

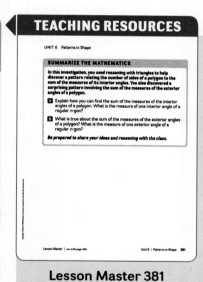

✅ CHECK YOUR UNDERSTANDING

Being able to recognize traffic signs by their shape and color is important when driving and is often tested on exams for a driver's license. Examine the school crossing sign at the right.

a. Identify the shape of the sign and describe the symmetries of this shape.

b. Use the design specifications shown and symmetry to find the lengths of the remaining sides of the sign.

c. Find the measures of the remaining interior angles.

d. On a copy of the shape, extend the sides to form an exterior angle at each vertex. Find the measure of each exterior angle.

INVESTIGATION 3

Patterns with Polygons

One of the most common and interesting applications of polygon shapes is their use as tiles for floors and walls. The photo below shows portions of two different *tilings* at the Center for Mathematics and Computing at Carleton College in Northfield, Minnesota. The portion of the tiling in the center of the photo is based on special tiles and a procedure for placing them created by Sir Roger Penrose, a British mathematician at the University of Oxford. Can you identify the types of polygons used for the Penrose tiles?

Later in this lesson you will have the opportunity to explore the variety of patterns that can be created with these tiles. Researchers have recently discovered that certain chemicals naturally organize themselves in similar patterns, some of which are used to make nonstick coating for pots and pans.

As you work on the following problems, make notes that will help you answer this question:

Which polygons or combinations of polygons will tile the plane?

Lesson 2 | Polygons and Their Properties **407**

✅ CHECK YOUR UNDERSTANDING

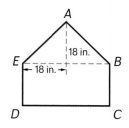

a. The shape is a pentagon. Ignoring the figures in the sign, the sign has line symmetry through A and the middle of the sign post.

b. $BC = 18.5$ in.; $AE = \sqrt{18^2 + 18^2} \approx 25.5$ in.; $AB \approx 25.5$

c. By symmetry, $m\angle C = 90°$ and $m\angle E = 135°$. Since the sum of the measures of the interior angles of a pentagon is $540°$, $m\angle A = 540° - 2(135°) - 2(90°) = 90°$.

d.

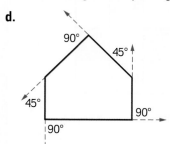

INVESTIGATION **3** **CCSS** G-MG.1, G-MG.2

Patterns with Polygons

Some regular polygons are repeatedly used in designs because they fit together to make a tiling or tessellation. In the first part of this investigation, students explore tessellations that can be generated by a single polygon. In the second part, they investigate tessellations formed by using more than one polygon shape with the restriction that the polygons be regular polygons. In this unit, we will only be interested in edge-to-edge tessellations.

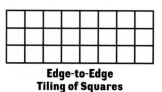

Edge-to-Edge Tiling of Squares

The intent of this investigation is for students to use characteristics they have previously discovered about triangles, parallelograms, and so on. For example, in Problem 2, Part c, push students beyond simply saying that "every triangle I tried makes a tessellation; therefore, all triangles will tessellate." You might ask them:

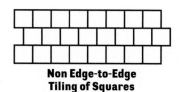

Non Edge-to-Edge Tiling of Squares

> *What features of your patterns suggest that any triangle will tile the plane?*

They might observe, for example, that you can always make a parallelogram by rotating any triangle about the midpoint of a side, and that the parallel sides of the parallelogram guide the placement of the adjoining parallelogram. Or, you might ask them to mark, with symbols or colors, the angles of the basic triangle and then ask them:

> *How do these angles appear at the vertices where the edges come together?*
> (Two of each color at each vertex.)

If students seem to be trying to place their shapes at random, point out pieces of sides that do not match, and remark that it will be difficult to repeat exactly that measurement elsewhere in the pattern. Trying to match edges and vertices will be more productive in terms of repeating the pattern.

In this investigation students will find the "Tilings with Regular Polygons" custom app particularly useful when exploring possible semiregular tessellations.

In Investigation 4 of Lesson 3, students will explore how regular polygons can be used to build regular polyhedra in three-dimensional space.

1 **Tilings with Triangles or Quadrilaterals** The figures below show portions of **tilings** or **tessellations** of equilateral triangles and squares. The tilings are made of repeated copies of a shape placed edge-to-edge so that they completely cover a region without overlaps or gaps.

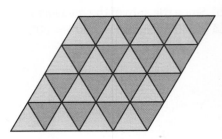 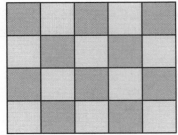

a. Assume that the tilings are extended indefinitely in all directions to cover the plane.

   i. Describe the various ways that you can *slide* a tracing of each tiling so that it coincides with the original tiling. These tilings have **translation symmetry**.

   ii. How could you describe the translation symmetries using arrows?

   iii. Do the extended tilings have any reflection symmetry? If so, describe the lines of symmetry.

   iv. Do the extended tilings have any rotational symmetries? If so, describe the centers and angles of rotation.

b. For these two tilings:

   i. what is the sum of the measures of the angles at a common vertex?

   ii. what is the measure of each angle at a common vertex?

c. In the tiling with equilateral triangles, identify other common polygons formed by two or more adjoined triangles that also produce a tiling. Sketch each and show the equilateral triangles that form the new tile. What does this suggest about other polygons that could be used to tile? Explain your reasoning.

2 Now explore if other triangles can be used as tiles.

a. Working in groups, each member should cut from poster board a small triangle that is not equilateral. Each member's triangle should have a different shape. Individually, explore whether a tiling of a plane can be made by using repeated tracings of your triangle. Draw and compare sketches of the tilings you made.

b. Can more than one tiling pattern be made by using copies of one triangle? If so, illustrate with sketches.

c. Do you think any triangle could be used to tile a plane? Explain your reasoning. You may find software like the "Tilings with Triangles or Quadrilaterals" custom app helpful in exploring this question.

1 **a.** **i.** You could slide the tilings to the right, to the left, or on the diagonal (up or down) to coincide with each other.

ii. You could use an arrow to show the direction to slide the tiling. The length of the arrow could indicate how far to slide the tiling.

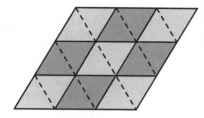

iii. The triangle tiling has line reflection across any line that connects a vertex and a midpoint of the opposite side of a triangle. The square tiling has line reflection across any diagonal or line connecting the midpoints of opposite sides.

iv. The triangle tiling has 120° and 240° rotational symmetries about any center of a triangle. There is also 120° and 240° rotational symmetry about any vertex of an equilateral triangle. The square tiling has 90°, 180°, and 270° rotational symmetry.

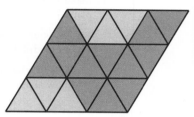

The square tiling has 90°, 180°, and 270° rotational symmetries about any center of a square. There is also 180° rotational symmetry about any vertex of a square.

b. **i.** The sum of the measures of the angles at a common vertex is 360°.

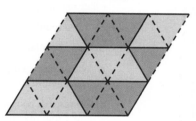

ii. Each angle at a common vertex measures 60° or 90°, respectively, for the triangle and square tilings.

c. Other common polygons made up of equilateral triangles are a rhombus, a regular hexagon, or isosceles trapezoids (as seen at the right). Any polygon made from equilateral triangles should be able to tile the plane. (Recall that unless otherwise stated, "polygon" refers to a convex polygon.)

2 **a.** Every triangle will tile the plane.

b. Many edge-to-edge patterns are possible, here are two:

- A parallelogram is formed when a triangle is rotated about the midpoint of one of its sides, and that parallelogram will tile the plane by translating repeatedly in the directions of its edges.

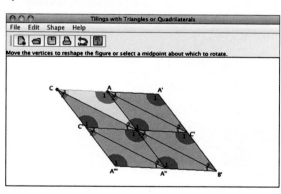

- When a triangle is reflected over any one of its sides, the resulting quadrilateral will tile the plane by rotating around the midpoints of the sides. This quadrilateral is a kite or a nonconvex quadrilateral with two pairs of consecutive sides congruent (dart).

c. Any triangle can be used to tile the plane because the sum of the measures of the interior angles is 180°. At any vertex of a tiling, two of each of the angles of the triangle will fit exactly; that is, without overlapping or having a gap. Side lengths must also match.

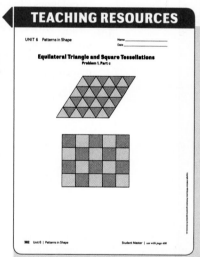
TECHNOLOGY NOTE

The "Tilings with Triangles and Quadrilaterals" custom app could be used to support student exploration and thinking.

3 The most common tiling is by squares. In this problem, you will explore other quadrilaterals that can be used to make a tiling.

a. Each member of your group should cut a nonsquare quadrilateral from poster board. Again, each of the quadrilaterals should be shaped differently. Individually, investigate whether a tiling of a plane can be made with the different quadrilaterals. Draw sketches of the tilings you made.

b. Can more than one tiling pattern be made using the same quadrilateral shape? If so, illustrate and explain.

c. Make a conjecture about which quadrilaterals can be used to tile a plane.

   i. Test your conjecture using software like the "Tilings wih Triangles or Quadrilaterals" custom app.

   ii. Explain why your conjecture makes sense in terms of what you know about angles of quadrilaterals.

4 You have seen two regular polygons that tile the plane. Now explore other regular polygons that could be used to make a tiling.

a. Can a regular pentagon tile the plane? Explain your reasoning.

b. Can a regular hexagon tile the plane? Explain.

c. Will any regular polygon of more than six sides tile the plane? Provide an argument to support your conjecture.

d. Tilings that consist of repeated copies of a single regular polygon with edges that match exactly are called **regular tessellations**. Which regular polygons can be used to make a regular tessellation?

5 **Tilings with More than One Polygon** As you saw at the beginning of this investigation, tilings can involve more than one type of shape. Another example of such a tiling is shown below. This tiling is from the Taj Mahal mausoleum in India.

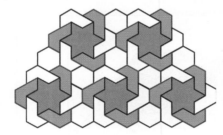

a. How many different shapes are used in the tiling? Draw a sketch of each shape.

b. Each shape can be divided into equilateral triangles, so this tiling is related to the tiling in Problem 1. On a copy of the tiling, show the equilateral triangles that make up each shape.

Lesson 2 | Polygons and Their Properties **409**

UNIT 6

INSTRUCTIONAL NOTE You may want to encourage students to try quadrilaterals of very different types, including nonconvex ones. As you circulate, ask them to describe their strategies. This reminds them to think in geometric terms about the moves their hands are making. For parallelograms, simple sliding works. However, other quadrilaterals are more instructive. Suggest they keep track of the placement by coloring or coding the angles of the quadrilateral. You might ask:

How many quadrilaterals come together at a vertex? What do you have to do when you move your shape to a new position? How do you know these moves could be repeated forever with this quadrilateral? Will your strategy work with other quadrilaterals?

a. All quadrilaterals will tile the plane, since the sum of the angle measures is 360°. The plane is tessellated by rotating the quadrilateral about the midpoints of each of the sides.

b. Parallelograms without right angles and trapezoids have two tiling patterns. The second type of pattern involves the use of line reflections. See diagrams for examples.

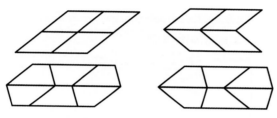

c. All quadrilaterals will tile the plane. Since the sum of the measures of the interior angles of a quadrilateral is 360°, you can place four copies of the quadrilateral at a vertex so that side lengths also match, and this block of four will translate to tile the plane.

4 **a.** A regular pentagon does not tile. One argument would relate to the angles at a point: $3 \times 108° = 324°$, which leaves 36° unfilled at each vertex, and $4 \times 108° = 432°$, so the tiles overlap.

b. A regular hexagon tiles the plane. Each interior angle is 120° and three fit without a gap or overlap around each point. All sides of a regular hexagon are the same length and thus will match.

c. The measure of each interior angle of a regular polygon with more than six sides is greater than 120°. The next largest integer that is both greater than 120° and a factor of 360° is 180°. Since the measure of an interior angle of a regular polygon is less than 180°, there is no regular polygon of more than six sides that tiles the plane.

d. Six equilateral triangle, four squares, or three hexagons will form regular tessellations. The sum of the measures of the angles at each vertex of the regular tessellation is 360°.

5 **a.** There are three different shapes, as shown below at the left.

b. The equilateral triangles that form each shape are shown below at the right.

6 Combinations of regular octagons and squares are frequently used to tile hallways and kitchens of homes. They are also often used in the design of outdoor patios.

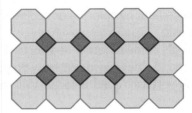

a. Explain why the polygons fit together with no overlaps or gaps. At each vertex, is there the same arrangement of polygons?

b. Tessellations of two or more regular polygons that have the same arrangement of polygons at each vertex are called **semiregular tessellations**. Use tiles made from poster board or software like the "Tilings with Regular Polygons" custom app to test whether there can be a semiregular tessellation that has at each vertex a regular hexagon, two squares, and an equilateral triangle. If possible, draw a sketch of such a tessellation.

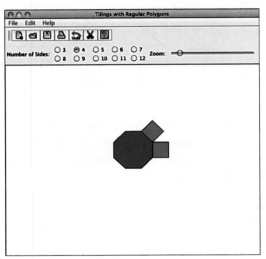

c. Semiregular tessellations are coded by listing the number of sides of the polygons that meet at a single vertex. The numbers are arranged in order with a smallest number first. The tessellation above Part a is coded 4, 8, 8, for square, octagon, octagon.

   i. Use this code to describe the tessellation you drew in Part b. Give the code for each of the three possible regular tessellations.

   ii. Determine if the vertex arrangement 3, 6, 3, 6 describes a semiregular tessellation.

   iii. Is there another semiregular tessellation that can be formed using equilateral triangles and regular hexagons? Explain.

Photodisc/Getty Images

6 **a.** Each interior angle in a regular octagon is 135°, and each interior angle in a square is 90°. At each vertex of the first tessellation, there are two regular octagons and one square, so 135° + 135° + 90° = 360°. At each vertex there is the same arrangement of polygons, two regular octagons and one square. The side lengths of the square and the hexagon are the same.

b.

> **INSTRUCTIONAL NOTE** The "Tilings with Regular Polygons" custom app allows quick, visual explorations for this task. For each tiling pattern produced, students should be prepared to explain mathematically why the pattern is possible.
>
> You may wish to have students use the software individually to create their own designs. Alternatively, groups could experiment on a couple of class computers as they reach this exploration. If some groups are waiting for computer access, they could begin the Check Your Understanding task on page 411. Alternatively, a master is provided to make regular polygon tiles from posterboard or colored acetate used for transparencies.

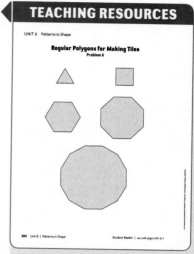

Students should notice that all side lengths are congruent and 120° + 90° + 90° + 60° = 360°.

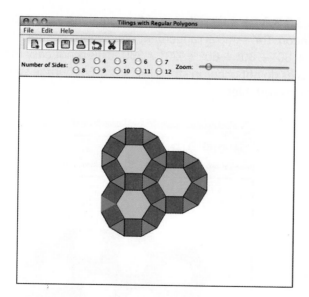

c. **i.** The code for Part b is 3, 4, 6, 4.
The code for equilateral triangles is 3, 3, 3, 3, 3, 3.
The code for squares is 4, 4, 4, 4.
The code for regular hexagons is 6, 6, 6.

ii. 3, 6, 3, 6 is a tessellation of two equilateral triangles and two regular hexagons as shown below. (60° + 120° + 60° + 120° = 360°)

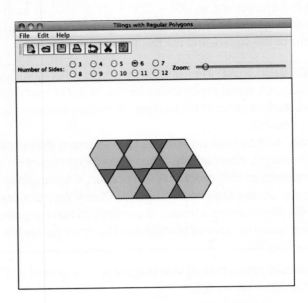

iii. Yes, 3, 3, 3, 3, 6 is a tessellation of four equilateral triangles and one regular hexagon. The same arrangement of polygons occurs at each vertex and 60° + 60° + 60° + 60° + 120° = 360°. This is not easy to find because the tiles do not occur in strips like 4, 8, 8. Encourage students to build up vertices with tiles.

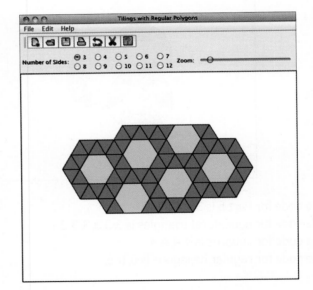

Students may also say that the tessellation below is semiregular, but it is not. Ask them why. (Not all vertex figures are the same!) 3, 3, 6, 6 is not possible for a semiregular tessellation.

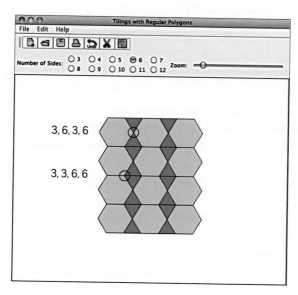

d. There are eight different semiregular tessellations. You have examples of four of them. Find at least one more example and name it using the vertex arrangement code in Part c. Compare your findings with those of other classmates.

SUMMARIZE THE MATHEMATICS

In this investigation, you explored special polygons that tile the plane. You also investigated how combinations of those special polygons can lead to more complex patterns in the plane.

a Write a summarizing statement describing which triangles and which quadrilaterals tile the plane.

b Which regular polygons tile the plane? How do you know there are no others? Explain your reasoning.

c How do semiregular tessellations differ from regular tessellations? How can number codes be used to describe semiregular tessellations?

Be prepared to discuss your ideas with the class.

✅ **CHECK YOUR UNDERSTANDING**

You have seen that a regular pentagon will not tessellate the plane. There are nonregular convex pentagons that will tessellate. But not many. Researchers have identified only 14 types. Whether there are more remains an open question.

a. Using a copy of the figure below, find a pentagon in the figure that will tile the plane. Shade it.

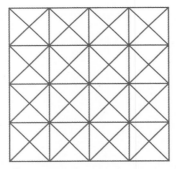

b. Show as many different tiling patterns using your pentagon as you can.

d. The other four semiregular tessellations are coded by: 3, 12, 12; 4, 6, 12; 3, 3, 3, 4, 4; and 3, 3, 4, 3, 4.

SUMMARIZE THE MATHEMATICS

a All triangles and quadrilaterals tile the plane. One way to construct the tiling is to rotate the shape 180° about the midpoints of the sides. Copies of the 4 angles of the quadrilateral and two copies of each of the 3 angles of a triangle will sum to 360° at each vertex of the tiling.

b Equilateral triangles, squares, and hexagons are the only regular polygons that tile the plane because the measure of each interior angle is a factor of 360. This allows congruent copies to be placed at each vertex without overlap or leaving space between the first and last copy. The measure of each interior angle of a regular polygon with more than six sides is greater than 120°. The next largest integer that is both greater than 120° and a factor of 360° is 180°. Since the measure of an interior angle of a regular polygon is less than 180°, there is no regular polygon of more than six sides that tiles the plane.

c Semiregular tessellations involve the same arrangement of two or more types of regular polygons at each vertex, whereas a regular tessellation has only one type of polygon whose copies fit together at each vertex.

A compact way to describe semiregular tessellations is by indicating the number of sides of the polygons at each vertex. Convention is to use the smallest number first (or one of the smallest numbers) and then list the number of sides of the shapes as you move around the vertex.

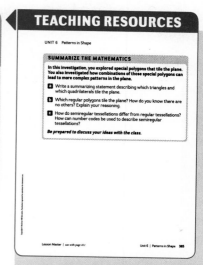
✔ CHECK YOUR UNDERSTANDING

a–b. Colored pencils will help students shade the tiling pattern. Three possible pentagons made from the figure in the student text and their tiling patterns are shown below. If students ignore the grid, the pentagon in Figure 1 can also tile the plane in the manner shown in Figure 2.

Figure 1 **Figure 2** **Figure 3**

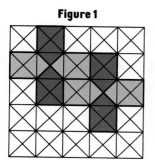 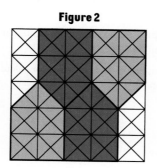 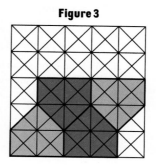

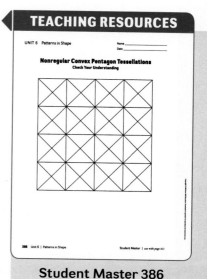

ON YOUR OWN

APPLICATIONS

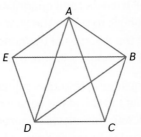

1. In regular pentagon *ABCDE*, four diagonals have been drawn.

   a. Use careful reasoning to explain why $\overline{AD} \cong \overline{AC}$.

   b. Is diagonal $\overline{AD}$ congruent to diagonal $\overline{DB}$? Explain your reasoning.

   c. Give an argument for why diagonal $\overline{AD}$ is congruent to diagonal $\overline{EB}$.

   d. Are all the diagonals of a regular pentagon congruent? Explain your reasoning.

2. Suppose every student in your mathematics class shook hands with each of the other students at the beginning of your next class. What would be the total number of handshakes?

   a. Show how you can represent this problem with a polygon for the case of just 4 students.

      i. How many handshakes were involved?

      ii. How is your answer related to the components of the polygon?

   b. Represent and solve the problem for the special case of 5 students. Of 6 students.

   c. How did you represent students in your models? How did you represent handshakes between students?

   d. Use any numerical or visual pattern in your models to help solve the original problem.

   e. In addition to using patterns to solve problems, it is also important to be able to explain and, whenever possible, generalize the patterns you discover. A student in a Wisconsin classroom claimed that a class of *n* students would involve $n^2 - 2n$ handshakes. The student reasoned as follows.

      > I thought of students as vertices of an *n*-gon and handshakes as the sides and diagonals. An *n*-gon has *n* sides and *n* angles. From each vertex, I can draw a diagonal to *n* − 3 other vertices. So, I can draw *n*(*n* − 3) diagonals. So, the number of handshakes is $n + n(n - 3) = n^2 - 2n$.

      i. Is this reasoning correct? If not, identify and correct errors in the reasoning.

      ii. Write a rule that expresses the number of handshakes as a function of the number of students *n*.

   f. Write an expression in symbols and in words for calculating the number of diagonals of an *n*-gon.

1 **a.** $AE = ED = AB = BC$ since $ABCDE$ is a regular pentagon. Also, $\angle E \cong \angle B$ since interior angles of a regular pentagon are congruent. Thus, $\triangle AED \cong \triangle ABC$ by the SAS congruence condition. Therefore, $\overline{AD} \cong \overline{AC}$ since they are corresponding sides of congruent triangles.

b. Yes, since $\triangle BCD \cong \triangle AED$ by reasoning similar to that used in Part a.

c. The same reasoning used in Parts a and b confirm that $\overline{AB} \cong \overline{EB}$.

d. Yes, all diagonals of a regular pentagon are congruent. Any diagonal can be used as the long side of a triangle. The other two sides will be used as the consecutive sides of the regular pentagon. Thus, the SAS congruence condition provides that all diagonals are congruent.

2 Student diagrams may vary. Below is one option.

a.

1   2

4   3

i. 6 handshakes were involved.

ii. There are 4 vertices representing students and 6 segments representing handshakes.

b.

For 5 students, there are 10 handshakes.

For 6 students, there are 15 handshakes.

c. Students were represented as vertices of an n-gon, where n was the number of students. Handshakes were represented by segments drawn between each vertex to every other vertex (sides of the n-gon and diagonals).

d. Student responses should be the same based on classroom makeup.

e. **i.** No. The student counted each diagonal twice, once at each end of the segment. To correct this, divide $n(n - 3)$ by 2.

ii. The number of handshakes h in a class of n students is $h = n + \dfrac{n(n - 3)}{2}$.

f. The number of diagonals of an n-gon is $\dfrac{n(n - 3)}{2}$ or one half the product of the number of sides and three fewer than the number of sides.

3 Objects in nature are often approximately symmetric in form.

a. The shapes below are single-celled sea plants called *diatoms*.

i. Identify all of the symmetries of these diatoms. Ignore interior details.

ii. For those with reflection symmetry, sketch the shape and show the lines of symmetry.

iii. For those with rotational symmetry, describe the angles of rotation.

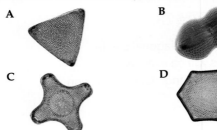

A B

C D

b. Identify all of the symmetries of the two flowers shown below.

i. If the flower has line symmetry, sketch the shape and draw all lines of symmetry.

ii. If the flower has rotational symmetry, describe the angles of rotation.

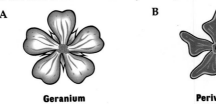

A B

Geranium   **Periwinkle**

c. It has been said that no two snowflakes are identical. Yet every snowflake has some common geometric properties.

i. Identify the symmetries of the snowflakes below.

ii. In terms of their symmetry, how are the snowflakes alike?

4 Polygons and symmetry are important components of the arts and crafts of many cultures.

a. Examine the Native American rug at the right.

i. Describe the line and rotational symmetries of this rug. Sketch two design elements within the rug that have rotational symmetry. Describe the angles through which each can be turned.

Native American rug

3 a. Diatom A:

reflection symmetry (3 lines)
rotational symmetry (120°, 240°)

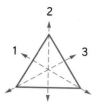

Diatom B:

reflection symmetry (2 lines)
rotational symmetry (180°)

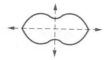

Diatom C:

reflection symmetry (4 lines)
rotational symmetry (90°, 180°, 270°)

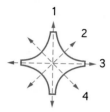

Diatom D:

reflection symmetry (6 lines)
rotational symmetry (60°, 120°, 180°, 240°, 300°)

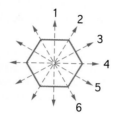

b. Flower A:

line symmetry (5 lines)
rotational symmetry (72°, 144°, 216°, 288°)

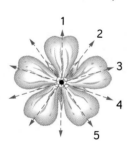

Flower B:

no line symmetry
rotational symmetry (72°, 144°, 216°, 288°)

c. i. The snowflakes all have line symmetry (6 lines) and rotational symmetry (60°, 120°, 180°, 240°, 300°).

ii. So, although their designs are different, the snowflakes are exactly alike in symmetry.

4 a. i. The rug has vertical and horizontal line symmetry across lines containing the center of the rug. It has 180° rotational symmetry about the center point of the rug.

ii. Sketch two design elements within the rug that have line symmetry. Draw the line(s) of symmetry.

iii. Are there any design elements which have both rotational and line symmetry? If so, identify them. Where is the center of rotation in relation to the lines of symmetry?

b. The design of the quilt to the left is called "Star of Bethlehem."

   i. What rotational symmetries do you see in the fundamental "pinwheel stars"? Give the angles of rotation for each of these symmetries.

   ii. Is there line symmetry in the "pinwheel stars"? Explain.

   iii. Does the quilt as a whole, including the pinwheel stars, have rotational or line symmetry? Describe each symmetry you find.

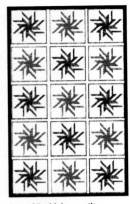

Star of Bethlehem quilt

5. Here is a two-person game that can be played on any regular polygon. To play, place a penny on each vertex of the polygon. Take turns removing one or two pennies from adjacent vertices. The player who picks up the last coin is the winner.

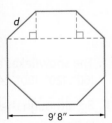

a. Suppose the game is played on a nonagon, as shown at the right. Try to find a strategy using symmetry that will permit the second player to win always. Write a description of your strategy.

b. Will the strategy you found work if the game is played on any polygon with an odd number of vertices? Explain your reasoning.

c. Suppose the game is played on a polygon with an even number of vertices, say an octagon. Try to find a strategy that will guarantee that the second player still can win always. Write a description of this strategy.

6. In designing this mall garden, the architect proposed a gazebo in the shape of a regular octagon. The octagonal roof cupola was to have a width of 9 feet 8 inches. What should be the dimensions of each side? (*Hint*: Use the *auxiliary lines* drawn to help guide your thinking.)

Michael Lynch/Alamy

ii. See student sketches.

iii. The element at the center of the rug that shows a square-shaped "X" design has 180° rotational symmetry and vertical and horizontal line symmetry. Each symmetry line contains the center point of the rug. The center of the rotation is the intersection point of the two lines of symmetry, again the center point of the rug. This is also true for other elements that are rectangular and have two intersecting lines of symmetry, such as the shapes near each of the four corners of the rug.

b. **i.** The center of rotational symmetry of each star is the intersection of the diagonals of the square that contains the star. The magnitudes of the rotation are 45°, 90°, 135°, 180°, 225°, 270°, and 315°.

ii. There is no line symmetry in the stars because the dark and light parts of the stars are not line symmetric.

iii. With color, the whole quilt has 180° rotational symmetry and no line symmetry.

5 **a.** If your opponent selects 1 coin, visually draw the line of symmetry which contains the empty vertex and choose the 2 symmetrically-placed coins. Using the same line of reflection, always choose the mirror image of your opponent's play. If your opponent selects 2 coins, draw the symmetry line between the 2 vertices. Then choose the one coin on that symmetry line (see diagram). Proceed as before, always choosing the mirror image of your opponent's play.

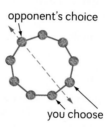

opponent's choice

you choose

b. Yes, as long as the regular polygon has an odd number of vertices, it will have lines of symmetry as in the diagram.

c. With an even number of vertices, you again would draw the symmetry line either containing the 1 coin or between the 2 coins your opponent chose. Mirror your opponent's play.

6 Each interior angle of the octagon measures 135°, so the smaller angles in the right triangle in the diagram are 45°. The width of the roof is $d + 2x = 116"$. (This is the same as the perimeter of the right triangle.) Since $x^2 + x^2 = d^2$, $2x^2 = d^2$, and $\sqrt{2}x = d$. (You may wish to refer students to Connections Task 20 on page 392 to remind them of this relationship.) $\sqrt{2}x + 2x = 116"$, so $x \approx 34"$. Students might use symbolic reasoning or tables to solve for x. $d = \sqrt{2}x = \sqrt{2}(34) \approx 48"$ or 4 feet.

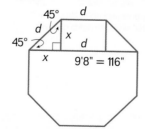

7 Bees produce honeycomb cells with cross sections that are approximately the shape of a regular hexagon.

a. If all the cells are to be congruent, what other regular polygon shapes might they have used?

b. Suppose the perimeter of a cross section of one cell of a honeycomb is 24 mm. Find the area of the cross section, assuming the cell has the following shape.

   i. an equilateral triangle

   ii. a square

   iii. a regular hexagon

c. Which cell has the greatest cross-sectional area for a fixed perimeter of 24 mm? As the number of sides of a regular polygon with fixed perimeter increases, how does the corresponding area change?

d. Write a statement summarizing how shape is an important factor in the design of the cells of a honeycomb.

8 It is possible to create intriguing tessellations by carefully modifying the sides of a polygon. The Dutch artist M.C. Escher was a master of these modifications. He created this tessellation of *Pegasus*, the mythical winged horse.

a. Assuming the tessellation at the right is extended indefinitely in all directions, describe its symmetries.

M.C. Escher's "Symmetry Drawing E105" ©2013 The M.C. Escher Company-The Netherlands. All rights reserved. www.mcescher.com

(t)imagebroker/Alamy

Lesson 2 | Polygons and Their Properties **415**

7 a. Bees might have used equilateral triangles or squares because these regular polygons also tile the plane. Tiling is helpful because there will be no gaps between the cells that might cause some of the honey to be wasted.

b. **i.** Area $\approx \frac{1}{2} \cdot 8 \cdot 6.93 = 27.72$ mm²

$h = \sqrt{64 - 16} = \sqrt{48} \approx 6.93$ mm

ii. Area $= 36$ mm²

iii. The central angle of a regular hexagon is 60° and the interior angles are 120°. So, $\triangle ABC$ is an equilateral triangle. The area of the hexagon is

$6 \cdot \frac{1}{2} \cdot 4 \cdot \sqrt{16 - 4} = 12\sqrt{12} \approx 41.57$ mm².

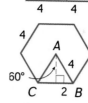

c. The regular hexagon has the largest cross-sectional area for a fixed perimeter of 24 mm.

The area for a fixed perimeter increases when the number of sides of a regular polygon increases.

d. By building a honeycomb out of shapes that tessellate, the walls of a cell perform double duty as walls for two cells. This saves on work time and on building materials (wax). It also means that honey will not be wasted by falling between openings that would occur if bees used shapes that did not tessellate. When comparing honeycomb cells with either regular triangular, square, or regular hexagonal shaped openings of a fixed perimeter, a regular hexagonal shape will provide the greatest cross-sectional area. (For the volume comparison see Extensions Task 23 on page 452.) Bees produce the shape that provides the most storage space for the amount of materials needed.

8 a. The tessellation has translation symmetry. The translations can be horizontal, vertical, or diagonal.

ON YOUR OWN

b. Study the process below which illustrates how Escher may have created his "flying horse" tessellation from a square.

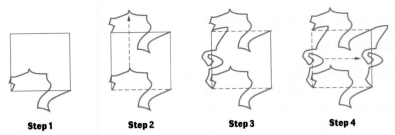

Step 1   Step 2   Step 3   Step 4

    i. Use tracing paper to verify how the modifications of sides are translated to the opposite sides.

    ii. How does the area of the Pegasus compare to the area of the initial square?

c. Start with a square, rectangle, or other parallelogram and use a similar process to create your own Escher-type tessellation. Verify that your shape does tile the plane.

9 A beautiful tiling for paving or wallpaper can be made with leaf-like tiles based on a rhombus. Study the process below, which illustrates how this tile may be created.

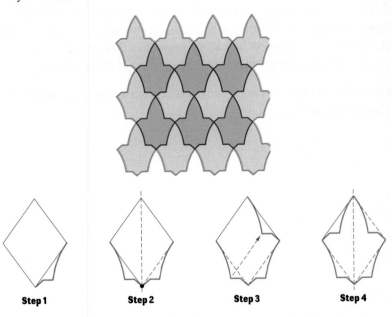

Step 1   Step 2   Step 3   Step 4

a. Use tracing paper to verify how the modifications of sides of the rhombus are reflected or translated to produce the other sides of the leaf tile.

b. How does the area of the leaf tile compare to the area of the rhombus?

c. Start with a rhombus and use a similar process to create your own paving or wallpaper design.

b. **i.** Students should verify translations with tracing paper or visually.

   ii. The area of the Pegasus is the same as that of the square. Any change in the area of a figure when a new side is created will be balanced out when that side is translated to the opposite side of the figure.

c. Student tessellations will vary.

9 **a.** Students will examine the tile construction.

b. The area of the tile is the same as the area of the rhombus.

c. See student designs.

CONNECTIONS

10 Psychologists often use figures like that below in their study of human perception.

a. What do you see?

b. Name the colored polygons involved in this task.

c. Which polygons are convex? Nonconvex?

d. Which polygons have symmetry? Describe the symmetries.

11 Graphs of various functions relating variables x and y are shown below. The scale on the axes is 1.

a. For each graph, locate any line(s) of symmetry.

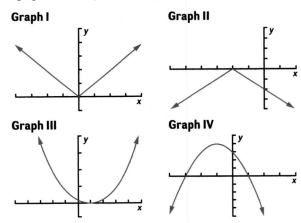

Graph I

Graph II

Graph III

Graph IV

b. What pattern do you see in the coordinates of the points on each line of symmetry? Write the equation of the symmetry line(s).

c. Suppose you have a graph, and its line of symmetry is the y-axis. If one point on the graph has coordinates $(-8, -23)$, what is the y-coordinate of the point on the graph with x-coordinate 8? Explain your reasoning.

12 The initial and first two stages in making a triangular Sierpinski carpet are shown below. In the *Exponential Functions* unit, you explored the area of carpet remaining as a function of the cutout stage. Describe the symmetries that the triangular carpet has at each stage of the process.

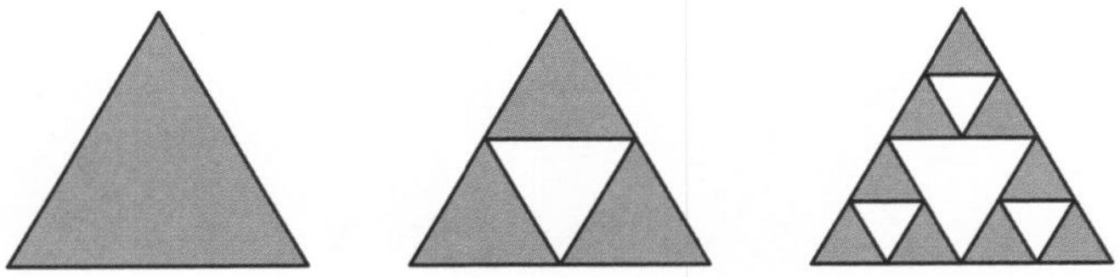

Stage 0

Stage 1

Stage 2

Lesson 2 | Polygons and Their Properties **417**

10 **a.** Students should see the word "LOVE."

b. The polygons from left to right are rectangle (or quadrilateral), decagon, rectangle (or quadrilateral), hexagon, triangle, decagon, and dodecagon.

c. The quadrilaterals and triangle are convex. The decagons, hexagon, and dodecagon are nonconvex.

d. The rectangles, triangle, and dodecagon have line symmetry. The rectangles also have 180° rotational symmetry.

11 **a.** The lines of symmetry are vertical lines through the lowest point on Graphs I and III and the highest points on Graphs II and IV.

b The equations for the lines of symmetry are:

Graph I; $x = 0$
Graph II; $x = -2$
Graph III; $x = 1$
Graphy IV; $x = -1$

c. Since the y-axis is a line of symmetry, the reflection of the point $(-8, -23)$ over the y-axis must be 8 units to the right of the y-axis and the same location vertically. This point has coordinates $(8, -23)$.

12 At every stage, the carpet has three reflection symmetries across the lines connecting a vertex and the midpoint of the opposite side of the original triangle. There are two 120° rotational symmetries about the point that is the center of the original triangle.

13 Make a sketch of a regular pentagon. Extend one of the sides to form an exterior angle. How could you use your knowledge of exterior angles to calculate the measure of an interior angle of a regular pentagon? Would your method work for other regular polygons? Explain your reasoning.

14 In Investigation 2, you discovered the rule $A = \dfrac{(n-2)180°}{n}$, which gives the measure A one interior angle of a regular n-gon.

a. As the number of sides of a regular polygon increases, how does the measure of each of its interior angles change? Is the rate of change constant? Explain.

b. Use your formula to find the measure of one interior angle of a regular 20-gon. Could a tessellation be made of regular 20-gons? Explain your reasoning.

c. When will the measure of each angle of a regular polygon be a whole number?

d. Use your calculator or computer software to produce a table of values for angle measures of various regular polygons. Use your table to help explain why the only regular tiling of the plane is one with regular polygons of 3, 4, or 6 sides.

15 The **dual** of a tessellation by regular polygons is a new tessellation obtained by connecting the centers of polygons that share a common edge. Use equilateral triangular (isometric) dot paper to complete Parts a and b and square dot paper to complete Part c.

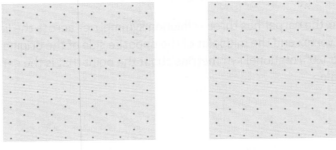

a. Draw a portion of a regular hexagon tessellation. Using a different colored pencil, draw and describe the dual of the tessellation.

b. Draw a portion of an equilateral triangle tessellation. Draw and describe the dual of this tessellation.

c. Draw and describe the dual of a tessellation of squares.

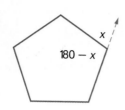

13 The sum of the five exterior angles of a regular pentagon is 360°; thus the measure of an interior angle is $180° - \frac{360°}{5} = 108°$. This method works for any regular polygon. Since the sum of the n exterior angles of a regular n-gon is 360°, the measure of an interior angle is $180° - \frac{360°}{n}$.

14 **a.** As the number of sides of a regular polygon increases, the measure of each of its angles increases as well. However, the change is *not* constant, as may be seen from the second column of the table in Part d.

b. 162°. No tiling could be made since multiples of 162° do not fit around a vertex.

c. The measure is a whole number when the number of sides is a factor of 360.

d. The only regular polygons with interior angles having measures that divide 360° (namely 60°, 90°, and 120°) are the 3-gon (triangle), 4-gon (square), and 6-gon (hexagon). Therefore, multiples of each of these three polygons fit evenly around a point.

Number of Sides of Regular Polygon	Measure of Each Interior Angle
3	60°
4	90°
5	108°
6	120°
7	$128\frac{4}{7}° \approx 128.6°$
8	135°
9	140°
10	144°
11	$147\frac{3}{11}° \approx 147.3°$
12	150°

15 **a.**  The dual of a regular hexagon tessellation is an equilateral triangle tessellation.

b. 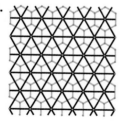 The dual of an equilateral triangle tessellation is a regular hexagon tessellation.

c. 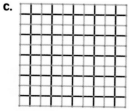 The dual of a tessellation of squares is another tessellation of the same size square, just translated half the length of a side of a diagonal.

TEACHING RESOURCES

UNIT 6 Patterns in Shape

Equilateral Triangular (Isometric) Dot Paper

448 Unit 6 | Patterns in Shape

Student Master | use with page 418

Student Master 448

ⓘ **GO DIGITAL**

INSTRUCTIONAL NOTE

Student Masters 403 and 448 containing these dot papers can be used.

16 Strip or *frieze* patterns are used in architecture and interior design. The portions of frieze patterns below came from the artwork on pottery of the San Ildefonso Pueblo, New Mexico.

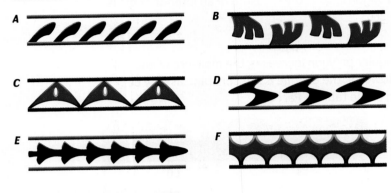

Source: Groups and Geometry in the Ceramic Art of San Ildefonso. *Algebras, Groups and Geometries 2,* no. 3 (September 1985).

Imagine that each frieze pattern extends indefinitely to the right and to the left.

a. Confirm that each pattern has translation symmetry.

b. Examine each frieze pattern for reflection and rotational symmetries. (If a strip has such a symmetry, the strip must appear the same before and after it is reflected across a line or rotated about a point.) Describe your findings for each pattern.

c. Pattern B has a symmetry called *glide-reflection symmetry*. Describe the translation and reflection combination that will move the motif so the pattern coincides with itself.

REFLECTIONS

17 Look up the word "polygon" in a dictionary. What is the meaning of its parts "poly" and "gon"? How do these meanings relate to your understanding of "polygon"?

18 A regular polygon is both equilateral and equiangular.

a. Give an example of an equilateral polygon that is not a regular polygon.

b. Give an example of an equiangular polygon that is not a regular polygon.

16 **a.** Yes, each figure in the pattern is the same size, and the pattern repeats itself by sliding over the same distance and direction each time. (You may need to remind students that they are looking for overall symmetry patterns, even though there are slight imperfections in the figures.)

b. Patterns C, F, and G have vertical line reflection symmetry. Patterns E and G have horizontal line reflection symmetry. Patterns D, F (if the center of rotation is carefully chosen), and G have 180° rotational symmetry.

c. This glide reflection combines a reflection (across a horizontal center line of the pattern) with a translation along the direction of the mirror line.

REFLECTIONS

17 "Poly" means more than one. "gon" means angle or corner. One usually thinks about polygons by the number of sides. But it has the same number of angles and vertices as sides. So, one could think about an n-gon as having n angles or vertices.

18 **a.** A rhombus that is not a square.

b. A rectangle that is not a square. (Any regular polygon can produce a nonregular equiangular polygon by cutting off part of it with a line parallel to one edge. See the sketch below.)

19 Suppose you are given two regular octagons. What is the minimum information you need to know in order to conclude they are congruent? How would your answer change if the two octagons are *not* regular?

20 Thumb through magazines or visit Internet sites to find company logos. Why do you think so many of the logo designs are symmetric? Draw three of the logos that have particularly interesting symmetries.

21 Cross-cultural studies suggest that symmetry is a fundamental idea that all people use to help understand, remember, compare, and reproduce forms. However, symmetry preferences have been found across cultures. One study found that symmetry about a vertical line was easier to recognize than symmetry about a horizontal line. The study also found that symmetry about a diagonal line was the most difficult to detect. (Source: Orientation and symmetry: effects of multiple, rotational, and near symmetries. *Journal of Experimental Psychology* 4[4]: 1978.)

a. Would the findings of the study apply to the way in which you perceive line symmetry?

b. Describe a simple experiment that you could conduct to test these findings.

22 Look back at your work on Applications Task 1. Do you think your finding applies to other regular polygons? Carefully draw a regular hexagon and label its vertices *PQRSTU*. Name the diagonals that are congruent to each other and give reasons to support your conclusions.

EXTENSIONS

23 Commercial artists sometimes use a device similar to the one shown for drawing mirror images. The linkage is assembled so that *APBP′* is a rhombus and the points at *P* and *P′* pivot freely as *A* and *B* slide along *ℓ*. As *P* traces out a figure, *P′* traces out its reflection image. Explain why this device works as it does.

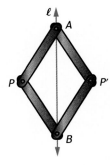

24 Use interactive geometry software or other tools to further investigate properties of regular polygons.

a. Is there a relationship between the measure of a central angle and the measure of an interior angle? If so, can you explain why that must *always* be the case?

b. Is there a relationship between the measure of a central angle and the measure of an exterior angle? If so, can you explain why?

19 The interior angles of the two regular octagons are 135°. So, you only need to know that a pair of sides, one from each of the two regular octagons, are congruent in order to conclude that the octagons are congruent. If the two octagons are not regular, you need to know that each side and angle on one octagon has a corresponding, congruent side and angle on the other octagon.

20 There are many reasons why logos are symmetric: symmetric figures are more pleasing to the eye; symmetry provides some balance to the figure; and symmetry generally helps us remember the figure. (Some students may want to visit Jill Britton's Web site at britton.disted.camosun.bc.ca/jbfunpatt.htm for links to this topic and many others in this unit.)

21 **a.** Responses may vary. A sample response could be: The findings of the Palmer and Henenway study would apply to the way in which I perceive line symmetry since the first line symmetry I look for is vertical, the second is horizontal, with "diagonal" last.

b. A simple experiment to test these findings would be to make copies of a shape with vertical, horizontal, and diagonal lines of symmetry, pass them out, and ask students to draw any lines of symmetry they see, labeling the lines 1, 2, 3, and so on, based on which one they saw first, second, etc.

22 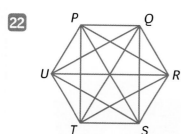 No, the findings for a regular pentagon do not apply to any other regular polygon except a square. For a regular hexagon, $\overline{PR} \cong \overline{QS} \cong \overline{RT} \cong \overline{SU} \cong \overline{TP} \cong \overline{UQ}$ and $\overline{PS} \cong \overline{QT} \cong \overline{RU}$. The first set of diagonals can be shown to be congruent by using the same reasoning used in Applications Task 1. $\overline{PS} \cong \overline{QT} \cong \overline{RU}$. The lengths of these segments are the sum of the lengths of 2 sides of the interior equilateral triangles. (Some students may notice that $\overline{PS}$, $\overline{QT}$, and $\overline{RU}$ are diameters of the circle that circumscribes the hexagon.)

EXTENSIONS

23 P' is the reflection image of P across line ℓ, since diagonal $\overline{AB}$ is the perpendicular bisector of diagonal $\overline{PP'}$. So, the reflection of whatever path P traces will be traced by P'.

24 **a.** The central angle forms an isosceles triangle. The sum of the measures of the two congruent base angles is the same as the measure of one interior angle. Since the three angle measures of the isosceles triangle sum to 180°, the sum of the central angle and an interior angle is also 180°. Alternatively, the measure of an interior angle is 180° minus the measure of the central angle.

b. The measure of the exterior angle is equal to the measure of the central angle. This is true because the measures of the exterior and interior angles sum to 180°, and the sum of the measures of an interior angle and the central angle is 180°.

ON YOUR OWN

25 In Investigation 3, you explored semiregular tessellations by examining various arrangements of regular polygon shapes around a vertex. You can also examine the possibilities using algebra. The diagram below is a start. It shows the case of three regular polygons of m, n, and p sides completely surrounding a vertex with no overlapping.

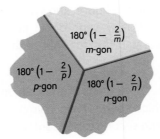

$180° \left(1 - \frac{2}{m}\right)$
m-gon

$180° \left(1 - \frac{2}{p}\right)$
p-gon

$180° \left(1 - \frac{2}{n}\right)$
n-gon

a. Why must the numbers m, n, and p all be integers greater than 2?

b. Explain why the measure of each interior angle is as shown.

c. Write an equation that must be satisfied if the polygons are to form a tessellation.

d. Show that your equation is equivalent to $\frac{1}{m} + \frac{1}{n} + \frac{1}{p} = \frac{1}{2}$. What are the whole number solutions to this equation?

e. Relate one of your solutions in Part d to a semiregular tessellation.

26 In Investigation 1, you explored how a two-mirror kaleidoscope could be used to create regular polygons. For this task, make a three-mirror kaleidoscope by fastening three congruent mirrors together to form an equilateral triangle at the base.

a. Explore what can be created by placing various patterns in the base like those shown below.

b. Can you create each regular tessellation by placing an appropriate pattern in the base of your kaleidoscope? If so, draw diagrams of the patterns.

c. Can you create a semiregular tessellation by placing an appropriate pattern in the base? If so, draw a diagram of the pattern.

d. How are ideas of symmetry related to your pattern-building explorations?

27 The first two tessellations on page 422 use the same isosceles triangle. Think of each tiling extended indefinitely to cover the plane. A tessellation that fits exactly on itself when translated is called **periodic**; it has translation symmetry. One that does not have translation symmetry is called **nonperiodic**.

a. Since you cannot have polygons with fewer than 3 sides, *m*, *n*, and *p* must all be greater than 2.

b. The measure of an interior angle for a regular *n*-gon is $180° - \frac{360°}{n}$ or $180°\left(1 - \frac{2}{n}\right)$ which is given.

c. $180°\left(1 - \frac{2}{m}\right) + 180°\left(1 - \frac{2}{n}\right) + 180°\left(1 - \frac{2}{p}\right) = 360°$

d. $180°\left(1 - \frac{2}{m}\right) + 180°\left(1 - \frac{2}{n}\right) + 180°\left(1 - \frac{2}{p}\right) = 360°$

$$180° - \frac{360°}{m} + 180° - \frac{360°}{n} + 180° - \frac{360°}{p} = 360°$$

$$\frac{360°}{m} + \frac{360°}{n} + \frac{360°}{p} = 180°$$

$$\frac{1}{m} + \frac{1}{n} + \frac{1}{p} = 12$$

Students may solve this equation using systematic substitution and checking or prepare a spreadsheet. The whole number solutions are **3, 12, 12**; 3, 10, 15; 3, 9, 18; 3, 8, 24; 3, 7, 42; **4, 8, 8**; **4, 6, 12**; 4, 5, 20; 5, 5, 10; and 6, 6, 6.

e. Solutions in boldface type can be extended to form semiregular tessellations. The tiling 4, 8, 8 is shown in Problem 6 (page 410).

> **DIFFERENTIATION** The integration of geometric and algebraic reasoning used in the solution of this problem can be extended even further. You might challenge your most able students to:
>
> • *Explain why there could also be 4, 5, or 6 regular polygons surrounding a vertex without overlapping, but no more.*
>
> • *Write, solve, and interpret the solutions of the three corresponding equations.*

 a. The first pattern creates a tessellation of large equilateral triangles formed by 6 of the shaded triangles.
The second pattern creates a semiregular tessellation of equilateral triangles and hexagons (3, 6, 3, 6).

b. A tessellation of equilateral triangles is created using the pattern on the left in Part a of the student text. A regular hexagon tessellation can be created by using the pattern at the right. You cannot make a tessellation of a square with a three-mirror kaleidoscope.

c. A semiregular tessellation can be formed by using the second pattern in Part a of the student text. Other examples follow.

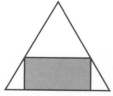 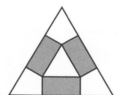 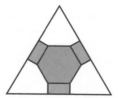

d. Mirrors create line reflections. The symmetry of repeated reflections creates distinguishable patterns or tessellations.

ON YOUR OWN

Many polygonal shapes (like the triangles below) will tile both periodically and nonperiodically. Many shapes (such as Escher's *Pegasus*) will tile *only* periodically.

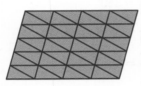
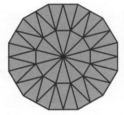

The diagram below at the left shows how the Penrose tiles at the beginning of Investigation 3 are formed from a particular rhombus. If the vertices are color-coded with black dots and gray dots as shown and only vertices with the same color dots are allowed to meet, then the only way these kite and dart shapes can tessellate is nonperiodically.

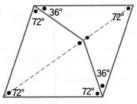
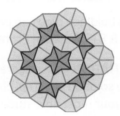

Use the "Tilings with Penrose Tiles" custom app or tracing paper to make a copy of the kite and dart shown above at the left. Then create two different nonperiodic tilings using the matching rule and explain why they are different.

REVIEW

28 There are three right triangles in each of the following diagrams. In each case, you are given three segment lengths.

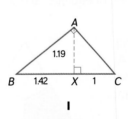
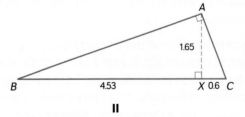

I **II**

a. Using the marked segment lengths, find *AB* and *AC* in each case.

b. Find the ratio *AB:AC* and *AX:XC* in each case.

29 Russell's department store is having a 25%-off sale. There is 6% sales tax on all items bought.

a. Liz found a dress she likes that usually costs $65. She has $50. Does she have enough money to buy the dress during this sale?

27 Student tilings will vary. They should explain how their tilings are different from each other.

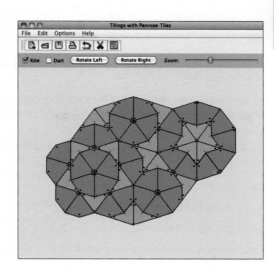

Additional Resources:

- Gardner, Martin. "Extraordinary nonperiodic tiling that enriches the theory of tiles," Mathematical Games, *Scientific American*, January, 1977, pp. 110–121.

- Grunbaum, B. and Shephard G. C., *Tilings and Patterns*, Freeman, 1987.

- www.uwgb.edu/dutchs/symmetry/penrose.htm

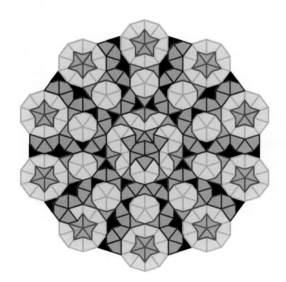

REVIEW

28 **a.** Triangle I: $AB = \sqrt{(1.42)^2 + (1.19)^2} \approx 1.85$

$AC = \sqrt{(1)^2 + (1.19)^2} \approx 1.55$

Triangle II: $AB = \sqrt{(4.53)^2 + (1.65)^2} \approx 4.82$

$AC = \sqrt{(0.6)^2 + (1.65)^2} \approx 1.76$

b. Triangle I: $\frac{AB}{AC} \approx 1.19$; $\frac{AX}{XC} = 1.19$

Triangle II: $\frac{AB}{AC} \approx 2.74$; $\frac{AX}{XC} = 2.75$

(Even if rounding makes these ratios seem unequal, they are exactly equal since $\triangle ABC$ and $\triangle ACX$ are similar.)

29 **a.** No. At $51.68, the dress costs more than $50.

b. Jerry bought a shirt on sale and paid a total of $22.26. What is the price of the shirt when it is not on sale?

c. Write a formula that describes the relationship between the original price of an item p and the amount of money that is needed to buy the item during this sale C.

d. Is the relationship described in Part c linear, exponential, or neither? Explain your reasoning.

30 Consider the rule $2x - 4 = y$.

a. How do the y values change as the x values increase by 1?

b. How do the y values change as the x values increase by 5?

c. Where does the graph of this rule intersect the y-axis?

31 Janelle creates and sells small ceramic figurines at arts and crafts fairs. How many figurine boxes, which are 3 inches long, 2 inches wide, and 3 inches tall, could she fit into the shipping box shown at the right?

18 in.

15 in.

12 in.

32 Write each of the following in a simpler equivalent exponential form that uses only positive exponents.

a. $(4x^3)^2$ **b.** $(5x^2y)(-3x^5y)$ **c.** $\frac{24t^6r^2}{8t^3r^5}$

d. $\left(\frac{-6d^4}{2}\right)^3$ **e.** $\left(\frac{5x^2y}{7x}\right)^5\left(\frac{-7x}{3y}\right)^2$

33 Write each expression in simplest equivalent form. Show your work.

a. $7(4 - x) + 15$ **b.** $36 - (50 - 15x) + 10x$

c. $0.5x(4 - 20) + \frac{6x + 4}{2}$ **d.** $7 + 4(5x - 7) - 2(15 - 9x)$

34 Complete each table so that its entries show an exponential pattern of change. Then write a rule that expresses y as a function of x.

a.

x	0	1	2	3	4
y	800	200	50		

b.

x	1	2	3	4	5
y	30	45	67.5		

c.

x	0	2	4	6	8
y	1	4	16		

35 Solve each equation.

a. $48 = 3(2^x)$ **b.** $129 = 6 + 3x$

c. $900(0.4^x) = 90$ **d.** $5(2x + 4) = 300$

36 Mariah wants to join a gym. In her community she has two choices. The First Street Gym charges a membership fee of $120 and a monthly fee of $35. Fitness Center has a $20 membership fee and charges $55 per month.

a. For what number of months will the total cost be the same at the two gyms?

b. Under what conditions will First Street Gym be less expensive?

Lesson 2 | Polygons and Their Properties **423**

b. $28

c. $C = 1.06(0.75p)$, or $C = 0.795p$

d. Linear, since it is of the form $y = ax + b$ where $a = 0.795$ and $b = 0$.

30 **a.** As the x values increase by 1, the y values increase by 2.

b. As the x values increase by 5, the y values increase by 10.

c. The y-intercept of the graph is at $(0, -4)$.

⏱ Just In Time

31 Janelle can place 30 small boxes in one layer on the bottom of the box. She can have 6 layers of small boxes. Thus, she can fit 180 small boxes into the big box.

32 **a.** $16x^6$　　　　**b.** $-15x^7y^2$　　　　**c.** $\dfrac{3t^3}{r^3}$

d. $-27d^{12}$　　　　**e.** $\dfrac{35}{9xy}$

33 **a.** $-7x + 43$　　　　**b.** $25x - 14$

c. $-5x + 2$　　　　**d.** $38x - 51$

34 **a.**

x	0	1	2	3	4
y	800	200	50	12.5	3.125

$y = 800\left(\dfrac{1}{4}\right)^x$

b.

x	1	2	3	4	5
y	30	45	67.5	101.25	151.875

$y = 20\left(\dfrac{3}{2}\right)^x$ or $y = 30\left(\dfrac{3}{2}\right)^{x-1}$

c.

x	0	2	4	6	8
y	1	4	16	64	256

$y = 2^x$

35 **a.** $x = 4$　　　　**b.** $x = 41$

c. $x \approx 2.51$　　　　**d.** $x = 28$

36 **a.** 5 months

b. If Mariah keeps her membership for more than 5 months, First Street Gym will be less expensive.

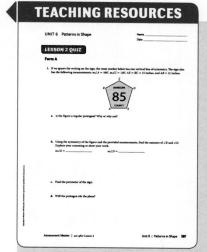

TEACHING RESOURCES

Assessment Masters 387–393

⏻ **GO DIGITAL**

UNIT 6

LESSON
3

Polyhedra and Their Properties

In the previous two lessons, you studied two-dimensional shapes and some of their important properties and applications in design, building, and art. In many cases, two-dimensional shapes and their properties have corresponding ideas in three dimensions. In three dimensions, as in two dimensions, the shape of an object helps to determine its possible uses.

In your history classes, you may have noticed that the Greeks and people in other ancient cultures often used columns in the design of their buildings. The Greek Parthenon shown above is made of marble. Thus, the columns had to support great weights. An important design consideration is the shape of the column.

424 UNIT 6 | Patterns in Shape

Polyhedra and Their Properties

This lesson continues the study, begun in the first two lessons, of properties of shapes and how these properties relate to possible functions of the shape. Students will recognize that in many cases, three-dimensional shapes and their properties have corresponding ideas in two dimensions. In Investigation 1, students explore (1) the definitions and properties of polyhedra, especially prisms and pyramids, by building and examining models and sketches of a variety of shapes. Investigation 2 focuses on visualizing and sketching three-dimensional shapes and (2) Euler's formula relating the number of vertices, edges, and faces of a polyhedron. In Investigation 3, students explore symmetries of polyhedra; rigidity, and Descartes' Theorem about angle defects. In Investigation 4, students explore some of the properties of regular polyhedra and determine why there are only five. Volume, surface area, and cross sections of selected three-dimensional shapes are explored in the On Your Own tasks.

Lesson Objectives

- Identify and describe important characteristics of common three-dimensional shapes including prisms, pyramids, cones, and cylinders

- Construct three-dimensional models of these shapes and describe their two-dimensional components

- Sketch three-dimensional shapes using different methods and recognize the advantages and disadvantages of each method

- Recognize and describe the plane and rotational symmetries of polyhedra

- Recognize whether a polyhedron is rigid and how to reinforce a polyhedron to produce one that is rigid

- Explore consequences of the Euler relationship involving the numbers of vertices, faces, and edges and of Descartes' Theorem concerning the face angles in any convex polyhedron

- Recall, justify derivations of, and use formulas for finding surface area and volume of common three-dimensional shapes

Common Core State Standards **CCSS**
Focused on:
G-GMD.2, G-GMD.3, G-MG.1
Connected to:
A-CED.2, G-GMD.4, G-MG.2. G-MG.3

THINK ABOUT THIS SITUATION

Suppose you made three columns by folding and taping sheets of 8.5 × 11-inch paper so that each column was 8.5 inches high with bases shaped, respectively, as equilateral triangles (pictured at the right), squares, and regular octagons. Imagine that you placed a small rectangular piece of cardboard (about 6 by 8 inches) on top of a column. Then you carefully placed a sequence of objects (like notebooks or textbooks) on the platform until the column collapsed.

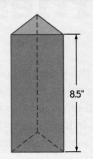

8.5"

a Which column shape do you think would collapse under the least weight?

b Which column shape do you think would hold the most weight before collapsing?

c Test your conjectures by conducting the experiment with your class. What happens to the maximum weight supported as the number of sides of the column base increases?

d Suppose another column is made with a regular hexagon base. Predict how the number of objects it would support before collapsing would compare to those of the three columns you made. Explain your reasoning.

e Why do you think the ancient Greeks chose to use cylindrical columns?

In this lesson, you will use properties of two-dimensional shapes to aid in examining three-dimensional shapes. You will learn how to identify and describe common three-dimensional shapes and how to construct three-dimensional models of them. You will develop skill in visualizing and sketching them in two dimensions and in identifying their symmetries and other important properties. You will also explore some of the many connections between two- and three-dimensional shapes.

 INVESTIGATION 1

Recognizing and Constructing Three-Dimensional Shapes

Like the columns of the Parthenon, most everyday three-dimensional shapes are designed with special characteristics in mind. In this investigation, you will consider the following questions:

What are important characteristics of common three-dimensional shapes?

How can three-dimensional models of these shapes be constructed?

This lesson is launched with an experiment comparing the relative strengths of columns that have various shapes. The launch is intended to illustrate that shape not only has practical importance in two dimensions, as students learned in the first two lessons, but also in three dimensions. One way to begin this launch is with a full-class discussion of whether the shape of the column is related to its weight-bearing strength in any way. Have students predict which of the column shapes will be strongest, and explain why they think so.

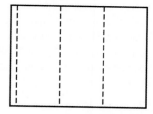

Next, check students' predictions by carrying out the experiment. Have the differently-shaped columns folded and taped in advance to save class time. To make triangular columns, measure and mark the paper $8\frac{1}{2}$" × 11" at 0.5 inches, 4.0 inches, and 7.5 inches (as pictured). It is important that the triangles be as close to equilateral as possible. A scalene or isosceles triangle does not hold as much weight as an equilateral triangle of the same perimeter.

To make square columns, fold the paper slightly off center, so that there is a half-inch extra on one end. The extra half-inch then should be folded. Unfold the paper at the center and then fold in the outer sides to the center fold.

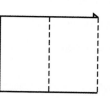

To make hexagonal columns, adjust these directions as needed. Relatively light, soft-cover books are better as weights than hard-bound textbooks, as one of the latter may cause some of the columns to collapse.

THINK ABOUT THIS SITUATION

The responses below assume that the class has tested how much weight the differently-shaped columns will support. Answers for Parts a and b may vary since they are predictions.

a The triangular column will collapse under the least amount of weight.

b A circular column will hold the most weight as your experiment will show.

c In general, the amount of weight a column will support increases as the number of sides of the column's base increases.

d A hexagonal column should hold more weight than the triangle or square column but less than the circular column. A hexagon has more sides than a triangle or a square, but less than a circle which can be thought of as having an infinite number of sides.

e A circular column is more and more closely approximated as the number of sides of the column's base increases without bound. As you saw in Part d, the more sides the base has, the more weight the column supports. Thus, a circular column will support the most weight. (A circular column might also be easier to construct than a many-sided column.)

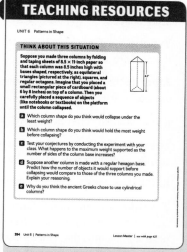

TEACHING RESOURCES

Lesson Master 394
GO DIGITAL

Think About This Situation, *page 425*

Before addressing the questions in the TATS, encourage students to think about the shapes of pillars they have seen used in buildings. The Parthenon pictured on page 424 is an example in which the pillars are roughly circular cylinders, but students may have seen square, or other shaped, pillars or supports in buildings at home or even at school.

Teacher: What shape do the columns appear to be in the Parthenon, pictured on page 424?

Tao: They look round and tall.

Teacher: Does anyone know the mathematical name for that shape?

Katie: I think they are called cylinders.

(Other students nod and murmur in agreement.)

Teacher: Does anyone know of any cylindrical columns around here—maybe at home or in buildings around town?

Chesney: There's a big house out on Highway 33—you know, just past the American Legion Post. It has columns like that in front.

(Other students share examples.)

Teacher: Many of us have seen columns that are circular cylinders. Do any of you know of any columns or pillars that have other shapes?

Yvonne: In our barn at home, the wooden columns that support the roof are square.

Alec: In the gym, the columns are square, too. And the ones on our porch are rectangles.

(Other students offer examples.)

Teacher: So square columns seem pretty common, too. Anyone seen any columns with other shapes?

Katie: I can't think of any, but there could be many shapes, I think.

Teacher: Columns could have many different shapes. Would some of the shapes hold more weight than others? For example, here are columns that I made from sheets of paper before class. *(Places the triangular, square, and octagonal columns on his flat-surfaced desk.)* Which shape would you predict would hold the least weight and which the most weight?

Chumani: The triangle one would hold the most—triangles are rigid. Probably the circular one would hold the least.

Charo: I'll say the square one holds the most weight because many pillars are square. I'm not sure about least. Maybe the triangle column since the top of the column looks smallest of the three shapes.

Nathan: I think they would all hold the same weight, because they are all made from a sheet of paper.

(Other students voice their agreement or disagreement. Nearly every ordering of shapes is named by at least one student.)

Teacher: Well, let's try it. I'll put this piece of cardboard on top of the triangular column. Chumani, you said the triangular column would hold the most weight. Would you carefully place these paperback books, one at a time on this column? We'll see how many it holds before it collapses.

(Chumani comes to the desk or table where the columns were placed.)

Chumani: Okay, that's one, hmmm ... two, three, four, fi... ooops *(as the column collapses)*. It held four books.

(Students who predicted that the square and octagonal columns would hold the most weight repeat this with those shapes, keeping the order of the books placed on the column the same. The results should be more for the square than the triangle and most for the octagon.)

Teacher: Now that we have these results, predict the number of books that this regular hexagonal column will hold before collapsing. *(Teacher places the regular hexagonal column on his desk.)*

Gino: I see a pattern here. If the pattern I observed continues, the column with a hexagon base should hold more weight than the square and less weight than the octagon. We might need to use a smaller unit of weight in an experiment to find this out though. Our books added quite a bit of weight each time we added one book.

Teacher: Why do you think that the ancient Greeks chose to use cylindrical columns?

Glyn: Well, if our experiment is right, the cylindrical columns hold the most weight.

Recognizing and Constructing Three-Dimensional Shapes

In this investigation, students construct three-dimensional shapes (polyhedra) by folding up two-dimensional nets composed of polygons, emphasizing that polyhedra are constructed from polygons. Students also classify polyhedra as pyramids, prisms, or neither, and they construct models for these polyhedra. Using these models, they discover Euler's relationship among the number of vertices, faces, and edges of a polyhedron. Finally, they briefly explore cones and cylinders, both as limiting cases of pyramids and prisms, respectively, and as solids of revolution.

You may want to begin this lesson with a whole-class discussion of the shapes of the pictured objects as addressed in Problem 1 Parts a and b. Encourage students to focus on mathematical characteristics such as *parallel edges, parallel faces, triangular or rectangular faces*, and *circular bases*. This problem provides an opportunity to access prior knowledge of geometric names of the shapes.

As you facilitate groups working on the investigation, check that students are correctly interpreting the definitions and using the mathematical terms properly. You will probably need to encourage students to explain their reasoning carefully and completely for each problem.

When students have completed Problems 1–4, they should have clear ideas of prisms and pyramids and their edges, faces, vertices, and bases.

Constructing the straw and pipe cleaner models in Problem 5 will help students develop their visualization skills as well as their understanding of specific polyhedra. Have each student construct one prism or one pyramid with each work group constructing all 9 models. Save these models for use in later investigations in this lesson.

To construct the models, you will need 5-cm and 8-cm pieces of thin straws or coffee stirrers and pipe cleaners. To assemble a model, use thin straws and a small piece of pipe cleaner to connect two straws at a common vertex. Additional pipe cleaner segments can be inserted at the same vertex to add edges. Continue the process to complete the model.

While students are making their models, it will help if you circulate among the groups and ask questions that focus students' attention on the properties of their models. For example, ask:

- How many differently-shaped faces does your model have?

- How is your model different from the models being constructed by others in your group?

1 As a class, examine the objects depicted below.

Popcorn Box   **Candy Package**   **Block "L"**   **Ice Cream Cone**

    a. Which of these objects have similar geometric characteristics? What are those characteristics?

    b. How would you describe the shapes of the above objects?

    c. A **polyhedron** (plural: *polyhedra*) is the three-dimensional counterpart of a polygon. It is made up of a set of polygons that encloses a single region of space. Exactly two polygons (*faces*) meet at each *edge* and three or more edges meet at a *vertex*. Furthermore, the vertices and edges of the polyhedron are vertices and edges of the polygon faces.

      i. Which of the above shapes are polyhedra? For each polyhedron, name the polygons that are its faces.

      ii. If a shape is not a polyhedron, explain why not.

    d. A **convex polyhedron** is a polyhedron in which no segment connecting any two vertices goes outside the polyhedron. Which of the above shapes are convex polyhedra?

    e. Name at least two other common objects with different polyhedron shapes.

2 **Building Polyhedra from Nets** Polyhedron-shaped boxes for packaging products like cereal and candy are often manufactured using a two-dimensional pattern, called a **net**, that can be folded along its edges to form the polyhedron.

Matt Meadows

1 **INSTRUCTIONAL NOTE** Students may use informal language to describe the shapes in this problem. Some students may already know the language of "prism" and "cone." The definitions of a prism and a pyramid are introduced in Problem 3.

a. All these shapes have at least one flat face. In the popcorn box, candy package, and the block "L," all faces are flat and each shape has some rectangular faces. In the popcorn box, all faces are rectangular. The popcorn box, candy package, and block "L" have at least one pair of faces that are parallel. (If students use a qualifying criteria of "polygon faces," then their response should indicate that the cone has nothing in common with the other shapes.) The ice cream cone is quite different from the other shapes, but it has one flat face, a circular one.

b. The popcorn box may be described as a rectangular box, the candy package as a triangular box, and the block "L" as a rectangular L-shaped box. The ice cream cone will likely be correctly identified as a cone.

c. **i.** The popcorn box, the candy package, and the block "L" are polyhedra. The popcorn box has 6 faces, all rectangles. The candy package has 3 rectangular faces and 2 triangular faces. The block "L" has 2 L-shaped faces and 6 rectangular faces.

   ii. The ice cream cone is not a polyhedron since it is not made up of joined polygons.

d. The popcorn box and the candy package are convex polyhedra.

e. There are many acceptable answers. For example, most books are in roughly the shape of a polyhedron, as are cereal boxes and many other grocery containers. Sugar cubes, the outline of many houses so long as the surfaces are flat, the pyramids of Egypt, and even soccer balls like the one pictured on page 442 are other examples of polyhedra.

a. A **cube** is a polyhedron with six congruent square faces. Examine enlarged copies of the three nets shown below. Which of these nets can be folded to make a cube? For nets that can be folded to make a cube, make matching tick marks on edges that match when the net is folded into a cube.

i.   ii.   iii.

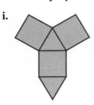 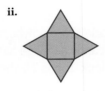 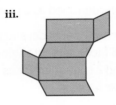

b. Draw a possible net for the candy package shown in Problem 1.

c. Using enlarged copies of the three nets pictured below, fold each net into a polyhedron. Divide the work among your classmates so that each student makes one polyhedron.

i.   ii.   iii.

d. Examine each vertex of the three polyhedra you made in Part c. What is the least number of faces that meet at a vertex? What is the least number of edges that meet at a vertex? Would it be possible for fewer faces or edges to meet at a vertex of any polyhedron? Explain your reasoning.

e. When polygons tile the plane, the sum of the measures of angles at a vertex is 360°.

    i. What is the sum of the measures of angles that meet at each vertex of the first two polyhedra in Part c?

    ii. What is the sum of the measures of the angles that meet at each vertex of the cube in Part a? Of the block "L" in Problem 1?

    iii. Make a conjecture about the sum of the measures of angles that meet at each vertex of a convex polyhedron.

2 **a.** Nets i and ii can be folded to make a cube. See the matching edges below.

i.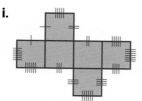

ii.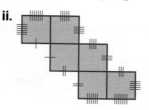

iii. This net cannot be folded to form a cube.

b.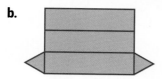

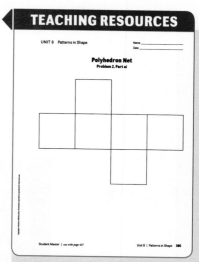
c. See student models.

d. At least 3 faces and at least 3 edges meet at a vertex. In both cases, this is the least number for any polyhedron. Two faces meeting at a vertex could not enclose a region of space. The 3 faces meet in pairs to form 3 edges that come together at the vertex.

e. **i.** The sum of the measures of the face angles at each vertex for Part ci is $90° + 90° + 60° = 240°$. For Part cii, the sum at each base vertex is $90° + 60° + 60° = 210°$, and the sum at the apex is $4 \times 60° = 240°$.

ii. For a cube, the sum of the measures of the face angles at each vertex is $3 \times 90° = 270°$.

For the block "L," the sum is 270° at most of the vertices. However, at the two vertices where the "L" bends, the sum is $270° + 90° + 90° = 450°$. See the figure at the right. The block "L" is nonconvex, but the other polyhedra considered above are convex.

Block "L"

iii. Students may conjecture that the sum of the angles of the faces that meet at any vertex of a convex polyhedron is less than 360°. If the sum is 360°, the faces would all lie in the same plane. If the sum is more than 360°, the faces at the vertex would overlap. To fold them, they would have to be turned outward, as in the nonconvex block "L".

3 **Characteristics of Prisms and Pyramids** Two important types of polyhedra are *prisms* and *pyramids*. Architects frequently use these shapes and an understanding of their characteristics in the design of buildings. For example, the Flat Iron Building, designed by David Burnham and the oldest surviving skyscraper in New York City, has an unusual prism shape. The glass pyramid, pictured on the right, was designed by I. M. Pei for the entrance to the Louvre museum in Paris, France.

a. A **prism** is a polyhedron with two parallel congruent faces with corresponding edges that are connected by parallelograms (called *lateral faces*). Which of the four polyhedra in Problem 2 are prisms?

b. Either one of a pair of congruent, parallel faces of a prism may be called a *base of the prism*. How many different faces of each of the prisms that you identified in Part a could be considered to be a base of the prism? Explain your answers.

c. Compare the prisms in Problem 2 Part c. One prism is a *right prism* and the other is an *oblique prism*. From what you know about other uses of the term "right" in mathematics, which prism is a right prism? Write a definition of a right prism.

d. A **pyramid** is a polyhedron in which all but one of the faces must be triangular, and the triangular faces share a common vertex called the *apex of the pyramid*. The triangular faces are called *lateral faces*. The face that does not contain the apex may have any polygonal shape, and this face is called the *base of the pyramid*. Identify the base and apex of the pyramid in Problem 2 Part c.

e. Prisms and pyramids are often named by the shapes of their bases. For example, a pyramid with a five-sided base is called a *pentagonal pyramid*. Use this naming method to name a cube as a prism. Name the other prisms and pyramids in Problem 2.

NOTE The polyhedra described in this solution are from Problem 2 in the student text.

a. In Problem 2, the polyhedra from Part a, Part ci, and Part ciii are prisms.

b. Since pairs of opposite faces are all parallel in the prism (cube) in Part a and the remaining lateral faces are squares and so also parallelograms, any of the 6 faces could be considered to be a base of the prism. Either of the 2 parallel triangular faces in Part ci may be considered to be a base of the prism. Note that the lateral faces are squares and squares are parallelograms. In Part ciii, all pairs of opposite faces are congruent and parallel and the remaining lateral faces are parallelograms, so any of the 6 faces could be considered to be a base of the prism.

c. The prism in Part ciii is an oblique prism, and the one in Part ci is a right prism. In mathematics, the term "right" is usually used to indicate the presence of right or 90° angles, as in Part ci. A **right prism** is a prism in which all lateral faces are rectangles.

d. Part cii is a net for a pyramid with a square base. The apex is the vertex shared by the 4 triangular faces.

e. Using this naming method, a cube is a square prism in which all edges are of equal length. The prism in Problem 2 Part ci is a triangular prism. The prism in Problem 2 Part ciii is an oblique parallelogram prism (also called a *parallelepiped*). The pyramid in Problem 2 Part cii is a square pyramid.

4 Now examine each of the shapes below.

a. Which shapes appear to be right prisms? Oblique prisms? Pyramids? None of these? Explain your choices based on the definitions in Problem 3.

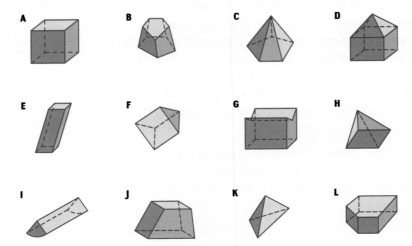

b. Which of the above polyhedra appear to be nonconvex? Explain.

Unless otherwise stated, in the remainder of this unit and in future units, prisms will be assumed to be convex, right prisms.

5 **Building and Analyzing Polyhedra Frames** Models for polyhedra can be hollow like a folded-up net or an empty box, or they can be solid like a candy bar or brick. Polyhedra can also be modeled as a skeleton that includes only the edges, as in a jungle gym.

Working in a group, make the following models from coffee stirrers or straws and pipe cleaners. Cut the pipe cleaners into short lengths that can be used to connect two straw edges at a vertex, as shown. Divide the work. Each student should build at least one prism and one pyramid. Save the models to explore properties of polyhedra later in this lesson.

Lesson 3 | Polyhedra and Their Properties **429**

4 **a.** A, F, G, J, and L appear to be right prisms since there are two congruent parallel faces and the remaining faces are rectangles. E appears to be an oblique prism because some of the lateral faces appear to be parallelograms that are not rectangles.

C, H, and K appear to be pyramids because the lateral faces are triangular and meet at a vertex.

B, D, and I are "none of these" (not prisms or pyramids). (B and D are polyhedra since they are made up of a set of polygons that enclose a region of space. I is not a polyhedron since each parallel face appears to be part of a circular region.)

b. The polyhedron in G is not convex since the segment joining two vertices—say, the top-right two vertices, goes outside the polyhedron.

a. cube: 5-cm edges

b. triangular prism: 5-cm edges on bases, 8-cm height

c. square prism: 5-cm edges on bases, 8-cm height

d. pentagonal prism: 5-cm edges on bases, 8-cm height

e. hexagonal prism: 5-cm edges on bases, 8-cm height

f. triangular pyramid: 5-cm edges on bases, other edges 5 cm

g. square pyramid: 5-cm edges on bases, other edges 8 cm

h. pentagonal pyramid: 5-cm edges on bases, other edges 8 cm

i. hexagonal pyramid: 5-cm edges on bases, other edges 8 cm

6 You learned earlier in this lesson that at least three faces and at least three edges must meet at any vertex of a polyhedron. There is a deeper and more surprising relationship among the numbers of vertices, faces, and edges in any polyhedron.

a. Complete a table, like the one below, that includes some of the polyhedra for which your class constructed models.

	Number of Vertices	Number of Faces	Number of Edges
Cube			
Triangular Prism			
Hexagonal Prism			
Triangular Pyramid			
Square Pyramid			

b. Describe one or two patterns in the table that you see.

c. Make a conjecture about the relationship among the numbers of faces F, vertices V, and edges E for each of these polyhedra. Compare your conjecture with others and resolve any differences.

d. Test the relationship you discovered in Part c using one of your other polyhedron models. Does it work for that polyhedron, too?

The formula relating the numbers of vertices, faces, and edges of convex polyhedra was first discovered by Swiss mathematician Leonhard Euler (1707–1783) and is called **Euler's Formula for Polyhedra**. The formula applies to all convex polyhedra.

7 Use Euler's Formula for Polyhedra to answer the following questions.

a. If a convex polyhedron has 10 vertices and 8 faces, how many edges does it have?

b. Can a convex polyhedron that has 8 faces, 12 edges, and 7 vertices be constructed? Give reasons for your answer.

8 *Cones* and *cylinders* are two other common three-dimensional shapes.

a. Are cones and cylinders polyhedra? Why or why not?

b. How do cones and cylinders compare to one another? How are they similar to and different from pyramids and prisms?

c. Use the interactive geometry "Generating Cones and Cylinders" custom app to see how these three-dimensional shapes can be generated from two-dimensional shapes.

Cone

Cylinder

6 **a.**

	Number of Vertices	Number of Faces	Number of Edges
Cube	8	6	12
Triangular prism	6	5	9
Hexagonal prism	12	8	18
Triangular pyramid	4	4	6
Square pyramid	5	5	8

b. Possible patterns are:

- The number of edges is always more than the number of vertices or faces.

- For a pyramid, the number of edges is 2n, where n is the number of edges of the base.

- For a prism, the number of edges is 3n, where n is the number of edges of the base.

- The number of faces is always less than or equal to the number of vertices.

- The sum of the number of vertices and faces is more than (or 2 more than) the number of edges.

c. The number of vertices V plus the number of faces F equals the number of edges E plus 2. In symbols, $V + F = E + 2$. Some students might express this as $V + F - 2 = E$.

d. This result is called Euler's Formula for Polyhedra. It is true for any convex polyhedron.

7 **a.** Using Euler's Formula, $10 + 8 = E + 2$ so $18 = E + 2$ and $E = 16$.

b. This is not possible, because Euler's Formula fails. $7 + 8 \neq 12 + 2$

8 **a.** Cones and cylinders are not polyhedra since they have circular rather than polygonal bases, and much of their surface is curved.

NOTE In this lesson, we restrict our attention to circular cones and cylinders.

b. Both cones and cylinders have circular bases, and a cylinder, like a prism, has two parallel congruent bases. A cone, on the other hand, is like a pyramid in that it has one base and an apex that lies above (or below) the base.

c. Students may describe the process of revolving a segment that is not parallel to an axis of rotation but with an endpoint that intersects that axis to generate a cone, or revolving a segment that is parallel to an axis of rotation to generate a cylinder. They may include *CPMP-Tools* screens showing how the shapes are generated.

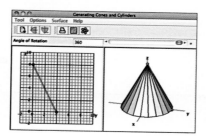
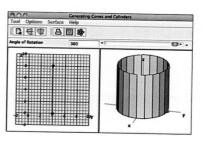

SUMMARIZE THE MATHEMATICS

In this investigation, you explored characteristics of commonly occurring three-dimensional shapes—prisms, pyramids, cylinders, and cones.

a In what ways are polyhedra like polygons? In what ways are they different?

b What is the least number of faces that can meet at a vertex of any polyhedron? What is the least number of edges that can meet at a vertex of any polyhedron?

c How are pyramids like prisms? How are they different?

d Consider a sequence of prisms in which each base is a regular polygon. The base of the first prism has 3 sides, the base of the second has 4 sides, the base of the third has 5 sides, and so on. As the number of sides in the base increases, what shape does the prism begin to resemble?

e Consider a sequence of pyramids with bases like those described in Part d. As the number of sides in the base of a pyramid increases, what shape does the pyramid begin to resemble?

f What formula relates the number of vertices, faces, and edges of the polyhedra that you explored in this investigation?

Be prepared to share your ideas and formula with the class.

✔️ CHECK YOUR UNDERSTANDING

Examine the photo of a cereal box shown at the right.

a. Explain why the box is an example of a polyhedron. Then name the polyhedron as precisely as you can.

b. Draw a net for a model of the box.

c. Betsy claimed that this three-dimensional shape is a prism and that any of its faces could be considered to be its base. Do you agree with Betsy? Explain why or why not.

d. If you were to make a model of this three-dimensional shape from straws and pipe cleaners:

  i. how many different length straws would you need?

  ii. how many straws of each length would be needed?

e. Verify that Euler's Formula is satisfied for the polyhedron represented by the cereal box.

Geoff Butler

Lesson 3 | Polyhedra and Their Properties **431**

After discussing Part f of the Summarize the Mathematics, ask students to compare Euler's Formula for Polyhedra to the one they found for vertex-edge graphs in Connections Task 13 of Lesson 1 of the *Discrete Mathematical Modeling* unit. To cement understanding of the definition of prism and the criteria for parallelogram lateral faces and when lateral faces can also be bases, use the straw hexagonal prism. This shape has lateral faces that cannot be bases.

SUMMARIZE THE MATHEMATICS

a Polyhedra are three-dimensional analogs of polygons. A polygon encloses a single region of the plane with pairs of sides that meet at a vertex, whereas a polyhedron encloses a single region of three-dimensional space with polygonal faces that meet in pairs at edges and edges that meet at a vertex.

b At least three faces and at least three edges must meet at a vertex of a polyhedron to enclose a region of space.

c Pyramids are similar to prisms in that both have only polygonal faces, and both are named by their bases. They are different in that pyramids have one base and triangular lateral faces that meet at a point, the apex, whereas prisms have two parallel, congruent bases and parallelogram (rectangular in a right prism) lateral faces.

d As the number of sides in the base of a prism increases, the prism approaches the shape of a cylinder.

e As the number of sides in the base of a pyramid increases, the pyramid approaches the shape of a cone.

f The formula, $V + F = E + 2$, is called Euler's Formula for Polyhedra.

PROMOTING MATHEMATICAL DISCOURSE

TEACHING RESOURCES

UNIT 6   Patterns in Shape

SUMMARIZE THE MATHEMATICS

In this investigation, you explored characteristics of commonly occurring three-dimensional shapes—prisms, pyramids, cylinders, and cones.

a In what ways are polyhedra like polygons? In what ways are they different?

b What is the least number of faces that can meet at a vertex of any polyhedron? What is the least number of edges that can meet at a vertex of any polyhedron?

c How are pyramids like prisms? How are they different?

d Consider a sequence of prisms in which each base is a regular polygon. The base of the first prism has 3 sides, the base of the second has 4 sides, the base of the third has 5 sides, and so on. As the number of sides in the base increases, what shape does the prism begin to resemble?

e Consider a sequence of pyramids with bases like those described in Part d. As the number of sides in the base of a pyramid increases, what shape does the pyramid begin to resemble?

f What formula relates the number of vertices, faces, and edges of the polyhedra that you explored in this investigation?

Be prepared to share your ideas and formula with the class.

402   Unit 6 | Patterns in Shape   Lesson Master | use with page 432

Lesson Master 402
ⓘ GO DIGITAL

MATH TOOLKIT

Sketch a prism, pyramid, cone, cylinder, and nonconvex polyhedron. Compare prisms and pyramids. Apply Euler's Theorem to one of your shapes.

✔ CHECK YOUR UNDERSTANDING

a. The cereal box is a polyhedron because it is a three-dimensional object that is made up of joined polygons and that encloses a single region of space. The cereal box is a right prism with a rectangular base, so it is called a rectangular prism.

b. One possible net is pictured here.

c. Betsy is right. Any pair of opposite faces are parallel and the lateral faces are parallelograms. Thus, any face could be considered to be a base.

d.   **i.** You would need three different lengths of straws—one for the height, one for the length, and one for the width.

   ii. You would need four straws of each length.

e. The cereal box has 8 vertices, 6 faces, and 12 edges. Euler's Formula is satisfied since $8 + 6 = 12 + 2$.

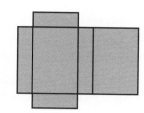

PROMOTING MATHEMATICAL DISCOURSE

Summarize the Mathematics, *page 431*

Teacher: In the first two lessons of this unit, we worked with two-dimensional shapes called polygons. The three-dimensional shapes that we studied in this lesson are similar in some ways and different in others from those two-dimensional shapes. In what ways are polyhedra like polygons, and in what ways are they different?

Cole: Well, they seem pretty different. Polygons are just flat figures, but polyhedra have three dimensions.

Tristan: They both have vertices and edges, so they're sort of alike except the polyhedra also have faces.

Alexa: Also, the sides of a polygon are in two-dimensional space, but the sides or faces of a polyhedron are in three-dimensional space.

Teacher: So, a polygon encloses a region in the plane, whereas a polyhedron encloses a region in three-dimensional space. What is the least number of faces and edges that can meet at a vertex of any polyhedron?

Chase: You need at least 3 faces to meet at a vertex because you need to be able to fold the shape to go three directions. This also means that there will be at least 3 edges of these faces that meet at a vertex.

Teacher: From your experience in Investigation 1, how would you say pyramids are like prisms and how are they different?

Angel: The faces of pyramids and prisms are polygons. *(Points to the square pyramid straw and pipe-cleaner model.)* See triangles here, and the base is a square. In both pyramids and prisms, the bases can be different polygons. The other faces are triangles for pyramids and rectangles for prisms.

Isaiah: The other faces in a prism don't have to be rectangles, do they? Like, if it is an oblique prism.

Cole: Oh, yeah, right. Then, the faces would be parallelograms, not rectangles.

Teacher: Okay, what can you say about the lateral faces of a pyramid?

Jaylen: They are triangles that all come together at this point, uh, vertex at the top.

Roco: Right, the triangles come together at the apex.

Teacher: So one difference between a prism and a pyramid is the shapes of their lateral faces. What other differences are there?

Chase: A pyramid has just one base, but a prism has two.

Reuben: Yeah, and the bases of a prism are parallel and congruent.

Teacher: Very good. Okay. I am going to want you to jot down your answer to this question, don't respond aloud, then I can make sure you all agree. I want you to think about a sequence of prisms. Let me describe them to you while you picture them in your head. Each prism has a base that is a regular polygon. The base of the first prism has 3 sides, (pause) the base of the second prism has 4 sides, (pause) the base of the third prism has 5 sides, (pause) and so on. Here is my question; jot down your answer. As the number of sides in the base of the prism increases, what shape does the prism begin to resemble? *(She gives students a moment to write their answers and looks around the room to make sure each student will have a written response to offer.)*

Teacher: Show your answer to other people in your group. What did you write down?

Misael: We all had cylinder for our answer.

Teacher: Did anyone have a different answer? *(No one offers a different choice.)*

Teacher: Let me ask that a different way. Raise your hand if you agree with the answer "cylinder." *(All the students indicate that they agree.)*

Teacher: What would happen if we considered a sequence of pyramids instead of prisms? As the number of sides in the base of the pyramid increases, what shape does the pyramid begin to resemble?

Tia: It would become a cone. Just think of the base having infinitely many sides—that would essentially make it a circle, and since it comes to a point it would be a cone.

Teacher: What do you think? Anyone disagree with Tia? *(No one disagrees.)*

Teacher: What formula relates the number of vertices, faces, and edges of the polyhedra that you explored in this investigation?

Rickey: Our group had the formula $V + F = E + 2$.

Teacher: Could someone tell me in words what Rickey's formula says?

Tristan: The number of vertices plus the number of faces is two more than the number of edges.

Rhianna: I think of it as add 2 to the number of edges and that will be the same as the sum of the number of vertices and faces.

Teacher: Does anyone think of it a different way?

Matteo: I think of it as edges is equal to vertices plus faces minus 2.

Roco: That's not the same, is it?

Keisha: Sure it is. For example, for the cube, there are 8 vertices plus 6 faces. So, $14 - 2$ or 12 edges are on a cube.

Leland: Oh, I see. And the formula could be written $V + F - 2 = E$. That is just subtracting 2 from each side of the equation.

Teacher: That's right. This formula could be written in different ways. Another way could be $V + F + E = 2$.

Misael: That doesn't make sense. There are way too many vertices, edges, and faces to add to only 2. You meant $V + F - E = 2$, didn't you?

Teacher: Good point! That is correct. What mistake did I make?

Syed: You subtracted E from one side of the equation and added it to the other side. That was a balancing mistake.

Teacher: That is an easy mistake to make. Thanks for catching it.

INVESTIGATION 2

Visualizing and Sketching Three-Dimensional Shapes

It is not always practical to construct models of three-dimensional shapes. For example, you cannot fax a scale model of an off-shore oil rig to an engineer in another country. Rather, the three-dimensional shape needs to be represented in two dimensions in a way that conveys the important information about the shape. In this investigation, you will explore these two main questions:

What are some effective ways to sketch three-dimensional shapes?

What information does each kind of sketch provide about the shape?

Orthographic Drawings There are several methods for representing a three-dimensional shape in a sketch, but since the sketch has only two dimensions, some information about the three-dimensional shape will necessarily be missing. One way to depict three-dimensional shapes is to sketch two-dimensional *face-views* such as a top view, a front view, and a right-side view. Architects commonly use this method, called an **orthographic drawing**. For the house below, *a top view*, *a front view*, and *a right-side view* are shown. Together, these views display the length, depth, and height of the building to scale. You'll notice the top view is different from the other two. Floor plans such as this are frequently used instead of an exterior top view.

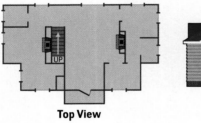

Top View **Front View** **Right-Side View**

1 An orthographic drawing of a model of a hotel made from cubes is shown below.

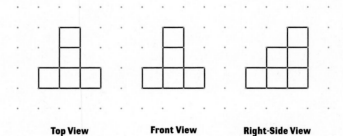

Top View **Front View** **Right-Side View**

Visualizing and Sketching Three-Dimensional Shapes

In the previous investigation, students constructed three-dimensional models of polyhedra. Such models probably are the best vehicles for visualizing and exploring the properties of three-dimensional shapes. However, for many practical purposes, two-dimensional representations, that is, sketches or drawings, are required. The focus of this investigation is on some ways to make such sketches.

The introduction to this investigation gives one example of the need to represent three-dimensional shapes in two dimensions. You can expand this into a class discussion; students will be able to give examples of two-dimensional drawings of three-dimensional shapes. Some examples are advertisements, directions for assembling an item, blueprints for construction, illustrations in textbooks, video game images, cartoon drawings, and landscaping plans. Let students know that, in addition to continuing to build spatial-visualization skills by working with three-dimensional shapes, in this investigation they will learn two ways to represent three-dimensional shapes. These are orthographic drawings (or face-views) and oblique drawings from a particular point of view showing hidden edges as dashed lines.

There are other, more specialized, drawing methods such as orthogonal and one-, two-, and three-point perspective drawings, but a great deal of time is required to teach and learn these methods. Furthermore, most drawings that people encounter in everyday life are drawn using one of the two methods that students learn about in this investigation. One-point perspective drawing is explored in an assessment project.

Many students have trouble visualizing how edges and plane surfaces in a three-dimensional model and a two-dimensional sketch of the same shape relate to each other. You may wish to supply interlocking cubes and polyhedra to help with visualization. As students construct and compare orthographic drawings and other sketches of the same three-dimensional shape, ask them regularly to tell you which edges, faces, or vertices must match in the different representations. Similarly, ask about the match between edges, faces, or vertices in their drawings and in the three-dimensional models that they are sketching. From their efforts to think about these matches, you will have an informal assessment of the progress they are making in developing visualization skills.

TECHNOLOGY NOTE

Students will need many opportunities to visualize three-dimensional shapes. The "Slicing or Unfolding Polyhedra" custom app will provide them these opportunities. Having access to technology tools frequently will help students become proficient at strategically choosing tools.

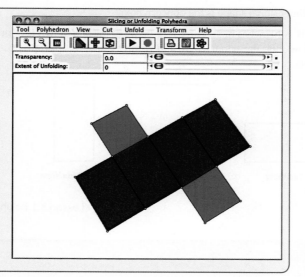

a. How many cubes make up the model?

b. Use blocks or sugar cubes to make a model of this hotel. Build your model on a sheet of paper or poster board that can be rotated.

c. Could you make the model using information from only two of these views? Explain.

2 Examine this model of a building built from cubes. Assume any cube above the bottom layer rests on another cube and that there are no other hidden cubes.

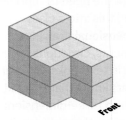

a. Make an orthographic sketch of this model.

b. How many cubes are in this model?

c. Would it be possible to make a model with fewer cubes that has the same top, front, and right-side views as this one? Explain.

3 **Oblique Drawings** Another way to represent a three-dimensional shape such as a popcorn box is shown below. The sketch on the right, called an **oblique drawing**, is a *top-front-right corner* view of the box as a geometer would draw it. The front face was translated in the direction of the arrow to produce the back face, then edges were drawn to connect vertices. The sketch gives a sense of depth even though it is not drawn in true perspective. The three edges of the box blocked from view are shown as dashed lines.

 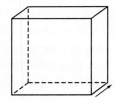

a. What three-dimensional shape is the popcorn box?

b. The actual box is 10 inches high. Three face-views of the box drawn to scale are given below. Find the actual length and width by making appropriate measurements.

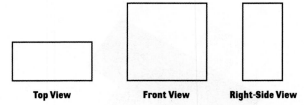

| Top View | Front View | Right-Side View |

Lesson 3 | Polyhedra and Their Properties **433**

1 **a.** There are 8 cubes in this model. Students may not give the correct number of cubes until after they build their model.

b. Students should build the model and verify that their model has the given top, front, and right-side views. Models should resemble the one drawn at the right.

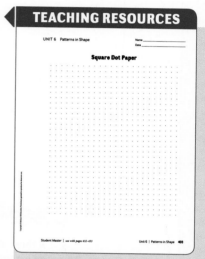

c. Using only the top and right-side views would allow you to construct the three-dimensional model correctly. (An extension of this problem is to ask students how they can change the model by changing only one view so that two views are not enough to determine the shape. One way is to add a cube on the bottom layer behind the right-most cube.)

2 **a.**

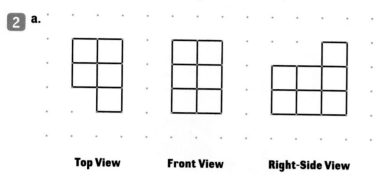

Top View	**Front View**	**Right-Side View**

b. This model is made of 12 cubes.

c. Yes, you could remove either top cube from the middle of the second row.

3 **a.** The popcorn box is a rectangular (right) prism.

b. The actual length and width of the box are 10 inches and 5 inches, respectively (assuming length is greater than width).

c. Now examine more carefully the sketch of the box from a top-front-right corner view.

    i. What appear to be the shapes of the faces as shown in the drawing? What are the shapes of the faces in the real box?

    ii. What edges are parallel in the real box? Are the corresponding edges in the sketch drawn parallel?

d. Sketch the box from a bottom-front-left corner view. Use dashed lines to show "hidden" edges.

4 For this problem, refer to the straw and pipe cleaner models you previously made. For each of the following models, place the model on your desk so that an edge of a base is parallel to an edge of your desk. Make an oblique sketch of the model. Compare your sketches and strategies for drawing these with those of your classmates.

a. cube

b. square prism

c. square pyramid

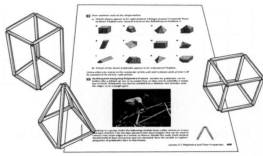

SUMMARIZE THE MATHEMATICS

A three-dimensional shape can be represented in two dimensions in various ways, including an orthographic (face-views) drawing or an oblique sketch from a particular point of view.

a When is it helpful to represent a three-dimensional shape by an orthographic drawing? By an oblique sketch?

b Discuss the similarities and differences between a top-front-right corner sketch of a right rectangular prism and the rectangular prism itself.

c Consider a convex polyhedron that is made up of two square pyramids sharing a common base. Make an orthographic drawing of this polyhedron. Assume an edge of the common base is parallel to an edge of your desk.

Be prepared to share your ideas and drawing with the class.

c. i. The front and back faces appear to be squares, as they are in the real box. The top, bottom, and side faces appear to be parallelograms, but not rectangles. In the real box, these faces are all rectangles.

ii. Opposite sides of the rectangular and parallelogram faces are parallel. Edges that are parallel in the real box are also parallel in the sketch. (For this reason, this type of drawing is called a parallel projection by geometers.)

d.

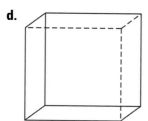

4 **a.** **b.** 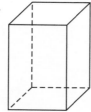 **c.**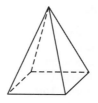

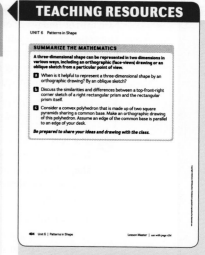

NOTE To locate the apex of the pyramid, draw the diagonals of the base to find its center. Then the apex is located on the line that is perpendicular to the base at its center.

SUMMARIZE THE MATHEMATICS

a It is helpful to use an orthographic drawing when you want the lengths of all the segments in the drawing to be a uniform scaling of the actual lengths. Architectural plans are often drawn this way in order to make the lengths, angles, and design of a structure as clear as possible. An oblique sketch is helpful when you want to see what a three-dimensional object actually looks like when viewed from a particular vantage point.

b The same pairs of edges are parallel in the sketch as in the rectangular prism. Lengths of front and back edges are in the same proportion in the sketch as in the prism. On the other hand, the front-to-back edges are not drawn to scale. All faces of a right rectangular prism are rectangles, whereas in the sketch only the front and back faces are rectangles. The other faces in the sketch are parallelograms that are not rectangular. Differences are unavoidable because the prism has three dimensions, but the sketch has only two dimensions.

c

Top View   **Front View**   **Right-Side View**

TEACHING RESOURCES

UNIT 6 Patterns in Shape

SUMMARIZE THE MATHEMATICS

A three-dimensional shape can be represented in two dimensions in various ways, including an orthographic (face-views) drawing or an oblique sketch from a particular point of view.

a When is it helpful to represent a three-dimensional shape by an orthographic drawing? By an oblique sketch?

b Discuss the similarities and differences between a top-front-right corner sketch of a right rectangular prism and the rectangular prism itself.

c Consider a convex polyhedron that is made up of two square pyramids sharing a common base. Make an orthographic drawing of this polyhedron. Assume an edge of the common base is parallel to an edge of your desk.

Be prepared to share your ideas and drawing with the class.

404 Unit 6 | Patterns in Shape   Lesson Master | use with page 434

Lesson Master 404
Ⓘ **GO DIGITAL**

PROCESSING PROMPT

Today _____ helped us
          (name)
visualize the shapes since
visualization is one of his/her
strengths; and _____
                    (name)
helped us ... .

✅ CHECK YOUR UNDERSTANDING

Consider the three-dimensional shape formed when a pentagonal pyramid is placed on top of a pentagonal prism. Assume the bases of the two shapes are congruent.

a. Make an orthographic drawing of this shape.

b. Is the shape a convex polyhedron? Explain.

c. Describe a possible real-world application of a shape with this design.

INVESTIGATION 3

Patterns in Polyhedra

Like polygons, polyhedra are most useful and interesting when they have certain regularities or symmetries. For example, an "A-frame" is a style of architecture sometimes used in building houses. This attractive shape has a balance, or symmetry, about a vertical plane that contains the top roof line. The symmetry plane splits the basic shape of the house into two parts that are mirror images of one another. In this investigation, you will explore symmetry and other properties of polyhedra. As you work on the following problems, look for clues to this general question:

How are properties of polyhedra such as symmetry and rigidity related to corresponding properties of polygons?

1 The basic shape of an A-frame house is a prism with isosceles triangle bases. In the diagram below, note how the vertical plane cuts the three-dimensional shape into two parts that are mirror images of each other. This plane is called a **symmetry plane** or **mirror plane**. The shape is said to have **reflection symmetry**.

a. Does this isosceles triangular prism have any other symmetry planes? If so, describe or sketch them. If not, explain why not.

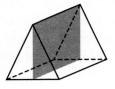

b. Next examine the cube and equilateral triangular pyramid models that your class made with straws and pipe cleaners. How many symmetry planes does each shape have? Describe or sketch them.

c. How are the symmetry planes for these three polyhedra related to the symmetry of their faces?

a.

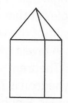

Top View　　**Front View**　　**Right-Side View**

b. This is a convex polyhedron, because there is no segment joining a pair of vertices that lies outside the polyhedron. All such segments either are edges of the polyhedron or are inside the polyhedron.

c. This shape could be used for a decorative candy container. It also could be used as an outside gazebo. The pyramid-shaped roof would help keep rain and snow from collecting.

INVESTIGATION 3 **CCSS** G-GMD.2, G-MG.1, A-CED.2

Patterns in Polyhedra

In earlier lessons in this unit, students investigated the symmetry and rigidity properties of polygons. This investigation extends that work to three dimensions by exploring these same properties for polyhedra. Students also explore a surprising property concerning the measures of a polyhedron's face angles. Students will need the models that they constructed in Problem 5 of Investigation 1.

For Problem 1, students will have an intuitive idea of reflection (or bilateral symmetry) in three dimensions as it is a natural extension of two-dimensional line reflection symmetry. If some students need more work with this idea, it may be helpful to have them describe the symmetry planes for some of the models that they constructed in Investigation 1. To discover reflection planes and to understand cross-sections (Extensions Problem 23), it is helpful to use a set of transparent solids with an aperture. Fill the transparent model to varying levels with water that has been tinted with food coloring. Rotating the model allows students to see the various cross-sectional shapes formed when planes intersect the three-dimensional model and decide when a plane divides the model into mirror-image halves. If solid or transparent models are available, rubber bands can be stretched around them to outline a cut by a plane.

Three-dimensional rotational symmetry is the focus of Problems 2 through 4. Again, emphasize the connection between rotational symmetry about a point in two dimensions and rotational symmetry about a line (or axis) in three dimensions.

In Problem 5, students examine the rigidity properties of the polyhedron models that they constructed in Investigation 1.

An interesting property of a convex polyhedron that sets limits on its face angles is the focus of Problem 6. The property has to do with the sum of the angle defects at all vertices of the polyhedron. The *vertex angle defect* is the positive difference between the sum of the measures of the face angles at that vertex and 360°. In other words, it is the angle measure of the gap that results if the vertex is opened out flat as in a net. (See the approach to regular polyhedra in Investigation 4.) Analogous to the Exterior Angle Theorem for polygons, Descartes' Theorem says that the sum of the angle defects at all vertices in any convex polyhedron is 720°. Students will see this result emerging in Problem 6 after a few examples. Emphasize that the examples are not a proof, and that the proof of Descartes' Theorem is beyond the scope of this course.

1 **a.** The plane that is perpendicular to the given symmetry plane and that contains the midpoint of the roofline is also a symmetry plane. The front half and back half of the house are mirror images when reflected across the plane.

b. A cube has 9 planes of symmetry, each containing parallel symmetry lines of opposite faces. Six of these symmetry planes contain parallel diagonals of opposite faces. An alternate way to describe these planes is to say that they contain opposite edges of the cube. The remaining 3 symmetry planes contain the lines connecting midpoints of opposite edges. All of the symmetry planes contain the center of the cube.

6 of

3 of

An equilateral triangular pyramid has 6 planes of symmetry. Each plane passes through one edge and the two altitudes or symmetry lines that meet at the midpoint of the opposite edge. Here also, all symmetry planes contain the center of the equilateral triangular pyramid.

6 of

> **INSTRUCTIONAL NOTE** Students may also describe these 6 planes as containing a vertex and an altitude of the triangular face opposite the vertex. If students take this approach, they may incorrectly determine 12 symmetry planes, not recognizing the duplications. Comparing these two approaches to visualizing the symmetry planes will help students recognize not only that both are correct, but also that working from the edges has the advantage of quickly reconstructing the number of symmetry planes.

c. Looking at the symmetry planes, you notice that these planes contain a symmetry line of each face they pass through.

2 Place a model of a square pyramid on the top of a desk or table. Rotate it about the line through its apex and the center of its base.

   a. What is the smallest angle that you can rotate the pyramid so that it appears to be in the same position as it was originally?

   b. As you rotate the pyramid through a complete 360° turn, at what other *angles of rotation* does it appear as it did in its original location?

   c. Can you rotate the pyramid through angles less than 360° about other lines so that it appears to be in the same position as originally? If so, describe them. If not, explain why not.

If there is a line about which a three-dimensional shape can be turned less than 360° in such a way that the rotated shape appears in exactly the same position as the original shape, the shape is said to have **rotational symmetry**. The line about which the three-dimensional shape is rotated is called an **axis of symmetry** or **rotation axis**.

3 Next examine the rotational symmetry of the equilateral triangular pyramid you constructed.

   a. How many axes of symmetry are there? Where are the axes of symmetry located?

   b. What are the angles of rotation for each axis of symmetry?

   c. How is the rotational symmetry of the triangular pyramid similar to that of the square pyramid, and how is it different?

4 Now examine the rotational symmetry of the cube model you constructed.

   a. How many axes of symmetry does the cube have? Where are the axes of symmetry located?

   b. What are the angles of rotation for each axis of symmetry?

   c. How is the symmetry of the faces related to the symmetry of the cube?

In addition to symmetry, another important consideration in the design of structures is *rigidity*. In Lesson 1, you discovered that any triangle is rigid; and that polygons with more than three sides can be made rigid by triangulating or bracing them with diagonals. In the next problem, you will investigate the rigidity of three-dimensional shapes.

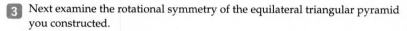

Jim Laser

2 **a.** The smallest angle is 90°.

b. The pyramid appears to be in its original position after rotations of 90°, 180°, and 270°.

c. No. For any other line that allows rotation, such as symmetry lines of the faces, or a line through the centers of opposite faces, an angle of 360° is needed to return to the original position.

3 **a.** There are seven axes of symmetry. Four axes of symmetry are lines containing an apex and the center of the opposite face called the base. Three other axes of symmetry connect midpoints of opposite edges.

b. The angles of rotation for the four axes through the centers of faces are 120° and 240°. The angle of rotation of the three axes through midpoints of opposite edges is 180°.

c. Some axes of symmetry for the two pyramids are described the same way, namely, the line containing the apex and center of the base. Since the triangular pyramid has all edges the same length, any face could be the base, and it thus has four of this type of axis of symmetry. The triangular pyramid has angles of rotation of 120° and 240°. This rotation symmetry is also called three-fold symmetry. The square pyramid has angles of rotation of 90°, 180°, and 270°. This rotation symmetry is also called four-fold symmetry. The square pyramid does not have axes of symmetry connecting midpoints of opposite edges.

4 **a.** A cube has 13 axes of symmetry. The axes of rotational symmetry are (1) the six lines that join the midpoints of opposite edges, (2) the three lines that join the centers of opposite faces, and (3) the four diagonal lines that join opposite corners.

b. Type (1) lines have 180° angles of rotation. Type (2) lines have angles of rotation of 90°, 180°, and 270°. Type (3) lines have 120° and 240° angles of rotation.

c. Each square face has the same rotational symmetries about its center as that described for type (2) lines in Part b. Type (2) lines, as described in Part a, go through the centers of opposite faces.

5 Consider the models that you made in Problem 5 on page 429.

   a. Which of the models represent rigid shapes?

   b. Add bracing straws to your model of a triangular prism to make it rigid.

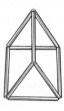

   i. Describe where you placed the bracing straws and why you placed them there.

   ii. Could you have placed the braces in different positions and still made the triangular prism rigid? Could you have used fewer bracing straws? Explain and illustrate.

   c. Add braces to your model of a cube so that it becomes a rigid structure. Note the number of bracing straws that you used and describe the position of each straw. Could you have used fewer bracing straws?

   d. Think of a different way to reinforce the cube so that it becomes a rigid structure. Describe the pattern of reinforcing straws.

   e. Of the methods you used to reinforce the cube, which could best be used to make a rectangular prism-shaped building stand rigidly?

6 **A Surprising Property of Polyhedra** Another interesting property of convex polyhedra has to do with the face angles that meet at each vertex. You saw in Investigation 1 that the sum of the measures of the face angles that meet at any vertex of any convex polyhedron must be less than 360°. The positive difference between the angle sum at a vertex and 360° is called the **vertex angle defect**. It is a measure of how close that corner is to being flat.

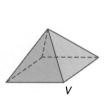

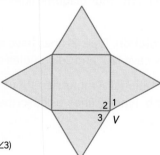

angle defect at V:
$360° - (m\angle 1 + m\angle 2 + m\angle 3)$

   a. What is the angle defect at each vertex of a cube? What is the sum of the angle defects at all vertices of a cube?

   b. In a similar way, find the sum of the angle defects for an equiangular triangular pyramid.

5 **a.** Only the triangular pyramid is rigid.

b. **i.** Subdividing the three rectangular faces into triangles makes the triangular prism rigid. If two of the rectangular faces are triangulated, then it will also be rigid.

   ii. Either diagonal of each lateral face may be used. Also, any combination of two diagonals of different faces will make the triangular prism rigid.

c. You can triangulate each face using a diagonal to make the cube rigid. You could also triangulate any 3, 4, or 5 faces as long as for each pair of opposite faces, at least one of the faces is triangulated.

d. Another way to make the cube rigid would be to place 3 or 4 braces as diagonals through the center of the cube. Combinations including some braces through the center and some diagonals of faces could also be used.

e. Braces for the faces are typically used so that a beam does not run through the interior of the building and cause design or space problems.

6 **a.** The angle defect at each vertex is $90°$. There are 8 vertices, so the sum of the angle defects of a cube is $8 \times 90° = 720°$.

b. The sum of the face angles at each vertex of the equiangular triangular pyramid is $180°$, so the angle defect at each vertex is also $180°$. There are 4 vertices, so the sum of the angle defects at all vertices is $4 \times 180° = 720°$

c. In the right equiangular triangular prism, each base is an equiangular triangle and the lateral faces are rectangles. At all 6 vertices, 2 rectangular faces and 1 equiangular triangular face meet, so the sum of the face angles is $60° + 90° + 90° = 240°$. The angle defect at each vertex is $360° - 240° = 120°$. So, the sum of the angle defects at all 6 vertices is $6 \times 120° = 720°$.

  Similarly, in the right regular hexagonal prism, there are 12 vertices each with an angle defect of $360° - (120° + 2 \times 90°) = 60°$, so again the sum of the angle defects at all vertices is $12 \times 60° = 720°$.

c. Find the sum of the angle defects for an equiangular triangular prism and for a regular hexagonal prism. Share the work with a partner.

d. Make a conjecture about the sum of the angle defects in any convex polyhedron. Test your conjecture using a pyramid with a quadrilateral base. Does your conjecture hold true in this case, too?

e. Compare your investigation of the face angles and angle defects in convex polyhedra to what you learned in Lesson 2 about angles of convex polygons. How are the ideas and the results alike? How are they different?

French philosopher and mathematician René Descartes (1596–1650) first discovered that the sum of the angle defects of any convex polyhedron is a constant. The result is called **Descartes' Theorem**.

SUMMARIZE THE MATHEMATICS

In this investigation, you explored two types of symmetry in three dimensions: reflection symmetry and rotational symmetry. You examined the rigidity of different polyhedra. You also discovered a property about the sum of the angle defects of a polyhedron.

a Describe how to identify reflection symmetry and rotational symmetry in a polyhedron.

b Name the rigid polyhedron with the fewest faces and edges.

c What methods can be used to make a polyhedron rigid?

d What is true of the sum of the vertex angle defects for the polyhedra that you studied in this investigation?

Be prepared to share your ideas with the entire class.

 CHECK YOUR UNDERSTANDING

Consider a polyhedron with all edges congruent that looks like a square pyramid joined to the top of a cube.

a. Is this a convex polyhedron? Explain.

b. Describe the reflection symmetry and rotational symmetry of the shape.

c. Describe two ways to add bracing to make this polyhedron rigid. What is the least number of braces needed? Explain.

d. Calculate the sum of the angle defects for this polyhedron and verify that Descartes' Theorem is satisfied.

d. A reasonable conjecture is that the sum of the angle defects of any convex polyhedron is 720°. Students will likely first think about finding the angle defect for each vertex separately, as before. But they should soon recognize that this approach will not work for a general quadrilateral base since we do not know each angle measure. We do know that the sum of the angles of the base is 360° and the sum of the angles for each triangle is 180°. So, the total angle defect can be found as follows:

$$360° \times 5 - 360° - 180° \times 4 = 720°.$$

A net similar to the one on page 437 may help students analyze the problem.

e. In convex polygons, the measure of an exterior angle at each vertex is the difference between 180° and the measure of the interior angle at that vertex. The sum of all the exterior angles in any polygon is 360°. In polyhedra, the angle defect at a vertex is the difference between 360° and the sum of the measures of the angles of the polyhedra that meet at that vertex. Like the sum of the exterior angles of a polygon, the sum of the angle defects at all vertices of a polyhedron is constant, but it is 720° rather than 360°.

NOTE The solution to Problem 6 Part c is on page T437.

INSTRUCTIONAL NOTE

The reasoning described in Part d applies also to oblique convex polyhedra. If students do not consider oblique prisms, you may wish to come back to this conjecture after they complete Connections Task 15 on page 449.

SUMMARIZE THE MATHEMATICS

a A polyhedron has reflection symmetry if there is a plane that divides the polyhedron so that the two parts are mirror images of one another. In identifying the reflection symmetry of a polyhedron, it is helpful to look at the line symmetry of the faces, and also to see if a reflection plane can contain opposite edges.

A polyhedron has rotational symmetry if there is a line, called an axis of symmetry, for which a rotation about the line of less than 360° leaves the shape appearing as if it were in its original position. In identifying the rotational symmetry of the polyhedron, it is helpful to look at the rotational symmetry of the faces, and also to see if an axis of symmetry can contain midpoints of opposite edges or contain opposite vertices.

b A triangular pyramid is the simplest rigid polyhedron, since it has just four faces, the minimum for a polyhedron, and all faces are rigid.

c To make a polyhedron rigid you can: (1) triangulate each face; (2) triangulate with fewer reinforcements until the polyhedron is rigid; or (3) put reinforcements through the interior of the polyhedron.

d The sum of the vertex angle defects for all the polyhedra investigated here was 720°. (Descartes' Theorem says that the sum of the vertex angle defects in any convex polyhedron is 720°.)

TEACHING RESOURCES

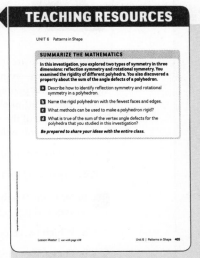

Lesson Master 405
⊙ GO DIGITAL

NOTE The solution to the Check Your Understanding is on page T439.

INVESTIGATION 4

Regular Polyhedra

In Lesson 2, you studied regular polygons and their properties. The three-dimensional counterpart of a regular polygon is a regular polyhedron. A **regular polyhedron**, also called a **Platonic solid**, is a convex polyhedron in which all faces are congruent, regular polygons. Furthermore, the arrangement of faces and edges is the same at each vertex. The regular polyhedron "globe" of the Earth shown here was created by R. Buckminster Fuller, inventor of the geodesic dome.

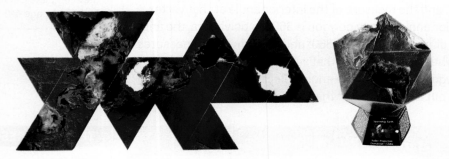

Recall that there are infinitely many different regular polygons, named by the number of sides—regular (or equilateral) triangle, regular quadrilateral (or square), regular pentagon, regular hexagon, and so on. You might think that there would also be infinitely many regular polyhedra. However, that is not the case! That fact is one of the more famous results in the history of geometry. In this investigation, you will explore these two related questions:

How many differently shaped regular polyhedra are possible and why?

What are some of the properties of these polyhedra?

1. Refer to the 9 polyhedra models you constructed in Investigation 1 using straws and pipe cleaners.

   a. Which two models represent regular polyhedra? Explain why.

   b. For each of these regular polyhedra, how many faces meet at each vertex?

2. To see whether other regular polyhedra can be constructed, begin by exploring how three or more congruent regular polygons can be arranged at a vertex of a polyhedron.

   a. What is the sum of measures of the face angles that meet at any vertex of a regular triangular pyramid? Draw a partial net to illustrate your answer.

   b. Next suppose 4 equilateral triangles meet at a vertex. If a regular polyhedron with vertices like this could be constructed, what would be the sum of the face angles at each vertex?

   c. Repeat Part b for the case when 5 equilateral triangles meet at a vertex.

   d. Explain why it is impossible for more than 5 equilateral triangles to meet at a vertex of a regular polyhedron.

a. The polyhedron is convex, because no segment joining any pair of vertices lies outside the polyhedron.

b. There are four planes of symmetry. Two contain diagonals of the base and the apex of the pyramid.

 The polyhedron has 90°, 180°, and 270° rotational symmetry where the axis of symmetry is the line containing the apex of the pyramid and the center of the base of the square pyramid.

c. Any bracing of the cube to make it rigid will make the whole shape rigid because the base of the pyramid would be rigid. For possible combinations, see the solution for Problem 5 Parts c and d on page 437. The minimum number of braces is 3.

d. The 4 vertices at the base of the figure each have angle defects of $360° - 270° = 90°$. The 4 vertices where the pyramid is joined to the cube each have angle defects of $360° - 300° = 60°$, and the angle defect of the apex of the pyramid is $360° - 240° = 120°$. Therefore, the sum of the angle defects is $4 \times 90° + 4 \times 60° + 120° = 720°$, and Descartes' Theorem holds for this polyhedron.

Regular Polyhedra

The regular polyhedra (or Platonic solids) have fascinated mathematicians, scientists, artists, and philosophers for many centuries. These polyhedra are regular in every way, a property that turns out to be very rare. There are only five differently-shaped polyhedra that achieve this level of uniformity. Yet this surprising fact, of such great interest through the ages, is not difficult to understand. This investigation provides students with the opportunity to develop their understanding of these beautiful shapes. The approach is to examine, for each regular polygon, how many congruent copies can meet at a vertex of a convex polyhedron, keeping in mind that the sum of the measures of the face angles at a vertex must be less than 360°. This line of reasoning is essentially Euclid's argument, and is reminiscent of the argument in two dimensions concerning which regular polygons tile the plane, although in the latter case the sum of the measures of the angles that meet at a point in a plane tiling must be equal to 360°. In this case, the sum of the face angles at any vertex must be less than 360°.

Two of the polyhedron models that students made with pipe cleaners and straws in Investigation 1 are regular polyhedra, namely, the cube and the regular triangular pyramid. This investigation begins by referring students in Problem 1 to these familiar models. In Problem 2, students explore the number of equilateral triangles that might meet at a vertex of a convex polyhedron. There are just three possibilities, namely, three, four, or five triangles. If six or more equilateral triangles meet at a point, the sum of the angles at that point is greater than or equal to 360°. The regular polyhedron formed by three equilateral triangles sharing a vertex is the regular triangular pyramid, already familiar to students. The regular polyhedra formed by four and five equilateral triangles meeting at a vertex are explored later in this investigation.

In Problem 3, the question is examined of whether three or more regular polygons with four or more sides could share a common vertex in a convex polyhedron. Again basing the argument on the measures of the angles in such polygons, students should see that just two more possibilities exist—three squares (which is the cube) and three regular pentagons. More than three squares and three regular polygons with more than five sides would result in the sum of the face angles at a vertex being greater than or equal to 360°, an impossibility in a convex polyhedron.

That leaves just the five possible arrangements of congruent regular polygonal faces at a vertex that are pictured in Problem 4. Students are asked to summarize the reasoning that led to the elimination of all other possible arrangements of faces at a vertex of a regular polyhedron. In Part c, this result is connected to Descartes' Theorem by using it to predict the number of vertices each regular polyhedron would have.

In the remainder of the investigation, students use copies of the partial nets of faces meeting at a vertex to construct the regular octahedron and regular dodecahedron. They also experiment with doing the same for the icosahedron but discover that the approach needs to be modified. Because of this, students are given a complete net to form the icosahedron. Next, the numbers of faces, vertices, and edges in each regular polyhedron are summarized and connected to the arrangements of faces at each vertex. Finally, students explore the plane and rotational symmetries of the regular octahedron.

ADDITIONAL RESOURCES

A video, "The Platonic Solids" (Key Curriculum Press), depicts in animation the argument as to why there are only five Platonic Solids and also presents several other aspects of Platonic Solids. If used, this video should follow the investigative work.

1 **a.** The cube and the equilateral triangular pyramid both satisfy the definition of a regular polyhedron. All faces of the cube are congruent regular quadrilaterals (squares). All faces of the pyramid are congruent regular triangles, (equilateral triangles).

b. The cube has square (regular quadrilateral) faces, and three of them meet at each vertex. The faces of the equilateral triangular pyramid are regular triangles, and three of them meet at each vertex.

2 **a.** The measure of each angle of an equilateral triangle is 60°. The sum of the face angles that meet at any vertex is $3 \times 60° = 180°$.

b. The sum of the face angles would be 240°.

c. The sum of the face angles would be $5 \times 60° = 300°$.

d. If 6 equilateral triangles met at a vertex, the sum of the face angles would be $6 \times 60° = 360°$. If more than 6 equilateral triangles met at a vertex, the sum of the face angles would be greater than 360°. Neither of these possibilities can occur in a convex polyhedron since the sum of the face angles at a vertex must be less than 360°.

3 Next, suppose the faces of a regular polyhedron have more than three edges. They might be squares, regular pentagons, regular hexagons, and so on.

   a. What is the sum of the measures of the face angles that meet at any vertex of a cube? Illustrate with a partial net.

   b. Why is it not possible for 4 or more squares to meet at a vertex of a regular polyhedron?

   c. Discuss whether 3 regular pentagons, 3 regular hexagons, or 3 regular septagons could meet at a vertex of a regular polyhedron.

   d. Explain why it is impossible for a regular polyhedron to have faces with more than 5 sides.

4 Putting together the steps of your reasoning in Problems 2 and 3, you have shown that there are at most 5 differently shaped regular polyhedra. The partial nets below show the different ways that regular polygon faces could meet at a single vertex of a regular polyhedron.

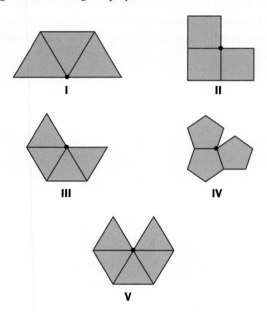

   a. Explain as precisely as you can why the above arrangements are the only ones possible.

   b. Your reasoning likely has much in common with the reasoning in Lesson 2 that showed that the only regular polygons that tile the plane are the regular quadrilateral, regular triangle, and regular hexagon. How are the two arguments similar? How are they different?

   c. For each of the partial nets above, assume that a regular polyhedron can be constructed for which the faces meet at each vertex as illustrated. What is the angle defect at each pictured vertex? How many vertices must each of the regular polyhedra have?

3 a. The measure of each angle of a square is 90°, and the sum of the measures of the face angles that meet at a vertex is 3 × 90° = 270°.

b. If four or more squares shared a common vertex, the sum of the measures of the angles at that vertex would be greater than or equal to 360°. That cannot happen in a convex polyhedron.

c. The measure of each interior angle of a regular pentagon is 108°. Since 3(108°) = 324°, 3 pentagons could meet at a vertex of a regular polyhedron. Each interior angle of a regular hexagon measures 120° and each interior angle of a regular septagon measures $128\frac{4}{7}$°. It is not possible for three of these shapes to meet at a vertex because in each case, the sum of the face angles would be greater than or equal to 360°.

d. Faces of a regular polyhedron must be regular polygons, and at least three faces must meet at a vertex of the polyhedron. Three regular polygons with more than five sides cannot meet at a vertex of a convex polyhedron because the sum of the face angles at the vertex would be 360° or more.

4 a. At least three regular polygonal faces must meet at each vertex of a regular polyhedron, and the sum of the face angles at each vertex must be less than 360°. Thus, the possibilities of faces meeting at each vertex are (1) three regular triangles; (2) three squares; (3) four regular triangles; (4) three regular pentagons, and (5) five regular triangles. More faces meeting at a vertex or more sides in each regular polygon face leads to the sum of measures of the face angles at a vertex that is greater than or equal to 360°. Therefore, there cannot be more than five differently-shaped regular polyhedra.

b. The arguments are similar in that they each consider the measure of an interior angle of various regular polygons. In the tiling argument, the goal is to find all regular polygons for which a whole number of angle measures total 360°, so when that number of polygons are placed together at a vertex they fill the plane. In the regular polyhedron argument, the goal is to find all regular polygons for which a whole number (3 or larger) of interior angle measures total less than 360°, so when that number of polygons are placed together at a vertex there is a gap that allows folding up to form a convex polyhedron.

c. The angle defects at the five types of vertices pictured in Problem 4 are, respectively, 180°, 90°, 120°, 36°, and 60°. Since all vertices of a regular polyhedron have the same defect, Descartes' Theorem says the number of vertices times the angle defect is 720°. By dividing 720° by each of these angle defects, the respective numbers of vertices must be 4, 8, 6, 20, and 12.

INSTRUCTIONAL NOTE

If students are struggling, you might ask, "Could you use Descartes' Theorem to help you?"

5 You have already constructed models of two of the five regular polyhedra, namely, an equilateral triangular pyramid, also called a **regular tetrahedron** (named from the Greek "tetra" for its 4 faces), and the cube, also called a **regular hexahedron** (named for its 6 faces).

   a. Collaborate with your classmates to construct models for a single "corner" of a regular polyhedron using copies of the third, fourth, and fifth partial nets shown in Problem 4. Each student should cut out one partial net, fold, and close the corner by joining two edges with tape. Compare your model to those of classmates who used the same net. Are the models based on the same net identical? If not, resolve the differences.

   b. Working in pairs, select either partial net III or IV in Problem 4 to complete the following tasks.

      i. Tape together as many partial nets as needed to form a model for a regular polyhedron. How many copies did you use?

      ii. Describe the polyhedron you formed. How many faces does it have? What would be a good name for the polyhedron? Why?

   c. Use the same procedure as in Part b to construct a model for a regular polyhedron using multiple copies of the fifth partial net in Problem 4. Discuss what happens.

   d. Although it cannot be constructed only from copies of its "corners" where 5 faces meet, there is a fifth regular polyhedron called a **regular icosahedron** (from the Greek "eikosi" meaning 20). Nets for the last three regular polyhedra are shown below. Construct a model of a regular icosahedron by cutting out a copy of its net and folding and taping.

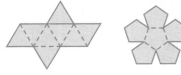 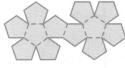 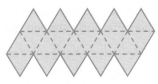

     Octahedron   **Dodecahedron**   **Icosahedron**

6 As you can see from examination of the models, regular polyhedra have many symmetries. You previously explored symmetries of a regular tetrahedron and a regular hexahedron. Study your model of a regular octahedron.

   a. How many planes of symmetry does it have? Describe their locations.

   b. As for rotational symmetry, a regular octahedron has 6 axes of 180° symmetry, 4 axes of 120° symmetry, and 3 axes of 90° symmetry. Describe the locations of the axes for each of these three types of rotational symmetry.

   c. How do the types and number of axes of symmetry for the regular octahedron compare with those of the cube?

5 **a.** Students will construct their own models.

  b. **i.** Two copies of vertex model III can be taped together to construct a regular 8-faced polyhedron. Four copies of vertex model IV are needed to construct a regular 12-faced polyhedron.

  ii. A good name for the polyhedron in part i formed using partial net III is regular octahedron because it has 8 faces where each face is a regular triangle. The polyhedron formed by using partial net IV has 12 regular pentagonal faces with 3 faces meeting at each vertex. The name for this polyhedron is regular dodecahedron because "do-deca" is a prefix meaning $2 + 10$ or 12.

  c. Descriptions may vary, but essentially the difficulty is that when two edges of two different copies of the fifth vertex model are taped together, the new vertices that are formed have just four triangular faces meeting there. Yet five triangular faces meet at the vertex in the model. Since the arrangements at each vertex must be identical in a regular polyhedron, an adjustment must be made to this approach to construct the fifth regular polyhedron. One way to obtain the polyhedron is to join vertex models by a band of 10 congruent regular triangles, as can be seen in the net shown in Part d.

  d. Students should construct the regular icosahedron by folding up and taping the edges of the complete net, or following the procedure described above.

6 **a.** The regular octahedron has symmetry planes similar to those of the cube. Three planes contain four edges that outline a square (the base of a square pyramid). Each of the other six planes cuts through opposite vertices and contains four altitudes of faces that also outline a square. These altitudes are symmetry lines of faces.

  b. The 6 axes of 180° symmetry contain midpoints of pairs of opposite edges. The 3 axes of 90° (180° and 270°) rotational symmetry are the lines containing pairs of opposite vertices. The 4 axes of 120° (and 240°) rotational symmetry contain the centers of opposite faces.

  c. Both the cube and the regular octahedron have 13 axes of symmetry. Furthermore, both have 6 axes of 180° symmetry, 3 axes of multiples-of-90° symmetry, and 4 axes of multiples-of-120° symmetry.

DIFFERENTIATION

Problem 6 may be considered optional for some students.

SUMMARIZE THE MATHEMATICS

In this investigation, you demonstrated that there are exactly 5 differently shaped regular polyhedra and examined some of their symmetries.

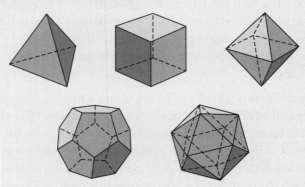

a Name all the regular polyhedra according to the number of faces of each. For each regular polyhedron, describe a face and give the number of faces that meet at each vertex.

b Explain why there cannot be more than 5 differently shaped regular polyhedra.

Be prepared to share your descriptions and explanation with the entire class.

 CHECK YOUR UNDERSTANDING

The design of a soccer ball is based on a **semiregular polyhedron**; that is, a polyhedron with faces that are congruent copies of two or more different regular polygons. As in a regular polyhedron, the arrangement of faces and edges is the same at each vertex.

a. Describe the three faces that meet at each vertex of the polyhedron that is used for the soccer ball.

b. What is the sum of the three face angles that meet at each vertex of the polyhedron? What is the angle defect at each vertex?

c. Find the number of vertices of the polyhedron.

d. The polyhedron consists of 20 hexagons and 12 pentagons. How many edges does it have?

SUMMARIZE THE MATHEMATICS

a A regular tetrahedron has 4 equilateral triangular faces with 3 faces meeting at each vertex.

A regular hexahedron (cube) has 6 square faces with 3 faces meeting at each vertex.

A regular octahedron has 8 equilateral triangular faces with 4 faces meeting at each vertex.

A regular dodecahedron has 12 regular pentagonal faces with 3 faces meeting at each vertex.

A regular icosahedron has 20 equilateral triangular faces with 5 faces meeting at each vertex.

b At least 3 regular polygonal faces must meet at each vertex of a regular polyhedron, and the sum of the interior angles at each vertex must be less than 360°. Thus, the possibilities of faces meeting at each vertex are (1) three regular triangles; (2) four regular triangles; (3) five regular triangles; (4) three squares; and (5) three regular pentagons. More faces meeting at a vertex or more sides in each regular polygon face leads to the sum of measures of the face angles at a vertex that is greater than or equal to 360°. Therefore, there cannot be more than 5 differently-shaped regular polyhedra.

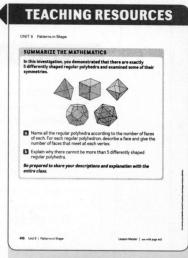
✔ CHECK YOUR UNDERSTANDING

a. Two regular hexagons and a regular pentagon meet at each vertex of the polyhedron.

b. The sum of the measures of the 3 face angles at each vertex is $2(120°) + 108° = 348°$, so the angle defect at each vertex is $360° - 348° = 12°$.

c. Since the sum of the angle defects is 720° by Descartes' Theorem, the polyhedron must have $\frac{720}{12} = 60$ vertices.

d. Using Euler's Formula, $V + F = E + 2$, $60 + 32 = E + 2$. Therefore, there are 90 edges in the polyhedron.

APPLICATIONS

1 Three-dimensional shapes are the basis of atomic structures as well as of common structures for work, living, and play. Often three-dimensional shapes are assembled from a combination of simpler shapes.

   a. Study this photograph of Big Ben in London, England. What three-dimensional shapes appear to be used in this tower? Which are prisms? Which are pyramids?

   b. Scientists use three-dimensional structures to model molecules of compounds, such as the model of a methane molecule shown below. Describe and name the polyhedron with the skeleton that would be formed by joining the outermost points of the four hydrogen atoms that are equally spaced around the central carbon atom.

Big Ben clock tower in London, England

2 Make a conjecture about the relationship between the circumference of a circular column and the weight it can support.

   a. Conduct an experiment to test your conjecture about the weight-bearing capability of circular columns. Use columns of the same height but with different circumferences.

   b. Organize your data in a table and display them in a graph.

   c. What appears to be true about the relationship between the circumference of a column and the weight it can support? Why do you think this happens?

3 A net for a square pyramid is shown below. Lateral faces are equilateral triangles.

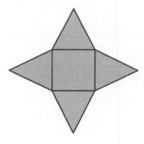

   a. Sketch two other nets that would fold into this pyramid.

   b. How many straight cuts are needed to cut out the net above? Each of the nets you sketched?

   c. Is there a net that requires even fewer straight cuts than the ones you have examined so far? Explain.

1 **a.** The base of the tower appears to be a square prism. The next level would then be a square pyramid with the top cut off. Above this there is another square prism. A square pyramid is on the top.

b. A regular tetrahedron surrounds the carbon atom.

2 **a–b.** Sample data (in this case a height of 8.5 inches with an overlap of 0.5 inch) are shown below for a paper circular column.

Circumference (in inches)	Trial Number of Books			
	1	2	3	4
8	10	8	8	11
6	7	6	6	7
5	5	5	4	4
3.75	3	4	4	4

Here is a scatterplot of the first trial data.

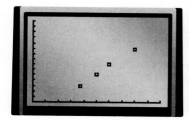 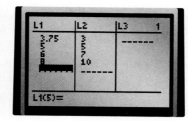 

c. Increasing the circumference increases the weight that is supported. This relationship is partially due to the fact that as the circumference increases, the lateral surface area of the column increases, giving more support for the weight.

3 **a.** Responses may vary. Some examples are shown below.

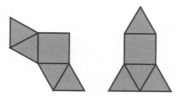

b. The net in the student text requires eight straight cuts. The net on the left above requires eight straight cuts, and the one on the right requires only seven. Seven straight cuts works on the right because two of the edges that need to be cut fall in a straight line.

c. There seems to be no net that could be cut out with less than seven straight cuts. (This may be a good example of the tendency to generalize too quickly. Student nets may all require eight straight cuts, and thus they may incorrectly assume that eight cuts is the fewest for a net. In fact, unless there is a systematic way to produce all nets and check them, we cannot be sure that seven is the fewest cuts.)

4 Building designers can test their designs by using identical cubes to represent rooms. They can use the cubes to try various arrangements of rooms. Study this drawing of a cube hotel.

a. How many cubes are there in the model? Assume any cube above the bottom layer rests on another cube.

b. Draw the top, front, and right-side orthographic views of this shape.

c. Is the model pictured on the right a polyhedron? If not, explain why not. If so, is it convex or nonconvex?

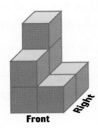

Front   Right

5 Three views of a cube model of a hotel are shown below.

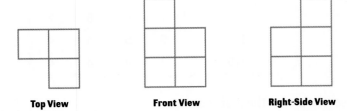

Top View   **Front View**   **Right-Side View**

a. Make an oblique drawing of this hotel model from a vantage point that shows clearly all the characteristics of the model. Assume any cube above the bottom layer rests on another cube.

b. Is there more than one model with these three views? If so, make a drawing of a second one from a vantage point that illustrates how this model differs from the one in Part a.

c. How many cubes are there in each hotel model?

6 Both portability and rigidity are design features of a folding "director's chair."

a. How are these features designed into the chair shown at the right?

b. The pair of legs at the front and back are attached at their midpoints. Draw and label a diagram of the front pair of legs and edge of the seat. Using congruent triangles and Connections Task 18, page 391, explain as carefully as you can why these conditions guarantee that the outstretched seat will be parallel to the ground surface.

c. Identify two other commonly used items that can collapse but must remain rigid when "unfolded." Analyze their designs.

Ingram Publishing/SuperStock

4 **a.** Seven cubes

b.

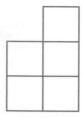

Top View　　　**Front View**　　　**Right-Side View**

c. This is a picture of a nonconvex polyhedron. This is the case because not all segments connecting any two vertices lie within the polyhedron.

5 **a–b.** As the sketches below illustrate, there is more than one model with these three views.

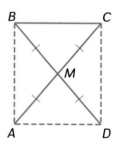

c. There are six cubes in the model on the left and seven cubes in the one on the right.

6 **a.** When opened and placed on the ground, the legs are positioned so that the director can sit on two rigid triangles connected at the vertices. One rigid triangle is formed by the legs of the chair and the small brace that will fold up. The other rigid triangle is then set by the top triangle and by the ground. The seat of the chair is made of fabric and the small brace folds up so that when the chair is picked up and collapsed, the rigid triangles are gone.

b. From Connections Task 18 on page 391, students now know that opposite sides of a parallelogram are parallel. So, if we show that $ABCD$ is a parallelogram then $\overline{AD}$ will be parallel to $\overline{BC}$. Since $\overline{BM} \cong \overline{DM}$, $\overline{AM} \cong \overline{CM}$, and $\angle BMC \cong \angle AMD$, it follows that $\triangle BCM \cong \triangle DAM$. Therefore, $\overline{BC} \cong \overline{AD}$ since they are corresponding sides in congruent triangles. Using similar reasoning, $\triangle CMD \cong \triangle AMB$ and $\overline{AB} \cong \overline{CD}$. So, $ABCD$ is a parallelogram because both pairs of opposite sides are congruent. Therefore, $\overleftrightarrow{BC}$ is parallel to $\overleftrightarrow{AD}$.

c. A ping-pong table and a fold-out TV tray are two examples. The legs of a ping-pong table usually are connected to the tabletop by cross bars running from the middle of each leg to the tabletop, forming a triangle. For TV trays, the tray and the legs usually snap together to create a triangle.

7 Symmetry can help to describe and also to construct a three-dimensional shape.

a. Describe the reflection symmetry and the rotational symmetry of these three-dimensional shapes.

  i. a right circular cylinder

  ii. a right circular cone

  iii. a prism with a parallelogram base

  iv. a regular pentagonal pyramid

  v. a sphere

b. Half of a polyhedron is shown below.

Front

  i. Sketch the entire polyhedron if it is symmetric about the plane containing the right face.

  ii. Sketch the entire polyhedron if it is symmetric about the plane containing the left face.

c. Are the polyhedra you sketched in Part b convex? Explain your answers.

d. For each polyhedron in Part b, count the vertices, faces, and edges. Verify that Euler's Formula holds for each polyhedron.

e. Using a polyhedron from Part b above as an example, explain why Descartes' Theorem does not make sense for nonconvex polyhedra.

8 A model of a square prism could be made from a potato or modeling clay. Consider the 5 × 5 × 6 square prism pictured below. The three lines (skewers) intersecting the prism contain the centers of opposite faces.

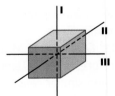

a. Explain why these lines are axes of symmetry for the prism.

b. What angles of rotation are associated with each axis of symmetry? Explain your reasoning.

c. Does this prism have other axes of symmetry? If so, describe their locations and give the angle of rotation associated with each.

d. How is the rotational symmetry of a cube similar to that of the square prism above? How is it different?

Lesson 3 | Polyhedra and Their Properties **445**

UNIT 6

7 **INSTRUCTIONAL NOTE** Students may want to construct models—in particular, for the less familiar prism with a parallelogram base in Part a, iii—to help find planes and axes of symmetry.

a. **i.** A right circular cylinder is symmetric about any plane containing the segment joining the centers of the bases. It also has reflection symmetry about the plane parallel to the bases, halfway between them. The line containing the centers of the bases of the cylinder is an axis of rotational symmetry through a rotation of any positive angle with measure less than 360°. Any line that is a perpendicular bisector of the segment containing the centers of the bases is an axis of 180° rotational symmetry.

   ii. A right circular cone is symmetric about any plane that contains the apex of the cone and the center of its base. The line through the apex and the center of the base is an axis of rotational symmetry through a rotation of any positive angle measure less than 360°.

   iii. A prism with a parallelogram base is symmetric about the plane parallel to the bases, halfway between them. The line through the centers of the parallelogram bases of this prism is an axis of 180° rotational symmetry.

   iv. A regular pentagonal pyramid is symmetric about any plane that contains a lateral edge and the midpoint of the opposite edge of the base of the pyramid. The line containing the apex and center of the base is an axis of 72°, 144°, 216°, and 288° rotational symmetry.

   v. A sphere is symmetric about any plane that contains its center. Any line that contains the center of the sphere is an axis of rotational symmetry through a rotation of any positive angle measure less than 360°.

b. **i.** 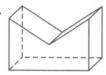   **ii.**

c. The polyhedron in Part bii is convex but the one in Part bi is not. In Part bi, the segment joining, say, one of the top-left and one of the top-right vertices lies outside the polyhedron.

d. Both polyhedra have 10 vertices, 7 faces, and 15 edges, so Euler's relationship is satisfied even though the polyhedron in Part bi is nonconvex.

> **NOTE** Euler's Formula holds for some, but not all, nonconvex polyhedra.

e. Consider the faces that meet at the vertex at the top and center of the front face of the nonconvex polyhedron in Part bi. The two top faces that meet there are rectangles, so the sum of their angle measures is 180°. The measure of the angle at this vertex of the front face is greater than 180°, so at this vertex the angle sum is greater than 360° and thus the angle defect is not defined (or is negative).

> **NOTE** The solution to Task 8 is on page T446.

ON YOUR OWN

9 The square pyramids at Giza in Egypt are pictured here. The lateral faces are isosceles, but not equilateral, triangles.

a. Describe the planes of symmetry and the rotational symmetr of one of the Giza pyramids.

b. In the steepest of these pyramids, the face angles at the apex are each about 40°. Find the angle defect at each of the 5 vertices of this pyramid. Verify that Descartes' Theorem holds for this pyramid.

CONNECTIONS

10 A pyramid has a square base that is 10 units on a side, and the other faces of the pyramid are congruent isosceles triangles.

a. Suppose you were going to make a model with straws and pipe cleaners of such a pyramid. Could the lateral edges to the apex be 5 units long? Could they be 10 units long? Could they be 20 units long?

b. Is there a minimum length for the lateral edges? Is there a maximum length for the lateral edges? If so, what are they? What property or properties from earlier lessons in this unit would justify your answers?

11 Imagine a model of a cube made of clay or cut from a potato. Make such a model if possible.

a. How many faces, edges, and vertices does a cube have?

b. Slice a corner off (as shown), making a small triangular face. How many faces, edges, and vertices does the new polyhedron have?

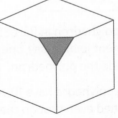

c. Repeat at each corner so that the slices do not overlap. Make a table showing the number of faces, edges, and vertices of the modified cube after each "corner slice."

d. Using *NOW* and *NEXT*, write a rule describing the pattern of change in the number of faces after a slice. Write similar *NOW-NEXT* rules for the number of edges and for the number of vertices after each slice.

8 a. Each line is an axis of symmetry because you can rotate the prism less than a 360° turn and it will appear to be in the original position.

b. The line containing the centers of the two square bases is an axis of symmetry with angles of rotation of 90°, 180°, and 270°. This is like the rotational symmetry of a square about its center. The other two lines, those containing centers of pairs of opposite rectangular faces, are axes of symmetry with a 180° angle of rotation. This is like the rotational symmetry of a rectangle about its center.

c. The two lines through the midpoints of opposite longer edges of the rectangular faces have angles of rotation of 180°.

d. All the above lines of symmetry are also lines of symmetry if the prism is a cube. In addition, in a cube but not in a square prism that is not a cube, the diagonals are axes of symmetry.

INSTRUCTIONAL NOTE

You may wish to have students make a paper model of the 5 × 5 × 6 square prism and physically rotate it about skewers.

9 a. There are four planes of symmetry, one through each of the lines of symmetry of the square base and perpendicular to the plane of the base. The line containing the apex of the pyramid and the center of its base is an axis of 90°, 180°, and 270° rotational symmetry.

b. The lateral faces of these pyramids are isosceles triangles with apex angles of 40°. Therefore, the base angles of each triangular face measure 70°. Further, each base is a square so its angles measure 90°. At the 4 vertices of the base, each angle sum is $90° + 70° + 70° = 230°$, which gives an angle defect of $360° - 230° = 130°$. At the apex, the angle sum is $4 \times 40° = 160°$, so the angle defect is $360° - 160° = 200°$. The sum of all angle defects is $4 \times 130° + 200° = 720°$, so Descartes' Theorem holds true.

CONNECTIONS

10 a. The lateral edges could be 10 or 20, but not 5, units long because of the Triangle Inequality, that is, the sum of the lengths of two sides of a triangle must be greater than the length of the third side.

b. The edges must be more than half the length of the diagonal of the square base, that is, they must be more than $5\sqrt{2}$, or about 7.1 units long. There is no theoretical maximum length, but, of course, there are practical limits for the length of straws in a model. This reasoning makes use of the Triangle Inequality.

11 a. A cube has 6 faces, 12 edges, and 8 vertices.

b. The new polyhedron has 7 faces, 15 edges, and 10 vertices.

c. These results assume nonoverlapping slices, as indicated in the student text.

d. For faces, $NEXT = NOW + 1$.
For edges, $NEXT = NOW + 3$.
For vertices, $NEXT = NOW + 2$.

	Faces	Edges	Vertices
Cube	6	12	8
First Slice	7	15	10
Second Slice	8	18	12
Third Slice	9	21	14
Fourth Slice	10	24	16

NOTE This is a partial table. The complete table contains 8 slices.

e. Do you think Euler's Formula will hold at each stage? Justify your answer using the *NOW-NEXT* rules in Part d.

f. How many faces, edges, and vertices does the new polyhedron have when all the corners are sliced off?

12 When filling three-dimensional containers like boxes or cylindrical cans, a measure of *volume* is needed. The volume of a three-dimensional shape of height 1 unit is numerically equal to the area of the base. For prisms and cylinders, imagine the first layer of 1-unit cubes as shown below.

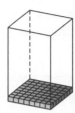

Then add additional layers until the prism or cylinder is filled. The number of layers is the shape's height. This suggests that the volume *V* of either a prism or a circular cylinder is the product of the *area of the base B* and the *height h*, a formula usually written symbolically as $V = Bh$.

a. Find the volume of a square prism with base edges of 7 cm and height of 10 cm. The volume is in what units?

b. Find the volume of a cylinder in which the radius of the base is 5 in. and the height is 9 in. Indicate the units.

c. Find the volume of a regular triangular prism if all edges are 4 ft long.

d. A right circular cylindrical can is packed snugly into a box as shown here. The base of the box is a square 8 cm on a side and the height of the box is 16 cm.

i. Find the volume of the space between the can and the box.

ii. Find the ratio of the volume of the cylinder to the volume of the box. What does the ratio tell you?

e. Suppose the length of the side of a square box as in Part d is *s* cm and the height is *h* cm.

i. What is the volume of the box in terms of *s* and *h*?

ii. What are the radius and height of the cylinder in terms of *s* and *h*?

iii. What is the volume of the cylinder in terms of *s* and *h*?

iv. What is the ratio of the volume of the cylinder to the volume of the box? What does the ratio tell you?

e. Euler's Formula: $V + F = E + 2$

Yes, the sum of the vertices and faces increases by 3 with each slice. This is evident from the constants added to *NOW* in the *NOW-NEXT* formulas. The number of edges also increases by 3, so the relationship holds true at each stage.

f. When all 8 corners are sliced off, there are 14 faces, 36 edges, and 24 vertices.

12 **a.** The volume is 490 cm³.

b. 225π in³, or about 707 in³

c. The equilateral triangular base has sides of length 4 ft, so its height is $2\sqrt{3}$ ft. The area of the base is $\frac{1}{2}(4)(2\sqrt{3}) = 4\sqrt{3}$ ft². The volume of the prism is the area of the base times the height, which is $(4\sqrt{3})(4) = 16\sqrt{3} \approx 27.7$ ft³.

d. **i.** The volume of the empty space is the volume of the box minus the volume of the can.

$$(8)(8)(16) - (16\pi)(16) = 1{,}024 - 256\pi \approx 219.8 \text{ cm}^3$$

ii. The ratio is comparing the volume of the cylinder to the volume of the box. Interpreting the decimal representation (the one students will likely use), $\frac{256\pi}{1{,}024} = \frac{\pi}{4} \approx 0.785$.

e. **i.** The volume of the square box is $s^2 h$.

ii. The radius of the cylinder is $\frac{s}{2}$ and its height is h.

iii. The volume of the cylinder is $\pi\left(\frac{s}{2}\right)^2 h = \frac{\pi s^2 h}{4}$.

iv. The ratio of the volume of the cylinder to the volume of the box is $\frac{\pi}{4}$. The volume of the cylinder is again approximately $\frac{\pi}{4}$ of the volume of the box. This ratio does not depend on s and h.

13 An important volume formula that holds for both prisms and cylinders is $V = Bh$ where B is the area of the base and h is the height, that is, the perpendicular distance between the bases. A related formula, $V = \frac{1}{3}Bh$, holds for pyramids.

a. The diagram below shows a triangular prism dissected into three triangular pyramids of equal volume. How could you use the diagram to develop the volume formula for a pyramid?

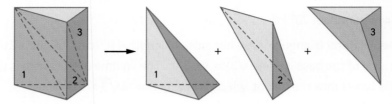

b. Imagine a sequence of pyramids with height h and regular n-gon bases starting at $n = 3$ sides and increasing by 10 sides at each stage. As n gets very large, what is the approximate shape of the figure formed? How would you calculate its volume?

c. Find the volume of the cube, pyramid, cylinder, and cone shown below. How do the volumes of these shapes compare?

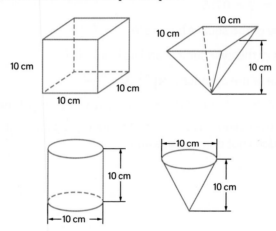

d. A movie theater sells different sizes of popcorn in different shaped containers. One is a cylinder with a height of 17 cm and radius of the base of 8 cm. It sells for $4.50. Another is a rectangular box (prism) with width 10 cm, length 16 cm, and height 18 cm. It sells for $3.75. Which is the better buy? Explain your answer.

e. A third popcorn container is a cone with a height of 24 cm and radius of the base of 10 cm. What is the most its price could be if it is the best buy of the three containers?

13 **a.** As the diagram shows, the prism can be dissected into three pyramids of equal volume. So, the volume of any one of the three pyramids is $\frac{1}{3}$ of the volume of the prism, $V = \frac{1}{3}Bh$.

b. The shape of the base of the figure becomes almost circular. The volume of this almost-conical figure can be approximated by $V = \frac{1}{3}Bh = \frac{1}{3}\pi r^2 h$, where r is the radius of the circle that circumscribes the many-sided n-gon base.

c. The volumes are as follows. cube: 1,000 cm³; pyramid: $\frac{1}{3}(100)(10) = 333\frac{1}{3}$ cm³; cylinder: $(\pi)(5^2)(10) = 250\pi \approx 785.4$ cm³; cone: $\frac{1}{3}(\pi)(5^2)(10) = \frac{250\pi}{3} \approx 261.8$ cm³.

The volumes of the pyramid and cone are one-third the volumes of the cube and cylinder, respectively.

d. The volume of the cylindrical container is $(\pi)(8^2)(17) = 1{,}152\pi \approx 3{,}418$ cm³. At $4.50 per container, you get $\frac{3{,}418}{4.5}$, or about 760 cm³ of popcorn per dollar. The volume of the rectangular box is $(10)(16)(18) = 2{,}880$ cm³. At $3.75 per box, you get $\frac{2{,}880}{3.75}$, or 768 cm³ of popcorn per dollar. Therefore, the box is the better buy.

e. The volume of the conical container is $\frac{1}{3}(\pi)(10^2)(24) \approx 2{,}513$ cm³. To be the best buy of the three containers, it must be priced so that customers get more than 768 cm³ of popcorn per dollar. In symbols, if p is the price of a conical container,

$$\frac{2{,}513}{p} > 768 \text{ and } 2{,}513 > 768p$$

$$p < \frac{2{,}513}{768} \text{ or } p < \$3.27$$

> **NOTE** Students may wonder why the three partitions of the prism have equal volumes. It is because the parts are pyramids with congruent bases and equal heights.

14 The stacks of paper below contain the same number of congruent sheets. If a single sheet of paper represents a cross section of each stack, then at every level, the cross sections have the same area. Bonaventura Cavalieri (1598–1647), an Italian mathematician, used this idea to compare the volumes of two solids.

Cavalieri's Principle
Consider two geometric solids and a plane. If every plane parallel to the given plane that intersects one of the solids also intersects the other so that resulting cross sections have the same area, then the solids have the same volume.

a. Explain how you could use Cavalieri's Principle in calculating the volumes of the *oblique prisms* shown below. Then find the volume of each prism.

i.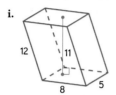

oblique prism with rectangular bases

ii.

oblique prism with equilateral triangle bases

iii.

oblique prism with triangular bases

b. Now use Cavalieri's Principle and the reasoning outlined below to provide a mathematical argument that the volume V of a sphere is $V = \frac{4}{3}\pi r^3$. The diagram shows a sphere and a right cylinder, each of radius r and height $2r$, situated so that they rest on the same plane. In the case of the cylinder, two identical cones have been removed. Each figure is sliced by a plane at a distance d from its center. The two identical hollowed-out cones meet at the center of the cylinder and each shares one of its bases.

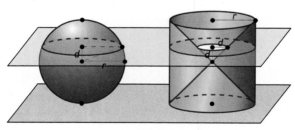

Step 1. Find the area of the cross section of the sphere.

Step 2. Find the area of the cross section of the cylinder with the cone removed.

Step 3. Find the volume of the cylindrical figure with the two cones removed.

Step 4. Find the volume of the sphere.

Lesson 3 | Polyhedra and Their Properties   **449**

14 **a.** For each of the prisms shown, a right prism with the same base and height could be sketched next to the oblique prism. Then every plane parallel to the base that intersects the oblique prism will intersect the right prism also. The area of the cross sections formed by every plane and the two prisms would be equal. Thus, the prisms have the same volume. So, to find the volume for each oblique prism below, find the area of the base and multiply that by the height as we would for a right prism.

   i. $V = 8 \times 5 \times 11 = 440$ cubic units

   ii. $V = 5 \times$ *area of the triangular base* $= 45\sqrt{3} \approx 78$ cubic units

   iii. By the converse of the Pythagorean Theorem, the bases are right triangles. $V = \frac{1}{2} \times 6 \times 8 \times 15 = 360$ cubic units

   b. **Step 1.** The radius of the circular cross section of the sphere is $\sqrt{r^2 - d^2}$ since it is the length of the leg of the right triangle shown by the auxiliary lines that has one leg of length d and the hypotenuse of length r. Thus, the area of any cross section of the sphere can be represented by $A = \pi(r^2 - d^2)$.

   Step 2. The area of the cross section of the cylinder is πr^2. The area of the removed disk is πd^2. So, the area of any cross section for this shape is also $A = \pi(r^2 - d^2)$.

   Step 3. $V = \pi r^2(2r) - 2\left(\frac{1}{3}\right)\pi r^3 = \frac{4}{3}\pi r^3$

   Step 4. By Cavalieri's Principle, the volume of a sphere is $V = \frac{4}{3}\pi r^3$.

ON YOUR OWN

15 Use your regular polyhedron models and the nets to complete a table like the one below.

	Edges per Face	Faces per Vertex	Number of Faces	Number of Vertices	Number of Edges
Tetrahedron		3	4		
Hexahedron		3		8	
Octahedron		4			12
Dodecahedron		3	12		
Icosahedron		5	20		

a. Describe at least two interesting patterns that you see in the table.

b. Check Euler's Formula for these polyhedra.

c. Eric conjectured that the number of edges in a regular polyhedron is the product of the number of edges per face and the number of faces. Do you agree with Eric? If so, explain why. If not, explain how to correct Eric's statement.

16 There are interesting and useful connections between pairs of regular polyhedra.

a. Refer to the regular tetrahedron pictured on the right. The center of each face is marked with a dot.

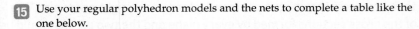

i. Imagine connecting the centers with segments. How many are there?

ii. Visualize the polyhedron having these segments as its edges. What are the shapes of its faces?

iii. What polyhedron is formed by connecting the centers of the faces of a tetrahedron?

b. Now using a model of a cube, imagine the center of its faces.

i. Imagine connecting with segments, each center to the center of the four *adjacent faces*. Adjacent faces are faces that have a common edge. How many such segments are there?

ii. Visualize the polyhedron having these segments as its edges. What are the shapes of its faces? How many faces are there?

iii. What polyhedros formed by connecting the centers of adjacent faces of a cube?

c. What polyhedron is formed by connecting the center of adjacent faces of a regular dodecahedron? Explain your reasoning.

UNIT 6

15

	Edges per Face	Faces per Vertex	Number of Faces	Number of Vertices	Number of Edges
Tetrahedron	3	3	4	4	6
Hexahedron	4	3	6	8	12
Octahedron	3	4	8	6	12
Dodecahedron	5	3	12	20	30
Icosahedron	3	5	20	12	30

a. Comparing the entries for the hexahedron and octahedron, you notice that the number of edges per face and per vertex are the opposite for the two polyhedra. The number of faces and vertices are also the opposite, but the number of edges is the same for the two polyhedra. A similar pattern is evident for the dodecahedron and the icosahedron. See also Part c.

b. Euler's Formula does hold.

c. Eric's relationship is not true. Since each edge of a face is paired with a second one to form an edge of the polyhedron, the product of the edges per face and the number of faces gives a double count of the total number of edges. Eric's method is easily fixed by dividing his product by 2 to get the correct count of edges of the polyhedron.

16 a. **i.** 4   **ii.** Triangles   **iii.** A tetrahedron

b. **i.** 12   **ii.** 8 triangular faces   **iii.** An octahedron

c. Using similar reasoning, a dodecahedron has 12 centers (faces) and 5 adjacent faces for each center. Thus, the new polyhedron has $\frac{12 \cdot 5}{2} = 30$ edges. Visualizing a face formed by these edges allows you to select the icosahedron as the new polyhedron.

ADDITIONAL RESOURCES

mathworld.wolfram.com/DualPolyhedron.html provides more information and an interactive dual polyhedron demonstration.

REFLECTIONS

17 The definitions are essentially the same. But, if all the faces of a polyhedron are convex polygons, then the polyhedron will not necessarily be convex. For example, consider the figure at the right with a pyramid inside the prism. All faces of this new polyhedron are convex, but the polyhedron itself is nonconvex since a segment connecting opposite vertices A and B on the top of the polyhedron is outside the shape.

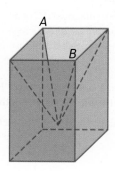

18 a. True. The plane that is parallel to both bases and halfway between them is a symmetry plane since the two halves in which this plane divides the prism are mirror images of one another.

b. False. As a counterexample, consider a right prism, the base of which is a scalene triangle. It has no rotational symmetry.

REFLECTIONS

17 Compare the definitions of convex polygon (page 404) and convex polyhedron (page 426). If all the faces of a polyhedron are convex polygons, must the polyhedron be convex? Explain.

18 Isaiah made the following two conjectures about the symmetry of a right prism. Indicate whether you agree or disagree with each, and write arguments in support of your positions. *Hint:* If you think a statement is false, one counterexample (that is, an example of a right prism that does not have the named symmetry) is a sufficient argument. A more general argument based on the properties of a right prism is required if you think a statement is true.

a. *Every right prism has at least one symmetry plane.*

b. *Every right prism has at least one axis of rotational symmetry.*

19 In this unit, as in previous units, you have engaged in a number of important mathematical practices that characterize the work of mathematicians and others who use mathematics regularly in their careers. Look back over the lessons in this unit and consider some of the mathematical practices you have used. Describe an example of where you used each of the following practices.

a. Made sense of a problem situation and persevered in solving it

b. Reasoned abstractly and quantitatively, making sense of quantities and their relationships in problem situations

c. Constructed a sound mathematical argument and critiqued the reasoning of others

d. Created a mathematical model for a real-world problem

EXTENSIONS

20 The faces of a cube are congruent squares. You know how to use the length of each edge of such a cube to find the lengths of the diagonals on the faces. Cubes also have "body" diagonals such as $\overline{AC}$ in the diagram at the right.

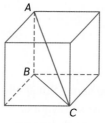

a. Find the length of the body diagonal $\overline{AC}$ of a cube when the cube edges are as given below. Express your answers in simplest radical form.

   i. 1 inch long   **ii.** 2 inches long   **iii.** 3 inches long

b. How many body diagonals does a cube have? Explain as precisely as you can why all body diagonals are the same length.

c. Find a formula for calculating the length of each body diagonal in a cube with edge length x.

UNIT 6

19 a. Good examples of tasks that required students to make sense of a problem and persevere in solving it by themselves are the oil refinery task (page 383) and the volume task (page 447).

b. In Lesson 2 Investigation 2, students reasoned quantitatively and abstractly as they developed formulas for the sum of the measures of the interior angles and the sum of the measures of the exterior angles of polygons. In Connections Task 14 (page 418), they explored the rate of change of the interior angle of a regular polygon as the number of sides increases.

c. Students constructed sound mathematical arguments in many problems. See Lesson 1 Investigation 3. They critiqued the reasoning of others in problems such as Problem 1 (page 374), but also when discussing their classmates' mathematical arguments.

d. In Lesson 1, students used physical models made of spaghetti and linkage strips to model relationships. In Lesson 3, they formulated algebraic models by representing the relations among the number of faces, edges, and vertices for a polyhedron with a formula. They also created geometric models using straws and pipe cleaners and created isometric and orthographic drawings.

> **NOTE** The solutions to Task 17 and 18 are on page T450.

> **CCSS CCSS MATHEMATICAL PRACTICE**
> Throughout this unit, students have employed these mathematical practices. Examples of each practice are given in Task 19. Also, note that some examples are listed with more than one mathematical practice. This is to emphasize that one problem or task in the curriculum usually employs multiple mathematical practices.

EXTENSIONS

20 a. The lengths below are found by a double application of the Pythagorean Theorem.

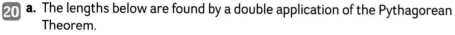

   i. $\sqrt{3}$ **ii.** $2\sqrt{3}$ **iii.** $3\sqrt{3}$

b. There are 4 "body" diagonals, since each vertex of the front face can be connected to the vertex on the back face that is opposite (such as A and C). Similar reasoning for the sides produces the same length because opposite vertices of a cube form the hypotenuse of congruent right triangles formed by one edge of the cube and one diagonal of a face. All edges are congruent and all face diagonals are congruent.

c. In general, the "body" diagonal will have length $L = x\sqrt{3}$, where x is the cube edge length.

ON YOUR OWN

21 Analysis of the formulas for the volume of a prism and for the volume of a cylinder suggests that multiplying the dimensions of the shape by a positive constant changes the volume in a predictable way.

   a. One large juice can has dimensions twice those of a smaller can. How do the volumes of the two cans compare?

   b. One cereal box has dimensions 3 times those of another. How do the volumes of the two boxes compare?

   c. If the dimensions of one prism are 5 times those of another, how do the volumes compare?

   d. If the dimensions of one prism are k times those of another, how do the volumes compare?

22 In Lesson 2, you identified polygons that tile the plane. In three-dimensional geometry, the related question is:

What three-dimensional shapes will fill space?

An obvious example of a space-filling, three-dimensional shape is a rectangular prism. In fact, the efficiency with which rectangular prisms can be stacked is what makes their shape so useful as boxes and other containers.

   a. What right prisms with regular polygonal bases will fill space? Explain how your answer is related to the regular polygons that will tile the plane.

   b. The cells of a honeycomb are approximated by regular hexagonal prisms, which form a three-dimensional tiling for storing honey. Suppose the perimeter of the base of one cell of a honeycomb is 24 mm and the height is 20 mm. What is the *lateral surface area* (surface area not including top and bottom) of a single cell? Explain.

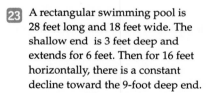

   c. Which of the three right prisms with regular polygonal bases that fill space (see Part a) produces the cell with the greatest volume when the perimeter of the base is 24 mm and the height is 20 mm? As the number of sides of the base of a prism with a regular polygonal base of fixed perimeter increases, how does the corresponding volume change?

   d. Write a statement summarizing how three-dimensional shape is an important factor in the building of the cells of a honeycomb.

23 A rectangular swimming pool is 28 feet long and 18 feet wide. The shallow end is 3 feet deep and extends for 6 feet. Then for 16 feet horizontally, there is a constant decline toward the 9-foot deep end.

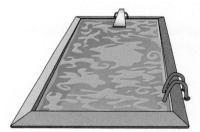

   a. Sketch the pool and indicate the measures on the sketch.

   b. How much water is needed to fill the pool within 6 inches of the top?

21　**a.** The large can is $2^3 = 8$ times the volume of the smaller can.

　b. The large box is $3^3 = 27$ times the volume of the smaller box.

　c. The large prism is $5^3 = 125$ times the volume of the smaller prism.

　d. The large prism is k^3 times the volume of the smaller prism.

22　**a.** A regular triangle, a square, and a regular hexagon are the only three regular polygons that tile the plane. For the same reason, right prisms with bases of one of these three shapes are the only right prisms with regular polygonal bases that fill space.

　b. The lateral surface area is (*perimeter of base*) • (*height*), or $(24)(20) = 480$ mm², because the six lateral faces are each 4 by 20 rectangles.

　c. If students completed Applications Task 7 on page 415, they can apply the knowledge that a regular hexagon of perimeter 24 mm has a larger area than a square or equilateral triangle with perimeter 24 mm. Since the volume of each of the three right prisms is the area of the base times the height and all three heights are the same, the regular hexagonal prism will have the largest volume. As the number of sides of the regular polygonal base of a prism increases, the volume increases.

　d. Of the three regular polygons that tessellate the plane, the (nearly) hexagonal cells of a honeycomb are the ones that maximize the volume for a fixed perimeter and height. As you tessellate the plane, you will need fewer hexagons to tile an area than either squares or triangles. This is because the hexagon has the largest area for a fixed perimeter.

23　**a.** This is a *hexagonal* prism.

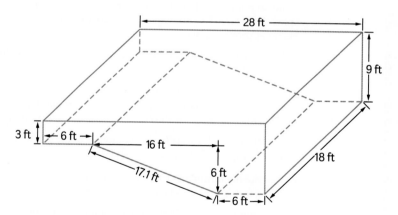

　b. The base of the prism, or the front of the pool as shown here, is comprised of a 3×28 rectangle, a right triangle with legs 16 and 6, and a 6×6 square. The area of this base is $3 \times 28 + 0.5 \times 16 \times 6 + 6 \times 6 = 84 + 48 + 36 = 168$ ft².

Volume of water = volume of pool
$$\qquad - \text{unfilled volume}$$
$$= (168 \text{ ft}^2 \times 18 \text{ ft})$$
$$\qquad - (28 \text{ ft} \times 0.5 \text{ ft} \times 18 \text{ ft})$$
$$= 2{,}772 \text{ ft}^3$$

　c. The area of the two bases (or sides of the pool) is 2(168) or 336 ft². There are 5 different rectangular surfaces to paint: (1) $3 \times 18 = 54$ ft²; (2) $6 \times 18 = 108$ ft²; (3) $17.1 \times 18 = 307.8$ ft²; (4) $6 \times 18 = 108$ ft²; and (5) $9 \times 18 = 162$ ft².

The total surface area to paint is the sum of the areas of the five rectangles plus the areas of the two bases (front and back of the pool), or 1,075.8 ft². So, $\frac{1{,}075}{75} = 14.344$ gallons of paint will be needed. Three 5-gallon cans of paint are needed to paint the pool.

　d. $(18 + 4)(28 + 4) = 22 \times 32 = 704$ ft²

DIFFERENTIATION

If students are having trouble with Task 21 Part c, suggest that they create a simple prism for which they know how to find the volume along with its counterpart that is 5 times the size.

c. One gallon of paint covers approximately 75 square feet of surface. How many gallons of paint are needed to paint the inside of the pool? If the pool paint comes in 5-gallon cans, how many cans should be purchased?

d. How much material is needed to make a rectangular pool cover that extends 2 feet beyond the pool on all sides?

e. About how many 6-inch square ceramic tiles are needed to tile the top 18 inches of the inside faces of the pool?

24 For each figure below, describe how a plane and a cube could intersect so that the intersection (or *cross section*) is the figure described. If the figure is not possible, explain your reasoning.

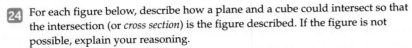

a. a point

b. a segment

c. a triangle

d. an equilateral triangle

e. a square

f. a rectangle

g. a pentagon

h. a hexagon

25 Use the interactive geometry "Slicing Cones and Cylinders" custom app to help answer the following questions.

a. Can a plane intersect a right circular cone so the cross section is each of the following? If so, illustrate with a sketch.

  i. a circle

  ii. a point

  iii. a triangle

  iv. an ellipse (oval)

  v. a rectangle

  vi. a segment

b. Answer Part a for the case of a right circular cylinder.

26 The volume formula for a sphere (see Connections Task 15) can be used to derive a formula for the *surface area* of a sphere. Consider a solid sphere with center at point O and radius r. Imagine a tiny polygon-like portion of the sphere's surface. This "polygon" is the base of a pyramid with vertex O and height approximately r.

a. If the area of the base of the polygon is B_1, what is the volume of the pyramid?

b. Next, imagine dividing the entire surface of the sphere into a large number n of tiny, nonoverlapping "polygons," with respective areas of $B_1, B_2, B_3, \ldots, B_n$. Write a formula for the surface area S in terms of $B_1, B_2, B_3, \ldots, B_n$.

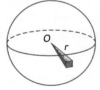

c. Explain why a formula for the volume V of the sphere is
$$V = \frac{1}{3}(B_1)(r) + \frac{1}{3}(B_2)(r) + \cdots + \frac{1}{3}(B_n)(r).$$

d. Rewrite the formula in Part c by (i) substituting $\frac{4}{3}\pi r^3$ for V and (ii) factoring the largest common factor from the right-hand side.

e. Use your result from Part d to write a formula for the surface area S of a sphere in terms of its radius r.

e. The perimeter of the pool is 92 feet. One row of six-inch tiles would require 184 tiles. In order to have 18 inches of tiling, you need three rows around the pool or 552 six-inch square tiles.

24 a. A plane could intersect the cube at a vertex only.

b. A plane could intersect a single edge of a cube.

c. A plane could cut off exactly one corner of the cube.

d. A plane could cut off equal lengths of the three edges that meet at a corner of the cube.

e. A plane parallel to a face intersects the cube in a square.

f. If a plane not parallel to any faces intersects opposite faces of a cube so that one pair of edges of the cross section is parallel to some edges of the cube, the intersection is a rectangle. Also, a plane could intersect two adjacent faces (as seen in the graphic in the student text). Here one pair of edges of the cross section is parallel to the common edge of the adjacent faces.

g. If a plane intersects the top, four lateral faces, and a vertex, the intersection is a pentagon. Imagine, in the drawing of the hexagon below, that the plane was slanted so that it went through the bottom vertex instead of intersecting the lower edges in two points.

h. A plane could intersect each of the six faces of the cube by cutting off opposite corners of the cube. When this plane cuts through the midpoints of the six edges, the cross section is a regular hexagon, and this cut divides the cube into two congruent halves.

25 a. In each part, the given shape is the cross section when the cone and the described plane intersect.

   i. Circle—a plane perpendicular to the axis at a non-vertex point of the axis

   ii. Point—a plane intersects the cone at the vertex only or at one point of the circular base

   iii. Triangle—a plane containing the axis

   iv. Ellipse—a plane oblique (not perpendicular) to the axis at a non-vertex point and not meeting the base

   v. The cross section cannot be a rectangle.

   vi. Segment—a plane tangent to the base and containing the cone's vertex

b. In each part, the given shape is the cross section when the cylinder and the described plane intersect.

   i. Circle—a plane perpendicular to the axis

   ii. Point—a plane tangent to one of the bases and intersecting the cylinder in just the point of tangency

   iii. The cross section cannot be a triangle.

   iv. Ellipse—a plane oblique to the axis and not intersecting either base

   v. Rectangle—a plane containing the axis or parallel to the axis

   vi. Segment—a plane tangent to the curved surface of the cylinder

NOTE The remainder of the solution to Task 23 is on page T452.

NOTE The intersections of planes with cones and cylinders will be explored in Extensions Task 25.

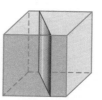

TECHNOLOGY NOTE

The "Slicing Cones and Cylinders" custom app in Geometry is available in *CPMP-Tools*. See the Unit Overview for more information.

NOTE The solution to Task 26 is on page T454.

ON YOUR OWN

REVIEW

27 Consider the following pairs of triangles. In each case, use a tracing of △ABC and rigid motions to see if it can be made to coincide with △PQR. If the shapes coincide, describe the rigid motion or sequence of rigid motions that were used. How are the shapes related?

a. 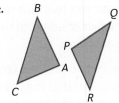 b.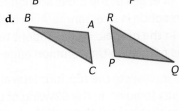

c.

d.

28 Population density is measured by the number of people per square unit of area. China has land area of 3.601 million square miles and in 2010 an approximate population of 1,340,000,000. The population density of the United States, with approximately 309 million people, was 87.3 people per square mile. Which country had the higher population density? How many times as large?

29 Examine the information given in the diagram at the left. Write and solve an equation to find the measure of ∠ABD.

30 Determine whether each of the following tables indicates a linear relationship between x and y. For those that are linear, find a rule that describes the relationship.

a.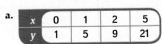

x	0	1	2	5
y	1	5	9	21

b.

x	0	1	2	3
y	1	5	7	37

c.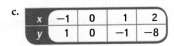

x	−1	0	1	2
y	1	0	−1	−8

31 Use algebraic reasoning to solve each equation or inequality.

a. $150 = 20 - 6x$ b. $150 > 20 - 6x$

c. $6(x + 8) = -72$ d. $6(x + 8) \geq -72$

32 Complete each sentence with the name of a polygon.

a. Every _____ has exactly two lines of symmetry.

b. Every rhombus is also a _____.

c. The diagonals of every _____ are lines of symmetry.

26 **a.** The volume of the pyramid is $\frac{1}{3}(B_1)(r)$.

b. $S = B_1 + B_2 + \cdots + B_n$

c. By dividing the entire surface of the cylinder into n polygonal regions, the volume is divided into n pyramids. Students found the volume of the first one in Part a. The volumes of the others are of the same form but with the appropriate change in subscript.

d. $V = \frac{1}{3}(B_1)(r) + \frac{1}{3}(B_2)(r) + \cdots + \frac{1}{3}(B_n)(r) = \frac{4}{3}\pi r^3 = \frac{1}{3}rS$

e. To complete the solution for S in Part d, divide both sides of the last equation by $\frac{1}{3}r$ to get $S = 4\pi r^2$.

REVIEW

27 **DIFFERENTIATION** Some students may wish to trace the left triangles and also, on another paper, trace both triangles for each part. This will allow them to move the left triangle in stages, marking intermediary triangles formed by slides, turns, and flips as needed.

a. $\triangle ABC$ coincides with $\triangle PQR$. The rigid motions students describe will vary. When the motion begins with vertex A or B, the two triangles coincide with a slide and a flip. If vertex C is mapped to vertex R, the triangles coincide after three motions: a slide, a turn, and a flip.

b. $\triangle ABC$ coincides with $\triangle PQR$. This can be accomplished with a slide, a turn, and a flip.

c. $\triangle ABC$ does not coincide with $\triangle PQR$.

d. $\triangle ABC$ coincides with $\triangle PQR$. This can be accomplished with a slide and a turn.

28 China had $\dfrac{1{,}340{,}000{,}000 \text{ people}}{3{,}601{,}000 \text{ square miles}} \approx 372.1$ people per square mile. China's population density was approximately 4.3 times that of the U.S.: $\dfrac{372.1 \text{ people per square mile}}{87.3 \text{ people per square mile}} \approx 4.3$.

29 $m\angle ABD + m\angle DAB = 90°$ since they are the two acute angles of a right triangle.

$$x + (x - 20°) = 90°$$
$$2x - 20° = 90°$$
$$2x = 110°$$
$$x = 55°$$

30 **a.** This is linear, with a constant rate of increase in y values of 4 for every increase of 1 in x values. The rule is $y = 4x + 1$.

b. This is not linear.

c. This looks linear at first, but the last pair indicates that the rate of change is not constant.

31 **a.** $x = -21.\overline{6}$ **b.** $x > -21.\overline{6}$

c. $x = -20$ **d.** $x \geq -20$

32 **a.** Rectangle or rhombus   **b.** Parallelogram or kite   **c.** Square

ON YOUR OWN

33 Andy kept track of the number of minutes he exercised each day for the last 30 days. His data are shown on the dot plot below.

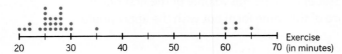

Exercise (in minutes)

a. What percentage of the days did Andy exercise for at least one hour?

b. Find the median number of minutes that Andy exercised for these 30 days.

c. Would you expect the mean number of minutes exercised to be greater than or less than the median number of minutes exercised? Explain your reasoning.

34 Produce a graph of the function $y = x^{10}$, for $0 < x < 2$. On the same set of axes, produce a graph of the function $y = 10^x$.

a. About where do the two graphs intersect?

b. Which function exceeds the other for sufficiently large values of x? Is this true for other pairs of functions of the form $y = x^b$ and $y = b^x$ for $b > 1$?

35 In almost all countries, temperature is measured in degrees Celsius. Temperature C in degrees Celsius is related to temperature F in degrees Fahrenheit by the formula

$$C = \frac{5}{9}(F - 32).$$

a. Describe, in words, how to convert from Fahrenheit to Celsius.

b. Write an equivalent formula that relates temperature C in degrees Celsius to temperature F in degrees Fahrenheit.

c. The temperature at Chicago O'hare International Airport reached a high of 103° Fahrenheit on July 6, 2012. Express this temperature in degrees Celsius.

36 Make a copy of the diagram below on a piece of grid paper or square dot paper. The legs of the right triangle each have a length of 1 unit.

a. What are the areas of the squares shown on the sides of the triangle?

b. On your paper, draw a similar diagram to show two squares, each with area 4 square units and a square with area 8 square units.

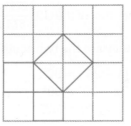

c. Use a similar diagram to draw a square with area 5 square units.

d. On your diagrams indicate line segments with lengths $\sqrt{2}$, $\sqrt{8}$, and $\sqrt{5}$.

e. From your diagrams, estimate the lengths $\sqrt{2}$, $\sqrt{8}$, and $\sqrt{5}$.

33 **a.** 5 days out of 30 days, or about 16.7% of the days

b. 27 minutes

c. The mean will be greater than the median. The 5 days on which Andy exercised more than an hour will increase the mean significantly.

34 **a.** The two graphs intersect at about (1.37, 23.5). (Student answers will vary depending on the window they use.)

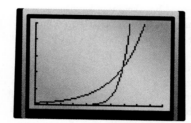
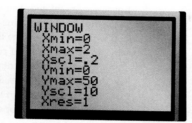

b. $y = 10^x$ exceeds $y = x^{10}$ for x values greater than the x value of the intersection point. For $b > 1$, $y = b^x$ will exceed $y = x^b$ for sufficiently large values of x.

35 **a.** The temperature in degrees Celsius is five-ninths of thirty-two degrees less than the temperature in Fahrenheit.

b. $C = \frac{5}{9}(F - 32)$

$\frac{9}{5}C = (F - 32)$

$\frac{9}{5}C + 32 = F$

(It is easier to use $C = \frac{5}{9}(F - 32)$ when degrees Fahrenheit is known and degrees Celsius is needed. It is easier to use $F = \frac{9}{5}C + 32$ when degrees Celsius is known and degrees Fahrenheit is needed.)

c. $C = \frac{5}{9}(103 - 32) = \frac{5}{9}(71) \approx 39°C$ or, alternatively,

$C = \frac{5}{9}(103) - \frac{160}{9} \approx 39°C$.

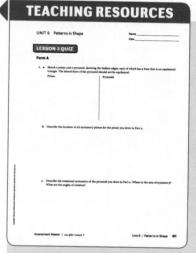

TEACHING RESOURCES

UNIT 6   Patterns in Shape

LESSON 3 QUIZ

Form A

Assessment Masters 411–417

🕐 **GO DIGITAL**

🕐 **JUST IN TIME**

36 **a–d.**

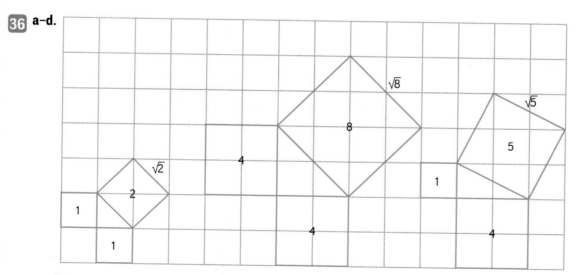

e. $\sqrt{2}$ is between 1 and 2, $\sqrt{8}$ is between 2 and 3, $\sqrt{5}$ is between 2 and 3.

UNIT 6

Looking Back

In this unit, you studied two- and three-dimensional shapes and how they are related. You learned how segment lengths and angle measures determine the shape of special polygons and how polygons determine the shape of polyhedra. You discovered ways to test triangles for congruence and how to use triangles to study useful properties of parallelograms and other polygons. You explored how to visualize three-dimensional shapes and how to represent them in two dimensions. You also learned about symmetry and other properties that make certain shapes useful in design, engineering, and construction. Finally, you learned how knowledge of a few basic properties of shapes could be used to reason to additional properties of those shapes.

The following tasks will help you review, pull together, and apply what you have learned in the process of solving several new problems.

1 Suppose you are given an envelope containing information on separate slips of paper about each of the three side lengths (AB, BC, AC) and each of the three angle measures ($m\angle A$, $m\angle B$, $m\angle C$) of a triangular truss. You randomly draw one slip at a time from the envelope.

a. What is the *largest* number of slips you would ever need to draw before you had enough information to build a congruent truss? Explain your reasoning.

b. What is the *smallest* number of slips you could draw and still build the truss? Explain.

Looking Back

This lesson includes 9 tasks and summary questions intended to provide a review of key ideas about shape of geometric figures. Tasks 8 and 9 and Part d of the Summarize the Mathematics are designed to help students synthesize corresponding ideas involving two- and three-dimensional shapes, specifically as they relate to polygons and polyhedra.

1 **a.** The largest number of slips needed is four. If three angles are selected, then one more draw is needed to determine the triangle. If one angle and two sides that are not both connected to the vertex of the drawn angle are selected, then another draw is needed.

   b. The smallest number of slips needed is three. Choices are SSS, SAS, ASA, and AAS.

CCSS

Common Core State Standards

This unit focused on the CCSS domains:

Congruence, G-CO

Similarity, Right Triangles, and Trigonometry, G-SRT

Geometric Measurement and Dimension, G-GMD

Modeling with Geometry*, G-MG

Plus the Modeling Conceptual Category

2 Some quadrilateral linkages can change rotary motion into "back-and-forth" motion and vice versa. In addition to being used in mechanical devices, the parallelogram linkage serves as the basis for a linkage called a *pantograph*. Pantographs are used for copying drawings and maps to a different scale.

The pantograph shown has been assembled so that *ABCE* is a rhombus; *AD* = *CF* and these lengths are the same as that of a side of the rhombus. The pantograph is held firm at point *D*. No matter how the linkage is moved, give reasons why:

a. *ABCE* will always be a rhombus.

b. *DE* = *EF*

c. Points *D*, *E*, and *F* will always be on a straight line.

3 Earlier in the unit you saw that the base angles of any isosceles triangle are congruent. This property can be restated as:

> *If two sides of a triangle are congruent, then the*
> *angles opposite those sides are congruent.*

a. Write the converse of this statement. Do you think the converse is a true statement?

b. Describe an experiment you could conduct to test whether the converse *might* be true.

c. The first diagram below shows △*ABC* with two congruent angles. The second diagram shows the same triangle with the bisector of ∠*A* drawn.

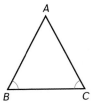
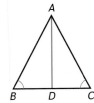

How could you use careful reasoning and the given information for the second diagram to show that the converse statement is true?

d. What would the experiment in Part b tell you about this situation? How does that differ from what the reasoning in Part c tells you?

4 Two farms, located at points *A* and *B*, are to be connected by separate wires to a transformer on a main power line ℓ.

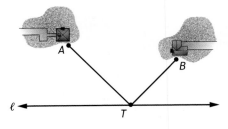

2 **a.** As the pantograph moves, the angles in quadrilateral *ABCE* will change, but the four sides will remain the same length, thereby keeping *ABCE* a rhombus.

b. Since opposite angles of a parallelogram (and therefore a rhombus) are congruent, ∠*BAE* ≅ ∠*BCE*. So, ∠*DAE* ≅ ∠*FCE*. It follows that, △*DAE* ≅ △*FCE* by the SAS congruence condition. $\overline{DE} ≅ \overline{FE}$ because they are corresponding sides of the congruent triangles. Therefore, *DE* = *EF*.

c. Using the diagram at the right, to show points *D*, *E*, and *F* are collinear, we need to establish that m∠1 + m∠2 + m∠3 = 180°.
We know that m∠1 + m∠4 + m∠5 = 180° because the sum of the measures of the angles of a triangle is 180°. Since △*DAE* ≅ △*ECF* by the SSS Congruence Condition, m∠4 = m∠3.
By substitution, m∠1 + m∠3 + m∠5 = 180°. Since *ABCE* is a rhombus, m∠2 + m∠6 = 180°. This means that m∠2 = m∠5.
So by substitution, m∠1 + m∠3 + m∠2 = 180°.
Since the sum of m∠1, m∠2, and m∠3 is 180°, points *D*, *E*, and *F* will always be on a straight line.

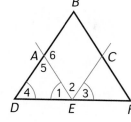

3 **a.** If two angles of a triangle are congruent, then the sides opposite those angles are congruent.

b. You could construct congruent acute angles on a segment drawn as a base of a triangle and then measure the sides of the triangle created by extending the sides of the angles.

c. ∠*B* ≅ ∠*C* is given, ∠1 ≅ ∠2 because $\overline{AD}$ bisects ∠*BAC*.
$\overline{AD}$ is a shared side of △*ABD* and △*ACD*.
△*ABD* ≅ △*ACD* by the AAS congruence condition.
(Students could also use ASA by observing that since
m∠*B* + m∠1 + m∠*ABD* = 180°,
m∠*C* + m∠2 + m∠*ADC* = 180°,
m∠*ADB* = m∠*ADC*.) So, $\overline{AB} ≅ \overline{AC}$ since they are corresponding sides of congruent triangles.

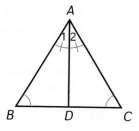

d. The experiment would provide evidence that the converse *may* be true. The careful reasoning in Part c shows that the converse *is* true.

Study the diagram below which shows a method for locating the position of the transformer.

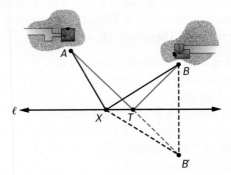

Point B' is located so that the power line ℓ is the perpendicular bisector of $\overline{BB'}$. Then the location T of the transformer is determined by sighting the line AB'. By locating the transformer at point T rather than at any other point X on the line, the power company uses the minimum amount of wire to bring electricity to the two farms.

a. Why is the length of the required wire, $AT + TB$, the same as the length AB'?

b. Explain as carefully and precisely as you can why if any other location X is chosen, then more wire would be required.

5 Make an accurate drawing of a regular decagon.

a. What must be the measure of an interior angle?

b. What must be the measure of an exterior angle?

c. Describe its lines of symmetry and its rotational symmetries.

d. Will a regular decagon tessellate a plane? Explain why or why not.

e. Will copies of an equilateral triangle, a regular decagon, and a regular 15-gon form a semiregular tessellation? Explain your reasoning.

6 Midland Packaging manufactures boxes for many different companies. The net for one type of box manufactured for a candy company is shown below.

a. Name the three-dimensional shape for which this is a net.

b. Sketch the box showing its hidden edges.

c. Sketch two other possible nets that could be used to manufacture the same box.

d. Find the volume of the box.

e. Find the surface area of the box.

f. Does the box have any symmetries? If so, explain how the symmetries are related to the symmetries of its faces.

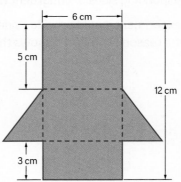

4 **a.** Label the point of intersections of ℓ and $\overline{BB'}$, C. Use the fact that ℓ is the perpendicular bisector to show that $\triangle TBC \cong \triangle TB'C$ by SAS. Then $\overline{TB} \cong \overline{TB'}$; or $TB = TB'$. Since T is on $\overline{AB'}$, $AB' = AT + TB' = AT + TB$.

b. If point X is any point on ℓ other than T, then A, X, and B' will form a triangle, $\triangle AXB'$. So $AX + XB' > AB'$ by the Triangle Inequality. Therefore, $AX + XB' > AT + TB$. This means that choosing any location other than T will require more wire.

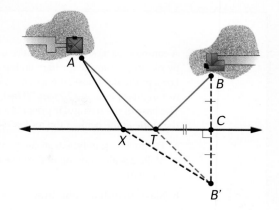

5 See student drawings.

a. $180° - \dfrac{360°}{10} = 180° - 36° = 144°$

b. $\dfrac{360°}{10} = 36°$ or $180° - 144° = 36°$

c. A regular decagon has five lines of reflection symmetry passing through pairs of opposite vertices. It also has another five lines of reflection symmetry passing through pairs of midpoints of opposite sides. A regular decagon has nine rotational symmetries: 36°, 72°, 108°, 144°, 180°, 216°, 252°, 288°, and 324°.

d. No. If such a tessellation existed, at least 3 decogons would meet at each vertex. For any particular vertex, the sum of the measures of the interior angles for meeting tiles must be 360°, but the measure of an interior angle for a regular decagon is 144°, and so this sum exceeds 360°. Thus this tessellation cannot exist.

e. No. While it is true that the three polygons can meet at a vertex and the angles at the vertex sum to 360°, no combination of equilateral triangle, regular decagon, and regular 15-gon can be extended to a semiregular tessellation.

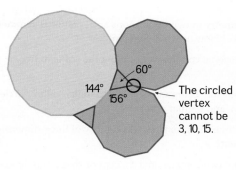

The circled vertex cannot be 3, 10, 15.

6 **a.** The shape is a triangular prism.

b. See the prism at the right.

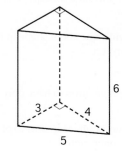

c. Two other possible nets are shown at the right.

d. $V = Bh = \dfrac{1}{2}(3 \times 4) \times 6 = 36 \text{ cm}^3$

e. $SA = 2\left(\dfrac{1}{2} \times 3 \times 4\right) + (6 \times 5) + (6 \times 4) + (6 \times 3) = 84 \text{ cm}^2$

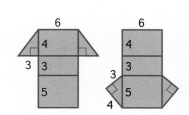

f. The box has a plane of symmetry positioned halfway between and parallel to the two triangular bases. The symmetry plane contains the horizontal lines of symmetry of all three lateral faces. (The lateral faces also have vertical lines of symmetry, but using any one of these lines through the opposite edge to form a plane does not produce a plane of symmetry.) The box has no rotational symmetries.

7. A common basic shape for a house is a polyhedron formed by placing a triangular prism on top of a rectangular prism. For a particular house, the length, width, and height of the rectangular prism are 70 feet, 50 feet, and 20 feet, respectively. The base of the triangular prism is an isosceles triangle, and the angle at the peak of the roof is 140°.

   a. The resulting polyhedron can be viewed as a single prism. Make a scale drawing of the base of the prism formed in this way.

   b. Make an orthographic drawing of this prism.

   c. Describe the reflection symmetry and the rotational symmetry of the prism.

   d. Determine the number of vertices, edges, and faces for this prism. Verify that Euler's Formula holds in this case.

   e. Find the angle defect at each vertex. Verify that Descartes' Theorem holds in this case.

8. Two-dimensional concepts often have corresponding, though not usually identical, concepts in three dimensions. Answer the following questions about some of these connections.

   a. What property of polygons is related to Descartes' Theorem in three dimensions?

   b. What is the three-dimensional counterpart of line symmetry in two dimensions?

   c. How are rotational symmetry in two dimensions and rotational symmetry in three dimensions alike? How are they different?

   d. What is the three-dimensional counterpart of tiling the plane in two dimensions?

   e. What are the three-dimensional counterparts of a triangle, square, circle, rectangle, parallelogram, and regular polygon?

   f. How is rigidity of two-dimensional shapes like rigidity of three-dimensional shapes? How is it different?

   g. Identify at least one more two-dimensional concept or shape and describe its counterpart in three dimensions.

9. Consider the following two statements, one about shape in two dimensions, the other about shape in three dimensions.

   • A regular hexagon tiles the plane.

   • It is not possible for a regular polyhedron to have only regular hexagonal faces.

   These two statements are true for very similar reasons. Explain why each statement is true, and explain their connections.

7 **a.**

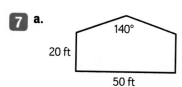

b. Students will likely choose to make an orthographic drawing using the bases of the prism as the sides of the house. Other selections for the placement of the prism are possible.

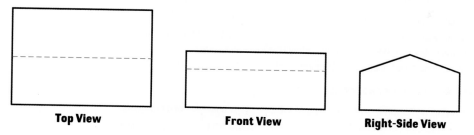

| Top View | Front View | Right-Side View |

c. The prism has two planes of reflection symmetry. One is perpendicular to the base of the house and contains the length of the peak (or the symmetry lines of the sides of the house). The other is perpendicular to the base of the house and contains the vertical symmetry lines of the 70-ft × 20-ft front and back of the house.

d.

Number of Vertices	Number of Edges	Number of Faces
10	15	7

Euler's Formula holds: $10 + 7 = 15 + 2$.

e. The four vertices at the base of the house have angle defect $360° - (90° + 90° + 90°) = 90°$, as seen at the right. The four vertices at the top of the walls have angle defect $360° - (90° + 90° + 90° + 20°) = 70°$. The two vertices at the peak of the roof have angle defect $360° - (90° + 90° + 140°) = 40°$. Descartes' Theorem holds: $4(90°) + 4(70°) + 2(40°) = 720°$.

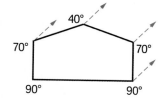

8 **a.** The sum of the exterior angles of a polygon is 360° and is the counterpart to Descartes' Theorem that says that the sum of the angle defects of any convex polyhedron is 720°.

b. Plane symmetry is the three-dimensional counterpart to line symmetry in two dimensions.

c. Rotational symmetries are alike because they must rotate through an angle of less than 360° and make the rotated figure coincide with the original figure. In a two-dimensional figure, the center of rotation is a point and the rotations occur in the plane of the shape. Three-dimensional figures have an axis or line about which they rotate in three dimensions.

d. The three-dimensional counterpart of tiling the plane is filling space with three-dimensional shapes so that there are no overlaps or gaps. One example would be continuing hexagonal prisms (such as bees make) in all directions.

e. The three-dimensional counterparts are tetrahedron, cube, sphere, right rectangular prism, oblique prism, and regular polyhedron, respectively. (Of course, not all regular polygons have counterparts in three dimensions since only 5 regular polyhedra can be formed.)

> **NOTE** The solutions to Task 8 Parts f and g and Task 9 are on page T460.

SUMMARIZE THE MATHEMATICS

Shape is a fundamental feature of the world in which you live. Understanding shape involves being able to identify and describe shapes, visualize and represent shapes with drawings, and analyze and apply properties of shapes.

a Triangles and quadrilaterals are special classes of shapes called polygons.

  i. What properties are true of every polygon?

  ii. What properties are true of every quadrilateral? What property of some quadrilaterals makes the shape widely useful as a linkage?

  iii. What properties are true of every triangle?

b What does it mean for two polygons to be congruent?

  i. What information is sufficient to test whether two triangles are congruent?

  ii. Which test in part i could be used to test whether two parallelograms are congruent?

  iii. How can you use the idea of triangle congruence to reason about properties of polygons and parallelograms in particular? What are some of those properties?

c If a statement is true, its converse may or may not be true. What is the converse of the Pythagorean Theorem? Explain why it is true. How is it used in applications?

d Polyhedra are three-dimensional counterparts of polygons.

  i. Compare and contrast polygons and polyhedra.

  ii. Describe a variety of ways that you can represent polyhedra.

  iii. In some cases, congruent copies of a polygon can be used to tile a plane. In other cases, they can be used to form a polyhedron. What must be true about the angle measures at a common vertex in each case?

  iv. Compare tests for symmetries of polygons and other two-dimensional shapes with tests for symmetries of polyhedra and other three-dimensional shapes.

  v. Rigidity is often an important consideration in the design of both two-dimensional and three-dimensional shapes. What is the key idea to bracing shapes for rigidity? Why does this work?

Be prepared to share your ideas and reasoning with the class.

 **CHECK YOUR UNDERSTANDING**

Write, in outline form, a summary of the important mathematical concepts and methods developed in this unit. Organize your summary so that it can be used as a quick reference in future units and courses.

f. Rigidity in two- and three-dimensional shapes is similar because you use additional supports to set edges (or vertices) in place. In both two- and three-dimensional shapes, this can be accomplished by placing braces from one vertex to all nonadjacent vertices. Braces in two-dimensional shapes are always in the interior of the shape. In three-dimensional shapes, unlike two-dimensional shapes, braces can be placed on the faces of the shape to allow the interior of the shape to remain "open."

g. • The area formula for parallelograms (bh, where b is the length of the base and h is the height), has a counterpart in three dimensions. The volume of prisms is Bh where B is the area of the base of the prism and h is its height.

• If an enlargement or reduction by a scale factor of k is made for a two-dimensional shape, the area will be changed by a scale factor of k^2. The three-dimensional counterpart is that the volume of a shape is changed by a scale factor of k^3 when the base and height are changed by a scale factor of k.

9 Three regular hexagons meet at a vertex to completely tile the plane since the angle sum at each vertex is $120° + 120° + 120° = 360°$. But, it is also because of this that there is no regular polyhedron with hexagonal faces. If there were, three or more regular hexagons would have to meet at each vertex. But since three regular hexagons meeting at a single vertex give an angle defect of $0°$, no convex polyhedron with regular hexagon faces can be created.

SUMMARIZE THE MATHEMATICS

a **i.** Every polygon is made up of pairs of connected edges (segments) joined at vertices (endpoints). Polygons enclose a single region of a plane. The sum of the measures of the interior angles of any (convex) polygon with n sides is $(n - 2)180°$. The sum of the measures of the exterior angles of any (convex) polygon is $360°$.

ii. The sum of the measures of the interior angles of every quadrilateral is $360°$. The sum of the lengths of any three sides must be greater than the fourth side length in order to create a quadrilateral. Every quadrilateral tiles the plane.

Quadrilaterals are not rigid figures. If the sum of the lengths of the shortest and longest sides is less than or equal to the sum of the lengths of the remaining two sides, then the shortest side of the linkage (crank) can rotate completely. When the shortest side is the frame, both cranks will rotate $360°$.

iii. The sum of the measures of the interior angles of every triangle is $180°$. Also, the sum of the lengths of any two sides will always be greater than the length of the third side. This property is called the Triangle Inequality. In addition, every triangle is a rigid shape. Every triangle tiles the plane.

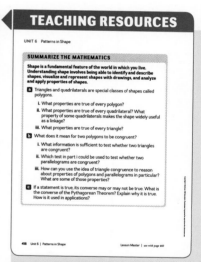

b Two polygons are congruent if there is a sequence of rigid motions that carries one onto the other. This is the principle of superposition. This means that all the corresponding angles and corresponding sides of the polygons are congruent.

   i. Each of the following sets of corresponding parts will be sufficient to test for congruence of two triangles:
   - three sides (SSS)
   - two sides and an included angle (SAS)
   - two angles and an included side (ASA) or
   - two angles and a non-included side (AAS)

   ii. In order to test whether two parallelograms are congruent, you would need a pair of corresponding adjacent sides congruent and any one pair of corresponding angles congruent. So, of the above tests, SAS could be used to test if two parallelograms are congruent.

   iii. If a polygon can be subdivided into triangles that can be shown to be congruent, then you can reason to properties of the polygon such as congruent sides, angles, or diagonals. For parallelograms, opposite angles are congruent and the measures of consecutive angles sum to 180°.

c The converse of the Pythagorean Theorem is: If a triangle has side lengths a, b, c satisifying $a^2 + b^2 = c^2$, then the triangle is a right triangle. The general idea behind the justification of the converse of the Pythagorean Theorem involves recognizing that if you have a triangle with side lengths $a, b,$ and c that satisfy $a^2 + b^2 = c^2$, then any right triangle that you would make with sides of length a and b would have a hypotenuse of length c (Pythagorean Theorem) and so would be congruent (by SSS) to the given triangle with side lengths $a, b,$ and c. Thus, that original triangle must also be a right triangle. The converse of the Pythagorean Theorem provides a way to test if a corner is square, that is, if it makes a right angle.

d **i.** Polyhedra are three-dimensional shapes formed from polygon shapes. A polygon encloses a region of the plane with edges that meet at vertices, while a polyhedron encloses a region of three-dimensional space with polygonal faces that meet in pairs at edges and edges that meet at vertices.

   ii. Polyhedra can be represented with three-dimensional models such as the straw and pipe-cleaner models or with clay or foam. They can also be represented in two dimensions with different views as in orthographic drawings, with oblique drawings, or with nets.

   iii The angle measures of congruent copies of polygons must add to 360° in order to tile the plane. In order to form a polyhedron, the sum of the angle measures must be less than 360° at each vertex.

   iv. Tests for line and plane symmetry for two-dimensional and three-dimensional shapes respectively involve looking for mirror images across a line or a plane. Tests for rotational symmetries in two- and three-dimensions involve looking for rotations (about a point or a line) less than 360° so that the figure and its image coincide.

   v. The key idea in bracing shapes is to stabilize the vertices of the shape. This is accomplished by adding braces to the shape to form triangles (triangulation) which are rigid shapes.

☑ CHECK YOUR UNDERSTANDING

Responses will vary. Above all, this should be something that is useful to the individual student. You may wish to have students use the Teaching Master, *Patterns in Shape* Unit Summary, to help them organize the information.

Practicing for Standardized Tests

Each Practicing for Standardized Tests master presents 10 questions that draw on all content strands. The questions are presented in the form of test items similar to how they often appear in standardized tests such as state assessment tests, the Preliminary Scholastic Aptitude Test (PSAT), or the ACT PLAN. We suggest using these practice sets following the unit assessment so students can become familiar with the formats of standardized tests and develop effective test-taking strategies for performing well on such tests. Answers are provided below.

Answers to Practice Set 6

1. (e)	**2.** (d)	**3.** (b)	**4.** (d)	**5.** (c)
6. (d)	**7.** (b)	**8.** (c)	**9.** (b)	**10.** (d)

Student Masters 420–423
ⓘ GO DIGITAL

Assessment Masters 424–445
ⓘ GO DIGITAL

Student Masters 446–447
ⓘ GO DIGITAL

UNIT 7

Quadratic Functions

When sport balls are kicked, thrown, or hit into the air, the flight paths are parabolas that can be described by quadratic functions like $y = -16x^2 + 40x + 5$. Quadratic functions also provide models for the shape of suspension bridge cables, television dish antennas, and the graphs of revenue and profit functions in business.

The understanding and skill you need to solve problems involving quadratic functions will develop from your work on problems in three lessons of this unit.

LESSONS

1 Quadratic Patterns

Explore typical quadratic relations and expressions to discover and explain connections among problem conditions, data tables, graphs, and function rules for quadratic patterns of change.

2 Equivalent Quadratic Expressions

Use algebraic properties of number systems to write quadratic expressions in convenient equivalent forms.

3 Solving Quadratic Equations

Solve quadratic equations by algebraic methods, including factoring and the quadratic formula.

Quadratic Functions

Unit Overview

In conventional high school algebra curricula, the most prominent nonlinear expressions and functions are quadratic polynomials. In *Core-Plus Mathematics* Course 1, earlier and greater attention is given to Exponential Functions due to their relevance and to capitalize on the connections with linear functions. This unit begins the study of Quadratic Functions that will be continued in future courses. Thus, this unit should be treated as an introduction to Quadratic Functions.

To be proficient in the use of quadratic functions for problem solving, students must have a clear and connected understanding of the numeric, graphic, verbal, and symbolic representations of quadratic functions and the ways that those representations can be applied to patterns in real data. The lessons of this unit are planned to develop each student's intuitive understanding of quadratic patterns of change and technical skills for reasoning with the various representations of those patterns. Understanding and skill in working with quadratic functions is developed in three lessons.

The first lesson develops students' understanding of the characteristics of quadratic functions and the connections among the various representations. Special attention is given to discovering the way each term of a quadratic expression influences the patterns in tables of (x, y) values and the shapes of graphs for quadratics. Lesson 2 explores ways of constructing symbolic expressions for quadratic function rules by reasoning and by data modeling, and strategies for rewriting quadratic expressions in equivalent forms by expanding products of two binomials and/or one monomial and one binomial factor. Lesson 3 explores strategies for solving quadratic equations algebraically by reducing to $x^2 = n$, by factoring, or using the quadratic formula. The final lesson takes a look back and reviews the key concepts and skills of the unit.

The unit was written assuming that most students entering this curriculum will have had modest prior experience with quadratic functions and equations. However, most of that experience may have focused on "finding the unknown x," not on how a function rule like $y = ax^2 + bx + c$ relates all values of x to values of y. The emphasis in this unit is on quadratic functions, and quadratic equations arise as a way of expressing questions about quadratic functions. The approach in the unit assumes that the development of an understanding of quadratic functions in realistic situations will make manipulating symbols much more meaningful.

Further work toward developing proficiency with manipulating symbols occurs in subsequent units and courses. Practice for the skills developed in this unit is incorporated in the On Your Own tasks.

- Recognize patterns in tables of sample values, in problem conditions, and in data plots that can be described by quadratic functions

- Write quadratic function rules to describe quadratic, or approximately quadratic, patterns in graphs or numerical data

- Use table, graph, or symbolic representations of quadratic functions to answer questions about the situations they represent: (1) Calculate y for a given x (i.e., evaluate functions); (2) Find x for a given y (i.e., solve equations and inequalities); and (3) Describe the rate at which y changes as x changes

- Rewrite simple quadratic expressions in equivalent forms by expanding or factoring given expressions and/or by combining like terms

CCSS and CPMP Pathways

The two pathways for this unit are nearly identical and include all of the algebraic concepts and skills in the unit. Your honors or STEM students would be well advised to complete Extensions tasks beyond those listed in the Unit Planning Guide for all students.

Lesson Objectives	Pathways: Pacing and OYO Assignments*	Resources
Lesson 1 Quadratic Patterns • Determine patterns of change associated with quadratic functions • Use tables of values and graphs to estimate answers for questions about situations modeled by quadratic functions • Describe the effects of each parameter in the function rule $y = ax^2 + bx + c$	CCSS Pathway (10 days, includes assessment) **Investigation 1:** OYO—choose two of A1–A4, C9, C10, R15, E19 or E20, Rv27–Rv29 **Investigation 2:** OYO—A5, A6, C11, C12, R16, E22, Rv30–Rv33 **Investigation 3:** OYO—A7, A8, C13, C14, R17, R18, E23, E24, Rv34, Rv35 **CPMP Pathway** (10 days, includes assessment) Use CCSS Pathway	• Spreadsheet software available in *CPMP-Tools* • Unit Resource Masters
Lesson 2 Equivalent Quadratic Expressions • Find symbolic rules for quadratic functions using data modeling and reasoning • Determine whether two given quadratic expressions are equivalent • Decide on most useful equivalent forms of quadratics for different question types • Create equivalent quadratic expressions by expanding products of linear factors • Factor quadratic expressions by extracting common linear factors	CCSS Pathway (7 days, includes assessment) **Investigation 1:** OYO—A1, A2 or A3, C10, R14, E18, Rv26–Rv28 **Investigation 2:** OYO—A4–A8, C11–C13, choose two of R15–R17, choose one of E19–E24, E25, Rv29–Rv32 **CPMP Pathway** (7 days, includes assessment) Use CCSS Pathway plus **Investigation 2:** OYO—C9	• CAS technology available in *CPMP-Tools* • Unit Resource Masters
Lesson 3 Solving Quadratic Equations • Write quadratic equations and inequalities to express questions about quadratic functions • Find exact values of solutions for quadratic equations in the form $ax^2 + c = d$ and $ax^2 + bx = 0$ by reasoning and factoring • Relate factored forms of quadratic expressions to x-intercepts of graphs for the related functions • Solve quadratic equations by using the quadratic formula • Describe the possible number of real solutions for quadratic equations and illustrate the possibilities with graphs	CCSS Pathway (6 days, no formal assessment) **Investigation 1:** OYO—A1, A2 or A3, A4–A6, C9–C11, R15 Part a, choose one of E19–E21, Rv27, Rv28, Rv30 **Investigation 2:** OYO—A7, A8, choose two of C12–C14, R15 Part b, choose one of R16–R18, choose one of E22–E26, Rv31–Rv35 **CPMP Pathway** (6 days, no formal assessment) Use CCSS Pathway	• CAS technology for E24 • Spreadsheet software for E25 • Unit Resource Masters
Lesson 4 Looking Back • Review and synthesize the major objectives of the unit	(2 days, includes unit assessment)	• Unit Resource Masters

* When choice is indicated, it is important to leave the choice to the student.
Note: *It is best if Connections tasks are discussed as a whole class after they have been assigned as homework.*
Note: *The Planning Guide assumes students have access to technology for homework.*

1

Quadratic Patterns

The town of Rehoboth Beach, Delaware, is a popular summer vacation spot along the Atlantic Ocean coast. When Labor Day passes, most beach people leave until the following summer. However, many return in the Fall to nearby Royal Farms in Bridgeville for the annual *Punkin' Chunkin'* festival. The main attraction of this weekend is a "World Championship" contest to see which team of amateur engineers devised the best machine for launching pumpkins a long distance.

(t)John Larew, (b)World Championship Punkin Chunkin Association

462 UNIT 7 | Quadratic Functions

Quadratic Patterns

The purpose of this lesson is to explore the properties of quadratic functions $y = ax^2 + bx + c$. Most students require a great deal of time to learn how to solve quadratic equations and to factor quadratic expressions. Factoring will be introduced on a basic level later in this unit and developed further in future units. The vertex form $y = a(x - h) + k$ will be studied in Course 3.

Rethinking the role of different algebraic forms and procedures in light of emerging technology calls into question continued emphasis on factoring quadratic expressions. First, if one thinks about curricular priorities on the basis of applicability in genuine problem situations, other functions (notably exponential and periodic) are more widely useful than quadratics or higher-degree polynomials. Second, while quadratic polynomials were generally more manageable than exponential or periodic functions in an era of paper-and-pencil calculation, technology makes more useful models as accessible as polynomials. Skill in factoring and expanding polynomial expressions is not prerequisite for solving important and interesting problems.

There are useful concepts concerning quadratics appropriate for introduction at this stage. Accordingly, this lesson analyzes a variety of patterns that can be modeled by quadratic functions and ways that questions corresponding to quadratic equations and inequalities can be solved numerically and graphically.

The emphasis here, as in other algebraic units and lessons, is on the use of algebraic expressions to represent functional relations between quantitative variables. By the end of the lesson, students should have the ability to predict the shape of a graph from inspection of a quadratic function rule and to use calculator or computer tools to evaluate function values and solve equations and to find the maximum or minimum value of quadratic functions.

Lesson Objectives

- Determine patterns of change associated with quadratic functions
- Use tables of values and graphs to estimate answers for questions about situations modeled by quadratic functions
- Describe the effects of each parameter in the function rule $y = ax^2 + bx + c$

Common Core State Standards CCSS

Focused on:
A-SSE.1, A-SSE.3, A-CED.2, A-REI.10, F-IF.4, F-IF.5, F-IF.7, F-IF.8, F-BF.1, F-BF.3, F-LE.3

Connected to:
A-SSE.2, A-REI.4, F-IF.1, G-GMD.4, S-ID.6

THINK ABOUT THIS SITUATION

The current distance record for Punkin' Chunkin' is nearly 5,000 feet, just short of one mile. Such a flight would take the pumpkin very high in the air, as well.

a Which of these graphs is most likely to fit the pattern relating pumpkin height to time in flight? Explain your choice.

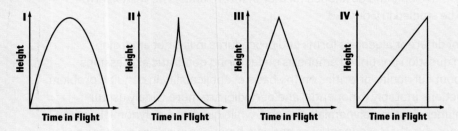

b What pattern would you expect to find in data tables relating pumpkin height to elapsed time?

In work on investigations of this lesson, you will explore several strategies for recognizing, modeling, and analyzing patterns like those involved in the motion of a flying pumpkin.

INVESTIGATION 1

Pumpkins in Flight

It turns out that the height of a flying pumpkin can be modeled well by a *quadratic* function of elapsed time. You can develop rules for such functions by reasoning from basic principles of science. Then you can use a variety of strategies to answer questions about the relationships. As you work on the problems of this investigation, look for answers to these questions:

*What patterns of change appear in tables and graphs of
(time, height) values for flying pumpkins
and other projectiles?*

What functions model those patterns of change?

You may not have any students that use the language of a "quadratic relationship" (though some may use the title of the unit as an indication). Do not discourage incomplete conceptions at this time, but do encourage students to document their ideas. This will give students opportunities to compare any changes in their thoughts as the lesson and unit progresses.

THINK ABOUT THIS SITUATION

a Graph I fits the pattern relating pumpkin height to time in flight. The pumpkin height increases quickly at first, then slows as the pumpkin reaches its maximum height. As the pumpkin falls to the ground, its height decreases at an increasing rate.

(Since students may be visualizing the path of the pumpkin, they may all select Graph I. In order to get them to at least consider the other graphs, you might ask, "Are you thinking about the path of the pumpkin rather than (*time*, *height*)?" This should encourage them to consider the other options also. It is not necessary to correct this misconception at this point, but when students do Problem 1, you might ask them whether $d = 16t^2$ represents the path of the dropped pumpkin.)

b Data tables relating pumpkin height to elapsed time should reveal heights increasing at a decreasing rate until a maximum height is reached and then decreasing at an increasing rate.

TEACHING RESOURCES

Lesson Master 449
() GO DIGITAL

INVESTIGATION 1

CCSS A-SSE.1, A-CED.2, A-REI.10, F-IF.4, F-IF.5, F-IF.7, F-BF.1, A-SSE.2, A-REI.4, F-IF.1, S-ID.6

Pumpkins in Flight

In this investigation, students will build a general quadratic rule for the height (in feet) of a projectile over time (in seconds). They first explore the constant term and then the linear term. As they investigate a pumpkin's height above the ground, students will probably use the table function to find specific answers. Ask them to use the graph, also, so they can see that the graph does not look like the physical representation of the very straight drop of the pumpkin, nor the long arc of the pumpkin flight.

(You can find interactive Galileo experiments and more at www.pbs.org/wgbh/nova/physics/galileo-experiments.html.)

POSSIBLE MISCONCEPTION

In TATS Part a, students will likely choose Graph I and be thinking of the path of the pumpkin rather than a (*time*, *height*) graph. See note.

COLLABORATION SKILL

Help our group check thinking or solutions.

CCSS MATHEMATICAL PRACTICE

This is a good time to reiterate the importance of both realizing and indicating the units of measure in different situations. This involves reasoning abstractly and quantitatively. This same practice is evident throughout this unit as students decontextualize and then recontextualize situations.

Punkin' Droppin' At Old Dominion University in Norfolk, Virginia, physics students have their own flying pumpkin contest. Each year they see who can drop pumpkins on a target from 10 stories up in a tall building while listening to music by the group The Smashing Pumpkins.

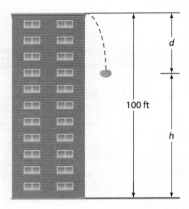

By timing the flight of the falling pumpkins, the students can test scientific discoveries made by Galileo Galilei, nearly 400 years ago. Galileo used clever experiments to discover that gravity exerts force on any free-falling object so that d, the distance fallen, will be related to time t by the function

$$d = 16t^2 \text{ (time in seconds and distance in feet)}.$$

For example, suppose that the students dropped a pumpkin from a point that is 100 feet above the ground. At a time 0.7 seconds after being dropped, the pumpkin will have fallen $16(0.7)^2 \approx 7.84$ feet, leaving it $100 - 7.84 = 92.16$ feet above the ground.

This model ignores the resisting effects of the air as the pumpkin falls. But, for fairly compact and heavy objects, the function $d = 16t^2$ describes motion of falling bodies quite well.

1 Create a table like the one below to show estimates for the pumpkin's distance fallen and height above ground in feet at various times between 0 and 3 seconds.

Time t	Distance Fallen d	Height Above Ground h
0	0	100
0.5	4	$100 - 4 = 96$
1		
1.5		
2		
2.5		
3		

courtesy Susie Flentie

1 Some students may need additional assistance completing the table.

Time t	Distance Fallen d	Height Above Ground h
0	0	100
0.50	4	$100 - 4 = 96$
1.00	16	$100 - 16 = 84$
1.50	36	$100 - 36 = 64$
2.00	64	$100 - 64 = 36$
2.50	100	$100 - 100 = 0$
3.00	144	$100 - 144 = -44$

INSTRUCTIONAL NOTE

Ask students what is happening—or has happened—when the table shows negative values of h.

TEACHING RESOURCES

Student Master 450

⟳ GO DIGITAL

2 Use data relating height and time to answer the following questions about flight of a pumpkin dropped from a position 100 feet above the ground.

   a. What function rule shows how the pumpkin's height h is related to time t?

   b. What equation can be solved to find the time when the pumpkin is 10 feet from the ground? What is your best estimate for the solution of that equation?

   c. What equation can be solved to find the time when the pumpkin hits the ground? What is your best estimate for the solution of that equation?

   d. How would your answers to Parts a, b, and c change if the pumpkin were to be dropped from a spot 75 feet above the ground?

High Punkin' Chunkin' Compressed-air cannons, medieval catapults, and whirling slings are used for the punkin' chunkin' competitions.

Imagine pointing a punkin' chunkin' cannon straight upward. The pumpkin height at any time t will depend on its speed and height when it leaves the cannon.

3 Suppose a pumpkin is fired straight upward from the barrel of a compressed-air cannon at a point 20 feet above the ground, at a speed of 90 feet per second (about 60 miles per hour).

   a. If there were no gravitational force pulling the pumpkin back toward the ground, how would the pumpkin's height above the ground change as time passes?

   b. What function rule would relate height above the ground h in feet to time in the air t in seconds?

Lesson 1 | Quadratic Patterns   **465**

2 **a.** $h = 100 - 16t^2$

b. $100 - 16t^2 = 10$; $t \approx 2.37$ seconds. (-2.37 is also a solution of the equation, but this time does not make sense in the context of the problem.)

c. $100 - 16t^2 = 0$; $t = 2.5$ seconds. (-2.5 is also a solution of the equation, but this time does not make sense in the context of the problem.)

d. The following changes would be made:

Part a: $h = 75 - 16t^2$
Part b: $75 - 16t^2 = 10$; $t \approx 2.02$ seconds (disregard $t \approx -2.02$)
Part c: $75 - 16t^2 = 0$; $t \approx 2.17$ seconds (disregard $t \approx -2.17$)

3 | **INSTRUCTIONAL NOTE** This may require a bit of "creative encouragement" for some students. There actually are other factors that influence the flight of the ball, such as air resistance and wind. We have made simplifying assumptions here in order to make the model more manageable.

a. The height would change at a constant rate of 90 feet per second.

b. $h = 20 + 90t$ would relate height h in feet to time in the air t in seconds.

c. How would you change the function rule in Part b if the punkin' chunker used a stronger cannon that fired the pumpkin straight up into the air with a velocity of 120 feet per second?

d. How would you change the function rule in Part b if the end of the cannon barrel was only 15 feet above the ground, instead of 20 feet?

4 Now think about how the flight of a launched pumpkin results from the combination of three factors:

- initial height of the pumpkin's release,

- initial upward velocity produced by the pumpkin-launching device, and

- gravity pulling the pumpkin down toward the ground.

a. Suppose a compressed-air cannon fires a pumpkin straight up into the air from a height of 20 feet and provides an initial upward velocity of 90 feet per second. What function rule would combine these conditions and the effect of gravity to give a relation between the pumpkin's height h in feet and its flight time t in seconds?

b. How would you change your function rule in Part a if the pumpkin is launched at a height of 15 feet with an initial upward velocity of 120 feet per second?

5 By now you may have recognized that the height of a pumpkin shot straight up into the air at any time in its flight will be given by a function that can be expressed with a rule in the general form

$$h = h_0 + v_0 t - 16t^2.$$

In those functions, h is measured in feet and t in seconds.

a. What does the value of h_0 represent? What units are used to measure h_0?

b. What does the value of v_0 represent? What units are used to measure v_0?

When a pumpkin is not launched straight up into the air, we can break its velocity into a vertical component and a horizontal component. The vertical component, the *upward velocity*, can be used to find a function that predicts change over time in the pumpkin's height. The horizontal component can be used to find a function that predicts change over time in the horizontal distance traveled.

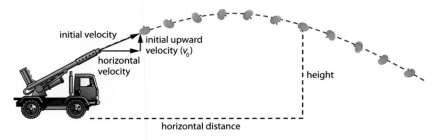

c. $h = 20 + 120t$

d. $h = 15 + 90t$

4 | **INSTRUCTIONAL NOTE** Students may need to refer back to the Punkin' Droppin' scenario in Problems 1 and 2 in this lesson to remember how gravity factors into a mathematical model of height versus time.

a. $h = 20 + 90t - 16t^2$

b. $h = 15 + 120t - 16t^2$

5 **a.** h_0 is the initial height in feet from which the object is launched.

b. v_0 is the initial upward velocity in feet per second with which the object is launched.

6 The pumpkin's height in feet t seconds after it is launched will still be given by $h = h_0 + v_0 t - 16t^2$. It is fairly easy to measure the initial height (h_0) from which the pumpkin is launched, but it is not so easy to measure the initial upward velocity (v_0).

  a. Suppose that a pumpkin leaves a cannon at a point 24 feet above the ground when $t = 0$. What does that fact tell about the rule giving height h as a function of time in flight t?

  b. Suppose you were able to use a stopwatch to discover that the pumpkin shot described in Part a returned to the ground after 6 seconds. Use that information to find the value of v_0.

7 Suppose that you were able to use a ranging tool that records the height of a flying pumpkin every half-second from the time it left a cannon. A sample of the data for one pumpkin launch appears in the following table.

Time (in seconds)	0	0.5	1.0	1.5	2.0	2.5	3.0	3.5	4.0
Height (in feet)	15	40	60	70	70	65	50	30	0

  a. Plot the data on a graph and experiment with several values of v_0 and h_0 in search of a function that models the data pattern well.

  b. Use a calculator or computer tool that offers quadratic curve-fitting to find a quadratic model for the sample data pattern. Compare that automatic curve-fit to what you found with your own experimentation.

  c. Use the rule that you found in Part b to write and solve equations and inequalities matching these questions about the pumpkin shot.

   i. When was the pumpkin 60 feet above the ground?

   ii. For which time(s) was the pumpkin at least 60 feet above the ground?

  d. Use the rule you found in Part b to answer the following questions.

   i. What is your best estimate for the maximum height of the pumpkin?

   ii. How do you know if you have a good estimate? When does the pumpkin reach that height?

6 | **INSTRUCTIONAL NOTE** For Part b, you might ask the following questions. What is the value of h when $t = 6$? How can you use that information to write and solve an equation involving only v_0?

    a. Since h_0 is 24 feet, the function will be given by a rule in the form
$h = 24 + v_0 t - 16t^2$.

    b. $24 + v_0(6) - 16(6)^2 = 0$
$v_0 = 92$ ft/sec

TECHNOLOGY NOTE For Problem 7, if you have access to and are familiar with a CBL or CBR, then we strongly encourage you to use it to create your own data set. This would be a great opportunity for the students to see that the gravity constant is authentic and is not just passed down from some numerical authority.

    What follows are a few settings and pointers for use of the CBL in this particular situation.

    After selecting the "Data Logger" option from the main menu, the settings should read as seen at the right. (This will yield quite different data from that given in Problem 7, as the initial height and velocity will not be feasible to reproduce by tossing a ball into the air.) If you have some groups use meters, the gravity coefficient corresponding to meters can also be achieved.

    You may notice that the suggested number of samples is 20. Students may notice when looking at the gathered data that there is "visual noise" at the beginning and end of the graph. This "noise" is a result of the movement of hands tossing and catching the ball. You will have an option to change the domain of the data in order to focus on the time interval of interest (and to view a solely quadratic relationship).

7 Encourage students to try several initial velocities and heights before using their curve-fitting calculator tool in Part b. As they try different starting values, they may begin to see the effects that each has on the flight of the pumpkin.

    a. The function $h = 15 + 60t - 16t^2$ fits the data well.

    b. The quadratic regression model is approximately $h = -15.87t^2 + 59.63t + 15.09$. The coefficients of the regression equation are close to those found in Part a.

    c.   **i.** Using $-15.87t^2 + 59.63t + 15.09 = 60$, the pumpkin was 60 feet high after approximately 1.04 seconds and 2.72 seconds.

        ii. Using $-15.87t^2 + 59.63t + 15.09 \geq 60$, the pumpkin was at least 60 feet high between approximately 1.04 seconds and 2.72 seconds.

    d. Using the regression equation above:

        i. The maximum height is 71.12 feet reached at about $t = 1.88$ seconds.

        ii. The maximum height was slightly higher than 70 feet. One can see from the table that maximum height occurred between 1.5 and 2 seconds, closer to 2 seconds.

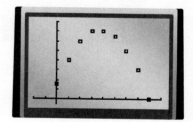

COMMON ERROR

Students sometimes just read the maximum value in the table as the maximum height. Depending on the table interval, this may be a poor estimate.

SUMMARIZE THE MATHEMATICS

In this investigation, you used several strategies to find rules for quadratic functions that relate the position of flying objects to time in flight. You used those function rules and resulting tables and graphs to answer questions about the problem situations.

a How can the height from which an object is dropped or launched be seen:

　　i. In a table of (*time, height*) values?

　　ii. On a graph of height over time?

　　iii. In a rule of the form $h = h_0 + v_0 t - 16t^2$ giving height as a function of time?

b How could you determine the initial upward velocity of a flying object from a rule in the form $h = h_0 + v_0 t - 16t^2$ giving height as a function of time?

c What strategies can you use to answer questions about the height of a flying object over time?

Be prepared to share your ideas and strategies with others in your class.

✓ CHECK YOUR UNDERSTANDING

In Game 3 of the 1970 NBA championship series, the L.A. Lakers were down by two points with three seconds left in the game. The ball was inbounded to Jerry West, whose image is silhouetted in today's NBA logo. He launched and made a miraculous shot from beyond midcourt, a distance of 60 feet, to send the game into overtime (there was no 3-point line at that time).

Through careful analysis of the game tape, one could determine the height at which Jerry West released the ball, as well as the amount of time that elapsed between the time the ball left his hands and the time the ball reached the basket.

This information could then be used to write a rule for the ball's height *h* in feet as a function of time in flight *t* in seconds.

a. Suppose the basketball left West's hands at a point 8 feet above the ground. What does that information tell about the rule giving *h* as a function of *t*?

b. Suppose also that the basketball reached the basket (at a height of 10 feet) 2.5 seconds after it left West's hands. Use this information to determine the initial upward velocity of the basketball.

c. Write a rule giving *h* as a function of *t*.

Martin Mills/Getty Images Sport/Getty Images

Summary

This is intended to be in part an informal start on quadratic functions, so complete analysis should not be expected.

SUMMARIZE THE MATHEMATICS

a The height from which an object is dropped or launched can be seen as:

　i. the value of h corresponding to a value of 0 for t in a table of values.

　ii. the y-intercept of the graph.

　iii. the constant term of the function rule.

b The initial upward velocity is the coefficient of the linear term in the function rule (v_0).

c Students' methods probably vary greatly, but at this point they most likely fall into one of three categories: tables, graphs (with trace, intersection, or maximum features), or solving with a CAS.

✅ CHECK YOUR UNDERSTANDING

a. It tells us the initial height or the constant term of the function rule.
$h = 8 + v_0t - 16t^2$

b. Solve $8 + v_0(2.5) - 16(2.5)^2 = 10$ for v_0 to get $v_0 = 40.8$ ft/s.

c. $h = 8 + 40.8t - 16t^2$

PROCESSING PROMPT

We checked our own thinking by ... .

d. Use the function you developed in Part c to write and solve equations and inequalities to answer these questions about the basketball shot.

    i. At what other time(s) was the ball at the height of the rim (10 feet)?

    ii. For how long was the ball higher than 30 feet above the floor?

    iii. If the ball had missed the rim and backboard, when would it have hit the floor?

e. What was the maximum height of the shot, and when did the ball reach that point?

INVESTIGATION 2

Golden Gate Quadratics

The quadratic functions that describe the rise and fall of flying pumpkins are examples of a larger family of relationships described by rules in the general form $y = ax^2 + bx + c$. The particular numerical values of the coefficients a and b and the constant c depend on problem conditions. As you work through this investigation, look for answers to these questions:

How can tables, graphs, and rules for quadratic functions be used to answer questions about the situations they represent?

What patterns of change appear in tables and graphs of quadratic functions?

Suspension Bridges Some of the longest bridges in the world are suspended from cables that hang in parabolic arcs between towers. One of the most famous suspension bridges is the Golden Gate Bridge in San Francisco, California.

Digital Vision/Getty Images

If you think of one bridge tower as the y-axis of a coordinate system and the bridge surface as the x-axis, the shape of the main suspension cable is like the graph of a quadratic function. For example, if the function defining the curve of one

Lesson 1 | Quadratic Patterns **469**

d. **i.** $8 + 40.8t - 16t^2 = 10$

This equation has two solutions, $t = 0.05$ seconds and $t = 2.5$ seconds. Therefore, the ball was at a height of 10 feet 0.05 seconds and 2.5 seconds after it left West's hands.

ii. $8 + 40.8t - 16t^2 > 30$

The ball is more than 30 feet above the floor on the interval: $0.78 \leq t \leq 1.77$ seconds. The ball was more than 30 feet above the floor for approximately 1 second.

iii. $8 + 40.8t - 16t^2 = 0$

This equation has two solutions, $t \approx 2.7$ seconds and $t \approx -0.2$ seconds. The solution of approximately 2.7 seconds is the only one that makes sense for the situation. If the ball had missed the rim and backboard, it would have hit the floor 2.7 seconds after leaving West's hands.

e. The maximum height of 34.01 feet occurred 1.275 seconds after the ball left West's hands.

INVESTIGATION **2** A-CED.2, A-REI.10, F-IF.4, F-IF.5, F-IF.7, F-BF.1, A-REI.4, F-IF.1

Golden Gate Quadratics

In this investigation, students will explore two other situations that can be modeled by quadratic functions. The first situation involves the height of a suspension bridge cable above the surface of the bridge. This situation provides an opportunity for students to study a quadratic function that opens upward. The second situation returns to the kinds of business questions that were first raised in the "Physics and Business at Five Star Amusement Park" investigation in Lesson 1 of *Patterns of Change*. These problems provide an opportunity for students to build and study a quadratic function with a rule in a non-standard form and a graph with a negative *y*-intercept.

Following Problem 1, for a short introduction to set the scene for the remainder of the investigation, you may want to use the introduction on page 470 and Problem 2 as a mini-launch in a whole-class discussion. Then students can work in groups on Problems 3–5, exploring how quadratics can occur in quite different situations than the height situations of the previous problems. A whole-class discussion about how sales, income, and profit are each different functions of price could provide the needed key to what follows. This combination of economic concepts and algebraic thinking might be difficult for some students.

The focus in Problem 3 should be on setting up the function rules and equations, not writing them in simplest form. The writing of equivalent expressions is the focus of the next lesson.

suspension cable is $y = 0.002x^2 - x + 150$, where x and y are measured in feet, the graph will look like that below.

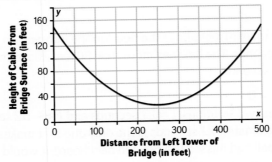

Distance from Left Tower of Bridge (in feet)

1 Use the function $y = 0.002x^2 - x + 150$ to answer the following questions.

a. What is the approximate height (from the bridge surface) of the towers from which the cable is suspended?

b. What is the shortest distance from the cable to the bridge surface, and where does it occur?

c. For what interval(s) is the suspension cable at least 75 feet above the bridge surface?

d. Recall that the height function for dropping pumpkins was $h = 100 - 16t^2$ and for a basketball long shot was $h = 8 + 40.8t - 16t^2$.

   i. How is the graph of the suspension cable function similar to and different from the graphs of these two functions?

   ii. How is the rule of the suspension cable function similar to and how is it different from the rules of these two functions?

Fundraising In 1996, the first Tibetan Freedom Concert, regarded by many as the single greatest cultural event in modern rock history, took place in Golden Gate Park in San Francisco. This was the first in a series of benefit concerts organized by the Milarepa Fund to raise awareness about nonviolence and the Tibetan struggle for freedom, as well as to encourage youth activism.

The primary goal for the Tibetan Freedom Concerts was to raise awareness, not money. However, careful planning was needed to ensure that the event would reach a large audience and that it would not *lose* money. The profit from any event will be the difference between income and operating expenses.

1 **a.** Each tower is roughly 150 feet high.

b. The shortest distance from the cable to the bridge surface is about 25 feet and it occurs 250 feet from the base of each tower.

c. The cable is at least 75 feet above the bridge surface on the intervals: $0 \leq x \leq 91.89$ and $408.11 \leq x \leq 500$ (where x is the distance from the "left" tower), or within 91.89 feet of the "left" and "right" towers.

d. **i.** The graphs of the suspension cables, punkin' chunkin, and basketball long shot functions all have the same shape (except for opening upward or downward) and they all have a positive y-intercept. Differences include that the bridge graph opens upward, and the bridge graph doesn't cross the x-axis.

ii. The rules are all of the form $y = ax^2 + bx + c$, or equivalently, $y = c + bx + ax^2$. Two noticeable differences in the rules are that a is positive in the bridge rule and b is negative.

2 **a.** The number of people that buy tickets and attend a concert depends on the ticket price, publicity for the concert, and the concert group's popularity.

b. For benefits like the Tibetan Freedom Concert performers donate their time, but publicity and the hiring of professional concert managers, production managers, and promoters present large upfront expenses not dependent on the number of tickets sold. The higher the number of tickets sold, the more money needs to be spent on catering, renting portable toilets, hiring security and cleanup crews.

> **INSTRUCTIONAL NOTE** You might give students the following information and ask what this suggests about the expenses for the first Tibetan Freedom Concert. It's rather eye-opening! Tickets cost $25 each. The event attracted 100,000 attendees and raised $800,000.

2 As organizers planned for the event, they had many variables to consider.

   a. What factors will affect the number of tickets sold for the event?

   b. What kinds of expenses will reduce profit from tickets sales, and how will those expenses depend on the number of people who buy tickets and attend?

3 Suppose that a group of students decided to organize a local concert to raise awareness and funds for the Tibetan struggle, and that planning for the concert led to this information:

   - The relationship between number of tickets sold s and ticket price x in dollars can be approximated by the linear function $s = 4{,}000 - 250x$.

   - Expenses for promoting and operating the concert will include \$1,000 for advertising, \$3,000 for pavilion rental, \$1,500 for security, and \$2,000 for catering and event T-shirts for volunteer staff and band members.

   a. Find a function that can be used to predict income I for any ticket price x.

   b. Find a function that can be used to predict profit P for any ticket price x.

   c. How do predicted income and profit change as the concert organizers consider ticket prices ranging from \$1 to \$20? How are those patterns of change shown in graphs of the income and profit functions?

   d. What ticket price(s) seem likely to give maximum income and maximum profit for the concert? What are those maximum income and profit values? How many tickets will be sold at the price(s) that maximize income and profit?

   e. If event planners are more interested in attracting a large audience without *losing* money on the event than in maximizing profit, what range of ticket prices should they consider? Explain your reasoning.

4 The **break-even point** is the ticket price for which the event's income will equal expenses. Another way to think of the break-even point is the ticket price when profit is \$0.

   a. Write and solve an equation that can be used to find the break-even ticket price for this particular planned concert.

   b. Write and solve an inequality that can be used to find ticket prices for which the planned concert will make a positive profit.

   c. Write and solve an inequality that can be used to find ticket prices for which the planned concert will lose money.

5 What similarities and differences do you see in tables, graphs, and rules of the functions relating number of tickets sold, income, and profit to the proposed ticket price?

3 | **INSTRUCTIONAL NOTE** It will be practical for students both to use and understand phrases like "increasing at a decreasing rate" and "decreasing at an increasing rate," which you might introduce at this time. As you observe groups, be sure students are recognizing that *Profit = Income − Expenses*.

NOTE The solution to Problem 2 is on page T470.

a. $I = x(4,000 − 250x)$

b. $P = x(4,000 − 250x) − 7,500$

c. They both increase faster at first, and then more slowly, until the "peak" is reached, and then both decrease, slower at first and then more quickly.
   Both graphs increase and then decrease. They start out very steep and get less steep until a maximum income or profit is reached. Then the graphs change direction and get more steep as ticket price increases until the income or profit is $0.

d. A price of $8 gives both the maximum profit and income. The maximum income would be $16,000 while the maximum profit would be $8,500. This would result from 2,000 tickets being sold since $s = 4,000 − 250(8) = 2,000$.

e. The event will not lose money if ticket prices range from $2.17 to $13.83, but once ticket prices exceed $8, both audience size and income/profit decline. So, they would want to consider ticket prices ranging from $2.17 to $8. For example, a ticket price of $4 would result in 3,000 tickets being sold for a profit of $4,500. This is $4,000 less profit than the maximum profit determined in Part d, but 1,000 more attendees.

4 | **INSTRUCTIONAL NOTE** More techniques for solving quadratic equations and inequalities will be presented later in the unit; at this point, using tables and graphs is expected. The focus should be on being able to set up such equations and inequalities and on understanding the meaning of these solutions.

a. $0 = x(4,000 − 250x) − 7,500$; break-even prices would be $13.83 and $2.17.

b. $x(4,000 − 250x) − 7,500 > 0$; positive profit would be gained with the following ticket price interval: $2.17 < x < $13.83.

c. $x(4,000 − 250x) − 7,500 < 0$; loss would occur on the following ticket price intervals: 0 (*free*) $\leq x < $2.17 or $x > $13.83. (Some students may wish to include x values less than 0, as well. This is reasonable, as paying people to come to a concert would definitely lead to a loss.)

5 Students should note that the ticket sales function is linear, while the other two are quadratic. This observation should allow them to make comments on the shape of the graphs, the pattern of change in the tables and graphs, and the differences in the structure of the rules. Other observations are:

- The income and profit graphs are quite similar, and that every y value of the income function is exactly 7,500 more than the corresponding y value of the profit function.

- The income and ticket sales have a common x-intercept.

SUMMARIZE THE MATHEMATICS

In this investigation, you used several strategies to find and use rules for quadratic functions in different problem situations.

 a How are patterns in the tables of values, graphs, and rules of the quadratic function examples in Investigations 1 and 2 similar to each other, and how do they differ from each other?

b How are tables, graphs, and rules of quadratic functions similar to and different from those of other types of functions you have worked with in earlier studies?

c What strategies can you use to:

   i. Produce functions that model problem conditions?

   ii. Solve quadratic equations or inequalities?

   iii. Find maximum or minimum values of quadratic functions?

Be prepared to share your ideas and strategies with others in your class.

✅ CHECK YOUR UNDERSTANDING

The physical forces that determine the shape of a suspension bridge and business factors that determine the graph of profit prospects for a concert apply to other situations as well. For example, the parabolic reflectors that are used to send and receive microwaves and sounds have shapes determined by quadratic functions.

Suppose that the profile of one such parabolic dish is given by the graph of $y = 0.05x^2 - 1.2x$, where dish width x and depth y are in feet.

a. Sketch a graph of the function $y = 0.05x^2 - 1.2x$ for $0 \le x \le 25$. Then write calculations, equations, and inequalities that would provide answers for parts i–iv. Use algebraic, numeric, or graphic reasoning strategies to find the answers, and label (with coordinates) the points on the graph corresponding to your answers.

   i. If the edge of the dish is represented by the points where $y = 0$, how wide is the dish?

   ii. What is the depth of the dish at points 6 feet in from the edge?

   iii. How far in from the edge will the depth of the dish be 2 feet?

   iv. How far in from the edge will the depth of the dish be at least 3 feet?

b. What is the maximum depth of the dish and at what distance from the edge will that occur? Label the point (with coordinates) on your graph of $y = 0.05x^2 - 1.2x$.

Edmond Van Hoorick/Getty Images

Summary

This investigation is intended to be, in part, an informal start on quadratic graphing, so no complete analysis should be expected.

SUMMARIZE THE MATHEMATICS

a At this point, students should note among the similarities the general U-shape, the non-constant rate of change, the increasing and decreasing characteristics of each graph, the fact that each graph has a y-intercept, and the similar structure of the rules. Differences observed may include the x-intercepts (or lack of x-intercepts); whether the graph opens upward or downward, increases and then decreases or vice versa, has a maximum or a minimum point.

b Observations may include: linear and exponential functions appear to always be either increasing or decreasing, while the quadratic functions "change" at some maximum or minimum point; linear functions have a constant rate of change, while exponential and quadratic functions' rates of change are non-constant.

c **i.** In Problem 3, students' reasoning from the problem conditions required substituting an expression for number of tickets sold s to build the expressions for income and profit.
   ii. Student methods at this point will most likely include tables, graphs (with trace or intersection features), or solving with a CAS.
   iii. Students might make use of the maximum and minimum features on their calculators, or, again, use of the trace or table features.

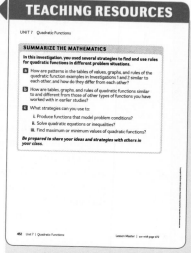
MATH TOOLKIT

Describe and sketch the patterns shown by quadratic functions. Compare these patterns to linear and exponential function patterns.

✔ CHECK YOUR UNDERSTANDING

PROCESSING PROMPT

We made sure all members were included in discussions by ... .

INSTRUCTIONAL NOTE Some students may not be able to visualize this problem well. Ask students to explain the relationship between the picture of the parabolic dish and the equation. Other students should be able to explain that the equation represents the curve that could be traced from any point on the edge of the dish following the shortest path through the center to the opposite side.

a. **i.** $0 = 0.05x^2 - 1.2x$
   The x-intercepts are at $(0, 0)$ and $(0, 24)$, so the dish is 24 feet wide.

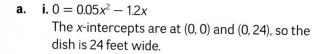

   ii. $y = 0.05(6)^2 - 1.2(6)$ and $y = 0.05(18)^2 - 1.2(18)$
   When $x = 6$ (and when $x = 24 - 6$, or 18), $y = -5.4$.
   So, the dish is 5.4 feet deep 6 feet in from the edge.

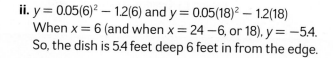

NOTE The remainder of the solution is on page T473.

INVESTIGATION **3**

Patterns in Tables, Graphs, and Rules

In your work on the problems of Investigations 1 and 2, you examined a variety of rules, tables, and graphs for quadratic functions. For example,

A pumpkin's height above ground (in feet) is given by $h = 100 - 16t^2$.

A suspension cable's height above a bridge surface (in feet) is given by $y = 0.002x^2 - x + 150$.

Income for a concert (in dollars) is given by $I = x(4{,}000 - 250x)$.

Profit for a concert (in dollars) is given by $p = x(4{,}000 - 250x) - 7{,}500$.

It turns out that the expressions used in all of these functions are equivalent to expressions in the general form $ax^2 + bx + c$. To solve problems involving quadratic functions, it helps to know how patterns in the expressions $ax^2 + bx + c$ are related to patterns in tables and graphs of the related quadratic functions $y = ax^2 + bx + c$. As you work on the following problems, look for answers to this question:

How are the values of a, b, and c related to patterns in the graphs and tables of values for quadratic functions $y = ax^2 + bx + c$?

To answer a question like this, it helps to use your calculator or CAS software to produce tables and graphs of many examples in which the coefficients a and b and the constant c are varied systematically. The problems of this investigation suggest ways you could do such explorations and some questions that might help in summarizing patterns you notice. Make informal notes of what you observe in the experiments and then share your ideas with your teacher and other students to formulate some general conclusions.

The Basic Quadratic Function When distance traveled by a falling pumpkin is measured in feet, the rule giving distance as a function of time is $d = 16t^2$. When such gravitational effects are studied on the Moon, the rule becomes $d = 2.6t^2$. When distance is measured in meters, the rule is $d = 4.9t^2$ on Earth and $d = 0.8t^2$ on the Moon.

These are all examples of the simplest quadratic functions—those defined by rules in the form $y = ax^2$.

How can you predict the shape and location of graphs of quadratic functions with rules in the form $y = ax^2$?

iii. $-2 = 0.05x^2 - 1.2x$

$y = -2$ when $x = 1.8$ (and when $x = 22.2$). So, about 1.8 feet in from the edge, the dish will be 2 feet deep.

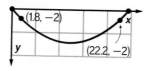

iv. $0.05x^2 - 1.2x \leq -3$

$y \leq -3$ when $2.84 \leq x \leq 21.16$. So, the dish will be at least 3 feet deep between approximately 2.84 and 21.16 feet in from the edge.

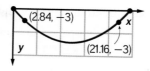

b. The maximum depth of 7.2 feet occurs 12 feet in from the edge.

INVESTIGATION **3** **CCSS** A-SSE.1, A-SSE.3, A-CED.2, A-REI.10, F-IF.4, F-IF.7, F-IF.8, F-BF.3, F-LE.3, F-IF.1, G-GMD.4

Patterns in Tables, Graphs, and Rules

The key point of this investigation is to generalize the patterns of quadratic tables and graphs that students may have observed in the previous investigations. This generalization is encouraged by a series of technology-based explorations, in which many examples are studied to find patterns relating the parameters in quadratic functions to the resulting tables and graphs.

The explorations will lead to two basic points, which are (1) a negative leading coefficient makes the graph open down and a positive leading coefficient makes the graph open up, and (2) the constant term indicates the y-intercept in any case. Another, more general point the students should see is that the effect of the linear term can only be interpreted as it interacts with the sign of the leading coefficient. In general, when the coefficient of the linear term is nonzero, the graph will be shifted left or right from its position symmetric across the y-axis. At this point, it is not necessary to stress anything more than that.

One of the risks of doing open-ended exploration of connections between functions and their graphs is that students may note patterns in a few special cases that do not hold in general. Even for the correct generalizations, there may be only the observation of a pattern without any underlying explanations of why these patterns occur. For those reasons, it is critical to follow the investigation with careful class discussion in which observations are shared and explanations sought.

The problems of this investigation suggest ways for students to move toward the goal of discovering the effect of each of a, b, and c on tables and graphs of functions $y = ax^2 + bx + c$. To avoid time-consuming writing of full sentence answers in this investigation, we suggest that students explore tables and graphs of the suggested examples (and others of their choosing), make some informal notes of what they see, and prepare to share their ideas in summary class discussion. You might want to have such summary discussions at several points in the investigation; for example, after Problems 1, 2, and 5. Possible questions to pose in those summary discussions have been inserted following each problem solution.

1 Study the tables and graphs produced by such functions for several *positive* values of a. For example, you might start by comparing tables and graphs of $y = x^2$, $y = 2x^2$, and $y = 0.5x^2$ for $-10 \leq x \leq 10$.

   a. What do all the graphs have in common? How about all the tables?

   b. How is the pattern in a table or graph of $y = ax^2$ related to the value of the coefficient a when $a > 0$?

2 Next study the tables and graphs produced by such functions for several *negative* values of a. For example, you might start by comparing tables and graphs of $y = -x^2$, $y = -2x^2$, and $y = -0.5x^2$ for $-10 \leq x \leq 10$.

   a. What do all these tables have in common? How about all the graphs?

   b. How is the pattern in a table or graph of $y = ax^2$ related to the value of the coefficient a, when $a < 0$?

3 Now think about *why* the patterns in tables and graphs of functions $y = ax^2$ occur and *why* the coefficient a is helpful in predicting behavior of any particular quadratic in this form.

   a. Consider first the functions $y = ax^2$ when $a > 0$.

      i. Why are the values of y always greater than or equal to zero?

      ii. Why are the graphs always symmetric curves with a minimum point $(0, 0)$?

   b. Consider next the functions $y = ax^2$ when $a < 0$.

      i. Why are the values of y always less than or equal to zero?

      ii. Why are the graphs always symmetric curves with a maximum point $(0, 0)$?

Adding a Constant When you designed a quadratic function to model position of a pumpkin at various times after it is dropped from a 100-foot tall building, the rules that made sense were $y = 100 - 16t^2$ or $y = -16t^2 + 100$.

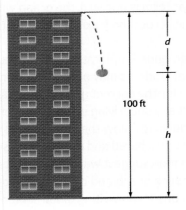

1 **a.** Among student responses might be: The graphs are symmetric about the y-axis, open upward, and have a minimum point at the origin (0, 0). Starting with negative x values, the y values in the tables decrease at a decreasing rate until an x value of 0 is reached ($y = 0$) and then the y values increase at an increasing rate.

b. When $a > 1$, for the same x values, the y values are larger than the y values of $y = x^2$. When $0 < a < 1$, for the same x values, the y values are smaller than the y values for $y = x^2$. The graphs of the functions with $a > 1$ appear to be "skinnier" while the graphs with $0 < a < 1$ appear to be "wider" than the $y = x^2$ graph.

2 **a.** Starting with negative x values, the y values in the tables increase at a decreasing rate until $x = 0$, and then decrease at an increasing rate. The graphs are symmetric about the y-axis, open downward, and have a maximum point at the origin (0, 0).

b. Students should recognize the graphs of the corresponding functions $y = ax^2$ and $y = -ax^2$ as reflections of each other across the x-axis. Students should also make observations similar to those in Problem 1 Part b.

3 **INSTRUCTIONAL NOTE** This is a good opportunity to reinforce order of operations. Also, the squaring process on a calculator: $(-5)^2$ is not -5^2. You may wish to introduce the terms "odd" and "even" functions at this time if students need to know this idea for state testing.

a. **i.** For each of the examples, one should first square the x value and then multiply the result by the coefficient. Students should recall that the x values squared will never be negative. If a is positive, then the product of a and x^2 will always be a non-negative number.

ii. The graph will always have a minimum value of zero since (0, 0) is a point on the graph, and the value of y can never be less than zero (no point will be below the y-axis). The graph will always be symmetric about the y-axis because $a(-x)^2 = ax^2$. This means that for any particular x value, the y values at x and at $-x$ are the same.

b. **i.** The squared x value will never be negative. If a is negative, then the product of a and x^2 will always be a nonpositive number.

ii. The graph will always have a maximum point at (0, 0) since that point will always satisfy the equation $y = ax^2$. There will be no points above (0, 0) on the graph when a is negative since y cannot be positive in this case. Symmetry about the y-axis can be explained by realizing that $a(-x)^2 = ax^2$. This means that for any particular x value, the y values at x and at $-x$ are the same.

If the building from which pumpkins are to be dropped were taller or shorter, the rules might be $y = -16t^2 + 150$ or $y = -16t^2 + 60$.

These are all examples of another family of quadratic functions—those defined by rules in the form $y = ax^2 + c$.

> *How can you predict the shape and location of graphs of quadratic functions with rules in the form $y = ax^2 + c$?*

4 Study tables and graphs produced by such functions for several combinations of positive and negative values of a and c. You might start by comparing these sets of functions:

Set 1	Set 2	Set 3
$y = x^2$	$y = -x^2$	$y = 2x^2$
$y = x^2 + 3$	$y = -x^2 + 5$	$y = 2x^2 + 1$
$y = x^2 - 4$	$y = -x^2 - 1$	$y = 2x^2 - 3$

a. How is the graph of $y = ax^2 + c$ related to the graph of $y = ax^2$?

b. How is the relationship between $y = ax^2 + c$ and $y = ax^2$ shown in tables of (x, y) values for the functions?

c. What are the values of $y = ax^2 + c$ and $y = ax^2$ when $x = 0$? How do these results help to explain the patterns relating the types of quadratics that you described in Parts a and b?

Factored and Expanded Forms When you studied problems about income from an amusement park bungee jump and promotion of a concert, you looked at functions relating income to ticket price. The resulting income rules had similar forms:

Bungee Jump: $I = p(50 - p)$

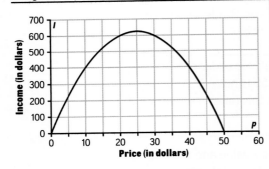

Concert Promotion: $I = x(4,000 - 250x)$

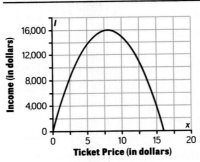

Just as you did with linear expressions in Unit 3, you can apply properties of numbers and operations to rewrite these rules in equivalent *expanded* form.

4 **a.** The graphs have the same shape. The graph of $y = ax^2 + c$ is the graph of $y = ax^2$ moved vertically (up or down) c units.

b. The y values in the table for $y = ax^2 + c$ are all c units greater or less than the corresponding y values in the table for $y = ax^2$.

c. When $x = 0$, $y = c$. This means that c is the y value at which the graph crosses the y-axis and the minimum or maximum value of the function. The patterns observed in graphs should confirm that the y-intercept is $(0, c)$. This pattern still holds in the case of $y = ax^2$ since $c = 0$ in this case.

These results show that in each equation, the first operation is the squaring of x, followed by the multiplication by a. In this respect, the values of y when $y = ax^2 + c$ are similar to the values of y when $y = ax^2$. The last step of adding c is what separates the two forms and produces both a vertical shift in the graph of $y = ax^2$ and a constant difference of c between the two tables of y values.

INSTRUCTIONAL NOTE You may wish to have different groups share their functions. Possible summary discussion questions for Problems 1–4:

- What do you know about the shape and location of the graph for any function with rule $y = ax^2$?

- How does the way one calculates $y = ax^2$ help explain the patterns observed?

- What do you know about the shape and location of the graph for any function with rule $y = ax^2 + c$ when compared to $y = ax^2$?

- What does the value of c tell about the shape of the graph and the pattern in the table of values when compared to $y = ax^2$?

- How does the way one calculates $y = ax^2 + c$ help explain the patterns observed?

- How does the effect of changing c in $y = ax^2 + c$ compare to the effect of changing a in $y = ax^2$?

5 To rewrite the rule $I = p(50 - p)$, a student at Sauk Prairie High School reasoned like this:

> Applying the distributive property, $p(50 - p) = 50p - p^2$.
> Rearranging terms, $50p - p^2 = -p^2 + 50p$.
> So $I = -p^2 + 50p$, showing that income is a quadratic function of ticket price.

a. Use similar ideas to rewrite $x(4{,}000 - 250x)$ in an equivalent expanded form.

b. Study graphs of the two income functions: $I = p(50 - p)$ and $I = x(4{,}000 - 250x)$. In each case, find coordinates of:

   i. the y-intercept,

   ii. the x-intercepts, and

   iii. the maximum point.

c. How could you find these special points in Part b by analyzing the symbolic function rules in factored and/or expanded forms?

d. The Sauk Prairie student made the following observations. How do you think the student arrived at those ideas? Do you agree with them? If not, explain why not.

   i. It is easiest to find the y-intercept from the *expanded* form $-p^2 + 50p$.

   ii. It is easiest to find x-intercepts of the income function graph from the *factored* form $p(50 - p)$.

   iii. It is easiest to find the maximum point on the income graph from the x-intercepts.

6 The planning committee for Lake Aid, an annual benefit talent show at Wilde Lake High School, surveyed students to see how much they would be willing to pay for tickets. Suppose the committee developed the function

$I = -75p^2 + 950p$ to estimate income I in dollars for various ticket prices p in dollars. Use the patterns you observed in Problem 5 to help answer the following questions.

a. Write the function for income using an equivalent factored form of the expression given. What information is shown well in the factored form that is not shown as well in the expanded form?

b. For what ticket prices does the committee expect an income of $0?

c. What ticket price will generate the greatest income? How much income is expected at that ticket price?

d. Use your answers to Parts b and c to sketch a graph of $I = -75p^2 + 950p$.

5 **a.** $x(4{,}000 - 250x) = 4{,}000x - 250x^2$ (distributive property)

$4{,}000x - 250x^2 = -250x^2 + 4{,}000x$ (rearranging terms)

INSTRUCTIONAL NOTE

In Lesson 2, students will be expected to write expressions in equivalent forms, so don't dwell too long on it here.

b. For the bungee-jump situation:

   i. the y-intercept is $(0, 0)$.

   ii. the two x-intercepts are $(0, 0)$ and $(50, 0)$.

   iii. the maximum occurs at the point $(25, 625)$.

For the concert promotion situation:

   i. the y-intercept is $(0, 0)$.

   ii. the two x-intercepts are $(0, 0)$ and $(16, 0)$.

   iii. the maximum occurs at the point $(8, 16{,}000)$.

c. **INSTRUCTIONAL NOTE** This problem allows students to think about the information carried by factored and expanded forms before considering the points of view in Part d. It is fine if their responses here are not thorough. They will think more deeply in Part d.

Students may mention that the factored form allows you to find the x-intercepts and thus the x-coordinate of the max/min point. They may also indicate that the expanded form allows you to quickly note the y-intercept.

d. **i.** It is easy to see from the form $-p^2 + 50p$ that the value of the function is 0 when $p = 0$. Students may argue that this is also easy to see from the form $p(50 - p)$.

INSTRUCTIONAL NOTE

The value of different forms of quadratic rules would be an appropriate class discussion topic.

   ii. The x-intercepts indicate ticket prices for which income will be $0. Clearly, income will be $0 if tickets are free ($0) and if tickets are so expensive ($50) that no one will buy a ticket. This is easiest to see in the form $I = p(50 - p)$. When either 0 or 50 is substituted for p in the rule, the result is 0 for the income.

   iii. Due to the symmetry of quadratic functions, the maximum will occur at a point halfway between the x-intercepts. So for the bungee-jump situation, the maximum will occur when $p = 25$. Substituting into either form of the rule gives a maximum income of $625.

6 **a.** $I = p(-75p + 950)$ or $I = p(950 - 75p)$ are possible equivalent forms. The x-intercepts are easier to determine in factored form. The factored form also shows that ticket sales s depend on price p according to the rule $s = 950 - 75p$.

b. An income of $0 can be expected if the ticket prices are set at either $0 (they don't charge for tickets) or $12.67 or more(nobody buys a ticket).

c. The greatest income will be gained from a ticket price of about$6.33 (halfway between $0 and $12.67). This will generate an income of $3,008.

d. See the sketch at the right.

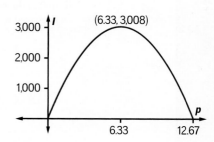

Adding a Linear Term The income functions you studied in Problems 5 and 6 are examples of another family of quadratics, those with rules in the form $y = ax^2 + bx$.

How can you predict the shape and location of graphs of quadratic functions with rules in the form $y = ax^2 + bx$?

7 Study tables and graphs produced by such functions for several combinations of positive and negative values of a and b. You might start by comparing graphs of the following sets of functions:

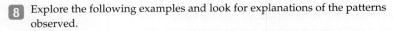

Set 1	Set 2	Set 3
$y = x^2$	$y = -x^2$	$y = 2x^2$
$y = x^2 + 4x$	$y = -x^2 + 5x$	$y = 2x^2 + 6x$
$y = x^2 - 4x$	$y = -x^2 - 5x$	$y = 2x^2 - 6x$

Look at graphs of the functions given above to see if you can find patterns that relate the values of a and b in the rules $y = ax^2 + bx$ to location of the features below. It might help to think about the functions using the equivalent factored form, $x(ax + b)$.

a. y-intercepts

b. x-intercepts

c. maximum or minimum point

Putting Things Together The graphs of all quadratic functions are curves called *parabolas*. In work on Problems 1–7, you have learned how to predict the patterns in graphs for three special types of quadratic functions: $y = ax^2$, $y = ax^2 + c$, and $y = ax^2 + bx$. You can use what you know about these quadratic functions to reason about graphs produced by functions when the coefficients a and b and the constant c are not zero.

8 Explore the following examples and look for explanations of the patterns observed.

a. The diagram at the right gives graphs for three of the four quadratic functions below.

$$y = x^2 - 4x$$
$$y = x^2 - 4x + 6$$
$$y = -x^2 - 4x$$
$$y = x^2 - 4x - 5$$

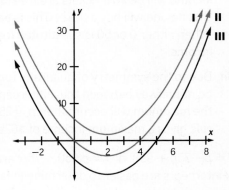

Without using graphing technology:

i. determine the function with the graph that is missing on the diagram.

ii. match the remaining functions to their graphs, and be prepared to explain your reasoning.

7 **a.** The graph of any function in the form $y = ax^2 + bx$ will go through the origin. Therefore, the y-intercept is at 0.

b. The graph will have x-intercepts at 0 and $\frac{-b}{a}$.

c. The x-coordinate of the maximum (if $a < 0$) or minimum (if $a > 0$) point will be $\frac{1}{2}\left(\frac{-b}{a}\right)$ or $\frac{-b}{2a}$.

The y-coordinate can be found by substituting $\frac{-b}{2a}$ for x in the rule.

> **INSTRUCTIONAL NOTE** Possible summary discussion question for Problem 7:
> - What do you know about the shape and location of the graph for any function with rule $y = ax^2 + bx$?

8 **a.** **i.** None of the graphs opens downward, therefore, $y = -x^2 - 4x$ must be the function with the missing graph.

ii. $y = x^2 - 4x$ must be Graph II because it goes through the origin.

$y = x^2 - 4x + 6$ must be Graph I because it has a positive y-intercept less than 10.

$y = x^2 - 4x - 5$ must be the bottom graph because it has a negative y-intercept greater than -10.

Alternatively, students might choose to answer this problem by describing the graph of $y = x^2 - 4x + 6$ in terms of a vertical shift of the graph of $y = x^2 - 4x$ up 6 units and the graph of $y = x^2 - 4x - 5$ in terms of a vertical shift of the graph of $y = x^2 - 4x$ down 5 units.

> **DIFFERENTIATION**
>
> Problem 8 Part c can be omitted for students who struggle.

b. Without using graphing technology, sketch the pattern of graphs you would expect for the next set of quadratic functions. Explain your reasoning in making the sketch. Then check your ideas with the help of technology.

$$y = x^2 + 4x$$
$$y = x^2 + 4x - 6$$
$$y = x^2 + 4x + 5$$

c. How would a sketch showing graphs of the following functions be similar to and different from those in Parts a and b? Explain your reasoning. Then check your ideas with the help of technology.

$$y = -x^2 + 4x$$
$$y = -x^2 + 4x - 6$$
$$y = -x^2 + 4x + 5$$

d. How can properties of the special quadratic functions $y = ax^2$, $y = ax^2 + c$, and $y = ax^2 + bx$ help in reasoning about shape and location of graphs for functions in the form $y = ax^2 + bx + c$?

SUMMARIZE THE MATHEMATICS

In this investigation, you discovered some facts about the ways that patterns in tables and graphs of quadratic functions $y = ax^2 + bx + c$ ($a \neq 0$) are determined by the values of a, b, and c.

a What does the sign of a tell about the patterns of change and graphs of quadratic functions given by rules in the form $y = ax^2$? What does the absolute value of a tell you?

b How are the patterns of change and graphs of quadratic functions given by rules like $y = ax^2 + c$ related to those of the basic quadratic function $y = ax^2$? What does the value of c tell about the graph?

c How are the graphs of functions defined by rules like $y = ax^2 + bx$ ($b \neq 0$) different from those of functions with rules like $y = ax^2$? What does the value of b tell about the graph?

d How can you use what you know about quadratic functions with rules $y = ax^2$, $y = ax^2 + c$, and $y = ax^2 + bx$ to predict the shape and location of graphs for quadratic functions with rules $y = ax^2 + bx + c$ in which none of a, b, or c is 0?

Be prepared to share your ideas with the class.

b. Students' explanations may vary. The intent is that students start with $y = x^2 + 4x$ that is easily rewritten as $y = x(x + 4)$ to identify the x-intercepts. The other two graphs will be vertical shifts of this one. Alternatively, students may recognize that these three functions differ from the three in Part a only in that the linear term is now positive. The graphs of the three functions are shown below.

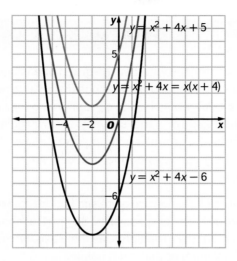

c. Students may recognize that the graphs of the functions in Part c are reflections of those in Part a across the x-axis. Not quite as apparent is that those in Part b are 180° rotations of those in Part c with the same y-intercepts.

d. The sign of a determines whether the graph will open up or down: since $y = ax^2 + bx = x(ax + b)$ has x-intercepts $(0, 0)$ and $\left(\frac{-b}{a}, 0\right)$ and $y = ax^2 + bx + c$ is a vertical shift up or down c units of $y = ax^2 + bx$, the points $(0, c)$ and $\left(\frac{-b}{a}, c\right)$ are on the graph of $y = ax^2 + bx + c$. The maximum or minimum point will be at $x - \frac{-b}{2a}$.

Summary

Have groups discuss the answers in preparation for class presentations. Have a different group present their thoughts on a problem followed by questions from other groups.

PROMOTING MATHEMATICAL DISCOURSE

TEACHING RESOURCES

UNIT 7   Quadratic Functions

SUMMARIZE THE MATHEMATICS

In this investigation, you discovered some facts about the ways that patterns in tables and graphs of quadratic functions $y = ax^2 + bx + c$ ($a \neq 0$) are determined by the values of a, b, and c.

a What does the sign of a tell about the patterns of change and graphs of quadratic functions given by rules in the form $y = ax^2$? What does the absolute value of a tell you?

b How are the patterns of change and graphs of quadratic functions given by rules like $y = ax^2 + c$ related to those of the basic quadratic function $y = ax^2$? What does the value of c tell about the graph?

c How are the graphs of functions defined by rules like $y = ax^2 + bx$ ($b \neq 0$) different from those of functions with rules like $y = ax^2$? What does the value of b tell about the graph?

d How can you use what you know about quadratic functions with rules $y = ax^2$, $y = ax^2 + c$, and $y = ax^2 + bx$ to predict the shape and location of graphs for quadratic functions with rules $y = ax^2 + bx + c$ in which none of a, b, or c is 0?

Be prepared to share your ideas with the class.

Lesson Master   use with page 478   Unit 7 | Quadratic Functions   **453**

Lesson Master 453

Ⓘ **GO DIGITAL**

MATH TOOLKIT

Describe or sketch the graph of $y = ax^2 + bx$ using specific numbers of your choice for a and b. Using a and b, complete the following for
$y = ax^2 + bx$.
x-intercepts: (__ , __), (__ , __)
y-intercept: (__ , __)
Minimum or maximum value of the function occurs when
$x =$ _____

UNIT 7

SUMMARIZE THE MATHEMATICS

a The sign determines whether the graph opens upward or downward. A graph with function that has a positive a value opens upward and a negative a value would lead to a graph that opens downward. The larger the absolute value of a, the "skinnier" the parabola will be. (Students may describe the graph as growing faster, as well.) When a is between -1 and 1, the graph will be wider. (Students may describe these graphs as more slowly.)

b The patterns of change are quite similar; the corresponding y values will each differ by c. The graphs will be symmetric about the y-axis. The value of c tells where the graph crosses the y-axis, or the y-intercept $(0, c)$ and also the maximum or minimum point.

c Graphs of functions in the form $y = ax^2 + bx$ will always go through $(0, 0)$, but $(0, 0)$ will be the minimum or maximum point only when $b = 0$. Graphs of the form $y = ax^2$ will always have a maximum or minimum point at the origin.

Graphs of functions in the form $y = ax^2$ will always be symmetric about the y-axis, while graphs of functions in the form $y = ax^2 + bx$ will be symmetric about the line $x = \frac{-b}{2a}$.

Graphs of functions in the form $y = ax^2$ have one x-intercept, while graphs of functions in the form $y = ax^2 + bx$ will have exactly two x-intercepts, at $(0, 0)$ and $\left(\frac{-b}{a}, 0\right)$.

The value of b in $y = ax^2 + bx$ helps determine where the maximum or minimum point of the graph will be located.

d Students are likely to quickly agree that the sign and the unsigned, or absolute value, of the a coefficient helps to determine the overall shape of the graph, as well as that the c value determines the y-intercept. They may refer to the $y = ax^2 + bx$ graph and how the $y = ax^2 + bx + c$ graph will be the same, only translated up or down c units.

Summarize the Mathematics, *page 478*

Teacher: In this investigation you examined how the patterns in tables and graphs of quadratic functions $y = ax^2 + bx + c$ are determined by the values of a, b, and c. To summarize this investigation, I would like your groups to talk about all parts of the Summarize the Mathematics and prepare a presentation on one part. Make sure you think about questions other students may have regarding your part of the STM and be prepared to answer them.

Teacher: *(The teacher assigns Parts a, b, and d to Groups 1, 2, and 3. She breaks up Part c, assigning the first question in Part c to Group 4 and the second question to Group 5. She gives students time to think about the summary questions and prepare an informal class presentation.)*

Teacher: Group 1. Are you ready to present?

Bret: We are ready. *(The group moves to the front of the room.)* I will be the moderator for our presentation. Our question was, "What does the sign of a tell about the patterns of change and graphs of quadratic functions given by rules in the form $y = ax^2$?"

Juliet: The sign of a tells you whether the parabola opens up or down. If a is positive the parabola opens upward and if a is negative then it opens downward.

Bret: We looked at both the tables and the graphs for x values between -10 and 10. We answered the question about graphs and table patterns separately. Okay, Marcus, what does that mean in terms of the pattern in a graph?

Marcus: If the parabola opens up then the pattern in the graph is decreasing to a minimum value and then increasing. If it opens down, then the pattern is just the opposite. First the function increases then it decreases and there is a maximum value instead of a minimum value.

Bret: Kim, what does that mean in terms of the pattern in a table?

Kim: You would see the same pattern in the table. If a is positive you would see values decreasing to zero and then increasing. So, like Marcus said, if a is positive then you have a minimum value of zero. If a is negative then the function values would increase to zero then decrease, so in this case you have a maximum value of zero.

Bret: *(Back to Juliet.)* What does the absolute value of a tell you?

Juliet: The absolute value of a tells you how "skinny" the graph will be. The bigger the value of a the "skinnier" the graph.

Bret: Any questions?

Destin: How can you see "skinnier" in a table?

Bret: We didn't discuss that but we can use the overhead calculator to look at it now. *(Bret's group accesses the overhead calculator.)* Let's look at $y = 2x^2$ and $y = 5x^2$. Let me pose the question to the class. "What do you notice in the patterns in the table?"

Karly: It looks like when a is bigger there are bigger gaps between the numbers. Look at the values between 0 and 5. Y_1 (the function $y = 2x^2$) goes from 0 to 50 but Y_2 ($y = 5x^2$) goes from 0 to 125. That is a much bigger jump.

Tim: It looks like the bigger a is, the larger the gap between y values in the table.

Bret: Any other questions for us? *(None are offered.)*

Destin: But how do the bigger gaps relate to a skinnier graph? Shouldn't the graph be "fatter"?

Bret: Oh, I see. You must be thinking that bigger gaps means a wider graph. The table values are the y values of the function. So bigger gaps in y values mean that its graph is taller than the one with smaller gaps in the y values. Does that make sense?

Rhonda: Sure, a skinnier graph will have larger y values in the table. It will go up faster than the other function both on the graph and in the table.

Teacher: Thank you, Group 1. Group 2. *(Group 1 returns to their seats and Group 2 comes up to the front.)*

Silvia: We split our roles up a little differently than Group 1. My part is to talk about how the graphs of functions with rules like $y = ax^2 + c$ relate to those of the basic quadratic function $y = ax^2$. The c value just tells how much the basic function shifts up or down. c is just the vertical shift; if c is positive the graph shifts up and if c is negative, the graph shifts down.

Katie: I drew examples on a transparency. You can see that we compared $y = 2x^2$ to $y = 2x^2 + 3$. So there is just a vertical shift up 3. The parabola still opens up and still has a minimum value but this time instead of the minimum at (0, 0) it is at (0, 3). You can see if I just slide the $y = 2x^2$ up 3 it will lay right on top of $y = 2x^2 + 3$. *(Katie has used two transparencies in order to physically demonstrate the vertical shift.)* Then before Mary Anne talks about our other example, Jon has to talk about his part.

Jon: We looked at the patterns in tables, too. *(Jon uses the overhead calculator to show the values for $y = 2x^2$ to $y = 2x^2 + 3$.)* We noticed that the y values for $y = 2x^2 + 3$ were just 3 more than each of the y values for $y = 2x^2$.

PROMOTING MATHEMATICAL DISCOURSE

Mary Anne: Okay. Now look at our other example. This time we used $y = 2x^2$ to $y = 2x^2 - 4$. In the graph you can see that for c equal to -4, the graph just moves down 4. *(Like Katie, Mary Anne demonstrates the shift by physically sliding one graph to lie on top of the other.)*

Jon: Then in the tables we see that all the y values are just 4 less than the other y values.

Silvia: To summarize, the value of c in $y = ax^2 + c$ determines the vertical shift of the more basic function $y = ax^2$.

Jon: Any questions? *(No questions are asked.)*

Teacher: I have one. What name do we give to that c value on the graph, in the cases that you examined?

Mary Anne: Do you mean the y-intercept?

Jon: Yeah, it's the y-intercept.

Teacher: Can you say anything about the symmetry of both $y = ax^2$ and $y = ax^2 + c$?

Katie: They both have the y-axis as the axis of symmetry. It makes sense that they would since one is just a vertical shift of the other. You are not shifting the graphs sideways.

Teacher: Thank you, Group 2. Group 3?

Maverick: We had to consider how the functions described by rules like $y = ax^2 + bx$, where a and b cannot be equal to zero, are different from those described by rules like $y = ax^2 + c$. We found that $y = ax^2 + bx$ is shifted both horizontally and vertically from $y = ax^2 + c$.

Dan: We said that the axis of symmetry is different since the graphs were shifted horizontally. So we thought about where the x-intercepts would be located.

Barrett: I will talk about the intercepts first then Dan will talk more about the minimum and maximum points. So, like Dan said, we looked at the x-intercepts first. $(0, 0)$ will always be one of the x-intercepts in $y = ax^2 + bx$ and actually the y-intercept, too; the other intercept will be at $\left(\frac{-b}{a}, 0\right)$. You can see that better if you factor $y = ax^2 + bx$ into $y = x(ax + b)$ like we did in Problem 7 of the investigation. In the case of $y = ax^2 + c$, $(0, 0)$ is not the y-intercept unless c is 0. The y-intercept is always $(0, c)$.

Dan: All right, back to the axis of symmetry. Since we found that the x-intercepts for $y = ax^2 + bx$ are at $\left(\frac{-b}{a}, 0\right)$. and $(0, 0)$ we knew that the axis of symmetry would be in the middle of those two intercepts. So, the axis of symmetry is where x is equal to $\frac{-b}{2a}$.

Shantel: I have to talk about the x-intercepts of the two different kinds of functions. First think about the equation $y = ax^2 + c$. Group 2, talked about how c just shifts the basic parabola up or down. So, let's look at that with two transparencies. I will just shift

my parabola up and down on top of the graph showing the x- and y-axes. Can you tell me about the x-intercepts? *(Shantel moves the parabolic graph up and down on the overhead copy of the coordinate grid.)* Jasmin, what can you say about the x-intercepts?

Jasmin: It looks like you can have no intercepts, one intercept, or two intercepts.

Shantel: Does anyone disagree with Jasmin? *(No disagreement is offered.)*

Teacher: I wonder when which one occurs and why.

Shantel: Do you want me to talk about that now?

Teacher: If you would like to, or you can offer it as a question to the class, if you prefer.

Shantel: I think we can describe what happens by using these transparencies. If the parabola opens up and c is positive then the graph will not cross the x-axis. If c is 0 then the parabola touches the axis at $(0, 0)$. And if c is negative then the minimum of the parabola will be below the x-axis so the graph will cross the axis twice. Does that make sense to everyone?

Hollie: I think you also have to consider the cases when the parabola opens down, when a is negative. Can I say what would happen then?

Shantel: Sure.

Hollie: Okay, turn your parabola upside down then slide it up and down the y-axis. *(Shantel moves the parabola as Hollie suggests.)* Now, we can see that if c is positive, this time there are two intercepts, and if c is 0, one intercept and, finally, if c is negative, no intercepts.

Shantel: Thanks, Hollie. Are there any other questions for our group? *(None are offered.)*

Teacher: Thank you, Group 3. You are all doing a nice job on these summaries. Group 4, are you ready? *(Group 4 comes up to the front of the classroom.)*

Jordan: We had to discuss the question, "What do the values of a, b, and c tell about the graphs?"

Yvonne: We made a chart on big paper to share. *(Yvonne tapes the chart on the front board.)* Okay, a tells whether the graph of the parabola opens up or down; up when a is positive and down when a is negative.

Rachelle: And a also determines how "skinny" the graph will be. The bigger the absolute value of a the "skinnier" the graph.

John: The value of b in $y = ax^2 + bx$ determines where the minimum or maximum point will be found on the graph; it will be located on the line that goes through the x-axis at $\frac{-b}{2a}$.

Jordan: The value of c in $y = ax^2 + c$ tells that the minimum or maximum point is located on the graph at $(0, c)$ and so is the y-intercept.

Jordan: Any question on our chart? (*No questions are asked.*)

Teacher: Thank you, Group 4. Group 5.

Sally: We had to think about how we can use the quadratic functions with rules $y = ax^2$, $y = ax^2 + c$, and $y = ax^2 + bx$ to predict the shape and location of graphs for quadratic functions with rules $y = ax^2 + bx + c$ where none of a, b, or c is 0.

Carmen: In all the cases, a will tell the shape and direction of the graph, that is, up or down, and "skinny" or "fat."

Tommy: We also agreed that c will be the y-intercept similar to how it was in $y = ax^2 + c$ but in this case $(0, c)$ will not be the minimum or maximum point of the graph.

Michael: You can think of the graph of $y = ax^2 + bx + c$ as a vertical shift of the graph of $y = ax^2 + bx$. Just like when we shifted $y = ax^2$, c units up or down to get the graph of $y = ax^2 + c$.

Sally: Any questions? (*No questions are offered.*)

Teacher: Nice work. There was a lot to summarize in this investigation. It will be important to add what we have talked about today to your Math Toolkit.

✅ **CHECK YOUR UNDERSTANDING**

Use what you know about the relationship between rules and graphs for quadratic functions to match the functions with their graphs. Graphs were all produced with the same windows.

Rule I $y = x^2 + 2$ **Rule II** $y = x^2 - 5x + 2$

Rule III $y = -x^2 + 2$ **Rule IV** $y = -0.5x^2 + 2$

Rule V $y = x^2 + 5x + 2$

A

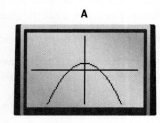

B

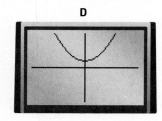

C

D

E

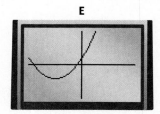

✓ CHECK YOUR UNDERSTANDING

Rule I: Graph D
Rule II: Graph C
Rule III: Graph A
Rule IV: Graph B
Rule V: Graph E

ON YOUR OWN

APPLICATIONS

1 A first-time diver was a bit nervous about his first dive at a swimming pool. To ease his worries about hitting the water after a fall of 15 feet, he decided to push a tennis ball off the edge of the platform to see the effect of landing in the water.

  a. What rule shows how the ball's height above the water h is related to elapsed time in the dive t?

  b. Estimate the time it will take the ball to hit the water.

2 Katie, a goalie for Riverside High School's soccer team, needs to get the ball downfield to her teammates on the offensive end of the field. She punts the ball from a point 2 feet above the ground with an initial upward velocity of 40 feet per second.

  a. Write a function rule that relates the ball's height above the field h to its time in the air t.

  b. Use this function rule to estimate the time when the ball will hit the ground.

  c. Suppose Katie were to kick the ball right off the ground with the same initial upward velocity. Do you think the ball would be in the air the same amount of time, for more time, or for less time? Check your thinking.

3 The opening of the cannon pictured at the left is 16 feet above the ground. The daredevil, who is shot out of the cannon, reaches a maximum height of 55 feet after about 1.56 seconds and hits a net that is 9.5 feet off the ground after 3.25 seconds. Use this information to answer the following questions.

  a. Write a rule that relates the daredevil's height above the ground h at a time t seconds after the cannon is fired.

  b. At what upward velocity is the daredevil shot from the cannon?

  c. If, for some unfortunate reason, the net slipped to the ground at the firing of the cannon, when would the daredevil hit the ground?

4 When a punkin' chunker launches a pumpkin, the goal is long distance, not height. Suppose the relationship between horizontal distance d (in feet) and time t (in seconds) is given by the function rule $d = 70t$, when the height is given by $h = 20 + 50t - 16t^2$.

  a. How long will the pumpkin be in the air?

  b. How far will the pumpkin travel from the chunker by the time it hits the ground?

  c. When will the pumpkin reach its maximum height, and what will that height be?

  d. How far from the chunker will the pumpkin be (horizontally) when it reaches its maximum height?

Mario Tama/Getty Images News/Getty Images

INSTRUCTIONAL NOTE In Applications Tasks 1–6, students are expected to use tables, graphs, or substitution to determine answers. Encourage them to use a variety of methods and not always resort to their favorite methods. You may wish to discuss advantages of various methods.

1 **a.** $h = -16t^2 + 15$

b. Solve the equation $0 = -16t^2 + 15$. The ball would hit the water after about 0.97 seconds.

2 **a.** $h = -16t^2 + 40t + 2$

b. Solve $0 = -16t^2 + 40t + 2$. The ball would hit the ground approximately 2.55 seconds after it is kicked.

c. Student initial conjectures may vary. If she kicked the ball right off of the ground (modeled by $h = -16t^2 + 40t$), it would hit the ground after 2.5 seconds, which is 0.05 fewer seconds in the air. (The graphs of the two functions give insight into this situation since the ball kicked from the ground does not fly as high as the other kicked ball.)

3 **a.** $h = 16 + 50t - 16t^2$
Students could use a variety of methods including quadratic regression to determine that $v_0 = 50$. Other methods involve substituting $(1.56, 55)$ or $(3.25, 9.5)$ into $h = 16 + v_0 t - 16t^2$ and solving for v_0.

b. The initial upward velocity was 50 feet per second.

c. Solving $0 = -16t^2 + 50t + 16$ gives $t \approx 3.42$ seconds as the time that the daredevil hits the ground.

4 **a.** Solve $20 + 50t - 16t^2 = 0$. The pumpkin will be in the air for approximately 3.48 seconds.

b. $70(3.48) = 243.6$. The pumpkin will travel nearly 244 feet.

c. The pumpkin will reach its maximum height of about 59 feet about 1.57 seconds after it is chunked.

d. $70(1.57) = 109.9$. The pumpkin will be nearly 110 feet (horizontally) from the chunker when it reaches its maximum height.

5 Imagine you are in charge of constructing a two-tower suspension bridge over the Potlatch River. You have planned that the curve of the main suspension cables can be modeled by the function $y = 0.004x^2 - x + 80$ where y represents height of the cable above the bridge surface and x represents distance along the bridge surface from one tower toward the other. The values of x and y are measured in feet.

a. What is the approximate height (from the bridge surface) of each tower from which the cable is suspended?

b. What is the shortest distance from the cable to the bridge surface and where does it occur?

c. At which points is the suspension cable at least 50 feet above the bridge surface? Write an inequality that represents this question and express the solution as an inequality.

6 One formula used by highway safety engineers relates minimum stopping distance d in feet to vehicle speed s in miles per hour with the rule $d = 0.05s^2 + 1.1s$.

a. Create a table of sample (*speed, stopping distance*) values for a reasonable range of speeds. Plot the sample (*speed, stopping distance*) values on a coordinate graph. Then describe how stopping distance changes as speed increases.

b. Use the stopping distance function to answer the following questions.

   i. What is the approximate stopping distance for a car traveling 60 miles per hour?

   ii. If a car stopped in 120 feet, what is the fastest it could have been traveling when the driver first noticed the need to stop?

c. Estimate solutions for the following quadratic equations and explain what each solution tells about stopping distance and speed.

   i. $180 = 0.05s^2 + 1.1s$

   ii. $95 = 0.05s^2 + 1.1s$

Lesson 1 | Quadratic Patterns **481**

5 **a.** The towers are each approximately 80 feet above the bridge surface.

   b. The shortest distance of 17.5 feet occurs 125 feet from each of the towers.

   c. The inequality is $0.004x^2 - x + 80 \geq 50$. The cable is at least 50 feet above the bridge on two intervals. Note that the x values represent the distance from the "left" tower. One such interval is $0 \leq x \leq 34.86$ and the other is $215.14 \leq x \leq 250$.

6 **a.** Students may argue as to what is a reasonable range for speeds, but one possible table of values is given below. As speed increases, it appears as if stopping distance increases at an increasing rate.

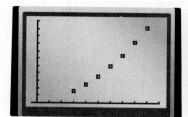 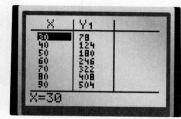 

   b.   **i.** The stopping distance for a car traveling 60 miles per hour would be about 246 feet.

      ii. The fastest the car could have been traveling is about 39.2 miles per hour.

   c.   **i.** $s = 50$. This tells us that at a speed of 50 miles per hour, a car will travel 180 feet before stopping.

      ii. $s \approx 34$. This solution means that 95 feet are needed to stop when traveling 34 miles per hour.

ON YOUR OWN

7 Use what you know about the connection between rules and graphs for quadratic functions to match the given functions with their graphs that appear below. Each graph is shown in the standard viewing window ($-10 \leq x \leq 10$ and $-10 \leq y \leq 10$).

Rule I $y = x^2 - 4$ **Rule II** $y = 2x^2 + 4$

Rule III $y = -x^2 + 2x + 4$ **Rule IV** $y = -0.5x^2 + 4$

A

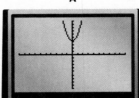

B

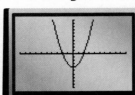

C

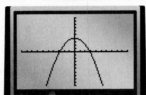

D

8 In Applications Tasks 1, 2, 5, and 6, you worked with several different quadratic functions. The function rules are restated in Parts a–d below. For each function, explain what you can learn about the shape and location of its graph by looking at the coefficients and constant term in the rule.

a. $h = 15 - 16t^2$ **b.** $h = 2 + 40t - 16t^2$

c. $y = 0.004x^2 - x + 80$ **d.** $d = 0.05s^2 + 1.1s$

CONNECTIONS

9 The following experiment can be used to measure a person's *reaction time*, the amount of time it takes a person to react to something he or she sees.

Hold a ruler at the end that reads 12 inches and let it hang down. Have the subject hold his or her thumb and forefinger opposite the 0-inch mark without touching the ruler. Tell your subject that you will drop the ruler within the next 10 seconds and that he or she is supposed to grasp the ruler as quickly as possible after it is dropped.

The spot on the ruler where it is caught indicates the distance that the ruler dropped.

Jim Laser

UNIT 7

7 Rule I: Graph B
   Rule II: Graph A
   Rule III: Graph D
   Rule IV: Graph C

8 **a.** $a = -16$ indicates that the graph will open downward and will be "skinnier" than $y = x^2$. $b = 0$ indicates that the graph will be symmetric about the y-axis. The maximum value of the function occurs at the y-intercept, which is $(0, 15)$ since $c = 15$.

   b. $a = -16$ indicates that the graph will open downward and will be "skinnier" than $y = x^2$. $c = 2$ indicates that the y-intercept is $(0, 2)$. $b = 40$, combined with $a = -16$, indicates that the x-coordinate of the maximum point is 1.25, and the graph is symmetric about the line $x = 1.25$.

   c. $a = 0.004$ indicates that the graph will open upward and will be "wider" than $y = x^2$. $c = 80$ indicates that the y-intercept is $(0, 80)$. $b = -1$, combined with $a = 0.004$, indicates that the x-coordinate of the minimum point is 125, and the graph is symmetric about the line $x = 125$.

   d. $a = 0.05$ indicates that the graph will open upward and will be "wider" than $y = x^2$. $c = 0$ indicates that the y-intercept is $(0, 0)$. $b = 1.1$, combined with $a = 0.05$, indicates that the x-intercepts are $(0, 0)$ and $(-22, 0)$. The x-coordinate of the minimum point is -11, and the graph is symmetric about the line $x = -11$.

a. What function describes the distance d in feet that the ruler has fallen after t seconds?

b. Use what you know about the relationship between feet and inches and your function from Part a to estimate the reaction time of a person who grasps the ruler at the 4-inch mark.

c. Conduct this experiment several times and estimate the reaction times of your subjects.

10 Consider some other familiar measurement formulas.

a. Match the formulas A–D to the measurement calculations they express:

   I   volume of a cube   **A** $y = s^2$

   II   surface area of a cube   **B** $y = s^3$

   III area of a square   **C** $y = 4s$

   IV   perimeter of a square   **D** $y = 6s^2$

b. Which of the formulas from Part a are those of quadratic functions?

11 The formula $A = \pi r^2$ shows how to calculate the area of a circle from its radius. You can also think about this formula as a quadratic function.

a. With respect to the general form of a quadratic function $y = ax^2 + bx + c$, what are the a, b, and c values for the area-of-a-circle function?

b. For $r > 0$, how does the shape of the graph $A = \pi r^2$ compare to that of $A = r^2$?

c. If the radius of a circle is 6 cm, what is its area?

d. If the area of a circle is about 154 cm^2, what is the approximate radius of the circle?

12 Sketch graphs of the functions $y = 2x$, $y = x^2$, and $y = 2^x$ for $0 \leq x \leq 5$.

a. In what ways are the graphs similar to each other?

b. In what ways do the graphs differ from each other?

c. The values of y for the three functions when x is between 0 and 1 show that $x^2 < 2x < 2^x$. Compare the values of y for the three graphs for the intervals for x below.

   i. between 1 and 2

   ii. between 2 and 3

   iii. between 3 and 4

   iv. greater than 4

9 **a.** $d = 16t^2$

b. Solving the equation $\frac{4}{12} = 16t^2$ would estimate the reaction time. The reaction time is approximately 0.14 seconds.

c. Student results will vary. They will likely find the reaction times will decrease as more trials are completed.

10 **a.** I—B   II—D   III—A   IV—C

b. $y = s^2$ and $y = 6s^2$ are quadratic.

11 **a.** $a = \pi, b = 0, c = 0$

b. Both of the graphs will be half of a parabola in the first quadrant beginning just after $(0, 0)$. The graph of the area-of-a-circle function will increase at a faster rate than the graph of $y = r^2$. This is a result of the a coefficient, π, being larger than 1.

c. To find the area, one could substitute 6 for the r in the formula. $A = 36\pi$, or approximately 113.1 cm^2.

d. The radius is approximately 7.
$\pi r^2 \approx 154$
$r^2 \approx 49$
$r \approx \pm 7$

12 The three graphs are shown to the right.

a. All three graphs have non-negative y values and are increasing on this interval. Both $y = x^2$ and $y = 2^x$ are increasing at an increasing rate. Both $y = 2x$ and $y = x^2$ have y-intercepts at the origin.

b. $y = 2x$ is increasing at a constant rate; while $y = x^2$ and $y = 2^x$ are increasing at an increasing rate. The y-intercept of $y = 2^x$ is $(0, 1)$; while $y = 2x$ and $y = x^2$ have y-intercepts at the origin.

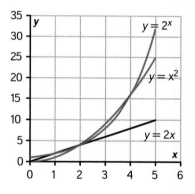

c. **i.** $x^2 < 2^x < 2x$ when $1 < x < 2$. (When $x = 2$, $x^2 = 2^x = 2x = 4$.)

ii. $2x < 2^x < x^2$ when $2 < x < 3$.

iii. $2x < 2^x < x^2$ when $3 < x < 4$. (When $x = 4$, $x^2 = 2^x = 16$.)

iv. $2x < x^2 < 2^x$ when $x > 4$.

ON YOUR OWN

13 Suppose that a pumpkin is dropped from an airplane flying about 5,280 feet above the ground (one mile up in the air). The function $h = 5,280 - 16t^2$ can be used to predict the height of that pumpkin at a point t seconds after it is dropped. But this mathematical model ignores the effects of air resistance.

a. How would you expect a height function that does account for air resistance to be different from the function $h = 5,280 - 16t^2$ that ignores those effects?

b. The speed of the falling pumpkin at a time t seconds after it is dropped can be predicted by the function $s_1 = 32t$, if you ignore air resistance. If air resistance is considered, the function $s_2 = 120(1 - 0.74^t)$ will better represent the relationship between speed and time.

   i. Make tables of (*time, speed*) values for each function s_1 and s_2 with values of t from 0 to 10 seconds.

   ii. Sketch graphs showing the patterns of change in speed implied by the two functions.

   iii. Describe similarities and differences in patterns of change predicted by the two (*time, speed*) functions.

c. Air resistance on the falling pumpkin causes the speed of descent to approach a limit called *terminal velocity*. Explore the pattern of (*time, speed*) values for the function $s_2 = 120(1 - 0.74^t)$ for larger and larger values of t to see if you can discover the terminal velocity implied by that speed function.

14 Graphs of quadratic functions are curves called parabolas. Parabolas and other curves can also be viewed as cross sections of a cone—called **conic sections**.

a. Describe how you could position a plane intersecting a cone so that the cross section is a parabola.

b. How could you position a plane intersecting a cone so that the cross section is a circle?

c. What other curve(s) are formed by a plane intersecting a cone? Illustrate your answer.

13 a. One would expect a height function that accounts for the effects of air resistance to decrease less steeply over time.

b. i.

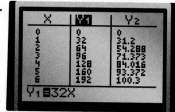 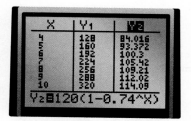

ii.

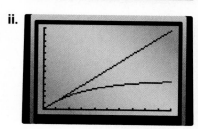 

iii. Both functions are increasing; however, s_1 is increasing at a constant rate, while s_2 is increasing at a decreasing rate.

c. The function $s_2 = 120(1 - 0.74^t)$ very quickly approaches the value 120, suggesting a terminal speed of 120 feet per second.

14 a. Position the plane so that it passes through the cone parallel to one edge of the cone.

b. Position the plane so that it passes through the cone parallel to the base of the cone.

c. An ellipse can be formed by passing the plane through the cone so that it is not parallel to the base and does not intersect the base.

(Some students may suggest that a point, a V-shaped curve, or a line segment might be generated. These are "degenerate" cases of conic sections.)

REFLECTIONS

15 Suppose that a skateboard rider travels from the top of one side to the top of the other side on a half-pipe ramp.

Which of the following graphs is the best model for the relationship between the rider's speed and distance traveled? Explain your choice.

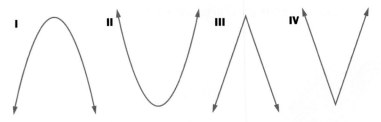

16 Calculators and computer graphing software help in quickly producing tables and graphs of quadratic functions.

a. In what ways might such tool-produced graphs give incomplete or misleading information about a quadratic or other type of function?

b. How does reasoning about equivalent expressions for quadratic functions give information that a tool-produced graph or table does not?

17 A student first studying quadratic functions had the idea that in the rule $y = ax^2 + bx + c$, the value of b should tell the slope of the graph and c should tell the y-intercept. Do you agree? How could you use a graph of the function $y = x^2 + 2x + 3$ and other reasoning to support or dispute the student's idea?

18 All linear functions can be described by rules in the form $y = a + bx$. All exponential functions can be described by rules in the form $y = a(b^x)$. All quadratic functions can be described by rules in the form $y = ax^2 + bx + c$. The letters a, b, and c take on specific values in each of the three function forms. What information about each type of function can be learned from the values taken on by the letters a, b, and c?

15 Graph I best represents the rider's speed as a function of distance traveled left to right. As the rider descends the ramp, his or her speed will increase, then as the rider goes up the other side of the ramp, his or her speed will decrease. If the ramp was flat, then the rates of increase then decrease in speed would be constant, but the ramp becomes less steep, then more steep from top to bottom to top; therefore, the speed will increase at a decreasing rate, then decrease at an increasing rate.

> CCSS **MATHEMATICAL PRACTICE**
> These tasks are designed to have students think about modeling with mathematics, use appropriate tools strategically, and look for and make sense of structure.

16 **a.** Calculator or computer tables show only a small sample of values for the function; graphs show more values, but still only a limited part of the domain and range. Graphs can also be misleading when one chooses the scales for the axes in unfortunate ways (and you might not see the graph at all if you do not set the window right).

b. Formal methods can express a function rule in forms that immediately reveal information like when to expect a maximum or minimum value, the y-intercept, and (when factored) the zeroes. They also show exact solutions (not the approximations inherent in calculator table or graph methods), and can even generate formulas for solution of any quadratic equation regardless of coefficients (e.g., the quadratic formula).

17 While b tells the slope of the graph of the function $y = a + bx$, b does not tell the slope of the graph of the function $y = ax^2 + bx + c$. One might use the graph of $y = x^2 + 2x + 3$ to show that the "slope" of the graph is changing. The rate of change between $(-2, 3)$ and $(-1, 2)$ is -1; between $(-1, 2)$ and $(0, 3)$ it is 1; and between $(0, 3)$ and $(1, 6)$ it is 3.

18 In the linear rule $y = a + bx$, the value of b indicates whether the graph is increasing (positive b) or decreasing (negative b), and also the constant rate of increase or decrease. The value of a indicates the y-intercept of the graph but does not affect the pattern of change.

In the exponential rule $y = a(b^x)$, the value of b indicates whether the graph is increasing ($b > 1$) or decreasing ($0 < b < 1$), and also the multiplicative rate of increase or decrease. The value of a indicates the y-intercept of the graph but does not affect the pattern of change.

In the quadratic rule $y = ax^2 + bx + c$, the value of a indicates whether the graph opens upward (positive a) or opens downward (negative a). Also, the larger the absolute value of a, the greater the rate of change in the rate of increase or decrease. The value of c indicates the y-coordinate of the y-intercept of the graph. The value of b shifts the graph horizontally but does not affect the overall pattern of change. The maximum or minimum point will have an x-coordinate of $\frac{-b}{2a}$, and the line $x = \frac{-b}{2a}$ is the axis of symmetry.

ON YOUR OWN

EXTENSIONS

19 For anything that moves, *average speed* can be calculated by dividing the total distance traveled by the total time taken to travel that distance.

ATHENS 2004

For example, a diver who falls from a 35-foot platform in about 1.5 seconds has an average speed of $\frac{35}{1.5}$, or about 23.3 feet per second. That diver will not be falling at that average speed throughout the dive.

a. If a diver falls from 35 feet to approximately 31 feet in the first 0.5 seconds of a dive, what estimate of speed would seem reasonable for the diver midway through that time interval—that is, how fast might the diver be moving at 0.25 seconds?

b. The relation between height above the water and the diver's time in flight can be described by the function $h = 35 - 16t^2$, if time is measured in seconds and distance in feet. Use that function rule to make a table of (*time, height*) data and then estimate the diver's speed at 6 points using your data. Make a table and a graph of the (*time, speed*) estimates.

c. What do the patterns in (*time, speed*) data and the graph tell you about the diver's speed on the way to the water?

d. About how fast is the diver traveling when he hits the water?

e. Write a rule for speed *s* as a function of time *t* that seems to fit the data in your table and graph. Use your calculator or computer software to check the function against the data in Part b.

20 When a pumpkin is shot from an air cannon chunker, its motion has two components—vertical and horizontal. Suppose that a pumpkin is shot at an angle of 40° with initial velocity of 150 feet per second and initial height 30 feet. The vertical component of its velocity will be about 96 feet per second; the horizontal component of its velocity will be about 115 feet per second.

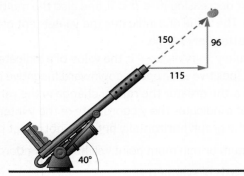

150   96

115

40°

Jamie Squire/Getty Images Sport/Getty Images

19 **a.** Since the diver fell 4 feet in 0.5 seconds, a reasonable estimate of speed would be 8 feet per second (4 ft/0.5 sec).

b. The speeds in the following table are average speeds in the time interval from $t - 0.1$ to $t + 0.1$. There are several efficient ways to get these results using a graphing calculator or computer software, with Y_1 defined to be $35 - 16X^2$.

A table can be created calculating $\dfrac{Y_1(X - 0.1) - Y_1(X + 0.1)}{0.2}$, using x values beginning at 0.1 and changing in steps of 0.2.

Time (in sec)	0.1	0.3	0.5	0.7	0.9	1.1	1.3
Speed (in ft/sec)	3.2	9.6	16	22.4	28.8	35.2	41.6

c. The diver's speed increases as he approaches the water. The speed is increasing at a constant rate of 6.4 feet per second for every 0.2 seconds (or, equivalently, 32 feet per second for every 1 second).

d. He is traveling approximately 48 ft/sec when he hits the water after about 1.5 seconds.

e. $s = 32t$

a. What function gives the height h of the pumpkin shot at any time t seconds after it leaves the chunker?

b. What function gives the horizontal distance d traveled by the pumpkin at any time t seconds after it leaves the chunker?

c. Use the functions in Parts a and b to find the horizontal distance traveled by the pumpkin by the time it hits the ground.

d. Rewrite the relation between time and distance in Part b to give time as a function of distance.

e. Combine the rule giving time as a function of horizontal distance and the rule giving height as a function of time to write a function rule giving height as a function of horizontal distance. (*Hint:* Replace each occurrence of t by an equivalent expression involving d.)

f. Use the function developed in Part e to estimate the distance traveled by the pumpkin when it hits the ground. Then compare the result obtained in this way to your answer to Part c.

21 You may have heard of *terminal velocity* in connection with skydiving. Scientific principles predict that a function like $h_2 = 5{,}680 - 120t - 400(0.74^t)$ will predict the height of a pumpkin (in feet) at any time t seconds after it is dropped from an airplane flying at an altitude of one mile. This function (in contrast to the more familiar $h_1 = 5{,}280 - 16t^2$) accounts for the slowing effect of air resistance on the falling pumpkin.

a. Use your calculator to produce a table showing predictions for height of the pumpkin using the functions h_1 and h_2 for times from 0 to 30 seconds. Record the data for times $t = 0, 5, 10, 15, 20, 25,$ and 30 seconds. Describe the patterns of change in height over time that are shown in the (*time, height*) values of the two functions.

b. Extend your table of (*time, height*) values to a point that gives estimates of the time it takes for the pumpkin to hit the ground.

c. Study the patterns of change in height for the last 10 seconds before the pumpkin hits the ground. Explain how the pattern of change in height for function h_2 illustrates the notion of terminal velocity that you explored in Connections Task 13 Part c.

22 Consider the two functions $y = 2^x$ and $y = x^2$.

a. How are the graphs of these two functions alike and how are they different?

b. How many solutions do you expect for the equation $2^x = x^2$? Explain your reasoning.

c. Estimate the solution(s) of the equation $2^x = x^2$ as accurately as possible. Explain or show how you estimated the solution(s).

23 Compare the quadratic function $y = x^2$ and the *absolute value function,* $y = |x|$.

a. Sketch graphs of these two functions and describe ways that they are similar and ways that they are different.

20 **a.** $h = 30 + 96t - 16t^2$

b. $d = 115t$

c. Solving $30 + 96t - 16t^2 = 0$, the pumpkin hits the ground after approximately 6.30 seconds. Evaluating $d = 115(6.30)$, the pumpkin has traveled 724.5 feet.

d. $t = \dfrac{d}{115}$

e. $h = 30 + 96\left(\dfrac{d}{115}\right) - 16\left(\dfrac{d}{115}\right)^2$

f. Solving $30 + 96\left(\dfrac{d}{115}\right) - 16\left(\dfrac{d}{115}\right)^2 = 0$, the pumpkin will have traveled about 724.2 feet when it hits the ground.

21 **a.**

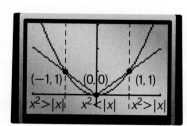

$h_1 = 5{,}280 - 16t^2$ decreases at an increasing rate.
$h_2 = 5{,}680 - 120t - 400(0.74)^t$ decreases at a less and less increasing rate that becomes constant.

b. $h_1 = 5{,}280 - 16t^2$ gives an estimate of 18.17 seconds.
$h_2 = 5{,}680 - 120t - 400(0.74)^t$ gives an estimate of 47.33 seconds.

c. During the last 10 seconds before the pumpkin hits the ground, its height is decreasing at a constant rate of 120 feet per second, the terminal velocity determined in Connections Task 13.

22 **a.** Possible differences: $y = 2^x$ is always increasing and is always above the x-axis; $y = x^2$ is symmetric across the y-axis and touches the x-axis at the origin. Possible similarities: both functions have nonconstant rates of change; both of the functions' y values are non-negative.

b. Most students will expect two solutions. A quick sketch of the two functions suggests the graphs will intersect once to the left of the y-axis and once to the right. However, at the first point of intersection to the right of the y-axis, $y = 2^x$ is increasing more slowly than $y = x^2$, and students should reason that $y = 2^x$ will eventually increase faster than $y = x^2$, and they will intersect again, giving three solutions.

c. Students may use tables, zoom and trace, or intersect features of a graphing calculator. The three solutions are $x = 2$, $x = 4$, and $x \approx -0.77$.

23 **a.** The graphs are similar because, from left to right, they both decrease to $(0, 0)$ and then increase. They are both symmetric about the y-axis and have non-negative y values.

The graphs are different because the rate of decrease and increase for $y = |x|$ is constant, whereas the rate for $y = x^2$ decreases at a decreasing rate and then increases at an increasing rate.

b. Find solutions for $x^2 = |x|$ by reasoning with the symbols themselves and then label the graph points representing the solutions with their coordinates.

c. Find the value(s) of x for which $x^2 > |x|$ and for which $x^2 < |x|$. Then indicate points on the graph representing the coordinates of those solutions.

24 Consider the quadratic functions defined by these rules:

Rule I $y = 3x^2 - 5x + 9$ **Rule II** $y = 1.5x^2 - 5x + 9$

Rule III $y = 3x^2 + 4x - 23$ **Rule IV** $y = x^2 - 5x - 23$

a. Examine graphs and/or tables of the functions to determine which of the functions have values that are relatively close to each other for large values of x.

b. Based on your findings in Part a, which coefficient (a or b) in the quadratic standard form determines **right end behavior**—the values of y for large positive values of x?

c. Can the same be said for **left end behavior** (which you may have guessed is for negative values of x with large absolute values)?

25 A computer spreadsheet can be a useful tool for exploring the effect of each coefficient and the constant term on the pattern of change of a quadratic function with rule $y = ax^2 + bx + c$. For example, the table below was produced with a spreadsheet to study $y = 2x^2 - 5x + 7$.

Quadratic Patterns.xlsx

	A	B	C	D	E	F	G
1	x	ax^2	bx	c	$ax^2 + bx + c$	$a =$	2
2	−5	50	25	7	82	$b =$	−5
3	−4	32	20	7	59	$c =$	7
4	−3	18	15	7	40		
5	−2	8	10	7	25		
6	−1	2	5	7	14		
7	0	0	0	7	7		
8	1	2	−5	7	4		
9	2	8	−10	7	5		
10	3	18	−15	7	10		
11	4	32	−20	7	19		
12	5	50	−25	7	32		

a. What numerical and formula entries and other spreadsheet techniques are needed to produce the x values in cells **A2–A12**?

b. What spreadsheet formulas can be used to produce entries in cells **B2**, **C2**, **D2**, and **E2**?

c. What formulas will appear in cells **B3**, **C3**, **D3**, and **E3**?

d. How could the spreadsheet be modified to study the function $y = x^2 + 3x - 5$?

b. Solutions are $x = -1, 0,$ and 1 since for each number, the absolute value of the number is equal to the square of the number.

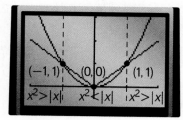

c. $x^2 > |x|$ for $x < -1$ and $x > 1$.
$x^2 < |x|$ for $-1 < x < 1$ and $x \neq 0$.

24 **a.** As x values get significantly large, the y values of the first and third functions become closer and closer.

b. Students should determine that the a term dictates right end behavior.

c. The same can be said for the left end behavior.

25 **a.** A2=−5
A3=A2+1
Fill down from **A3** to cell **A12**.

b. B2=$G$1*A2^2
C2=$G$2*A2
D2=$G$3
E2=B2+C2+D2

c. B3=$G$1*A3^2
C3=$G$2*A3
D3=$G$3
E3=B3+C3+D3

d. Change the values in cells **G1**, **G2**, and **G3** to **1**, **3**, and **−5**, respectively.

26 Important questions about quadratic functions sometimes require solving inequalities like $10 > x^2 + 2x - 5$ or $-2x^2 + 6x \geq -8$.

a. What is the goal of the process in each case?

b. How can you use graphs to solve the inequalities?

c. How can you use tables of values to solve the inequalities?

d. How many solutions would you expect for a quadratic inequality?

REVIEW

27 At many basketball games, there is a popular half-time contest to see if a fan can make a half-court shot. Some of these contests offer prizes of up to $1,000,000! You may wonder how schools and other organizations could afford such payouts. In many cases, the organization offering the contest has purchased insurance to cover the costs, in the rare event that someone happens to make the shot. Imagine you've decided to start *Notgonnahappen Insurance* and your company will specialize in insuring $1 million prizes.

a. If you charge organizations $2,000 per contest for insurance, how many contests would you need to insure to cover the cost of a single event in which a contestant makes a million dollar half-court shot?

b. Suppose that for the first $1,000,000 you collect in insurance fees, there are no payouts. You decide to invest this money in a savings account for future contests.

   i. If the account earns 4% interest compounded annually, how much would the account be worth in one year if no deposits or withdrawals were made?

   ii. Write two rules for calculating the account balance b at the end of t years—one using the *NOW-NEXT* approach and the other "$b = \ldots$."

   iii. How much would the account be worth in 10 years if no deposits or withdrawals were made?

28 Write an equation for the line that:

a. Contains the points $(0, 4)$ and $(5, -3)$.

b. Contains the points $(-2, 3)$ and $(-5, 6)$.

c. Contains the point $(7, 5)$ and has slope $\frac{2}{3}$.

d. Contains the point $(-2, 5)$ and is parallel to the line with equation $y = 1.5x + 6$.

29 In the diagram at the right, $\overline{AC} \cong \overline{BD}$ and $\angle BAC \cong \angle ABD$. Using only this information:

a. Explain why $\triangle ABC \cong \triangle BAD$.

b. Explain why $\overline{AD} \cong \overline{BC}$.

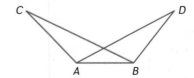

Lesson 1 | Quadratic Patterns **489**

26 a. For the first inequality, you want to know what values of x give a value for the quadratic expression that is less than 10. For the second inequality, you want to know what values of x give a value for the quadratic expression that is greater than or equal to -8.

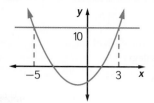

b. By finding the x values where $y = x^2 + 2x - 5$ is below $y = 10$, you solve the inequality $10 > x^2 + 2x - 5$. Thus, the solution is $-5 < x < 3$.

By finding the x values where $y = -2x^2 + 6x$ is at or above $y = -8$, you solve the inequality $-2x^2 + 6x \geq -8$. Thus, the solution is $-1 \leq x \leq 4$.

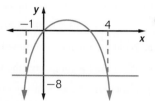

c. By inspecting the tables at the right, you can determine the values for x that satisfy the inequality. You can see in the first table that for $-5 < x < 3$ the value of the quadratic expression $x^2 + 2x - 5$ will be less than 10.

In the second table, you can see that the value of the quadratic expression $-2x^2 + 6x$ will be greater than or equal to -8 when $-1 \leq x \leq 4$.

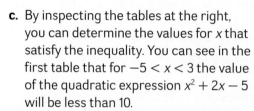

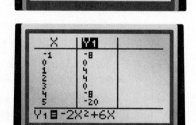

d. You would expect an infinite number of solutions since there will be an interval of x values possible. It is also possible that there could be one solution, e.g., $x^2 + 2x - 5 \leq -6$, or no solutions, e.g., $x^2 + 2x - 5 < -8$.

REVIEW

27 a. One would need to insure 500 contests to cover the $1,000,000, because $500 \cdot 2,000 = 1,000,000$.

b. i. The account would be worth $1,040,000.

ii. $NEXT = 1.04 \cdot NOW$ or $NEXT = NOW + 0.04 \cdot NOW$, starting at $1,000,000$; $b = 1,000,000(1.04)^t$

iii. The account would be worth about $1,480,244.29 in ten years.

28 a. $y = -\dfrac{7}{5}x + 4$
b. $y = -x + 1$
c. $y = \dfrac{2}{3}x + \dfrac{1}{3}$
d. $y = 1.5x + 8$

29 a. $\triangle ABC$ and $\triangle BAD$ have a common side $\overline{AB}$. So, the triangles are congruent by the SAS congruence condition.

b. $\overline{AD} \cong \overline{BC}$ because they are corresponding sides of the congruent triangles.

30 Write each of the following exponential expressions in the form 5^x for some integer x.

a. $(5^3)(5^4)$

b. $5^7 \div 5^3$

c. $(5^2)^3$

d. $4(5^3) + 5^3$

31 Suppose that the 15 numbers below are a sample of fares (in dollars) collected by drivers for *Fast Eddy's Taxi* company from trips on one typical day.

$$13, 23, 20, 22, 27, 21, 29, 31, 12, 10, 11, 21, 5, 19, 36$$

a. What are the mean and median of this sample of fares collected?

b. What are the range and the standard deviation of the sample of fares?

c. If there is a $2 local government tax on each taxi fare, what are the mean, median, range, and standard deviation of the sample of fares after taxes have been deducted?

Fast Eddy's Taxi allows each driver to keep 70% of each after-tax fare as her or his pay.

d. What are the mean and median driver earnings from the sample of trips?

e. What are the range and standard deviation of driver earnings from the sample of trips?

32 In the *Patterns in Shape* unit, you revisited how to calculate areas and volumes of shapes.

a. What is the area of an equilateral triangle with side lengths of 10 units?

b. What is the area of a regular hexagon with side lengths of 10 units?

c. What additional information do you need to find the volume of a prism with a regular hexagonal base that has side lengths of 10 units?

d. How would the volumes of a prism and a pyramid compare if they had the same hexagonal base and same height?

33 Find the prime factorization of each number.

a. 28

b. 105

c. 72

d. 297

34 Rewrite each expression in a simpler equivalent form by first using the distributive property and then combining like terms.

a. $6x(3x - 5) + 12x$

b. $22 - 2(15 - 4x)$

c. $\frac{1}{2}(12x + 7) + \frac{2}{3}(9 - 15x)$

d. $15 - (3x - 8) + 5x(6 + 3x)$

35 Sketch a cylinder with radius r and height h. What will change the volume of the cylinder more, doubling the radius or doubling the height? Explain your reasoning.

490 UNIT 7 | Quadratic Functions

30 **a.** 5^7 **b.** 5^4

c. 5^6 **d.** 5^4

31 **a.** The mean is $20.
The median is $21.

b. The range is $31.
The standard deviation is approximately 8.63.

c. The mean is $18.
The median is $19.
The range is $31.
The standard deviation is approximately 8.63.

d. The mean is $12.60.
The median is $13.30.

e. The range is $21.70.
The standard deviation is approximately 6.04.

32

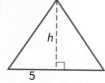

a. Using the Pythagorean Theorem: $h^2 = 10^2 - 5^2 = 75$, so $h \approx 8.66$.
Area of triangle $= 0.5(10)(8.66) = 43.3$ square units.

b. The hexagon is made of six equilateral triangles so the area is approximately 260 square units.

c. The volume of the prism would be base area times height. We know the base area from Part b, but we need information about the height.

d. The pyramid would have $\frac{1}{3}$ the volume of the prism.

33 **a.** $2 \cdot 2 \cdot 7$ **b.** $3 \cdot 5 \cdot 7$

c. $2 \cdot 2 \cdot 2 \cdot 3 \cdot 3$ **d.** $3 \cdot 3 \cdot 3 \cdot 11$

⏱ JUST IN TIME

34 **a.** $18x^2 - 30x + 12x = 18x^2 - 18x$

b. $22 - 30 + 8x = 8x - 8$

c. $6x + \frac{7}{2} + 6 - 10x = -4x + \frac{19}{2}$

d. $15 - 3x + 8 + 30x + 15x^2 = 15x^2 + 27x + 23$

35

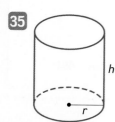

Since $V = \pi r^2 h$, doubling the height will double the volume. But doubling the radius will increase the volume by a factor of 4 because the radius is squared. So, doubling the radius increases the volume more than doubling the height.

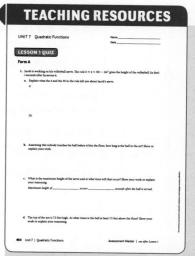

LESSON 2

Equivalent Quadratic Expressions

When the freshman class officers at Sturgis High School were making plans for the annual end-of-year class party, they had a number of variables to consider:

- the number of students purchasing tickets and attending the party

- the price charged for tickets

- expenses, including food, a DJ, security, and clean-up.

Equivalent Quadratic Expressions

The symbolic rules for quadratic functions come in two common forms—the standard polynomial form $ax^2 + bx + c$ and the factored form $(ax + b)(cx + d)$. Each form conveys its own useful information. For example, the standard expanded form reveals the y-intercept of the parabola graph $(0, c)$, the line of symmetry for the graph $x = \frac{-b}{2a}$, and whether the graph has a maximum or minimum point ($a < 0$ or $a > 0$). The factored form reveals the zeroes of the function and the x-intercepts of the graph $\left(\frac{-b}{a}, 0\right)$ and $\left(\frac{-d}{c}, 0\right)$. Depending on the situational information available to write the quadratic expression for the function, the form may represent context information and thus be in one of the common forms, or another form entirely as with *profit = income − expenses*.

Because of the usefulness of equivalent expanded and factored forms for quadratics (and other higher degree polynomials), it is helpful for students to develop some facility in transforming one form into the other. In fact, this skill (complete with its almost universally known, albeit of limited applicability, mnemonic device FOIL) consumes a substantial part of traditional algebra courses. Lesson 2 of *Quadratic Functions* is a modest beginning on developing student skill with expanding and factoring quadratic expressions. The primary emphasis is on expanding, rather than factoring, and we deal mostly with the more straightforward cases. Since widely available symbol manipulation software performs those formal operations automatically, and since expressions for many realistic quadratic functions are not factorable, we do not devote a great deal of time to developing extensive factoring and expanding skills. These skills will be revisited in Course 2.

The two essential ideas of this lesson:

> *Quadratic functions can be expressed with both factored and expanded symbolic forms.*
>
> *Depending on the questions to be answered, one or the other of the equivalent forms might be more useful.*

Lesson Objectives

- Find symbolic rules for quadratic functions using data modeling and reasoning
- Determine whether two given quadratic expressions are equivalent
- Decide on most useful equivalent forms of quadratics for different question types
- Create equivalent quadratic expressions by expanding products of linear factors
- Factor quadratic expressions by extracting common linear factors

Common Core State Standards CCSS

Focused on:
A-SSE.1, A-SSE.2, A-SSE.3, F-IF.8, F-BF.1

Connected to:
N-RN-2, F-IF.1, S-ID.6

A survey of class members showed that the number of students attending the party would depend on the price charged for tickets. Survey data suggested a linear model relating price x and number of tickets sold n: $n = 200 - 10x$.

The students responsible for pricing food estimated an expense of $5 per student.

The students responsible for getting a DJ reported that the person they wanted would charge $150 for the event.

The school principal said that costs of security and clean-up by school crews would add another $100 to the cost of the party.

THINK ABOUT THIS SITUATION

Think about how you could use the above information to set a price that would guarantee the freshman class would not lose money on the party.

a What party profit could be expected if ticket price is set at $5 per person? What if the ticket price is set at $10 per person?

b How could the given information be combined to figure out a price that would allow the class to break even or maybe even make some profit for the class treasury?

In this lesson, you will explore ways to develop expressions for functions that model quadratic patterns of change and to write and reason with equivalent forms of those expressions.

INVESTIGATION 1

Finding Expressions for Quadratic Patterns

When the freshman class officers at Sturgis High School listed all the variables to be considered in planning their party, they disagreed about how to set a price that would guarantee a profitable operation. To help settle those arguments, they tried to find a single function showing how profit would depend on the ticket price. They came up with two different profit functions and wondered whether they were algebraically equivalent. As you work on the problems in this investigation, look for answers to these questions:

What strategies are useful in finding rules for quadratic functions?

In deciding whether two quadratic expressions are equivalent?

In deciding when one form of quadratic expression is more useful than another?

Quantitative analysis of decisions usually requires combining several different variables and constraints. The aim of this TATS is to get students thinking about one such situation that will be the context for initial investigation of equivalent forms for quadratic expressions. Before focusing on the particular conditions described in the example concerning Sturgis High School's class party planning, you might find it helpful to pose questions to the class like the following:

- *If you and some fellow students were assigned responsibility for planning a class party, what are some of the questions you'd have to answer?*

- *How would you decide on a price to charge for the party?*

- *How would the price you set affect the number of students likely to come?*

- *What expense items would have to be predicted?*

Since a situation somewhat like this has been considered in the *Patterns of Change* unit (business prospects of running a bungee jump at Five Star Amusement Park), as well as in Lesson 1 of this unit, students should have some insights into this kind of analysis.

To provide more specific orientation to the situation that will be analyzed in Investigation 1, have students read through the information about the Sturgis class' planning and work out answers to TATS Part a. Then have only an informal brainstorming discussion of Part b, closing by indicating that the investigation will require more systematic analysis of one approach to this problem.

THINK ABOUT THIS SITUATION

a For the given conditions, the profit at a ticket price of $5 per person will be −$250. (The ticket price will yield 150 students at the party, $750 in ticket income, $750 in food expense, and $250 in other expenses.)

  The profit at a ticket price of $10 will be $250. (The ticket price will yield attendance of 100 students, $1,000 in ticket income, $500 in food expense, and $250 in other expenses.)

b Student ideas about how to combine all the information in a way that will help find an optimal price will probably vary.

  (It is not at all important to work out any of the ideas in detail at this time—the purpose of the question is to give you insight into the sophistication of thinking that the students bring to the problem. The investigation that follows gives scaffolding for development of one analysis approach.)

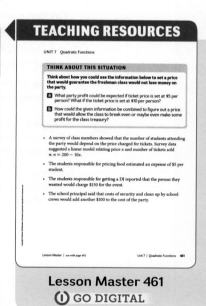

TEACHING RESOURCES

UNIT 7 Quadratic Functions

THINK ABOUT THIS SITUATION

Think about how you could use the information below to set a price that would guarantee the freshman class would not lose money on the party.

a What party profit could be expected if ticket price is set at $5 per person? What if the ticket price is set at $10 per person?

b How could the given information be combined to figure out a price that would allow the class to break even or maybe even make some profit for the class treasury?

- A survey of class members showed that the number of students attending the party would depend on the price charged for tickets. Survey data suggested a linear model relating price x and number of tickets sold n: $n = 200 − 10x$.

- The students responsible for pricing food estimated an expense of $5 per student.

- The students responsible for getting a DJ reported that the person they wanted would charge $150 for the event.

- The school principal said that costs of security and clean up by school crews would add another $100 to the cost of the party.

Lesson Master | *use with page 492* | Unit 7 | Quadratic Functions **461**

Lesson Master 461
① GO DIGITAL

1 One way to discover functions that model problem conditions is to consider a variety of specific pairs of (x, y) values and look for a pattern relating those values.

a. Use the information on page 492 to find ticket sales, income, costs, and profits for a sample of possible ticket prices. Record results in a table like this:

	Ticket Price (in $)				
	0	5	10	15	20
Number of Tickets Sold	200	150			
Income (in $)	0	750			
Food Cost (in $)	1,000				
DJ Cost (in $)	150				
Security/Cleanup Cost (in $)	100				
Profit (in $)	−1,250				

b. Plot the sample (*ticket price*, *profit*) values and describe the kind of function that you would expect to model the data pattern well.

2 Ms. Parkhurst, one of the Sturgis High School mathematics teachers, suggested another way to find a profit function that considers all factors. Check each step of her reasoning and explain why it is correct.

(1) Since the number of tickets sold *n* is related to the ticket price *x* by the linear function *n* = 200 − 10*x*, income from ticket sales will be related to ticket price by the function *I* = *x*(200 − 10*x*).

(2) The cost *c* for food is related to the number of tickets sold *n* by the function *c* = 5*n*, so the cost for food will be related to the ticket price by the function *c* = 5(200 − 10*x*).

(3) The costs for a DJ, security, and cleanup total $250, regardless of the number of students who attend the party.

(4) So, the profit of the party can be predicted from the ticket price *x* using the function *P* = *x*(200 − 10*x*) − 5(200 − 10*x*) − 250.

3 Some students followed Ms. Parkhurst's reasoning up to the point where she said the profit function would be $P = x(200 - 10x) - 5(200 - 10x) - 250$. But they expected a quadratic function like $P = ax^2 + bx + c$.

a. Is the expression $x(200 - 10x) - 5(200 - 10x) - 250$ equivalent to an expression in the $ax^2 + bx + c$ form? If so, what is the expression in that form? If not, how do you know?

b. What are the advantages of expanded and simplified expressions in reasoning about the function relating party profit to ticket price?

IS37/Alamy

UNIT 7

Finding Expressions for Quadratic Patterns

The goal of this investigation is to help students develop strategies that are useful in finding rules for quadratic functions, in deciding when two quadratic expressions are equivalent, and in deciding when one type of quadratic expression is more useful than another. The questions posed for student consideration illustrate two common strategies for generating function rules—using data analysis tools to model patterns in specific data points and using logical analysis to reason from problem conditions to a function rule. To highlight the contrasting styles and information content of standard and factored form quadratic expressions, the students are asked to generate some specific data, to find a standard form quadratic model (the data plot will suggest that form), and to follow reasoning that suggests a different, more analytic approach.

Two algebraic expressions are *equivalent* if and only if they produce identical outputs for identical input values of the independent variables involved. For example, $x^2 + 2x$ is equivalent to $x(x + 2)$ because the two expressions will always yield identical outputs if given identical inputs of x. There are useful informal ways of checking for equivalence that highlight this condition—comparing tables and graphs of input and output values gives vivid confirmation of equivalence (though not certain confirmation for all x).Reasoning from general properties of the number system is a more formal, though not always as convincing or insightful, strategy for proving equivalence. For example, the fact that $x^2 + 2x$ is equivalent to $x(x + 2)$ is a direct consequence of the Distributive Property of Multiplication over Addition.

Students have done some reasoning about equivalence of linear expressions in Unit 3, *Linear Functions*. This investigation extends that understanding and skill to focus on expansion and factoring of quadratic expressions. However, this investigation builds on the work with linear expressions, in particular with respect to rearrangement and combination of "like terms."

The development of the equivalence idea is not by an "explain and then practice" strategy. Instead, after finding some equivalent expressions, students are asked to consider the advantages of simplified and expanded expressions in Problem 3 Part b. At this point, students may or may not be able to reason through this idea. Full-class discussion of that question, after student exploration, is crucial for getting across the message of this investigation. Investigation 2 focuses more specifically on formal reasoning, so you need not linger in developing the familiar expanding and factoring skills.

1 **a.** The completed table of values will look like this:

	Ticket Price (in $)				
	0	**5**	**10**	**15**	**20**
Number of Tickets Sold	200	150	100	50	0
Income (in $)	0	750	1,000	750	0
Food Cost (in $)	1,000	750	500	250	0
DJ Cost (in $)	150	150	150	150	150
Security/Cleanup Cost (in $)	100	100	100	100	100
Profit (in $)	−1,250	−250	250	250	−250

b. The plot of (*ticket price, profit*) data will look like this:

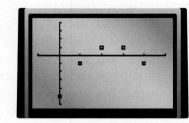

The quadratic regression model for this data pattern is
$y = -10x^2 + 250x - 1{,}250$.

2 **(1)** The teacher's reasoning is correct. In general
income = ticket price × number of customers, so the derived expression for
predicted *income* is correct.
     (It might take some discussion for students to see how the expression
$200 - 10x$ is just another way of writing *number of customers*.)

(2) The reasoning replaces *n* by the expression $200 - 10x$, involving *ticket price*, so
the resulting expression for *food cost* is correct.

(3) This reasoning is correct. The two fixed costs total $250 and do not depend on
the number of students who attend the party.
     (Some students, applying common sense to the situation, might argue that
if they expected no students to come, they would cancel the party and hope
to get money back from the DJ and security payments that planners had to
commit to in advance.)

(4) In general, *profit = income − food cost − (DJ cost + security/cleanup cost)*,
so the expression given in the problem is correct.

3 **a.** Student responses may be similar to the following:

If the two chunks involving parentheses are expanded, you get
$200x - 10x^2 - 1{,}000 + 50x - 250$. Then rearrange and combine these
terms to get $-10x^2 + 250x - 1{,}250$.

b. Student ideas will vary about the virtues of each profit expression. The basic ideas are that the longer form shows the contribution of each component (ticket income, food cost, fixed costs for DJ and security), while the shorter form immediately shows that profit is −$1,250 when tickets are free ($0) and the coefficient on the x^2 term of −10 indicates the profit will rise to a maximum amount and then go down. In addition, the shorter form would be more efficient for calculation of profit for various ticket prices.

4 Ms. Parkhurst's rule for the function relating party profit to ticket price involves products and sums of linear functions, but the result is a quadratic function. For each of the following pairs of linear functions:

i. Graph the sum and describe the type of function that results from that operation. For example, for the functions in Part a, the sum is $y = (x + 2) + 0.5x$.

ii. Graph the product and describe the type of function that results from that operation. For example, for the functions in Part a, the product is $y = (x + 2)(0.5x)$.

iii. Write each sum and product in simpler equivalent form.

Be prepared to explain the reasoning you used to produce the equivalent function expressions.

a. $y_1 = x + 2$ and $y_2 = 0.5x$ **b.** $y_1 = 2x - 3$ and $y_2 = -1.5x$

c. $y_1 = -3x$ and $y_2 = 5 - 0.5x$ **d.** $y_1 = x + 2$ and $y_2 = 2x + 1$

SUMMARIZE THE MATHEMATICS

In this investigation, you explored two ways to develop expressions for quadratic functions relating variables and ways to compare expressions to see if they are equivalent.

a What are the advantages of each strategy for developing rules for quadratic functions— looking for patterns in sample (x, y) data or using only reasoning about problem conditions?

b What does it mean to say that two algebraic expressions are equivalent?

c In what ways can you check to see whether two expressions are equivalent?

d Why might it be useful to write a quadratic expression in a different equivalent form?

e What graph and rule patterns would you expect from combining two linear functions by addition? By multiplication?

Be prepared to explain your ideas to the class.

 CHECK YOUR UNDERSTANDING

Use your understanding of equivalent expressions to help complete the following tasks.

a. Which of the following pairs of algebraic expressions are equivalent, and how do you know?

i. $x^2 + 5x$ and $x(x + 5)$

ii. $m(100 - m) + 25$ and $-m^2 + 100m + 25$

iii. $43 - 5(x - 10)$ and $33 - 5x$

4 | **INSTRUCTIONAL NOTE** The equivalence of the two profit functions studied in the preceding problems illustrates a general principle that the sum of two linear functions will always be a linear function, but the product of two linear functions will always be a quadratic function (except for the very special case when one or more of the linear functions is a constant function). This problem asks students to explore these principles graphically and, if possible, to use reasoning like that called for in Problem 3 Part a to confirm their observations. Noticing the general fact that a sum of linear functions is linear and the product is (in general) a quadratic should not be too hard. Proof will be harder in the cases of products, especially Part d.

Once again, there is more to come about the rules for manipulating quadratic expressions. Don't push to mastery on the symbol manipulation at this time.

DIFFERENTIATION

In a press for time, Problem 4 can be omitted without serious consequence. For stronger students or groups, it might make an extension exploration.

The window for the graphs below is Xmin $= -5$, Xmax $= 5$, Xscl $= 1$, Ymin $= -10$, Ymax $= 10$, Yscl $= 2$, unless otherwise indicated.

a. $y_1 = x + 2$ and $y_2 = 0.5x$
The sum is $y = (x + 2) + 0.5x$
or $y = 1.5x + 2$.

The product is
$y = (x + 2)(0.5x)$
or $y = 0.5x^2 + x$.

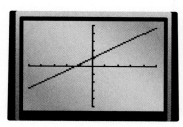 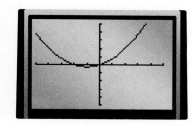

b. $y_1 = 2x - 3$ and $y_2 = -1.5x$
The sum is $y = (2x - 3) - 1.5x$
or $y = 0.5x - 3$.

The product is
$y = (2x - 3)(-1.5x)$
or $y = -3x^2 + 4.5x$.

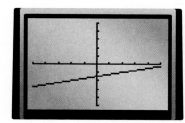 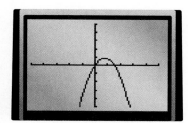

c. $y_1 = -3x$ and $y_2 = 5 - 0.5x$
The sum is
$y = (-3x) + (5 - 0.5x)$
or $y = -3.5x + 5$.

The product is
$y = (-3x)(5 - 0.5x)$
or $y = 1.5x^2 - 15x$.

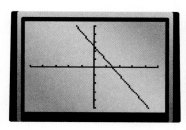 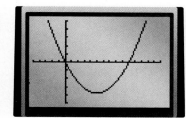 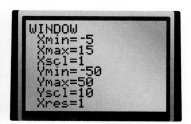

d. In this problem, it may be harder for students to reason through the product without your help! It is not essential to master at this point.

$y_1 = x + 2$ and $y_2 = 2x + 1$.

The sum is	The product is
$y = (x + 2) + (2x + 1)$	$y = (x + 2)(2x + 1)$
or $y = 3x + 3$.	or $y = 2x^2 + 5x + 2$.

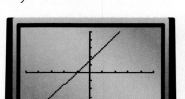
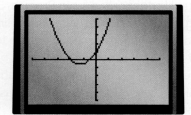

Summary

As you lead a class discussion of these questions, keep in mind the investigation goals—getting students to explore different strategies for developing rules for quadratic functions, clarifying meaning of equivalent expressions, and beginning to develop reasoning to verify equivalence and to produce useful equivalent forms of quadratics.

a Student ideas will vary about the virtues of data modeling and reasoning from verbal conditions in deriving a quadratic function rule.

Producing sample-specific (x, y) data pairs is often a helpful way to develop understanding of problem conditions. However, using a data-modeling utility seldom reveals *why* a particular model type makes sense (other than it fits the data pattern). Reasoning from given conditions does push one to really understand what those conditions imply. Furthermore, it can lead to a form of function rule that reveals directly how each of the problem conditions contributes to the overall relationship involved.

b Two algebraic expressions are equivalent if they produce identical outcome values when identical input values of the variables are substituted.

c One can run informal tests of equivalence by comparing tables and graphs produced by the functions $y_1 = $ *expression 1* and $y_2 = $ *expression 2*. Confirmation of the equivalence "for all x" can be provided by reasoning that shows how properties of numbers and operations can be applied to manipulate one expression into the other form.

d Writing quadratic expressions in equivalent forms often provides new insights into the graph (intercepts, maximum or minimum), the zeroes of the function, and more efficient calculation of output values (fewer required operations from input to output).

e The sum of two linear functions is always a linear function; the product of two linear functions is a quadratic function, unless one of the two factors is a constant. (No example of this is shown in Problem 4, so it is a fine point that students do not need to notice at this stage).

UNIT 7 Quadratic Functions

SUMMARIZE THE MATHEMATICS

In this investigation, you explored two ways to develop expressions for quadratic functions relating variables and ways to compare expressions to see if they are equivalent.

a What are the advantages of each strategy for developing rules for quadratic functions—looking for patterns in sample (x, y) data or using only reasoning about problem conditions?

b What does it mean to say that two algebraic expressions are equivalent?

c In what ways can you check to see whether two expressions are equivalent?

d Why might it be useful to write a quadratic expression in a different equivalent form?

e What graph and rule patterns would you expect from combining two linear functions by addition? By multiplication?

Be prepared to explain your ideas to the class.

Lesson Master | use with page 494   Unit 7 | Quadratic Functions **463**

Lesson Master 463
ⓘ **GO DIGITAL**

MATH TOOLKIT

- Give an example of equivalent algebraic expressions.
- Explain how to tell if they are equivalent.
- Why are equivalent forms useful?

✔ CHECK YOUR UNDERSTANDING

a. **i.** $x^2 + 5x$ is equivalent to $x(x + 5)$, seen by comparing tables or graphs and by application of the Distributive Property of Multiplication over Addition.

ii. $x(100 - x) + 25$ is equivalent to $-x^2 + 100x + 25$, seen by comparing tables or graphs and by application of the distributive property and then rearranging.

iii. $43 - 5(x - 10)$ is not equivalent to $33 - 5x$, seen by comparing tables or graphs and by applying the distributive property and rearranging and combining like terms in the first expression (it gives $93 - 5x$ in "simplest" form).

PROCESSING PROMPT

_____ added a new
(name)
mathematical idea to our discussion by ... .

b. Which of these functions are linear, which are quadratic, which are neither, and how can you justify your conclusions algebraically?

    i. $J = (4p)(7p - 3)$

    ii. $y = (3x + 2) - (2x - 4)$

    iii. $d = (6t - 4) \div (2t)$

INVESTIGATION **2**

Reasoning to Equivalent Expressions

In your work with linear functions, you learned that the form $y = mx + b$ was very useful for finding the slope and intercepts of graphs. However, you also found that linear functions sometimes arise in ways that make other equivalent expressions natural and informative. The work on party planning in Investigation 1 showed that the same thing can happen with quadratic relations.

   It is relatively easy to do some informal checking to see if two given quadratic expressions might be equivalent—comparing graphs or entries in tables of values. But there are also some ways that properties of numbers and operations can be used to prove equivalence of quadratic expressions and to write any given expression in useful equivalent forms. As you complete the following problems, look for answers to this question:

> *What strategies can be used to transform quadratic*
> *expressions into useful equivalent forms?*

One basic principle used again and again to produce equivalent expressions is the **Distributive Property of Multiplication over Addition** (and **Subtraction**). It states that for any numbers a, b, and c, $a(b + c) = (ab) + (ac)$ and $a(b - c) = (ab) - (ac)$. For example, $5(x + 7) = 5x + 35$ and $5(x - 7) = 5x - 35$.

1 Use the distributive property to expand and combine like terms to write each of the following expressions in equivalent standard form $ax^2 + bx + c$. Be prepared to explain your reasoning in each case.

a. $(3 + x)x$

b. $5x(4x - 11)$

c. $7x(11 - 4x)$

d. $7x(x + 2) - 19$

e. $-9(5 - 3x) + 7x(x + 4)$

f. $mx(x + n) + p$

b. **i.** $y = (4x)(7x - 3)$ is quadratic, $y = 28x^2 - 12x$ in standard form after applying the distributive property. Graphing $y = (4x)(7x - 3)$ will also yield a parabola.

ii. $y = (3x + 2) - (2x - 4)$ is linear, $y = x + 6$, seen by combining like terms, by observing the graph or the constant rate of change in a table for $y = (3x + 2) - (2x - 4)$, or by recognizing this expression as the sum of two linear terms.

iii. $y = (6x - 4) \div (2x)$ is neither linear nor quadratic. The "standard" form of the rule might be something like $y = 3 - \dfrac{2}{x}$.

> **NOTE** Inverse relationships such as $y = 3 - \dfrac{2}{x}$ will be studied in Course 2, Unit 1.

INVESTIGATION **2** **CCSS** A-SSE.1, A-SSE.2 A-SSE.3, F-IF.8

Reasoning to Equivalent Expressions

The goal of this investigation is to build on the introduction of Investigation 1 and focus more generally on symbol manipulation that produces equivalent expanded expressions (standard polynomial forms) equivalent to given factored forms. Although it might be helpful to refer back to the party planning context of Investigation 1 to remind students of why it might be useful to do this sort of algebraic reasoning, the aim here is to begin building general context-free algebraic reasoning skills with quadratic expressions.

The first set of problems focuses on direct monomial-times-binomial applications of the distributive property. The next several problems look at fairly simple examples of products involving two binomials, with special focus on the case of squaring a single binomial and the product of the sum and difference of the same two terms. We do not recommend extensive practice of expanding or factoring quadratic expressions at this point. Distributed practice will occur in future lessons and additional development of these skills will occur in other units. The big idea is that students should recognize the information content that is provided most readily by the different forms.

You might launch the investigation by revisiting the *price × number of customers* example of the preceding investigation, asking students how they could check that $x(200 - 10x)$ is equivalent to $-10x^2 + 200x$ in several ways, including use of the distributive property. Then indicate that the problems of this investigation require similar reasoning.

You might want to stop the class for a mini-summary discussion of results after most students have completed a substantial part of Problems 1–3. Also after Problem 3, you may wish to demonstrate how a CAS can be used to expand and factor expressions like those in this investigation.

Depending on your students' middle school exposure to multiplying binomials, you may also wish to reason through the worked example presented in Problem 4 as a class. Connections Task 11 presents an area model for expanding a product of two binomials and asks students to use such a model to illustrate the square of a binomial and a product leading to a difference of squares.

1 **a.** $x^2 + 3x$

b. $20x^2 - 55x$

c. $-28x^2 + 77x$

d. $7x^2 + 14x - 19$

e. $7x^2 + 55x - 45$

f. $mx^2 + (mn)x + p$

2 Use the distributive property to write each of these quadratic expressions in equivalent form as a product of two linear factors. Be prepared to explain your reasoning in each case.

a. $7x^2 - 11x$

b. $12x + 4x^2$

c. $-3x^2 - 9x$

d. $ax^2 + bx$

3 Sometimes you need to combine expanding, factoring, and rearrangement of terms in a quadratic expression in order to produce a simpler form that gives useful information. For example, the following work shows how to write a complex expression in simpler expanded and factored forms.

$$5x(6x - 8) + 4x(2 - 3x) = 30x^2 - 40x + 8x - 12x^2$$
$$= 18x^2 - 32x$$
$$= 2x(9x - 16)$$

Use what you know about ways of writing algebraic expressions in equivalent forms to produce simplest possible expanded and (where possible) factored forms of these expressions.

a. $(14x^2 + 3x) - 7x(4 + x)$

b. $-x + 4x(9 - 2x) + 3x^2$

c. $5x(2x - 1) + 4x^2 - 2x$

d. $(5x^2 - 4) - 3(4x + 8x^2) - 25x$

The distributive property is used many places in algebra to write expressions in equivalent forms. In fact, the operations of *expanding* and *factoring* expressions like those for quadratic functions are now built into computer algebra systems. The following screen shows several results that should agree with answers you got in Problems 1, 2, and 3.

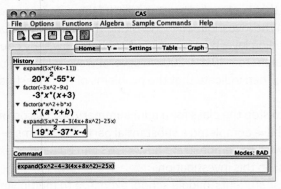

You can use such a computer algebra tool to check your answers as you learn how expanding and factoring work and when you meet problems that require complicated symbol manipulation.

2 **a.** $x(7x - 11)$

    b. $x(12 + 4x)$ or $4x(3 + x)$

    c. $x(-3x - 9)$ or $-3x(x + 3)$

    d. $x(ax + b)$

3 **a.** $7x^2 - 25x$ or $x(7x - 25)$

    b. $-5x^2 + 35x$ or $-5x(x - 7)$

    c. $14x^2 - 7x$ or $7x(2x - 1)$

    d. $-19x^2 - 37x - 4$

4 In some situations, a quadratic expression arises as the product of two linear expressions. In those cases, you can use the distributive property twice to expand the factored quadratic to standard form. Study the steps in these examples, and then apply similar reasoning to expand the expressions in Parts a–e.

Strategy 1

$$(x + 5)(x - 7) = (x + 5)x - (x + 5)7$$
$$= x^2 + 5x - 7x - 35$$
$$= x^2 - 2x - 35$$

Strategy 2

$$(x + 5)(x - 7) = x(x - 7) + 5(x - 7)$$
$$= x^2 - 7x + 5x - 35$$
$$= x^2 - 2x - 35$$

a. $(x + 5)(x + 6)$

b. $(x - 3)(x + 9)$

c. $(x + 10)(x - 10)$

d. $(x - 5)(x + 1)$

e. $(x + a)(x + b)$

5 The next five expressions have a special form $(x + a)^2$ in which both linear factors are the same. Use the distributive property to find equivalent expanded forms for each given expression and look for a consistent pattern in the calculations. Remember $(x + a)^2 = (x + a)(x + a)$.

a. $(x + 5)^2$

b. $(x - 3)^2$

c. $(x + 7)^2$

d. $(x - 4)^2$

e. $(x + a)^2$

6 The next four expressions also have a special form in which the product can be expanded to a standard-form quadratic. Use the distributive property to find expanded forms for each expression. Then look for a pattern and an explanation of why that pattern works.

a. $(x + 4)(x - 4)$

b. $(x + 5)(x - 5)$

c. $(3 - x)(3 + x)$

d. $(x + a)(x - a)$

7 When algebra students see the pattern $(x + a)(x - a) = x^2 - a^2$, they are often tempted to take some other "shortcuts" that lead to errors. How would you help another student to find and correct the mistakes in these calculations?

a. $(x + 5)(x - 3) = x^2 - 15$

b. $(m + 7)^2 = m^2 + 49$

Lesson 2 | Equivalent Quadratic Expressions   **497**

4 **a.** $x^2 + 11x + 30$

b. $x^2 + 6x - 27$

c. $x^2 - 100$

d. $x^2 - 4x - 5$

e. $x^2 + (a + b)x + ab$ or $x^2 + ax + bx + ab$

5 **a.** $x^2 + 10x + 25$

b. $x^2 - 6x + 9$

c. $x^2 + 14x + 49$

d. $x^2 - 8x + 16$

e. $x^2 + 2ax + a^2$

COMMON ERROR

Students often forget the middle term when squaring binomials.

6 **a.** $x^2 - 16$

b. $x^2 - 25$

c. $9 - x^2$ or $-x^2 + 9$

d. $x^2 - a^2$

In each case, the product of the sum and difference of the same two terms resulted in the difference of the squares of the terms. This works because the "middle terms" always "cancel each other out."

7 **a.** If the student applies the distributive property as follows, they should arrive at the correct answer.

$$(x + 5)(x - 3) = x(x - 3) + 5(x - 3)$$
$$= x^2 - 3x + 5x - 15$$
$$= x^2 + 2x - 15$$

b. $(m + 7)^2 = (m + 7)(m + 7) = m(m + 7) + 7(m + 7)$
$$= m^2 + 7m + 7m + 49$$
$$= m^2 + 14m + 49$$

POSSIBLE MISCONCEPTION

Many students believe that since $x^2 - a^2$ is factorable, $x^2 + a^2$ is also factorable.

8 The next screen shows how a computer algebra system would deal with the task of expanding products of linear expressions like those in Problems 4–6. Compare these results to your own work and resolve any differences.

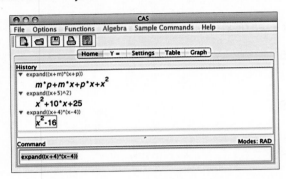

SUMMARIZE THE MATHEMATICS

In this investigation, you explored several of the most common ways that quadratic expressions can be written in equivalent factored and expanded forms.

a What is the standard expanded form equivalent to the product $2x(5x + 3)$?

b What is a factored form equivalent to $ax^2 + bx$?

c What is the standard expanded form equivalent to the product $(x + a)(x + b)$?

d What are the standard expanded forms equivalent to the products $(x + a)(x - a)$ and $(x + a)^2$?

Be prepared to compare your answers with those of your classmates.

 CHECK YOUR UNDERSTANDING

Write each of the following quadratic expressions in equivalent factored or expanded form.

a. $9x(4x - 5)$
b. $9x^2 + 72x$
c. $3(x^2 + 5x) - 7x$
d. $(x + 3)(x + 7)$
e. $(x + 2)^2$
f. $(x + 6)(x - 6)$

In Parts g and h, find values for the missing numbers that will make the given expressions equivalent.

g. $x^2 + 12x + \underline{\quad} = (x + 4)(x + \underline{\quad})$

h. $x^2 + \underline{\quad}x - 8 = (x + 4)(x + \underline{\quad})$

8 To produce displays like those shown in the student text, simply press function key F2 (Algebra), select option 3 (Expand), type in the desired expressions, close parentheses, and press return to get the result displayed. A typical CAS will deal with expressions that have numerical coefficients, but it will also work with expressions in which coefficients are expressed as letter parameters. The only caution for working with such examples, like $(ax + b)(cx + d)$, is that the typical CAS will treat ax as a single variable with a two-letter name. To be sure that the "a" is treated as a separate parameter, be sure to enter **a*x+b** and **c*x+d**.

SUMMARIZE THE MATHEMATICS

a $2x(5x + 3) = 10x^2 + 6x$

b $ax^2 + bx = x(ax + b)$

c $(x + a)(x + b) = x^2 + (a + b)x + ab$

d $(x + a)(x - a) = x^2 - a^2$
$(x + a)^2 = x^2 + 2ax + a^2$

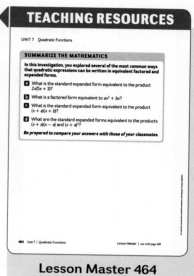
 CHECK YOUR UNDERSTANDING

There are a variety of equivalent forms for many items below.

a. $36x^2 - 45x$

b. $9x(x + 8)$

c. $3x^2 + 8x$ or $x(3x + 8)$

d. $x^2 + 10x + 21$

e. $x^2 + 4x + 4$

f. $x^2 - 36$

g. $x^2 + 12x + \underline{32} = (x + 4)(x + \underline{8})$

h. $x^2 + \underline{2}x - 8 = (x + 4)(x + \underline{(-2)})$

MATH TOOLKIT

Summarize some of the patterns related to equivalent expanded forms:

Factored Form	Expanded Form
$(x + a)(x - a)$	_____
$(x + a)(x + a)$	_____
$(x - a)(x - a)$	_____

APPLICATIONS

1 Planners of a school fund-raising carnival considered the following factors affecting profit prospects for a rental bungee jump attraction:

- The number of customers n will depend on the price per jump x (in dollars) according to the linear function $n = 100 - x$.

- Insurance will cost $4 per jumper.

- Costs include $250 for delivery and setup and $100 to pay a trained operator to supervise use of the jumping equipment.

a. Complete a table like that begun here, showing number of customers, income, costs, and profit expected for various possible prices.

	Price per Jump (in $)						
	0	**15**	**30**	**45**	**60**	**75**	**90**
Number of Customers							
Income (in $)							
Insurance Cost (in $)							
Delivery/Setup Cost (in $)							
Operator Pay (in $)							
Profit (in $)							

b. Plot the (*price per jump*, *profit*) data. Then find a function that models the pattern relating those variables.

c. Write a rule showing how profit p depends on price per jump x by replacing each variable name in the following verbal rule with an expression using numbers and symbols:

profit = income − insurance cost − delivery/setup cost − operator pay

d. Check to see if the expressions for profit derived in Parts b and c are equivalent and explain how you reached your conclusion.

Lesson 2 | Equivalent Quadratic Expressions **499**

1 **a.**

	Price per Jump (in $)						
	0	**15**	**30**	**45**	**60**	**75**	**90**
Number of Customers	100	85	70	55	40	25	10
Income (in $)	0	1,275	2,100	2,475	2,400	1,875	900
Insurance Cost (in $)	400	340	280	220	160	100	40
Delivery/Setup Cost (in $)	250	250	250	250	250	250	250
Operator Pay (in $)	100	100	100	100	100	100	100
Profit (in $)	−750	585	1,470	1,905	1,890	1,425	510

b.

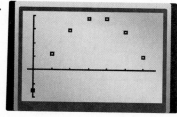   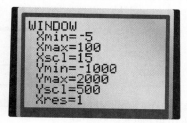

$p = -x^2 + 104x - 750$

c. $p = x(100 - x) - 4(100 - x) - 250 - 100$

d. The two expressions for *profit* are equivalent, which can be seen by comparing tables and graphs generated by each or by expanding the expression for p in Part c and combining "like terms."

ON YOUR OWN

2 Students in a child development class at Caledonia High School were assigned the task of designing and building a fenced playground attached to their school as shown in the following sketch. They had a total of 150 feet of fencing to work with.

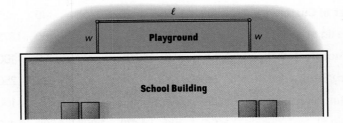

a. Complete a table like that begun here, showing how the length and area of the playground depend on choice of the width w.

Width (in feet)	10	20	30	40	50	60	70
Length (in feet)	130						
Area (in ft^2)	1,300						

b. Plot the data relating area to width and find the function that models the pattern in that relationship.

c. Write a function rule showing how length ℓ depends on width w and then another showing how area A depends on width.

d. Compare the two functions from Parts b and c relating area to width and decide whether they are equivalent. Explain evidence or reasoning that supports your answer.

e. Graph the area function and estimate the value of w that will produce the playground with largest possible area. Find the corresponding value of ℓ.

3 In many mountainous places, rope bridges provide the only way for people to get across fast rivers and deep valleys. A civil engineering class at a Colorado university got interested in one such rope bridge located in the mountains near their campus.

They came up with a function that they believed would give the distance in feet from the bridge to the river at any point. The function proposed was $d = 0.02x(x - 100) + 110$, where x measures horizontal distance (0 to 80 feet) from one side of the river to the other.

©Galen Rowell/Corbis

500 UNIT 7 | Quadratic Functions

2 **a.**

Width (in feet)	10	20	30	40	50	60	70
Length (in feet)	130	110	90	70	50	30	10
Area (in ft²)	1,300	2,200	2,700	2,800	2,500	1,800	700

b.

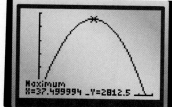 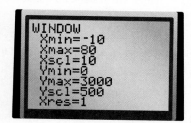

$A = -2w^2 + 150w$

c. $\ell = 150 - 2w$

$A = w(150 - 2w)$

d. The two functions are equivalent, as can be shown informally in comparison of tables and graphs of the area function and formally by expanding the expression $w(150 - 2w)$ and rearranging the terms.

e.

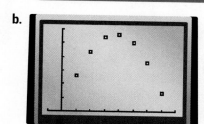 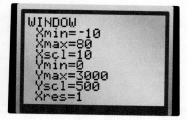

The maximum area (2,812.5 square feet) occurs when the width of the playground is 37.5 feet and the length is 75 feet.

a. Use the given function to calculate the distance from the bridge to the river below at points 0, 10, 20, 30, 40, 50, 60, 70, and 80 feet from one end of the bridge. Sketch a graph showing the bridge shape in relation to the mountain sides and to the river below.

b. Estimate the low point of the bridge and its height above the water.

c. One brave student decided to check the proposed model of the distance from the bridge to the river below. She walked across the bridge and used a range-finding device to get data relating bridge height to horizontal distance. Her data are shown in the following table.

Horizontal Distance x (in feet)	15	25	35	45	55	65	75
Distance to the River d (in feet)	85	70	65	60	60	65	75

Find a function that models the pattern in these data well.

d. Compare the function proposed by the civil engineering students (who used only a few data points to derive their model) to that based on the range-finder data and decide whether you think the two models are equivalent or nearly so.

e. Write the first function $d = 0.02x(x - 100) + 110$ in standard quadratic form and explain how that form either supports or undermines your decision in Part d.

4 Write each of the following quadratic expressions in equivalent standard form.

a. $(3x + 4)x$

b. $m(3m - 15)$

c. $2p(3p - 1)$

d. $3d(5d + 2) + 29$

5 Write each of these quadratic expressions in equivalent form as the product of two linear factors.

a. $3x^2 + 9x$

b. $2x - 5x^2$

c. $-7d^2 - 9d$

d. $cx + dx^2$

6 Write each of these quadratic expressions in two equivalent forms—one expanded and one factored—so that both are as short as possible.

a. $2x(5 - 3x) + 4x$

b. $-3(2s^2 + 4s) - (3s + 5)7s$

c. $(9m + 18)m - 3m^2 - 5m$

d. $6x(8x + 3) + 4(2x - 7) - 2x$

7 Expand each of the following products to equivalent expressions in standard quadratic form.

a. $(x + 2)(x + 7)$

b. $(p + 2)(p - 2)$

c. $(x + 6)(x - 6)$

d. $(x + 6)(x + 6)$

e. $(R + 1)(R - 4)$

f. $(m - 7)(7 + m)$

3 **a.**

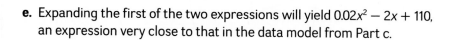

Horizontal Distance x (feet)	0	10	20	30	40	50	60	70	80
Distance to the River d (feet)	110	92	78	68	62	60	62	68	78

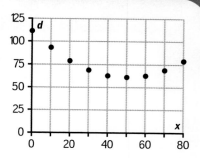

b. Using the table and graph, the low point is about 50 feet out from one side and the distance to the river is about 60 feet at this point.

c. A quadratic regression model for the data pattern given would be $d = 0.022x^2 - 2.14x + 112$.

d. The two function models are quite close in form and in data patterns as seen on a table and a graph.

> **INSTRUCTIONAL NOTE** The fact that only three data points are needed to find coefficients in a quadratic model is a general principle, like only two points are needed to determine a linear function rule.

e. Expanding the first of the two expressions will yield $0.02x^2 - 2x + 110$, an expression very close to that in the data model from Part c.

4 **a.** $3x^2 + 4x$ **b.** $3m^2 - 15m$

   c. $6p^2 - 2p$ **d.** $15d^2 + 6d + 29$

5 **a.** $3x(x + 3)$ or $x(3x + 9)$ **b.** $x(2 - 5x)$

   c. $-d(7d + 9)$ or $d(-7d - 9)$ **d.** $x(c + dx)$

6 **a.** $14x - 6x^2$ or $2x(7 - 3x)$ **b.** $-27s^2 - 47s$ or $-s(47 + 27s)$

   c. $6m^2 + 13m$ or $m(6m + 13)$ **d.** $48x^2 + 24x - 28$ or $4(12x^2 + 6x - 7)$

7 **a.** $x^2 + 9x + 14$ **b.** $p^2 - 4$

   c. $x^2 - 36$ **d.** $x^2 + 12x + 36$

   e. $R^2 - 3R - 4$ **f.** $m^2 - 49$

> **INSTRUCTIONAL NOTE**
>
> In Tasks 4–8, you may wish to encourage students to check using tables, graphs, or a CAS.

ON YOUR OWN

8 Expand each of the following products to equivalent expressions in standard quadratic form.

a. $(t + 9)(t - 5)$

b. $(m + 1)^2$

c. $(x + 9)(9 - x)$

d. $(3x + 6)(3x - 6)$

CONNECTIONS

9 The diagrams below are vertex-edge graphs that you can think of as maps that show cities and roads connecting them. In the first two "maps," every city can be reached from every other city by a direct road. In the third "map," every city can be reached from every other city, but some trips would require passing through another city along the way.

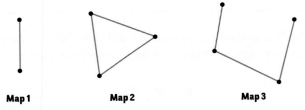

Map 1   Map 2   Map 3

a. Sketch maps with 5, 6, and 7 cities and the smallest number of connecting roads to enable travel from any city on the map to any other city. Record the (*number of cities, number of roads*) data in a table like this:

Number of Cities c	2	3	4	5	6	7	8	9
Number of Roads r	1	2	3					

  i. Use the pattern of results from the sketches to find a rule for calculating the number of roads r for any number of cities c if the number of connecting roads is to be a minimum in each case.

  ii. Describe the type of function relating r and c. Explain how the rule could be justified.

b. Next sketch maps with 4, 5, 6, and 7 cities and direct roads connecting each pair of cities. Record the (*number of cities, number of roads*) data in a table like this:

Number of Cities c	2	3	4	5	6	7	8
Number of Roads r	1	3					

  i. Use the pattern of results from the sketches to find a rule for calculating the number of direct roads r for any number of cities c.

8 **a.** $t^2 + 4t - 45$

b. $m^2 + 2m + 1$

ON YOUR OWN

c. $81 - x^2$

d. $9x^2 - 36$

CONNECTIONS

9 **a.**

Number of Cities c	2	3	4	5	6	7	8	9
Number of Roads r	1	2	3	4	5	6	7	8

i. $r = c - 1$

ii. This is a linear function. When you have two cities, you have one fewer roads than cities. After that, when a new city is added to the map, you need only one new road to connect it to one of the original cities and thus to the whole network.

b.

Number of Cities c	2	3	4	5	6	7	8	9
Number of Roads r	1	3	6	10	15	21	28	36

i. Rule: $r = 0.5c^2 - 0.5c$

ii. Study the following argument:

Each of the c cities must be connected by a road to the $c - 1$ other cities, so it looks like there must be $c(c - 1)$ direct roads. But that counting will include each road twice, so the actual number of direct roads r in a map with c cities is given by $r = \dfrac{c(c - 1)}{2}$.

Do the reasoning and the resulting function seem right?

iii. Explain how you know that the results from data analysis in part i and from the reasoning approach in part ii are or are not equivalent.

10 Your work with the Pythagorean Theorem often involved expressions with radicals like $\sqrt{49}$ or $\sqrt{2x^2}$, where $x > 0$. Write each of the following radical expressions in equivalent form with the simplest possible whole number or expression under the radical sign.

a. $\sqrt{18}$ **b.** $\sqrt{\dfrac{9}{4}}$ **c.** $\sqrt{2x^2}$ **d.** $\sqrt{\dfrac{3x^2}{4}}$

11 You can think of expanding products of linear expressions in terms of geometric models based on the area formula for rectangles.

a. What is the expanded form of $(x + 2)(x + 4)$? How is that result shown in the following diagram? (*Hint:* How can the area of the whole rectangle be calculated in two ways?)

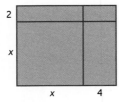

b. Find the expanded form of $(x + 3)(x + 7)$ and illustrate the result with a sketch similar to that given in Part a.

c. Make an area sketch like that in Part a to illustrate the general rule for expanding an expression in the form $(x + k)^2$.

d. What general result does the next sketch show?

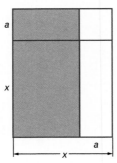

ii. The reasoning provided is correct.

iii. Equivalence of the expressions for the number of direct roads needed to connect c cities could be established informally by comparing entries in tables of (*number of cities, number of roads*) values or by expanding the second expression as follows:

$$\frac{c(c-1)}{2} = \frac{1}{2}(c(c-1))$$
$$= 0.5(c^2 - c)$$
$$= 0.5c^2 - 0.5c$$

10 **a.** $\sqrt{18} = 3\sqrt{2}$ **b.** $\sqrt{\frac{9}{4}} = \frac{3}{2}$

c. $\sqrt{2x^2} = x\sqrt{2}, x > 0$ **d.** $\sqrt{\frac{3x^2}{4}} = \frac{x}{2}\sqrt{3}, x > 0$

11 **a.** $(x + 2)(x + 4) = x^2 + 2x + 4x + 8$ or $x^2 + 6x + 8$
This is illustrated by the diagram in that the area of the rectangle can be calculated as the product of its length and width $(x + 2)(x + 4)$, or as the sum of the areas of the four smaller rectangles $x^2 + 2x + 4x + 8$ or $x^2 + 6x + 8$.

b. $(x + 3)(x + 7) = x^2 + 3x + 7x + 21$
$$= x^2 + 10x + 21$$

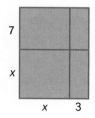

c. $(x + k)^2 = x^2 + 2kx + k^2$

d. $(x + a)(x - a) = x^2 + ax - ax - a^2$ or $x^2 - a^2$
The shaded portion of the diagram is a rectangle with a height of $x + a$ and a base of $x - a$, and thus an area of $(x + a)(x - a)$. The area of the shaded portion of the diagram can also be calculated by finding the area of the whole diagram $x(x + a) = x^2 + ax$ and then subtracting the areas of the unshaded portions ax and a^2 to get $x^2 - a^2$.

ON YOUR OWN

12 What kind of function do you think will result when two exponential functions are added or when the same two functions are multiplied? Use the examples in Parts a–d to develop conjectures from exploration of tables and graphs. Then summarize your ideas by answering Parts e and f, and use what you know about combining exponential expressions to confirm your ideas.

a. $y_1 = 1.5^x$ and $y_2 = 2^x$

b. $y_1 = 0.8^x$ and $y_2 = 2^x$

c. $y_1 = 0.5^x$ and $y_2 = 0.9^x$

d. $y_1 = 3^x$ and $y_2 = 2(3^x)$

Based on these examples (and others you might choose to test), how would you answer the questions in Parts e and f?

e. Is the sum of two exponential functions (always, sometimes, never) an exponential function?

f. Is the product of two exponential functions (always, sometimes, never) an exponential function?

13 When working with exponential growth functions it is often important to compare the value of the function at one time to the value at some future time. You can make the comparison by division or by subtraction.

a. What properties of numbers, operations, and exponents justify each step in this reasoning that claims $3^{x+1} - 3^x = 2(3^x)$?

$$3^{x+1} - 3^x = (3^x)(3^1) - (3^x)(1) \qquad\qquad (1)$$
$$= 3^x(3 - 1) \qquad\qquad (2)$$
$$= 2(3^x) \qquad\qquad (3)$$

b. Use similar reasoning to find an expression of the form $k(3^x)$ equivalent to $3^{x+2} - 3^x$.

c. Use similar reasoning to show that for any number n,
$3^{x+n} - 3^x = 3^x(3^n - 1)$.

d. What property of exponents guarantees that for any x, $\dfrac{3^{x+1}}{3^x} = 3$?

e. What property of exponents guarantees that for any x, $\dfrac{3^{x+n}}{3^x} = 3^n$?

REFLECTIONS

14 When you are working with a quadratic function with a rule like $y = 5x^2 + 15x$, what kinds of questions would be most easily answered using the rule in that standard form and what kinds of questions are easier to answer when the rule uses the equivalent expression $y = 5x(x + 3)$?

15 The following claims show some of the most common errors that people make when attempting to write quadratic expressions in equivalent forms by expanding, factoring, and rearranging terms. Spot the error(s) in each claim and tell how you would help the person who made the error correct his or her understanding.

12 a. The sum of $y_1 = 1.5^x$ and $y_2 = 2^x$ produces a graph that looks like an exponential function. However, in a table of values for $y = 1.5^x + 2^x$, with equal step increases in x, the ratios of successive y values will not be constant, thus, ruling out an exponential function.

The table at the right shows that pattern (here $y_1 = 1.5^x + 2^x$ and $y_2 = y_1(x) \div y_1(x - 1)$).

The product of the two functions is exponential with rule $y = 3^x$. This is a consequence of the property of exponents $(ab)^x = a^x b^x$.

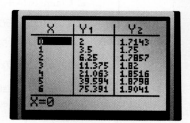

b. The sum of $y_1 = 0.8^x$ and $y_2 = 2^x$ is not exponential, but the product is exponential with rule $y = 1.6^x$, for the reasons cited in Part a.

c. The sum of $y_1 = 0.5^x$ and $y_2 = 0.9^x$ is not exponential, but the product is exponential with rule $y = 0.45^x$, for the reasons cited in Part a.

d. The sum of $y_1 = 3^x$ and $y_2 = 2(3^x)$ is exponential because $3^x + 2(3^x) = 3(3^x)$ or 3^{x+1}. The product is also exponential because $3^x \cdot 2(3^x) = 2 \cdot 3^{2x} = 2 \cdot 9^x$.

e. The sum of two exponential functions is exponential if and only if both expressions have the same base, or one base is a power of the other. For example, $2^x + 3(2)^x = 4(2^x)$, which is exponential.

f. The product of two exponential functions is always exponential (except in the degenerate cases: for example, $(a^x)\left(\dfrac{1}{a}\right)^x = 1^x$).

13 a. (1) Use $b^{x+y} = b^x b^y$ and $(a)(1) = a$.

(2) Use distributive property to factor out 3^x.

(3) Use arithmetic fact $3 - 1 = 2$ and Commutative Property of Multiplication.

b. $3^{x+2} - 3^x = (3^x)(3^2 - 1)$ or $8(3^x)$

c. $3^{x+n} - 3^x = (3^x)(3^n) - (3^x)(1)$
$$= 3^x(3^n - 1)$$

d. $\dfrac{3^{x+1}}{3^x} = 3$ because $\dfrac{a^x}{a^y} = a^{x-y}$ for positive values of a.

e. $\dfrac{3^{x+n}}{3^x} = 3n$ because $\dfrac{a^x}{a^y} = a^{x-y}$ for positive values of a.

REFLECTIONS

14 It is easier to see from the form $y = 5x^2 + 15x$ that the graph opens upward and that the y-intercept is $(0, 0)$. It is easier to see from the form $y = 5x(x + 3)$ that the x-intercepts are $(0, 0)$ and $(0, -3)$ and that the graph is symmetric across the line $x = -1.5$, which also gives the x-coordinate of the minimum.

   a. Claim: $5x(4 + 3x)$ is equivalent to $23x$.

   b. Claim: $7x - 5(2x + 4)$ is equivalent to $-3x + 20$.

   c. Claim: $5x^2 + 50x$ is equivalent to $5x(x + 50)$.

   d. Claim: $5x + 7x^2$ is equivalent to $12x^3$.

16 You know at least four different strategies for checking to see if two algebraic expressions are equivalent or not—comparing tables or graphs of (x, y) values, comparing the reasoning that led from the problem conditions to the expressions, or using algebraic reasoning based on number system properties like the distributive property.

   a. What do you see as the advantages and disadvantages of each strategy?

   b. How do you decide which strategy to use in a given situation?

   c. Which strategy gives you most confidence in your judgment about whether the given expressions are or are not equivalent?

17 A rectangle is divided into 4 regions by equal-length segments as shown.

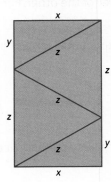

   a. Bushra says the area of the rectangle is $x(y + z)$. Is she correct? If so, explain the reasoning she likely used.

   b. Kareem says that the area of the rectangle is $\frac{1}{2}zx + \frac{1}{2}zx + \frac{1}{2}xy + \frac{1}{2}xy$. Is he correct? If so, explain his possible reasoning.

   c. Fatmeh says that the area is $2x + 2y + 2z$. Is she correct? If so, explain her reasoning.

   d. In reasoning about the questions in Parts a–c, you used your knowledge of area formulas for rectangles and triangles to analyze the given algebraic expressions. Show how knowledge about number system structure can be used to compare the expressions in Parts a–c.

   i. Why is $x(y + z)$ equivalent to $xy + xz$?

   ii. Why is $\frac{1}{2}zx + \frac{1}{2}zx + \frac{1}{2}xy + \frac{1}{2}xy$ equivalent to $zx + xy$?

   e. How does your work in Part d show the power of knowing how to reason with algebraic expressions without any context cues as guides?

Lesson 2 | Equivalent Quadratic Expressions   **505**

15 a. Error: did not distribute $5x$ times $3x$.

Use an area model (see Connections Task 11) to illustrate that $5x(4 + 3x) = 20x + 15x^2$.

b. Error: did not "distribute the negative."

Rewrite the expression as $7x + (-5)(2x + 4)$, then distribute and combine like terms: $-3x - 20$.

c. Error: did not factor the 5 from the $50x$.

Expand to show that $5x(x + 50) = 5x^2 + 250x$. $5x^2 + 50x = 5x(x + 10)$.

d. Error: combined unlike terms.

Use an area model to show they are not equal. Adding 7 squares x by x to a 5 by x rectangle does not result in 12 cubes of length x.

16 a. Comparing tables and graphs can be quite convincing and is particularly useful for illustrating when two expressions are *not* equivalent; however, the appearance of equivalence in tables and graphs cannot guarantee equivalence for all values of x.

Students may vary in how convincing they find both algebraic reasoning and reasoning from problem conditions. Reasoning from problem conditions can be very intuitive, but sometimes an error in translating such reasoning to symbols is easy to overlook. Algebraic reasoning is the only way to guarantee equivalence for all values of x; however, symbol manipulation techniques are prone to error, particularly when the manipulations become complicated, or particular techniques may be beyond one's current skill level.

It is probably best to use more than one technique to evaluate whether or not two expressions are equivalent.

b. Students may suggest that comparing graphs and tables can often quickly reveal when two expressions are not equivalent and can give an indication of potential equivalences. They may also comment on the complexity of the expressions as a reason they may choose to compare tables and graphs. If both expressions came from a problem situation, students may refer to the situation to examine equivalences; if both expressions represent the same thing in the situation, then they must be equivalent. Algebraic reasoning is sometimes the quickest way to verify equivalence.

c. Student responses may depend on their confidence with the strategies at this time in their mathematical development. (It is wise to check your thinking with a second strategy.)

17 a. Bushra is correct since for a rectangle, $area = length \times width = x(y + z)$.

b. Kareem is correct since he probably sees four triangles and uses the formula $0.5(base)(height)$. The two larger triangles have base z and height x. The two smaller triangles have base y and height x.

c. Fatmeh is not correct. She is representing the perimeter not the area.

d. **i.** $x(y + z)$ is equivalent to $xy + xz$ because of the distributive property.

ii. $\frac{1}{2}zx + \frac{1}{2}zx + \frac{1}{2}xy + \frac{1}{2}xy$ is equivalent to $zx + xy$ because of the distributive property and the fact that $\frac{1}{2} + \frac{1}{2} = 1$.

e. The work in Part d is guided by algebraic properties that produce equivalent expressions without reliance on contextual cues that might give quantitative meaning to the manipulations.

CCSS CCSS MATHEMATICAL PRACTICE
Task 17 highlights the practice: look for and make use of structure.

ON YOUR OWN

EXTENSIONS

18 Suppose that the conditions for operation of a rented bungee jump at the school carnival are as follows:

- The number of customers n will depend on the price per jump x (in dollars) according to the linear function $n = 80 - 0.75x$.

- Insurance will cost $500 plus $2 per jumper.

- Costs include $250 for delivery and setup and $3 per jumper to pay a trained operator to supervise use of the jumping equipment.

a. Write two rules for calculating projected profit for this attraction as a function of price per jump x. Write one rule in a form that shows how each income and cost factor contributes and another that is more efficient for calculation. Explain how you are sure that the two rules are equivalent.

b. Use one of the profit rules from Part a to estimate the price that will yield maximum profit and to find what that profit is.

c. Use one of the profit rules from Part a to estimate price(s) that will assure at least some profit (not a loss) for the attraction.

19 The sum of two linear expressions is always a linear expression, but the product of two linear expressions is *not always* a quadratic expression.

a. Use what you know about rearranging and combining terms in a linear expression to prove that $(ax + b) + (cx + d)$ is always a linear expression.

b. Find examples of linear expressions $ax + b$ and $cx + d$ for which the product $(ax + b)(cx + d)$ is not a quadratic expression.

c. Under what conditions will the product of two linear expressions *not be* a quadratic expression?

20 Consider the following mathematical question.

If a 5-ft tall person stands in one spot on the equator of Earth for 24 hours, how much farther will that person's head travel than his or her feet as Earth rotates about its axis?

a. Before doing any calculations, which of the following would you guess as an answer to the question?

1 foot	30 feet	300 feet	3,000 feet
1 mile	30 miles	300 miles	3,000 miles

b. Use the facts that the radius of Earth is about 4,000 miles at the equator and there are 5,280 feet in one mile to find the answer.

c. Use algebraic reasoning to answer this more general question:

If a tower that is k feet tall stands upright on the equator of a sphere of radius r feet, how much farther will the top of the tower travel than the base of the tower as the sphere makes one complete revolution about its axis?

Show that your answer works for the case of the person standing on Earth's equator.

18 **a.** *profit = income − insurance cost − delivery/setup cost − operator cost*
$$= x(80 − 0.75x) − (500 + 2(80 − 0.75x)) − 250 − 3(80 − 0.75x)$$
$$= −0.75x^2 + 83.75x − 1{,}150$$
It would be possible to compare the two expressions by inspecting patterns in tables or graphs, or by reasoning showing how the first expression actually condenses to the second by expanding and then combining like terms.

   b. The maximum profit occurs when $x ≈ 55.83$ and the profit at that price level is approximately \$1,188.

   c. The break-even point(s) are $x ≈ 16.03$ and $x ≈ 95.63$, so the attraction will make a positive profit for any ticket prices x, $16.03 < x < 95.63$.

19 **a.** $(ax + b) + (cx + d)$

$(ax + cx) + (b + d)$	Rearrangement
$(a + c)x + (b + d)$	Distributive property

The last expression represents a number times x plus a number. Thus, $(a + c)x + (b + d)$ is a linear expression.

   b. Any example where either a, c, or both are equal to 0 will yield a product that is not a quadratic expression.

   c. If one or both of the linear expressions are constants (numbers),then the product will not be quadratic. (The product of two linear expressions is quadratic if and only if the coefficients of x in both rules are not 0.)

20 **a.** Student guesses will likely vary.

   b. Feet will travel: $2π(4{,}000 \cdot 5{,}280)$, or about 132,700,874 feet.
Head will travel: $2π(4{,}000 \cdot 5{,}280 + 5) = 2π(4{,}000 \cdot 5{,}280) + 2π(5)$, or about 132,700,905 feet.
So, a 5-ft tall person's head will travel $10π ≈ 30$ feet farther than his or her head as Earth completes one revolution about its axis.

   c. Base will travel: $2πr$ feet
Top will travel: $2π(r + k)$, or $2πr + 2πk$ feet
So, the top of the tower will travel $2πk$ feet farther than the base.
Check: $2π(5) ≈ 31.4$ feet

d. The next sketch shows a disc inside a shaded ring. If the disc has radius 1 inch and the ring adds 0.25 inches to the radius of the figure, what is the area of the shaded ring?

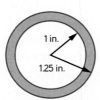

1 in.

1.25 in.

e. If a disc of radius *r* is inside a shaded ring that adds *k* to the radius, what rule gives the area of the shaded ring? Express that rule using the simplest possible expression involving *r* and *k*.

f. Natasha thought you might be able to calculate the area of the shaded ring by thinking about unwrapping the ring from around the disc. She said it would be pretty close to a rectangle, so its area could be estimated by multiplying the circumference of the ring by the width of the ring. She thought of three possible calculations to estimate this area.

$$2\pi rk \qquad 2\pi(r + k)k \qquad 2\pi\left(r + \frac{k}{2}\right)k$$

   i. What thinking would have led Natasha to each of these expressions for area of the shaded ring?

   ii. Which, if any, of the expressions gives a correct way of estimating the area of the shaded ring?

21 Study the geometric design in the figure below—a square with sides of length *s* surrounded by four congruent rectangles.

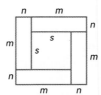

a. Express *s* in terms of *m* and *n*.

b. Express the area of the large square in two equivalent ways—each a function of *m* and *n*.

c. Equate the two expressions for area you found in Part b. Then explain how this equation implies that $(m + n)^2 \geq 4mn$ for any positive numbers *m* and *n*.

d. Use the result in Part c to explain why $\frac{m + n}{2} \geq \sqrt{mn}$ for any positive numbers *m* and *n*. This is known as the *arithmetic mean-geometric mean inequality*.

d. Area (shaded ring) = Area (larger circle) − Area (smaller circle)
$$= \pi(1.25)^2 - \pi(1)^2$$
$$= 0.5625\pi$$
$$\approx 1.77 \text{ square inches}$$

e. Area (shaded ring) = Area (larger circle) − Area (smaller circle)
$$= \pi(r + k)^2 - \pi r^2$$
$$= \pi r^2 + 2\pi kr + \pi k^2 - \pi r^2$$
$$= 2\pi kr + \pi k^2 \text{ or } \pi k(2r + k)$$

f. **i.** The first expression uses the smaller radius; the second expression uses the larger radius; and the last expression uses the average of the smaller and larger radii.

   ii. The last expression $2\pi\left(r + \frac{k}{2}\right)k$, which uses the average radius, gives a correct way of calculating the area of the shaded ring.
   $$2\pi\left(r + \frac{k}{2}\right)k = 2\pi kr + \pi k^2 \text{ as in Part e.}$$

21 **a.** $s = m - n$

   b. $A = (m + n)^2$ or $A = (m - n)^2 + 4mn$

   c. $(m + n)^2 = (m - n)^2 + 4mn$
   Since $(m - n)^2$ is always a non-negative number, $(m - n)^2 + 4mn \geq 4mn$.
   By substitution, we arrive at $(m + n)^2 \geq 4mn$ for any positive numbers m and n.

   d. $(m + n)^2 \geq 4mn$ Given

   $(m + n) \geq 2\sqrt{mn}$ Taking the square root of both sides

   $\frac{m + n}{2} \geq \sqrt{mn}$ Division by 2

ON YOUR OWN

22 Expand each expression and look for a pattern to shortcut the calculations.

a. $(3x + 5)(2x + 1)$ **b.** $(5x - 3)(x + 4)$

c. $(-2x + 7)(4x - 3)$ **d.** $(7x - 4)(x + 2)$

e. $(ax + b)(cx + d)$

23 Find equivalent expanded forms for each given expression and look for a pattern to shortcut the calculations.

a. $(3x + 5)^2$ **b.** $(5x - 3)^2$

c. $(-2x + 7)^2$ **d.** $(7x - 4)^2$

e. $(ax + b)^2$

24 Find equivalent expanded forms for each given expression and look for a pattern to shortcut the calculations.

a. $(3x + 5)(3x - 5)$ **b.** $(2x - 3)(2x + 3)$

c. $(-2x + 7)(-2x - 7)$ **d.** $(8 - 4x)(8 + 4x)$

e. $(ax + b)(ax - b)$

25 Consider all quadratic functions with rules of the form $y = ax^2 + bx$.

a. How can any expression $ax^2 + bx$ be written as a product of linear factors?

b. Why does the factored form in Part a imply that $ax^2 + bx = 0$ when $x = 0$ and when $x = \frac{-b}{a}$?

c. How does the information from Part b imply that the maximum or minimum point on the graph of any function $y = ax^2 + bx$ occurs where $x = \frac{-b}{2a}$?

REVIEW

26 Solve these linear equations.

a. $3.5x + 5 = 26$ **b.** $7(2x - 9) = 42$

c. $\frac{5x}{2} + 12 = 99$ **d.** $3.5x - 8 = 12 + 5x$

e. $7x + 4 = 4(x + 7)$ **f.** $3(x + 2) = 1.5(4 + 2x)$

27 Amy's last 10 scores on 50-point quizzes are 30, 32, 34, 34, 35, 35, 35, 36, 40, 42.

a. She says she can find her mean score by adding 3.0, 3.2, 3.4, 3.4, 3.5, 3.5, 3.5, 3.6, 4.0, and 4.2. Her friend Bart says she has to add and divide the total by 10,

$$\frac{30 + 32 + 34 + 34 + 35 + 35 + 35 + 36 + 40 + 42}{10}.$$

Who is correct? Explain why.

22 **a.** $6x^2 + 13x + 5$

    b. $5x^2 + 17x - 12$

    c. $-8x^2 + 34x - 21$

    d. $7x^2 + 10x - 8$

    e. $acx^2 + (bc + ad)x + bd$

INSTRUCTIONAL NOTE

In Extensions Tasks 22, 23, and 24, you may wish to have students express the patterns for the shortcut calculations in words.

23 **a.** $9x^2 + 30x + 25$

    b. $25x^2 - 30x + 9$

    c. $4x^2 - 28x + 49$

    d. $49x^2 - 56x + 16$

    e. $a^2x^2 + 2abx + b^2$ or $(ax)^2 + 2abx + b^2$

24 **a.** $9x^2 - 25$

    b. $4x^2 - 9$

    c. $4x^2 - 49$

    d. $-16x^2 + 64$

    e. $a^2x^2 - b^2$ or $(ax)^2 - b^2$

25 **a.** $ax^2 + bx = x(ax + b)$ or $ax\left(x + \dfrac{b}{a}\right)$

    b. In factored form, the product will be 0 if and only if at least one of the factors is 0. That occurs when $x = 0$ and when $x = \dfrac{-b}{a}$.

    c. Since students will very likely have discovered that all quadratics have parabolic graphs that are symmetric about a vertical line through the maximum or minimum point, the vertex occurs midway between the two x-intercepts. Those intercepts are 0 and $\dfrac{-b}{a}$. The midpoint of those two points on the x-axis is the average of those two x values or $\dfrac{0 + \frac{-b}{a}}{2} = \dfrac{-b}{2a}$.

REVIEW

 JUST IN TIME

26 **a.** $x = 6$

    b. $x = 7.5$

    c. $x = 34.8$

    d. $x = -13\frac{1}{3}$

    e. $x = 8$

    f. x is any number

27 **a.** They are both correct. Bart has the traditional method. Amy has divided each individual score by 10 since there are 10 scores. If you start with Bart's formula and use the distributive property you get Amy's calculation.

b. Amy is hoping for a 44 on the next 50-point quiz. If so, she says she will add 4.4 to her current mean to get the new mean. Is she correct?

c. Amy says that if she gets a 44 on the next quiz, her median score will increase. Bart disagrees. Who is correct? Explain.

28 In the diagram at the right, $\overline{AB} \cong \overline{BC}$ and m$\angle 1 = 100°$. Use geometric reasoning to determine:

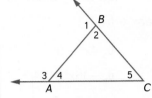

a. m$\angle 2$

b. m$\angle 4 +$ m$\angle 5$

c. m$\angle 4$

d. m$\angle 3$

29 Try using various values of a, b, and c to help you determine if each pair of expressions are equivalent. If you think they are not equivalent, show this with an example using values for a, b, and c. If you think they are equivalent, use algebraic reasoning to transform one into the other.

a. $(a + b)^2$ and $a^2 + b^2$

b. $a(b - c)$ and $ab - ac$

c. $\sqrt{a^2 + b^2}$ and $a + b$

d. $\dfrac{\sqrt{9a^2}}{3}$ and a $(a \geq 0)$

e. $(ab)^c$ and $a^c b^c$

f. $\sqrt[3]{a^3 b^6}$ and ab^2

30 Alex takes two servings of fruit with him every day to school. Suppose that there are always apples, oranges, grapes, and watermelon in his house.

a. List all the possibilities for his daily fruit if he wants two different types of fruit.

b. How much longer would your list be if he didn't care if the types of fruit were different? Explain your reasoning.

31 Draw a triangle that has a perimeter of 12 cm.

a. What are the lengths of the sides of your triangle?

b. Suppose that another student in your class drew a triangle with the same side lengths as yours. Will the two triangles be guaranteed to be congruent? Explain your reasoning.

c. Heather wants to draw a right triangle that has perimeter 12 cm. Give possible whole number lengths of the sides that she could use. Explain how you know they will give her a right triangle.

d. Christine indicates that the triangle she drew has sides of length 7 cm, 3 cm, and 2 cm. Is that possible? Explain why or why not.

32 Explain, as precisely as you can, why a rectangle with a pair of consecutive sides the same length is a square.

b. No, she is not correct. She now has 11 scores so if she divided each by 11 (not very convenient), then she would get the correct mean.

c. Bart is correct. The median will be 35 before and after the 11th quiz.

28 **a.** 80° **b.** 100° **c.** 50° **d.** 130°

🕐 **JUST IN TIME**

29 **a.** Not equivalent; for example, $(3 + 4)^2 \neq 3^2 + 4^2$ since $49 \neq 25$.

b. Equivalent by the distributive property

c. Not equivalent; for example, $\sqrt{3^2 + 4^2} \neq 3 + 4$ since $5 \neq 7$.

d. Equivalent; $\dfrac{\sqrt{9a^2}}{3} = \dfrac{3a}{3} = a \, (a \geq 0)$

e. Equivalent
$$\underbrace{(ab) \cdot (ab) \cdot \cdots \cdot (ab)}_{c \text{ times}} = \underbrace{(a \cdot a \cdot \cdots \cdot a)}_{c \text{ times}} \cdot \underbrace{(b \cdot b \cdot \cdots \cdot b)}_{c \text{ times}} = a^c b^c$$

f. Equivalent; $\sqrt[3]{a^3 b^6} = \sqrt[3]{(ab^2)^3} = ab^2$

30 **a.** The possible fruit combinations:
apple and orange
apple and grapes
apple and watermelon
orange and grapes
orange and watermelon
grapes and watermelon

b. The list of fruit combinations would include four more choices:
apple and apple
orange and orange
grapes and grapes
watermelon and watermelon

31 **a.** Answers will vary.

b. Yes; two triangles with the same side lengths are congruent by the SSS congruence condition.

c. Heather must have a triangle with side lengths of 3 cm, 4 cm, and 5 cm. It must be a right triangle since the Pythagorean Theorem holds true: $3^2 + 4^2 = 5^2$.

d. Such a triangle is not possible since $3 + 2 \leq 7$.

32 If a rectangle has a pair of consecutive sides the same length, then because the opposite sides are the same length, all four sides are the same length. Thus, the rectangle is a rhombus with a right angle, which by definition is a square.

INSTRUCTIONAL NOTE

For Task 32, students now have two different ways to show that a quadrilateral is a square: (1) a rhombus with one right angle and (2) a rectangle with two consecutive sides the same length.

TEACHING RESOURCES

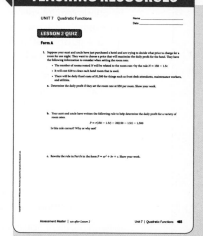

Assessment Masters 465–470
ⓘ **GO DIGITAL**

LESSON 3

Solving Quadratic Equations

Many key questions about quadratic functions require solving equations. For example, you used the function $h = 8 + 40.8t - 16t^2$ to answer questions about the flight of a long basketball shot.

> To find the time when the shot would reach the 10-foot height of the basket, you solved the equation
> $$8 + 40.8t - 16t^2 = 10.$$

> To find the time when an "air ball" would hit the floor, you solved the equation
> $$8 + 40.8t - 16t^2 = 0.$$

The values of t that satisfy the equations are called the **solutions** of the equations.

In each problem, you could get good estimates of the required solutions by searching in tables of values or by tracing coordinates of points on the graphs of the height function.

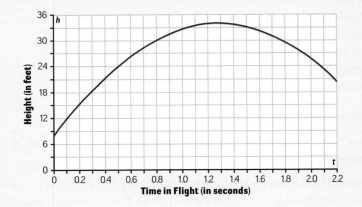

t	0	0.2	0.4	0.6	0.8	1.0	1.2	1.4	1.6	1.8	2.0	2.2
h	8	15.2	21.8	26.7	30.4	32.8	33.9	33.8	32.3	29.6	25.6	20.3

Frederic J. Brown/AFP/Getty Images

510 UNIT 7 | Quadratic Functions

UNIT 7

Solving Quadratic Equations

In standard high school algebra courses, a great deal of time is devoted to developing skill in solving quadratic equations. The most prominent strategy taught involves writing the equation in the form $ax^2 + bx + c = 0$, factoring the quadratic expression into a product of two linear factors, setting each linear factor equal to zero, and solving for x. Unfortunately, even when all coefficients are integers, only a small fraction of quadratic expressions can be factored over the integers. Thus, the strategy that is given so much time is not very practical for most applications of quadratic functions and equations.

This lesson addresses the very important topic of solving quadratic equations to answer questions about quadratic functions. However, it does not aim to develop students' factoring skill, except in the case of factoring a common monomial term by direct use of the distributive property. Instead of focusing on solving by factoring, the lesson emphasizes noncalculator strategies for solving quadratics of the form $ax^2 + c = d$ and $ax^2 + bx = 0$ and use of the quadratic formula for the form $ax^2 + bx + c = 0$ cases.

This lesson and unit comprise only the start of work on quadratics and other polynomials in the *Core-Plus Mathematics* program. The basic ideas will be extended in future courses and the skills will be reviewed periodically in future units. Furthermore, it is important that the focus on formal methods and symbol manipulation strategies should not cause students to forget that in practical problem solving they also have very useful estimation methods for solving quadratic equations by examining tables of function values or tracing points on graphs.

Lesson Objectives

- Write quadratic equations and inequalities to express questions about quadratic functions

- Find exact values of solutions for quadratic equations in the form $ax^2 + c = d$ and $ax^2 + bx = 0$ by reasoning and factoring

- Relate factored forms of quadratic expressions to x-intercepts of graphs for the related functions

- Solve quadratic equations by using the quadratic formula

- Describe the possible number of real solutions for quadratic equations and illustrate the possibilities with graphs

NOTE Quadratic equations are being addressed in the real number system at this point. Complex numbers will be introduced in Course 3.

Common Core State Standards CCSS
Focused on:
A-SSE.2, A-SSE.3, A-REI.4, A-REI.10, F-IF.7
Connected to:
A-APR.3, A-REI.7, F-IF.4

THINK ABOUT THIS SITUATION

Based on what you know about the tables and graphs of quadratic functions:

a How many solutions would you expect for each of these equations, and what strategies would you use to find those solutions?

    i. $8 + 40.8t - 16t^2 = 10$

    ii. $8 + 40.8t - 16t^2 = 0$

    iii. $8 + 40.8t - 16t^2 = 40$

    iv. $8 + 40.8t - 16t^2 = 34$

b How many solutions would you expect for other quadratic equations in the form $ax^2 + bx + c = d$?

In this lesson, you will explore methods for finding exact solutions of quadratic equations.

INVESTIGATION 1

Solving $ax^2 + c = d$ and $ax^2 + bx = 0$

Calculator or computer tables, graphs, and symbol manipulation tools are helpful in finding approximate or exact solutions for quadratic equations and inequalities. But there are times when it is easier to use algebraic reasoning alone. As you work on the problems of this investigation, look for answers to this question:

What are some effective methods for solving
quadratic equations algebraically?

1 Some quadratic equations can be solved by use of the fact that for any positive number n, the equation $x^2 = n$ is satisfied by two numbers: $\sqrt{n}$ and $-\sqrt{n}$.

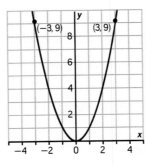

Students have already solved quadratic equations in several problem settings prior to this lesson. The purpose of this Think About This Situation is to remind students of the estimation methods with which they should be comfortable and to raise the general question of how many solutions can be expected for quadratic equations in general. It is not uncommon to find that when students examine tables or graphs to estimate solutions of equations, they find one solution and forget to look for others.

You might start a discussion on this TATS by helping students recall the function in Lesson 1, giving height of a basketball shot as a function of time in flight. Without showing the graph, you might ask questions like the following.

• *What information would you get by solving the equation $8 + 40.8t - 16t^2 = 10$?*

• *How about from solving the equation $8 + 40.8t - 16t^2 = 0$?*

Then you could display the graph and table in the text and ask students for their ideas about Part a.

THINK ABOUT THIS SITUATION

a   **i.** $8 + 40.8t - 16t^2 = 10$ has two solutions, $t \approx 0.05$ and $t \approx 2.5$ seconds.

ii. $8 + 40.8t - 16t^2 = 0$ has two solutions, $t \approx -0.2$ and $t \approx 2.7$ seconds.

iii. $8 + 40.8t - 16t^2 = 40$ has no solutions because the maximum height is about 34 feet.

iv. $8 + 40.8t - 16t^2 = 34$ appears to have only one solution, $t = 1.3$ seconds. The maximum value of h occurs when $t = 1.275$ seconds and that height is about 34.01 feet.

b   It is possible to find quadratic equations of the given form that have zero, one, or two solutions. Student answers to Part a might give them ideas about this general question. On the other hand, the idea of a Think About This Situation is mainly to raise an issue and to diagnose student ideas at the start of a lesson. It would be quite suitable to simply leave this as an open issue to be decided upon in the investigations that follow.

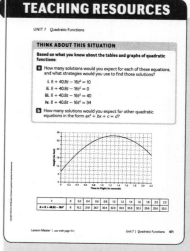
INVESTIGATION 1   A-SSE.2, A-SSE.3, A-REI.4, A-REI.10, F-IF.7, A-APR.3, F-IF.4

Solving $ax^2 + c = d$ and $ax^2 + bx = 0$

The goal of this investigation is to help students develop strategies that are useful in solving two types of quadratic equations by reasoning and direct symbol manipulation. These are types that can readily be solved. The specific examples used in the problems also highlight issues about how many solutions are possible, the connections between solving equations and finding *x*-intercepts of graphs, and connections with locating maximum or minimum points of parabolas.

INSTRUCTIONAL NOTE

For Part aiv, while technically the given equation has two solutions, the idea here is to simply raise the possibility that a quadratic might have only one solution. Working only from the graph information, that is a reasonable conjecture in this case.

COLLABORATION SKILL

Help clarify the discussion by asking questions or adding evidence to the discussion.

Use this principle and what you know about solving linear equations to solve the following quadratic equations. In each case, check your reasoning by substituting the proposed solution values for x in the original equation.

a. $x^2 = 25$

b. $x^2 = 12$

c. $5x^2 = 60$

d. $5x^2 + 8 = 8$

e. $5x^2 + 15 = 60$

f. $5x^2 + 75 = 60$

g. $-5x^2 + 75 = 60$

h. $x^2 = -16$

2 Use the methods you developed in reasoning to solutions for equations in Problem 1 to answer these questions about flight of a platform diver.

a. If the diver jumps off a 50-foot platform, what rule gives her or his distance fallen d (in feet) as a function of time t (in seconds)?

b. Write and solve an equation to find the time required for the diver to fall 20 feet.

c. What function gives the height h (in feet) of the diver at any time t (in seconds) after she or he jumps from the platform?

d. Write and solve an equation to find the time when the diver hits the water.

3 If a soccer player kicks the ball from a spot on the ground with initial upward velocity of 24 feet per second, the height of the ball h (in feet) at any time t seconds after the kick will be approximated by the quadratic function $h = 24t - 16t^2$. Finding the time when the ball hits the ground again requires solving the equation $24t - 16t^2 = 0$.

a. Check the reasoning in this proposed solution of the equation.

  i. The expression $24t - 16t^2$ is equivalent to $8t(3 - 2t)$. Why?

  ii. The expression $8t(3 - 2t)$ will equal 0 when $t = 0$ and when $3 - 2t = 0$. Why?

  iii. So, the solutions of the equation $24t - 16t^2 = 0$ will be 0 and 1.5. Why?

b. Adapt the reasoning in Part a to solve these quadratic equations.

  i. $0 = x^2 + 4x$

  ii. $0 = 3x^2 + 10x$

  iii. $0 = x^2 - 4x$

  iv. $-x^2 - 5x = 0$

  v. $-2x^2 - 6x = 0$

  vi. $x^2 + 5x = 6$

1 **a.** $x = \pm 5$

b. $x = \pm\sqrt{12} = \pm 2\sqrt{3}$ or $x \approx \pm 3.46$

c. $x = \pm\sqrt{12} = \pm 2\sqrt{3}$ or $x \approx \pm 3.46$

d. $x = 0$

e. $x = \pm 3$

f. No solutions

g. $x = \pm\sqrt{3}$ or $x \approx \pm 1.732$

h. No solutions

2 Students should ignore any force other than gravity, such as air resistance.

a. Distance fallen in feet: $d = 16t^2$

b. Time to fall 20 feet: $20 = 16t^2$
Solutions: $t \approx \pm 1.12$ seconds, but only 1.12 seconds makes sense here.

c. Height in feet after t seconds: $h = 50 - 16t^2$

d. Time to hit water in seconds: $0 = 50 - 16t^2$
Solutions: $t \approx \pm 1.77$ seconds, but only 1.77 seconds makes sense here.

3 **a.** **i.** $24t - 16t^2$ is equivalent to $8t(3 - 2t)$ because of the distributive property.

ii. $8t(3 - 2t)$ will equal 0 in case $t = 0$ and in case $3 - 2t = 0$ because a product is 0 if and only if at least one of the factors is 0.

iii. Solutions of the equation $24t - 16t^2 = 0$ will be 0 and 1.5 because those are the values of t that make the factors 0.

b. Student solutions should show that they can factor the expressions and identify each solution from the factored form set equal to 0.

i. $x = 0$ or $x = -4$

ii. $x = 0$ or $x = \dfrac{-10}{3}$

iii. $x = 0$ or $x = 4$

iv. $x = 0$ or $x = -5$

v. $x = 0$ or $x = -3$

vi. $x^2 + 5x = 6$: The procedure does not apply here! The equation cannot be solved by the same reasoning as equations of the form $ax^2 + bx = 0$. Using tables or graphs, $x = 1$ and $x = -6$.

4 Solving quadratic equations like $3x^2 - 15 = 0$ and $3x^2 - 15x = 0$ locates x-intercepts on the graphs of the quadratic functions $y = 3x^2 - 15$ and $y = 3x^2 - 15x$.

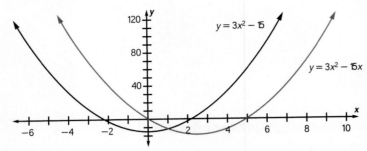

a. Using the graphs above, explain how the symmetry of these parabolas can be used to relate the location of the minimum (or maximum) point on the graph of a quadratic function to the x-intercepts.

b. Use the results of your work in Problem 3 to find coordinates of the maximum or minimum points on the graphs of these quadratic functions.

    i. $y = x^2 + 4x$ **ii.** $y = 3x^2 + 10x$

    iii. $y = x^2 - 4x$ **iv.** $y = -x^2 - 5x$

    v. $y = -2x^2 - 6x$ **vi.** $y = ax^2 + bx$

5 Use what you know about solving quadratic equations and the graphs of quadratic functions to answer these questions.

a. What choices of values for a and d will give equations in the form $ax^2 = d$ that have two solutions? Only one solution? No solutions? Explain the reasoning behind your answers and illustrate that reasoning with sketches of graphs for the related function $y = ax^2$.

b. What choices of values for a, c, and d will give equations in the form $ax^2 + c = d$ that have two solutions? Only one solution? No solutions? Explain the reasoning behind your answers and illustrate that reasoning with sketches of graphs for the related function $y = ax^2 + c$.

c. Why must every equation in the form $ax^2 + bx = 0$ (neither a nor b zero) have exactly two solutions? Explain the reasoning behind your answer and illustrate that reasoning with sketches of graphs for the related function $y = ax^2 + bx$.

4 **a.** The idea here is to recognize that due to the symmetry of parabolas, the max/min points will lie on the line of symmetry, located midway between the zeroes of the function.

b. **i.** Zeroes are 0 and -4, has minimum point $(-2, -4)$.

ii. Zeroes are 0 and $\frac{-10}{3}$, has minimum point $\left(\frac{-10}{6}, \frac{-25}{3}\right)$.

iii. Zeroes are 0 and 4, has minimum point $(2, -4)$.

iv. Zeroes are 0 and -5, has maximum point $(-2.5, 6.25)$.

v. Zeroes are 0 and -3, has maximum point $(-1.5, 4.5)$.

vi. Zeroes are $x = 0$ and $x = \frac{-b}{a}$, has max or min point at $\left(\frac{-b}{2a}, \frac{-b^2}{4a}\right)$.
(The formulas are not so important as realizing that the zeroes of $y = ax^2 + bx$ are always 0 and $\frac{-b}{a}$ and the x-coordinate of the max/min point is midway between the zeroes.)

5 | **INSTRUCTIONAL NOTE** You might use this item for a full-class discussion. Students should be beginning to move flexibly between the symbolic and visual representations of quadratic functions. Some students may use their visual understandings from Lesson 1 to support their answers. Encourage students to also reason algebraically as was done in this lesson. Questions to consider asking are:

- What is the solution?
- Under what conditions can you take the square root?

The discussion around STM Parts c and d provide an opportunity to make these connections secure.

a. Possible numbers of solutions are zero, one, and two. Students might cite examples from Problem 1 or generalize that the solutions are $\pm\sqrt{\frac{d}{a}}$ to recognize the following:

two solutions: $\frac{d}{a} > 0$ (both d and a have the same sign)

one solution: $\frac{d}{a} = 0$ $(d = 0)$

zero solutions: $\frac{d}{a} < 0$ (d and a have opposite signs)

Student-drawn sketches similar to those in the STM should support their algebraic reasoning.

b. Possible numbers of solutions are zero, one, and two.

two solutions: $\frac{d - c}{a} > 0$ ($d - c$ has the same sign as a)

one solution: $\frac{d - c}{a} = 0$ $(d - c = 0)$

zero solutions: $\frac{d - c}{a} < 0$ ($d - c$ has the opposite sign as a)

c. Since $ax^2 + bx = x(ax + b)$ and neither a nor b are 0, there are two solutions: $x = 0$ and $x = \frac{-b}{a}$.

SUMMARIZE THE MATHEMATICS

In this investigation, you learned how to find exact solutions for some forms of quadratic equations by algebraic reasoning.

a Describe a process that uses rules of algebra to find solutions for any quadratic equation in the form $ax^2 + c = d$.

b Describe a process that uses rules of algebra to find solutions for any quadratic equation in the form $ax^2 + bx = 0$.

c What are the possible numbers of solutions for equations in the form $ax^2 = d$? For equations in the form $ax^2 + c = d$? For equations in the form $ax^2 + bx = 0$?

d How can graphs of quadratic functions in the form $y = ax^2$, $y = ax^2 + c$, and $y = ax^2 + bx$ be used to illustrate your answers to Part c?

e How can you locate the maximum or minimum point on the graph of a quadratic function with rule in the form:

    i. $y = ax^2$ **ii.** $y = ax^2 + c$ **iii.** $y = ax^2 + bx$

Be prepared to share your ideas and reasoning strategies with the class.

 CHECK YOUR UNDERSTANDING

Quadratic equations, like linear equations, can often be solved more easily by algebraic reasoning than by estimation using a graph or table of values for the related quadratic function.

a. Solve each of these quadratic equations algebraically.

    i. $3x^2 = 36$

    ii. $-7x^2 = 28$

    iii. $5x^2 + 23 = 83$

    iv. $-2x^2 + 4 = 4$

    v. $7x^2 - 12x = 0$

    vi. $x^2 + 2x = 0$

b. Use algebraic methods to find coordinates of the maximum and minimum points on graphs of these quadratic functions.

    i. $y = -5x^2 - 2$

    ii. $y = 5x^2 + 3$

    iii. $y = x^2 - 8x$

    iv. $y = -x^2 + 2x$

UNIT 7

As you lead a class discussion of the Summarize the Mathematics, keep in mind the investigation goals—getting students to explore different strategies for solving quadratic equations by hand in two simple cases.

SUMMARIZE THE MATHEMATICS

a Students' articulation of their strategies will vary, but will probably involve something like this:

Subtract c from both sides to get $ax^2 = d - c$.

Divide both sides by a to get $x^2 = \dfrac{d-c}{a}$.

Take the square root of each side of the equation.

b Again, students' articulation of strategies will vary, but the key steps are: Factor the left side to get $x(ax + b) = 0$. Since the product $x(ax + b) = 0$, reason that solutions occur when factors are 0. One solution is $x = 0$ and the other is obtained by solving the linear equation $ax + b = 0$.

c Equations in the form $ax^2 = d$ and $ax^2 + c = d$ can have zero, one, or two solutions. Equations in the form $ax^2 + bx = 0$ always have exactly two solutions (as long as neither a nor b is 0).

d Illustrative graphs might look like the ones at the right.

Case $ax^2 = d$: Using the function $y = x^2$, zero, one, and two solutions exist for $x^2 = -2$, $x^2 = 0$, and $x^2 = 2$, respectively.

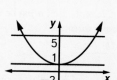

Case $ax^2 + c = d$: Using the function $y = x^2 + 1$, zero, one, and two solutions exist for $x^2 + 1 = -2$, $x^2 + 1 = 1$, and $x^2 + 1 = 5$, respectively.

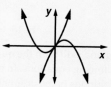

Case $ax^2 + bx = 0$: Using the functions $y = x^2 + 2x$ and $y = -x^2 + 2x$, you see that there are two solutions for each; one of which is at the origin.

e For each form, the function will have a maximum point if $a < 0$ and a minimum point if $a > 0$.

  i. For $y = ax^2$ examples, the max/min point will always be at $(0, 0)$.

  ii. For $y = ax^2 + c$ examples, the max/min point will be at $(0, c)$.

  iii. For $y = ax^2 + bx$, the max/min point will have x-coordinate midway between the solutions to $ax^2 + bx = 0$: $x = 0$ and $x = \dfrac{-b}{a}$.

  Substitute $x = \dfrac{-b}{2a}$ in the function rule to find the y-coordinate.

Lesson Master 472
Ⓘ **GO DIGITAL**

INSTRUCTIONAL NOTE

Possible discussion question is: What is the general equation form when the maximum or minimum point lies on the y-axis?

PROCESSING PROMPT

_____ helped clarify
(name)
our discussion by ...

MATH TOOLKIT

- Describe when each equation will have one, two, or no real solutions:
$$ax^2 = d$$
$$ax^2 + bx = 0$$

- Describe how to find the maximum or minimum point for:
$$y = ax^2$$
$$y = ax^2 + bx$$
$$y = ax^2 + bx + c$$

NOTE The solutions to the Check Your Understanding are on page T515.

INVESTIGATION 2

The Quadratic Formula

Many problems that require solving quadratic equations involve *trinomial* expressions like $15 + 90t - 16t^2$ that are not easily expressed in equivalent factored forms. So, solving equations like

$$15 + 90t - 16t^2 = 100$$

(When is a flying pumpkin 100 feet above the ground?)

is not as easy as solving equations like those in Investigation 1.

Fortunately, there is a **quadratic formula** that shows how to find all solutions of any quadratic equation in the form $ax^2 + bx + c = 0$. For any such equation, the solutions are

$$x = \frac{-b}{2a} + \frac{\sqrt{b^2 - 4ac}}{2a} \text{ and } x = \frac{-b}{2a} - \frac{\sqrt{b^2 - 4ac}}{2a}.$$

In Course 3 of *Core-Plus Mathematics*, you will prove that the quadratic formula gives the solutions to any quadratic equation. For now, to use the quadratic formula in any particular case, all you have to do is

- be sure that the quadratic expression is set equal to 0 as is prescribed by the formula;
- identify the values of a, b, and c; and
- substitute those values where they occur in the formula.

As you work on the problems in this investigation, make notes of answers to these questions:

What calculations in the quadratic formula give information on the number of solutions of the related quadratic equation?

What calculations provide information on the x-intercepts and maximum or minimum point of the graph of the related quadratic function?

1 Solve each quadratic equation by following the procedure for applying the quadratic formula.

- Give the values of a, b, and c that must be used to solve the equations by use of the quadratic formula.
- Evaluate $\frac{-b}{2a}$ and $\frac{\sqrt{b^2 - 4ac}}{2a}$.
- Evaluate $x = \frac{-b}{2a} + \frac{\sqrt{b^2 - 4ac}}{2a}$ and $x = \frac{-b}{2a} - \frac{\sqrt{b^2 - 4ac}}{2a}$.
- Check that the solutions produced by the formula actually satisfy the equation.

    a. $2x^2 - 2x - 12 = 0$ **b.** $15 + 90t - 16t^2 = 100$

2 Test your understanding and skill with the quadratic formula by using it to find solutions for the following equations. In each case, check your work by substituting proposed solutions in the original equation and by sketching a graph of the related quadratic function to show how the solutions appear as points on the graph.

    a. $x^2 - 7x + 10 = 0$ **b.** $x^2 - x - 8 = 0$

    c. $-x^2 - 3x + 10 = 0$ **d.** $2x^2 - 12x + 18 = 0$

    e. $13 - 6x + x^2 = 0$ **f.** $-x^2 - 4x - 2 = 2$

Lesson 3 | Solving Quadratic Equations **515**

✔️ CHECK YOUR UNDERSTANDING

a.   **i.** $x = \pm\sqrt{12}$ or $x \approx \pm 3.46$ **ii.** No solutions

     iii. $x = \pm\sqrt{12}$ or $x \approx \pm 3.46$ **iv.** $x = 0$

     v. $x = 0$ and $x = \dfrac{12}{7}$ **vi.** $x = 0$ and $x = -2$

b.   **i.** Maximum point at $(0, -2)$ **ii.** Minimum point at $(0, 3)$

     iii. Minimum point at $(4, -16)$ **iv.** Maximum point at $(1, 1)$

INVESTIGATION 2   **CCSS**   **A-REI.4,** A-REI.7, A-REI.10, F-IF.4, F-IF.7

The Quadratic Formula

The quadratic formula is introduced here with some development problems and straightforward practice tasks. Solving quadratic equations will be revisited in Course 2, Unit 5, *Nonlinear Functions and Equations*. Full proof of the formula, using completing-the-square and algebraic reasoning, will be developed in Course 3. Complex numbers are first introduced in Course 3 but revisited in Course 4.

Problems 1 and 2 provide guided practice in use of the formula. Then Problem 3 asks a series of questions designed to help students connect the formula to ideas of x-intercepts, symmetries, and maximum/minimum points of graphs.

1   **a.** $2x^2 - 2x - 12 = 0$

$a = 2, b = -2, c = -12$

$\dfrac{-b}{2a} = \dfrac{1}{2}, \dfrac{\sqrt{b^2 - 4ac}}{2a} = \dfrac{5}{2}$

$x = \dfrac{1}{2} + \dfrac{5}{2} = 3, x = \dfrac{1}{2} - \dfrac{5}{2} = -2$

Check:

$2(3)^2 - 2(3) - 12 = 0$

$2(-2)^2 - 2(-2) - 12 = 0$

b. $15 + 90t - 16t^2 = 100$ or

$-16t^2 + 90t - 85 = 0$

$a = -16, b = 90, c = -85$

$\dfrac{-b}{2a} = 2.8125, \dfrac{\sqrt{b^2 - 4ac}}{2a} \approx -1.6117$

$t \approx 2.8125 + (-1.6117) \approx 1.2,$

$t \approx 2.8125 - (-1.6117) \approx 4.4$

Check:

$15 + 90(1.2) - 16(1.2)^2 = 99.96 \approx 100$

$15 + 90(4.42) - 16(4.42)^2 = 100.22 \approx 100$

2   Students should check by substitution and sketch graphs showing the x-intercepts.

a. $x = 5$ and $x = 2$

b. $x = \dfrac{1}{2} \pm \dfrac{\sqrt{33}}{2} \approx 3.37$ and -2.37

c. $x = -5$ and $x = 2$

d. $x = 3$

e. No solutions

f. $x = -2$

> **POSSIBLE MISCONCEPTION**
>
> Some students think that $\sqrt{-x^2} = -x$. Remind them that if $b^2 - 4ac$ is negative, then there are no real solutions to the quadratic equation.

3 The formula for calculating solutions of quadratic equations is a complex set of directions. You can begin to make sense of the formula, by connecting it to patterns in the graphs of quadratic functions.

Consider the related quadratic functions:

$$y = 2x^2 - 12x$$
$$y = 2x^2 - 12x + 10$$
$$y = 2x^2 - 12x - 14$$
$$y = 2x^2 - 12x + 24$$

The graphs of these functions are shown in the following diagram.

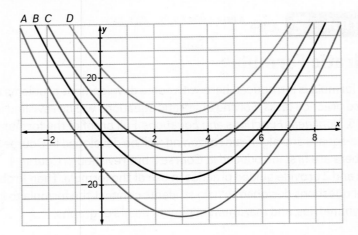

a. Match each function with its graph.

b. What are the x-coordinates of the minimum points on each graph? How (if at all) are those x-coordinates related to the x-intercepts of the graphs?

c. What are the coordinates of the x-intercepts on the graph of a quadratic function with rule $y = ax^2 + bx$? What is the x-coordinate of the minimum or maximum point for such a graph?

d. How will the x-coordinate of the maximum or minimum point of $y = ax^2 + bx + c$ be related to that of $y = ax^2 + bx$?

4 Now look back at the quadratic formula and think about how the results of Problem 3 help to explain the connections between these parts of the formula and the graph of $y = ax^2 + bx + c$.

a. $\dfrac{-b}{2a}$

b. $\dfrac{\sqrt{b^2 - 4ac}}{2a}$

c. $\dfrac{-b}{2a} + \dfrac{\sqrt{b^2 - 4ac}}{2a}$

d. $\dfrac{-b}{2a} - \dfrac{\sqrt{b^2 - 4ac}}{2a}$

3 **a.** $y = 2x^2 - 12x$ matches B (dark green).
$y = 2x^2 - 12x + 10$ matches C (teal).
$y = 2x^2 - 12x - 14$ matches A (orange).
$y = 2x^2 - 12x + 24$ matches D (light blue).

b. The x-coordinate of the minimum points on all graphs is 3. For the graphs that have x-intercepts, 3 is the average of the x-coordinates of the two x-intercepts.

c. For quadratics in the form $y = ax^2 + bx$, the x-intercepts are always at $(0, 0)$ and $\left(\dfrac{-b}{a}, 0\right)$. The x-coordinate of the max/min point is $\dfrac{-b}{2a}$.

d. The "$+ c$" simply moves the graph of $y = ax^2 + bx$ up or down, not left or right. So, you can average the x-intercepts of $y = ax^2 + bx$ to find the x-coordinate of the max/min point of $y = ax^2 + bx + c$. For quadratics in the form $y = ax^2 + bx + c$, the x-coordinate of the maximum or minimum point is always $\dfrac{-b}{2a}$, which is the same value as for quadratics of the form $y = ax^2 + bx$. The x-intercepts of $y = ax^2 + bx + c$, if they exist, are the same distance left or right of the x-intercepts of $y = ax^2 + bx$.

4 **a.** For $y = ax^2 + bx + c$ and $y = ax^2 + bx$, $\dfrac{-b}{2a}$ locates the x-coordinate of the max/min point midway between the two x-intercepts of $y = ax^2 + bx$. If the graphs have x-intercepts, $\dfrac{-b}{2a}$ will be midway between the two x-intercepts.

b. $\dfrac{\sqrt{b^2 - 4ac}}{2a}$ tells how far to the right and left of $\dfrac{-b}{2a}$ the x-intercepts are located.

c. $\dfrac{-b}{2a} + \dfrac{\sqrt{b^2 - 4ac}}{2a}$ gives the x-coordinate of one of the two x-intercepts if they exist (the greater of the two, unless the coefficient of x^2 is negative).

d. $\dfrac{-b}{2a} - \dfrac{\sqrt{b^2 - 4ac}}{2a}$ gives the x-coordinate of the other x-intercept if it exists (the lesser of the two, unless the coefficient of x^2 is negative).

INSTRUCTIONAL NOTE

This item can be used as a focal point for a summary class discussion.

SUMMARIZE THE MATHEMATICS

This investigation focused on a method for finding exact solutions for any quadratic equation.

a What are the key steps in using the quadratic formula to solve a quadratic equation?

b How can you tell from the calculation $\sqrt{b^2 - 4ac}$ that is part of the quadratic formula when a given quadratic equation has 2, 1, or 0 solutions? Give specific examples that illustrate the three possibilities.

c How are the locations of the maximum or minimum point and x-intercepts of a quadratic function graph shown by calculations in the quadratic formula?

d How do you choose among solution strategies—estimation using a table or graph, using arithmetic operations and square roots, factoring, or the quadratic formula—for the different quadratic equations that arise in solving problems?

Be prepared to share your thinking with the entire class.

 CHECK YOUR UNDERSTANDING

Use what you have learned about the quadratic formula to complete the following tasks.

a. Solve each of these equations. Show or explain the steps in each solution process.

  i. $x^2 - 6x + 8 = 0$ **ii.** $3x^2 - 8 = -2$

  iii. $x^2 - 2x + 8 = 2$ **iv.** $-7x + 8 + x^2 = 0$

  v. $15 = 7 + 4x^2$ **vi.** $x^2 = 36$

b. Suppose that a group of students made these statements in a summary of what they had learned about quadratic functions and equations. With which would you agree? For those that you don't believe to be true, what example or argument would you offer to correct the proposer's thinking?

  i. "Every quadratic equation has two solutions."

  ii. "The quadratic formula cannot be applied to an equation like $-7x + 8 + x^2 = 0$."

  iii. "To use the quadratic formula to solve $-7x + 8 + x^2 = 0$, you let $a = -7$; $b = 8$, and $c = 1$."

  iv. "To use the quadratic formula to solve $x^2 - 6x + 8 = 0$, you let $a = 0$, $b = 6$, and $c = 8$."

  v. "To use the quadratic formula to solve $3x^2 + 5x - 7 = 8$, you let $a = 3$, $b = 5$, and $c = -7$."

UNIT 7

SUMMARIZE THE MATHEMATICS

a The key steps in use of the quadratic formula are: (1) making sure that the equation is in the form $ax^2 + bx + c = 0$; (2) identifying the values of a, b, and c; and (3) substituting correctly in the parts of the formula.

b There can be zero, one, or two solutions for a quadratic equation. This is shown by the two parts of the formula. There are no solutions when the term $b^2 - 4ac$ is negative, 1 solution when $b^2 - 4ac$ is 0, and two solutions when $b^2 - 4ac$ is positive. See Problem 2 Parts e, d, and c, respectively, for specific examples.

c The location of the x-coordinate of the maximum or minimum point of a quadratic function graph is the term $\frac{-b}{2a}$ in the quadratic formula. The x-coordinates of the x-intercepts are $\frac{\sqrt{b^2 - 4ac}}{2a}$ to the right and left of $\frac{-b}{2a}$.

d Student responses may vary. However, students should choose applying simple arithmetic operations for solving equations of the form $y = ax^2$. They should choose factoring when a monomial involving x can be factored from the quadratic expression involved. Students should tend to prefer the quadratic formula when the quadratic equation has only integer values of a, b, and c. Estimation will most likely be preferred for non-integer values of a, b, and c.

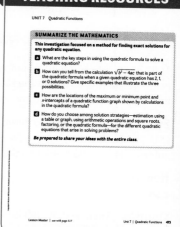
✔ CHECK YOUR UNDERSTANDING

a.   **i.** $x = 4$ or $x = 2$ **ii.** $x = \pm\sqrt{2}$ **iii.** No solutions

   iv. $x = \frac{7}{2} \pm \frac{\sqrt{17}}{2}$ or $x \approx 5.56$ or $x \approx 1.44$

   v. $x = \pm\sqrt{2}$ **vi.** $x = 6$ or $x = -6$

b.   **i.** False. Some quadratic equations have only one and some have no solutions. (Students could give a counterexample or explanation based on the quadratic formula.)

   ii. False. The equation is quadratic. The value of a is 1, the value of b is -7, and the value of c is 8.

   iii. False. The value of a is always the coefficient of the x^2 term, the value of b is the coefficient of the x term, and the value of c is always the constant term.

   iv. False. In this case $a = 1$, $b = -6$, and $c = 8$.

   v. False. The formula requires a quadratic expression set equal to 0, so the required value of c is -15, not -7.

Summarizing the Mathematics, *page 517*

Teacher: Let's summarize your work with the quadratic formula in Investigation 2. What are the key steps in using the quadratic formula to solve a quadratic equation?

Eva: Well, first you have to make sure the equation is set equal to 0. Say the equation is $5x^2 + 3x - 12 = 14$. Then you have to subtract 14 from both sides so that the equation equals 0.

Roman: After that, you have to figure out the values for a, b, and c so you can use them in the formula.

Quinton: Then all that's left is plugging the values in and calculating the solutions.

Teacher: How many solutions should you expect?

Kelsie: It depends on the quadratic equation you are trying to solve.

Teacher: Can you say more about that, Kelsie?

Kelsie: Well, some quadratic equations have two solutions, some have one, and some have none.

Teacher: How can you tell from the calculation $\sqrt{b^2 - 4ac}$ that is part of the quadratic formula whether a quadratic equation has one, two, or zero solutions?

Brody: If $b^2 - 4ac$ is negative you get no solutions.

Teacher: Brody, can you give a specific example?

Brody: Do you mean symbolically or a graph?

Teacher: Could you talk about both?

Brody: Well, graphically you would have a quadratic function that doesn't cross the x-axis. Symbolically, $4ac$ has to be larger than b^2, so, say if b is 1 and a and c are both 2. The equation would be $2x^2 + x + 2 = 0$. So you would have to take the $\sqrt{1^2 - 4(2)(2)}$, or $\sqrt{-15}$. So you get no solutions.

Teacher: Would someone else speak to the case of one solution?

Santiago: You have one solution when $b^2 - 4ac = 0$. On the graph that means that the parabola just touches the x-axis and then turns around. Using numbers, b^2 has to equal $4ac$ so that their difference is 0. An example would be if $b^2 = 16$ so b is 4, and a is 1 and c is 4. Then $4^2 - 4(1)(4) = 0$. The equation would be $x^2 + 4x + 4 = 0$.

Teacher: Okay. Who can talk about the case of two solutions?

Simone: You have two solutions when $b^2 - 4ac$ is a positive number. So b^2 has to be larger than $4ac$. For example, if b is 10 and a is 2 and c is 3. Then you have $10^2 =$ and $4(2)(3)$. Since $100 - 24$ is positive, you get two solutions.

Teacher: What does this particular case look like graphically?

Simone: The graph crosses the x-axis twice.

Teacher: So the quadratic formula tells us how many times the graph crosses the x-axis and the graph tells us how many solutions to expect using the quadratic formula. How are the locations of the maximum and minimum point and x-intercepts shown by calculations in the quadratic formula?

Reed: The maximum or minimum is found on the axis of symmetry of the graph. When you do the quadratic formula the axis of symmetry is $x = \frac{-b}{2a}$.

Gilberto: You can find the x-intercepts by starting at the axis of symmetry and counting over $\frac{\sqrt{b^2 - 4ac}}{2a}$ to the left and right.

Teacher: How do you choose among solution strategies for the different quadratic equations that arise in solving problems? How do you decide whether to estimate, factor, or use the quadratic formula?

Maddison: I always see if I can easily factor first. I just look at it and if I can't see a way to factor quickly then I just use the quadratic formula.

Rosemary: I do that, too, but first I check to see if I can just take the square root of both sides. You know the kind of equations where it is just something x^2 equals some number? I just get x^2 by itself then take the square root of both sides and estimate the solution with my calculator.

Maddison: I hadn't thought of that but I agree with Rosemary, I would check for that possibility first.

Darion: I usually just go straight to the quadratic formula since it works every time. It's pretty easy to calculate the solutions quickly.

Devyn: I prefer to factor, so I agree with Maddison. I usually try and factor first.

Teacher: It sounds like you have thought about the different strategies and are using those that make the most sense for you. While you work on the Check Your Understanding tasks tonight, keep in mind the different strategies we talked about and choose the one that might be considered the most efficient for each particular equation.

ELL TIP Whenever possible, group students in pairs, small groups, or cooperative learning situations to encourage verbal interaction and to allow ELLs to use other students as models for their communication. Use role-playing situations, like Promoting Mathematical Discourse, to reinforce concepts as well as to take advantage of students' more developed social language skills. Pair ELLs with English speakers to encourage collaboration and attainment of common goals.

ON YOUR OWN

APPLICATIONS

1 Solve each of these quadratic equations by using only arithmetic operations and square roots. Show the steps of your solution process and a check of the solutions.

a. $x^2 = 20$ **b.** $s^2 + 9 = 25$

c. $x^2 - 11 = -4$ **d.** $3m^2 + 9 = 5$

e. $-2x^2 + 24 = 2$ **f.** $29 - 3n^2 = 5$

2 An engineer designed a suspension bridge so that the main cables would lie along parabolas defined by the function $h = 0.04x^2 + 15$ where h is the distance from the cable to the bridge surface at a point x feet from the *center* of the bridge. The bridge is to be 50 feet long.

a. Sketch a graph of the function for $-25 \le x \le 25$ and indicate on that sketch the height of each tower and the shortest distance from the cable to the bridge surface.

b. Write and solve an equation to answer the question, "At what location(s) on the bridge surface is the suspension cable exactly 20 feet above the surface?"

3 The exterior of the St. Louis Abbey Church in Missouri shows a collection of parabolic faces.

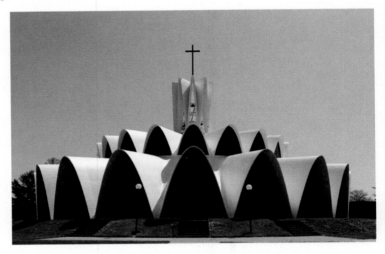

Suppose that an arch in the lower ring of the parabolic roof line is defined by the function $y = -0.075x^2 + 30$, with y giving the distance in feet from the roof to the ground at any point x feet from the line of symmetry for the arch.

a. What is the maximum height of the arch and how can you find that without any calculation?

UNIT 7

1 Students should include the steps to their solutions and provide a check of their solutions.

a. $x = \pm\sqrt{20} = \pm2\sqrt{5}$ or $x \approx \pm4.47$

b. $s = \pm4$

c. $x = \pm\sqrt{7}$ or $x \approx \pm2.65$

d. No solutions

e. $x = \pm\sqrt{11}$ or $x \approx \pm3.32$

f. $n = \pm\sqrt{8} = \pm2\sqrt{2}$ or $n \approx \pm2.83$

2 **a.**

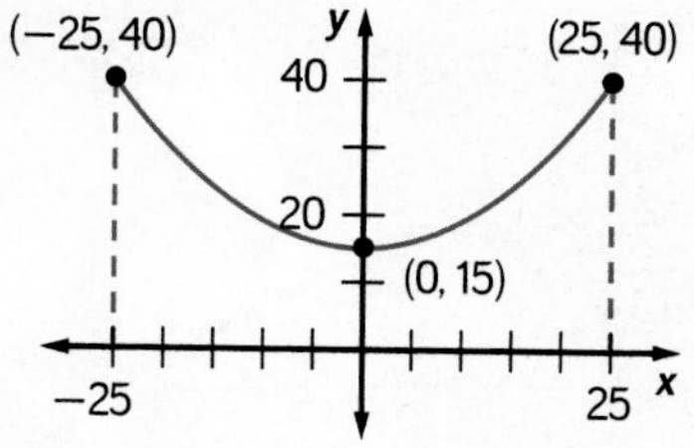

The height of each tower is 40 feet. The shortest distance from the cable to the bridge surface is 15 feet.

b. The equation $0.04x^2 + 15 = 20$ will answer the given question. The solutions are $x = \pm\sqrt{125} = \pm5\sqrt{5}$ or $x \approx \pm11.2$. The cable is 20 feet above the surface at $x \approx \pm11.2$.

3 **a.** Maximum height of the roofline arch is 30 feet. This can be deduced from the function by noting that when $x = 0$, $y = 30$ and that this type of quadratic function has the y-axis as a line of symmetry.

b. Write and solve an equation that determines the distance from the line of symmetry to the points where the arch would meet the ground.

c. Write and solve an equation that determines the points where the roof is exactly 15 feet above the ground.

4 Solve each of these quadratic equations algebraically. Show your work.

a. $5x^2 + 60x = 0$ **b.** $-5x^2 + 23x = 0$

c. $-12x + 7x^2 = 0$ **d.** $2x - x^2 = 0$

5 Without graphing, find coordinates of the maximum and minimum points on graphs of these quadratic functions.

a. $y = 5x^2 + 60x$ **b.** $y = -5x^2 + 23x$

c. $y = -12x + 7x^2$ **d.** $y = 2x - x^2$

6 In football, when a field goal attempt is kicked, it leaves the ground on a path for which the height of the ball h in feet at any time t seconds later might be given by a function like $h = 45t - 16t^2$.

a. Write and solve an equation that tells time(s) when the ball hits the ground at the end of its flight.

b. Write and solve an equation that tells time(s) when the ball is at the height of the end zone crossbar (10 feet above the ground).

c. Find the maximum height of the kick and when it occurs.

7 Using the quadratic function $y = x^2 - 3x + 2$, choose values of y to write equations that have the prescribed number of solutions. In each case, show on a graph of the function how the condition is satisfied.

a. Two solutions

b. One solution

c. No solutions

8 Test your understanding and skill with the quadratic formula by using it to find solutions for the following equations. In each case, check your work by substituting proposed solutions in the original equation and by sketching a graph of the related quadratic function.

a. $x^2 + 4x + 5 = 0$ **b.** $x^2 - 7x + 8 = -2$

c. $x^2 - x - 8 = 4$ **d.** $5x + x^2 - 3 = 0$

e. $3x^2 - 18x + 27 = 0$ **f.** $5x^2 - x = 8$

Lesson 3 | Solving Quadratic Equations **519**

b. The distance from the line of symmetry to the points where the arch meets the ground is 20 feet, found by solving:

$$-0.075x^2 + 30 = 0$$
$$x^2 = 400$$
$$x = \pm 20$$

c. $-0.075x^2 + 30 = 15$ has solutions $x = \pm\sqrt{200}$ or $x \approx \pm 14.1$.

4   **a.** $x = 0$ and $x = -12$ **b.** $x = 0$ and $x = 4.6$

   c. $x = 0$ and $x = \frac{12}{7}$ **d.** $x = 0$ and $x = 2$

5   **a.** minimum point: $(-6, -180)$ **b.** maximum point: $(2.3, 26.45)$

   c. minimum point: $\left(\frac{12}{14}, -5\frac{1}{7}\right)$ **d.** maximum point: $(1, 1)$

6   **a.** The predicted time to hit the ground in seconds will be found by solving $45t - 16t^2 = 0$. The solutions of this equation are $t = 0$ (the time when the ball was kicked) and $t = \frac{45}{16}$ or $t \approx 2.8$ seconds.

   b. The kick will be at 10 feet above the ground two times in its flight: $t \approx 0.24$ and $t \approx 2.57$ seconds. These times are found by solving the equation $45t - 16t^2 = 10$.

   c. The maximum height of the kick occurs when $t = \frac{45}{32}$ seconds. The height at that time is approximately 31.6 feet.

7 The graph at the right shows each condition. The scale on each axis is 1. Examples may vary.

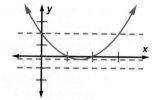

   a. $x^2 - 3x + 2 = 2$ has two solutions: $x = 0$ and $x = 3$. (Any $y > -0.25$ is correct.)

   b. Only the equation $x^2 - 3x + 2 = -0.25$ has one solution: $x = 1.5$.

   c. $x^2 - 3x + 2 = -1$ has no solutions. (Any $y > -0.25$ is correct.)

8 Students should provide a check by substitution for each solution and a sketch of each function showing solutions as points on the graph.

   a. No solutions because $4^2 - 4(1)(5)$ is negative.

   b. $x = 5$ and $x = 2$

   c. $x = 4$ and $x = -3$

   d. $x = \frac{-5}{2} \pm \frac{\sqrt{37}}{2}$ or $x \approx -5.54$ and $x \approx 0.54$

   e. $x = 3$

   f. $x = \frac{1}{10} \pm \frac{\sqrt{161}}{10}$ or $x \approx 1.37$ and $x \approx -1.17$

ON YOUR OWN

CONNECTIONS

9 The Pythagorean Theorem says that in any right triangle with legs of length a and b and hypotenuse of length c, $c^2 = a^2 + b^2$. Write and solve quadratic equations that provide answers for these questions.

   a. What is the length of the hypotenuse of a right triangle with legs of length 5 and 7?

   b. If a right triangle has one leg of length 9 and the hypotenuse of length 15, what is the length of the other leg?

   c. If a right triangle has hypotenuse of length 20 and one leg of length 10, what is the length of the other leg?

   d. What are the lengths of the sides of a square that has diagonal length 15?

10 Shown at the right is an equilateral triangle $\triangle ABC$. M is the midpoint of $\overline{AC}$.

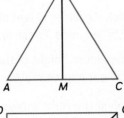

   a. What are the measures of the angles in $\triangle ABM$?

   b. If side $\overline{AB}$ has length 8, what is the length of side $\overline{AM}$? What is the length of side $\overline{MB}$?

   c. If side $\overline{AB}$ has length x, what are the lengths of sides $\overline{AM}$ and $\overline{MB}$ in terms of x?

11 At the right is square $ABCD$ with one diagonal drawn in.

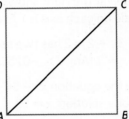

   a. If side $\overline{AB}$ has length 6, what is the length of the diagonal $\overline{AC}$?

   b. If side $\overline{AB}$ has length x, show that the length of the diagonal $\overline{AC}$ is $x\sqrt{2}$.

12 Consider all linear equations of the type $2x + 1 = k$.

   a. What are the greatest and the least numbers of solutions for such equations?

   b. How can your answer to Part a be supported with a sketch of the graph for the function $y = 2x + 1$?

13 Consider all equations of the type $5(2^x) = k$. How many solutions can there be for such equations? Give equations with specific values of k that illustrate the possibilities. How can you support your answer with a graph of the function $y = 5(2^x)$?

14 The quadratic formula gives a rule for finding all solutions of equations in the form $ax^2 + bx + c = 0$. Now consider all linear equations of the type $ax + b = k$ (where $a \neq 0$). Write a rule that shows how to calculate all solutions of such linear equations, using arithmetic operations involving the values of a, b, and k.

UNIT 7

9   **a.** $c = \sqrt{74} \approx 8.6$

    b. $a = \sqrt{144} = 12$

    c. $a = \sqrt{300} = 10\sqrt{3} \approx 17.3$

    d. $a = \sqrt{112.5} \approx 10.6$

10   **a.** $m\angle ABM = 30°; m\angle BAM = 60°; m\angle BMA = 90°$

    b. $AM = 4; 8^2 = 4^2 + MB^2, MB = \sqrt{48} = 4\sqrt{3} \approx 6.9$

    c. $AM = \frac{x}{2}; MB = \frac{x}{2}\sqrt{3}$

11   **a.** $AC^2 = 6^2 + 6^2; AC = 6\sqrt{2}$

    b. $AC^2 = x^2 + x^2 = 2x^2$
        $AC = \sqrt{2x^2} = x\sqrt{2}$

12   **a.** Every such equation has exactly one solution.

    b. The graph of $y = 2x + 1$ is a diagonal line with no lower or upper bound. So, any horizontal line $y = k$ will intersect the line $y = 2x + 1$. They will intersect at the point $\left(\frac{k-1}{2}, k\right)$.

13 If $k > 0$, there will be exactly one solution; if $k \leq 0$, there will be no solutions. Student examples will vary. The graph of $y = 5(2^x)$ is a curve that approaches but never reaches the x-axis to the left and rises rapidly on the right. So, the function values for $y = 5(2^x)$ will be all values $y > 0$. $k = 5(2^x)$ has one solution if $k > 0$. The graph of $y = 5(2^x)$ is never below the x-axis and thus when $k < 0$, $k = 5(2^x)$ has no solution.

14 The solution to any linear equation in the form $ax + b = k$ will be $x = \frac{k-b}{a}$, where $a \neq 0$.

REFLECTIONS

15 A quadratic equation may have 0, 1, or 2 solutions.

a. How would you use the graph of a quadratic function to explain those possibilities?

b. How are the possible numbers of solutions for a quadratic equation seen by examining the quadratic formula?

16 Mathematicians call "$x^2 + 5x + 6$" an expression and "$x^2 + 5x + 6 = 0$" an equation. How would you explain the difference between *expressions* and *equations*?

17 You previously learned how to solve quadratic equations by studying tables and graphs of the related quadratic functions. In this lesson, you learned ways of solving quadratic equations by reasoning about the algebraic expressions.

a. What reasons might there be to develop skill in solving quadratic equations and inequalities by algebraic reasoning, in addition to using calculator or computer tools?

b. What insight into a quadratic equation or inequality might be gained by studying a table of values or graph?

18 You now know three different ways to solve quadratic equations using algebraic methods: by reducing the problem to solving $x^2 = n$, by reducing the problem to solving $x(x + m) = 0$, and by using the quadratic formula.

a. What do you see as the advantages and disadvantages of each strategy?

b. Give an example of a quadratic equation that you would prefer to solve by factoring.

c. Give an example of a quadratic equation that you would prefer to solve by use of the quadratic formula.

EXTENSIONS

19 Find all solutions of the following equations that involve products of three or four linear terms. Then sketch graphs of the functions involved in these equations for $-5 \leq x \leq 5$ and explain how the solutions to the equations are shown on the graphs. Compare the pattern relating graphs and equations in these examples to the patterns you met in dealing with quadratic functions.

a. $x(x - 4)(x + 2) = 0$ **b.** $(2x + 3)(x - 1)(x + 3) = 0$

c. $x(2x + 3)(x - 1)(x + 3) = 0$ **d.** $x(x - 4)(x + 2) = -9$

20 Shown at the right are the dimensions for a multi-use gift box.

a. Will a pen 11 cm long fit in the bottom of the box? Explain why or why not.

b. Find the length of the longest pencil that will fit inside the box. Illustrate and explain how you found your answer.

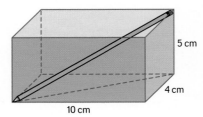

5 cm

4 cm

10 cm

UNIT 7

15 Quadratic equations can have zero, one, or two solutions.

NOTE The solution to Task 14 is on page T520.

  a. Any quadratic equation can be written in the form $ax^2 + bx + c = 0$. When the function $y = ax^2 + bx + c$ is graphed, the solutions to the equation are the x values where y is zero or the locations of the x-intercepts. If the graph is totally above or below the x-axis, there are no solutions. If the graph intersects the x-axis in one point, there is one solution. If the graph intersects the x-axis in two points, there are two solutions.

  b. The possible number of solutions is seen in the term $\dfrac{\sqrt{b^2 - 4ac}}{2a}$. If $\sqrt{b^2 - 4ac}$ is equal to 0, then there is one solution. If $\sqrt{b^2 - 4ac}$ is any real number other than 0, then the quadratic formula will produce two solutions. If $\dfrac{\sqrt{b^2 - 4ac}}{2a}$ is a nonreal number ($b^2 - 4ac$ is negative), then there will be no solutions.

16 *Expressions* define a procedure for a calculation. Expressions do not indicate the result of the calculation, or the output, only the actions on the input(s). Expressions contain only numbers, variables, and operations (no "="").

    Equations, as used in this text, represent questions about what input(s) for an expression will give a particular output, or what input(s) for two expressions will give the same output—in other words, where the graphs of the functions defined by two expressions will intersect. *Equation* may more broadly refer to any statement that two expressions are equivalent, as indicated by "=".

17 **a.** Developing skill in solving quadratic equations and inequalities by algebraic reasoning, in addition to using calculator or computer tools, gives ways of seeing general strategies, not only specific solution examples.

  b. Studying a table of values or graph gives insight into a quadratic equation or inequality by showing how solutions to an equation might change if some constants in the equation change. Also, tables and graphs give overall pictures of the relationship between variables involved in a situation, pictures that simply do not appear in the process of solving specific equations by formal algebraic methods.

18 **a.** Student responses might use the following and other ideas. An advantage of solving by reducing the problem to solving $x^2 = n$ is that it is generally quick; however, this method can only be used to solve quadratic equations that do not have a linear term ($b = 0$). An advantage of the quadratic formula is that it can be used to solve any quadratic equation. An advantage of factoring is that the solutions to the quadratic equation are easily seen in the factored form. A disadvantage of factoring is that not all quadratic expressions are factorable, so much time might be spent on trying to factor, thus making the process inefficient.

  b. Examples may vary; in general, equations of the form $ax^2 + bx = 0$.

  c. Examples may vary; in general, equations of the form $ax^2 + bx + c = 0$, where a, b, and $c \neq 0$.

19 | **NOTE** Polynomial functions will be studied in Course 3, Unit 5.

a. $x(x - 4)(x + 2) = 0$ has solutions
$x = 0$, $x = 4$, $x = -2$. The solutions
are the values at which the graph
crosses the x-axis.

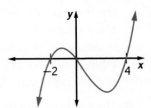

b. $(2x + 3)(x - 1)(x + 3) = 0$ has solutions
$x = -1.5$, $x = 1$, and $x = -3$. The solutions are
the values at which the graph crosses the x-axis.

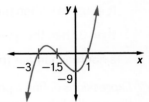

c. $x(2x + 3)(x - 1)(x + 3) = 0$ has solutions
$x = 0$, $x = -1.5$, $x = 1$, and $x = -3$. The solutions
are the values at which the graph crosses
the x-axis.

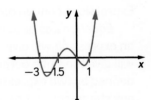

d. $x(x - 4)(x + 2) = -9$ has solutions
$x = 1$ and $x = \frac{1}{2} \pm \frac{\sqrt{37}}{2}$ or $x \approx -2.54$ and
$x \approx 3.54$. The solutions are the values of x
where the function crosses the line $y = -9$.

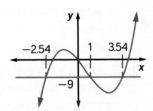

INSTRUCTIONAL NOTE Just as was the case with the factored form of the quadratic expressions $ax^2 + bx$ that students studied in this lesson, here too the factored expressions make it easy to find the x-intercepts of the graph. The cubic functions here (with three x-intercepts) have one local max *and* one local min value, whereas a quadratic function has only one local max *or* one local min value. Like quadratic functions, the end behavior is unbounded, but in these examples the left and right end behaviors are opposite, whereas the right and left end behaviors for a quadratic function are both either positive or negative. The quartic function has four x-intercepts and in this case two local min values and one local max value. Like quadratic functions, the right and left end behaviors of quartic functions are unbounded and are either both positive or both negative.

   (In general, a third-degree polynomial will have one, two, or three x-intercepts, and a fourth-degree polynomial will have zero, one, two, three, or four x-intercepts. When factors are repeated, the number of distinct x-intercepts is reduced, and the graph will be tangent to the x-axis at those x values.)

20 **a.** The pencil will not fit in the bottom because the diagonal is about 10.77 cm long.

b. The longest pencil that will fit diagonally is $\sqrt{141} \approx 11.87$ cm. This is found using a second application of the Pythagorean Theorem.

ON YOUR OWN

21 What values of x satisfy these quadratic inequalities?

a. $9 - x^2 < 0$ **b.** $9 - x^2 > 5$

c. $x^2 - 5x < 0$ **d.** $x^2 - 5x > 0$

22 In Investigation 1, you considered a quadratic model for a soccer ball kicked from a spot on the ground using the model $h = 24t - 16t^2$, where height was measured in feet and time in seconds.

a. What question can be answered by solving the inequality $24t - 16t^2 > 8$?

b. Solve the inequality and answer the question you posed.

c. Write an inequality that can be used to answer the question, "At what times in its flight is the ball within 8 feet of the ground?"

d. Solve the inequality you wrote in Part c.

23 Find rules for the functions with the graphs given below. Be prepared to explain how you developed the rules in each case.

a.

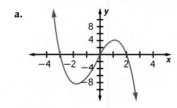

b.

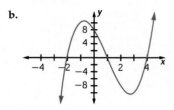

24 What results will you expect from entering these commands in a calculator or computer algebra system?

a. **solve(a*x^2+c=d,x)**

b. **solve(a*x^2+b*x=0,x)**

c. **solve(a*x^2+b*x+c=0,x)**

Execute the commands and resolve any differences between what you expected and what occurred.

25 If you had a job that required solving many quadratic equations in the form $ax^2 + bx + c = 0$, it might be helpful to write a spreadsheet program that would do the calculations after you entered the values of a, b, and c. The table that follows was produced with one such spreadsheet and the equation $3x^2 - 6x - 24$.

Quadratic Equations.xlsx ☐ ◱ ☒

◇	A	B	C	D	^
1	1	3	$a =$	3	
2	Solution 1=	−2	$b =$	−6	
3	Solution 2 =	4	$c =$	−24	

a. What formulas would you expect to find in cells **A1** and **B1**?

Digital Vision/Getty Images

21 Students might use symbolic reasoning, graphical reasoning of the related function, or a combination of these to solve the inequalities.

  a. $x < -3$ or $x > 3$

  b. $-2 < x < 2$

  c. $0 < x < 5$

  d. $x < 0$ or $x > 5$

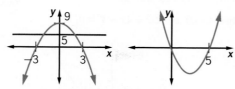

22 **a.** For what time period will the height of the ball be greater than 8 feet?

  b. The height will be more than 8 feet when the time is between 0.5 and 1 second after the kick. Students might use a variety of strategies including solving $-8 + 24t - 16t^2 = 0$ to locate the t values that produce a height of 0, or finding the intersection points of the graphs of $y = 8$ and $y = 24x - 16x^2$.

  c. $24t - 16t^2 < 8$

  d. The ball will be less than 8 feet high on the intervals of $0 \leq t < 0.5$, or $1 < t \leq 1.5$.

23 **a.** $y = -(x + 3)(x)(x - 2)$

  b. $y = (x + 2)(x - 1)(x - 4)$

24 **a.** Using the TI-Nspire, **solve(a*x^2+c=d,x)** will give this result:

  b. **solve(a*x^2+b*x=0,x)** will give:

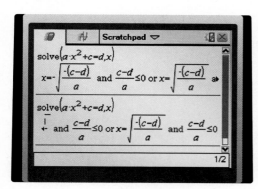

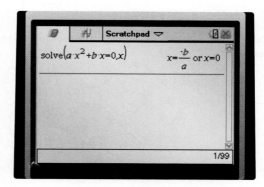

  c. **solve(a*x^2+b*x+c=0,x)** will give:

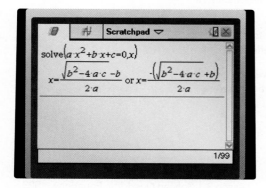

25 One possibility follows:

  a. Cell **A1: =−D2/(2*D1)**
    Cell **B1: =SQRT((D2)^2−4*D1*D3))/(2*D1)**

b. What formulas would you expect to find in cells **B2** and **B3**?

c. How could you modify the spreadsheet to solve $-2x^2 + 4x - 7 = 0$?

26 The graphs of $y_1 = x^2 + x - 8$ and $y_2 = 2x + 4$ are shown at the right.

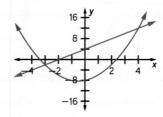

a. Estimate the coordinates of points where the two graphs intersect.

b. Solve the equation $x^2 + x - 8 = 2x + 4$ algebraically and compare the results to your estimate in Part a.

c. What are the possible numbers of solutions to an equation in the form *quadratic expression* = *linear expression*? Give examples and sketches of function graphs to illustrate your ideas.

REVIEW

27 Write each of the following radical expressions in equivalent form with the smallest possible integer inside the radical sign.

a. $\sqrt{24}$

b. $\sqrt{125}$

c. $\sqrt{\dfrac{25}{16}}$

d. $\sqrt{12}\sqrt{8}$

e. $\sqrt[3]{-1,000}$

f. $\sqrt[4]{16}$

28 Examine this portion of a semiregular tessellation made with regular octagons and squares.

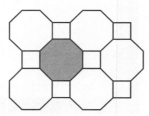

a. What is the measure of each angle in a regular octagon?

b. Explain why the octagons and squares in this semiregular tessellation fit together exactly.

c. If the shaded polygon is removed, in how many ways can the tile be replaced to fit the same outline, using both rotation and reflection?

29 Given that two vertex-edge graphs both have 8 edges and 6 vertices, which of the following statements is true? Give examples to support your answers.

a. The graphs must be identical.

b. Both graphs must have Euler circuits.

c. Both graphs must have Euler paths.

Lesson 3 | Solving Quadratic Equations **523**

b. Cell **B2:** $=$**A1**$-$**B1**
   Cell **B3:** $=$**A1**$+$**B1**

c. You could modify the spreadsheet to solve $-2x^2 = +4x - 7 = 0$ by changing the entry in **D1** to $-$**2**, the entry in **D2** to **4**, and the entry in **D3** to $-$**7**. If students modify the spreadsheet as described, cells **B1, B2,** and **B3** will become **#NUM!**. This happens because the value of $b^2 - 4ac$ is negative. Thus, there are no real number solutions.

26 **a.** It looks like the graphs intersect at $(-3, -2)$ and $(4, 12)$.

b. The estimate in Part a can be confirmed by reasoning like this:
   If $x^2 + x - 8 = 2x + 4$, then $x^2 - x - 12 = 0$. The quadratic formula gives $x = 4$ or $x = -3$. The y-coordinates can be confirmed by substituting the x values into either y_1 or y_2.

c. Student examples will vary but should include a sketch of graphs as support. Quadratic/linear systems can have zero, one, or two solutions.
   The example in Part b illustrates the case of two solutions, since the line cannot intersect the rising parabola at any more points than those shown. An example of a system with no solutions would be $y = x^2$ and $y = -1$, which leads to $x^2 = -1$. An example of a system with one solution would be $y = x^2$ and $y = 0$, which leads to $x^2 = 0$.

NOTE More interesting systems with exactly one solution are those that lead to $ax^2 + bx + c = bx + c$. The graph of $y = bx + c$ will always be tangent to the graph of $y = ax^2 + bx + c$ at $(0, c)$, the y-intercept of the graph. You can see why this occurs by looking at $y = ax^2 + bx + c$ as the sum of $y = ax^2$ and $y = bx + c$, with the term $y = ax^2$ always positive (or negative), so always adding to (or subtracting from) the graph of $y = bx + c$.

REVIEW

JUST IN TIME

27 **a.** $\sqrt{24} = 2\sqrt{6}$ **b.** $\sqrt{125} = 5\sqrt{5}$

   c. $\sqrt{\dfrac{25}{16}} = \dfrac{5}{4}$ **d.** $\sqrt{12}\,\sqrt{8} = 4\sqrt{6}$

   e. -10 **f.** 2

28 **a.** $135°$

b. Each interior angle of the octagon is $135°$ and each interior angle of the square is $90°$. At each vertex of the tessellation there are two octagons and one square, so $135° + 135° + 90° = 360°$.

c. The regular octagon can be replaced after reflecting across or rotating through any of its symmetries. The octagon has eight lines of symmetry—four through opposite vertices and four through opposite midpoints of edges. It also has $45°, 90°, 135°, 180°, 225°, 270°,$ and $315°$ rotational symmetries.

NOTE The solution to Task 29 is on page T524.

ON YOUR OWN

30 You know that the general form of a linear function is $y = mx + b$, and that the general form of an exponential function is $y = a(b^x)$.

a. What is the equation of a line with slope $\frac{2}{3}$ and y-intercept at $(0, 3)$?

Can you always write the equation of a line if you know its slope and y-intercept?

b. What is the equation of a line with slope $\frac{2}{3}$ and x-intercept at $(3, 0)$?

Can you always write the equation of a line if you know its slope and x-intercept?

c. What is the rule for an exponential function that has a graph with y-intercept at $(0, 5)$ and growth factor 2?

Can you always write the rule for an exponential function if you know the y-intercept of its graph and the growth factor?

d. Is there an exponential function matching a graph that has x-intercept at $(3, 0)$ and a decay factor of 0.5?

Can you always find an exponential function when given an x-intercept and a decay factor?

31 Determine if the triangles in each pair are congruent. If they are congruent, indicate how you know the triangles are congruent and write the congruence relation. If they are not congruent, explain how you know.

a.

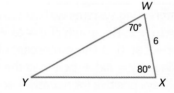

b.

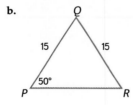
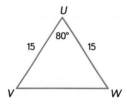

c.

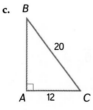
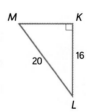

29 **a.** Not true. One counterexample is given below.

b. Not true. Neither of the graphs in Part a has an Euler circuit.

c. Not true. The first graph in Part a does not have an Euler path.

30 **a.** If the slope is $\frac{2}{3}$ and the y-intercept is $(0, 3)$, then the equation is $y = \frac{2}{3}x + 3$. Yes.

b. If the slope is $\frac{2}{3}$ and the x-intercept is $(3, 0)$, then the equation is $y = \frac{2}{3}x + b$. Substituting $(3, 0)$ into this equation gives $0 = \frac{2}{3}(3) + b$, so $b = -2$. So, the equation is $y = \frac{2}{3}x - 2$. Yes.

c. If the y-intercept is at $(0, 5)$ and the growth factor is 2, then the function rule is $y = 5(2^x)$. Yes.

d. Exponential functions are asymptotic to the x-axis, so there can be no x-intercept. Reasoning symbolically, any exponential function can be written $y = a(b^x)$. In the example given, the decay factor is 0.5, so this becomes $y = a(0.5x)$. Substituting $(3, 0)$ gives $0 = a(0.5)^3$. This can be true only if $a = 0$, but this will give us $y = 0(0.5^x)$ or $y = 0$, which would be a line and not an exponential function. No.

31 **a.**

Not congruent because angle measures are not all the same measures in the two triangles

b.

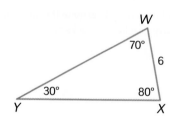

$\triangle PQR \cong \triangle VUW$ by ASA or SAS.

c.

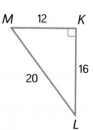

$\triangle ABC \cong \triangle KLM$ by SSS or SAS.

32 Write results of these calculations in standard scientific notation $N \times 10^x$, $1 \leq N < 10$.

a. $(5 \times 10^8)(4 \times 10^{11})$

b. $(5 \times 10^8)(4 \times 10^{-3})$

c. $(5 \times 10^8) \div (4 \times 10^5)$

d. If there are 6×10^3 molecules in a volume of 3×10^7 cubic centimeters, what is the average number of helium molecules per cubic centimeter?

33 Find the value of each absolute value expression.

a. $|-5|$

b. $-|6|$

c. $|7 - 4|$

d. $|4 - 7|$

e. $|3(-2) + 5|$

f. $|-3 - 10|$

34 In kite $ABCD$, $m\angle BAD = 78°$ and $m\angle BCD = 40°$. Calculate the measures of $m\angle ABC$ and $m\angle ADC$.

35 Jake starts with \$52 in a new savings account. Each week after opening the account, he deposits the same amount of money into the account and does not take any money out of the account. After 12 weeks, he has \$148 in the account.

a. Sketch a graph that shows the amount of money in the savings account after Jake makes each of the twelve deposits.

b. Write a function rule that could be used to determine the amount of money in Jake's savings account after any number of weeks n.

32 **a.** $20 \times 10^{19} = 2.0 \times 10^{20}$

b. $20 \times 10^5 = 2.0 \times 10^6$

c. 1.25×10^3

d. 2×10^{-4} helium molecules per cubic centimeter

 Just In Time

33 **a.** 5

b. -6

c. 3

d. 3

e. 1

f. 13

34 $m\angle ABC = 121°$
$m\angle ADC = 121°$

35 **a.**

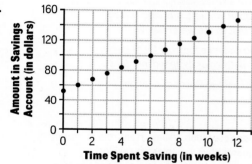

b. $T = 8n + 52$

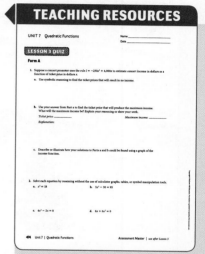

TEACHING RESOURCES

Assessment Masters 474–479

ⓘ GO DIGITAL

LESSON

4

Looking Back

In your work on problems and explorations of this unit, you studied patterns of change in variables that can be modeled well by quadratic functions.

The height of a basketball shot increases to a maximum and then falls toward the basket or the floor, as a function of time after the shot is taken.

The projected income from a business venture rises to a maximum and then falls, as a function of price charged for the business product.

The main cables of a suspension bridge dip from each tower to a point where the bridge surface is closest to the water below.

The stopping distance for a car increases in a quadratic pattern as its speed increases.

The functions that model these patterns of change can all be expressed with rules like

$$y = ax^2 + bx + c.$$

Since quadratic expressions play such an important role in reasoning about relations among quantitative variables, you explored a variety of strategies for combining and expanding those expressions to produce useful equivalent forms. You also learned how to solve quadratic equations by algebraic reasoning and use of the quadratic formula.

As a result of your work on Lessons 1–3, you should be better able to recognize situations in which variables are related by quadratic functions, to use data tables and graphs to display patterns in those relationships, to use symbolic expressions to describe and reason about the patterns, and to use graphing calculators and computer algebra systems to answer questions that involve quadratic functions.

In future units of *Core-Plus Mathematics*, you will extend your understanding and skill in use of quadratic functions and expressions to solve problems. The tasks in this final lesson ask you to put your current knowledge to work in solving several new problems.

Mystic Mountain Mike and Tanya grew up in the mountains of Idaho, but they are now mathematics teachers in a large eastern city. They have a dream of going into business with a restaurant and entertainment complex they plan to call Mystic Mountain. Not surprisingly, several of Mike and Tanya's ideas for Mystic Mountain involve quadratic functions and their graphs.

Image 100/Alamy

Looking Back

This lesson includes tasks intended to provide review and practice of key ideas developed throughout the unit and summary questions designed to stimulate student synthesis of the key principles and techniques. You might have different groups select two of Tasks 1–4 and all do Tasks 5 and 6. Having more than one group do Tasks 1–4 should allow more informed questions during group presentations.

CCSS

Common Core State Standards

This unit focused on the CCSS domains:

Seeing Structure in Expressions, A-SSE

Creating Equations★, A-CED

Reasoning with Equations and Inequalities, A-REI

Interpreting Functions, F-IF

Building Functions, F-BF

Linear, Quadratic, and Exponential Models★, F-LE

Plus the Modeling Conceptual Category

1 **The Entry Bridge** Their first idea is to have customers enter Mystic Mountain by walking across a rope bridge suspended over an indoor river that will be 40 feet wide. Tanya worked out the function $h = 0.02x^2 - 0.8x + 15$ to describe the arc of the bridge. In her rule, x gives horizontal distance from the entry point toward the other side of the river, and h gives height of the bridge above the water, both measured in feet.

   a. Sketch a graph of this function for $0 \leq x \leq 40$. On the sketch, show the coordinates of the starting and ending points and the point where the bridge surface is closest to the water.

   b. Show how coordinates for those key points on the graph can be calculated exactly from the rule, not simply estimated by tracing the graph or scanning a table.

   c. Write and estimate solutions for an equation that will locate point(s) on the bridge surface that are 10 feet above the water.

2 **Mike's Water Slide** Mike wanted to design a parabolic water slide for customers. The curve he wanted is shown in the following sketch. He wanted to have the entry to the slide at the point $(-10, 35)$, the low point to be $(0, 5)$, and the exit point to be $(5, 12.5)$.

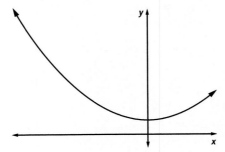

   a. What rule will define a function with a graph in the shape that Mike wants?

   b. Use the rule from Part a to write and solve an equation that gives the x-coordinate(s) of point(s) on the slide that are exactly 20 feet above the ground.

   c. Mike tried to find the rule he wanted by looking first at functions like $y = ax^2$. He started by trying to find a so that $(-10, 30)$ and $(0, 0)$ would be points on the graph.

      i. How do you suppose Mike was thinking about the problem that led him to this approach?

      ii. How could he have figured out the value of a with that start?

      iii. How could he then adjust the rule so the graph would go through the point $(-10, 35)$?

      iv. Verify that the graph of the adjusted rule in part iii goes through the point $(5, 12.5)$.

Lesson 4 | Looking Back   **527**

1 **a.**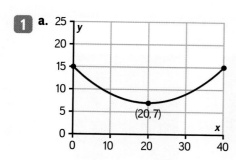

b. Calculations would be $0.02(0)^2 - 0.8(0) + 15$; $0.02(40)^2 - 0.8(40) + 15$; and $0.02(20)^2 - 0.8(20) + 15$.

(By this point in the unit, students should recognize that the constant term of a quadratic is the y-coordinate of the y-intercept and that the max/min point has x-coordinate $\frac{-b}{2a}$. In this case, that is $\frac{0.8}{0.04} = 20$.)

c. The point(s) where the bridge is 10 feet above the river will be solutions to the equation $0.02x^2 - 0.8x + 15 = 10$. Approximate solutions will be $x = 7.75$ feet and $x = 32.25$ feet.

2 **a.** The rule that will work is $y = 0.3x^2 + 5$.

(Students might get this by using the quadratic regression feature of their calculators with the three given data points.)

b. Solutions to the equation $0.3x^2 + 5 = 20$ will be exactly $x = \pm\sqrt{50}$ or $x \approx \pm 7.1$. In this situation, only the negative solution makes sense because the slide only goes out to $x = 5$.

c. **i.** The reasoning suggested might be based on getting the slide to go through $(0, 0)$ and $(-10, 30)$ and then sliding it up 5 feet to hit $(0, 5)$ and $(-10, 35)$.

ii. The rule containing the first two points would be in the form $y = ax^2$. To get a we could reason that $30 = a(-10)^2$ and solve for a to get the coefficient of 0.3.

iii. The adjustment is to add 5, since $0.3(-10)^2 + 5 = 35$.

iv. That graph does in fact go through the point $(5, 12.5)$, since $0.3(5)^2 + 5 = 12.5$.

> **INSTRUCTIONAL NOTE**
>
> Ask students to think about the difference between Mike's parabolic slide and a linear slide that starts and ends at the same points as the parabolic slide. How would the speed of the rides compare?

3 Flying Off the Slide Mike figured that people would come off the end of his water slide at the point (5, 12.5) with an upward speed of about 20 feet per second. He wanted to know about the resulting flight into the air and down to a splash in the pool lying at the end of the slide.

a. What rule would give good estimates of the slider's height above the water as a function of time (in seconds) after they leave the end of the slide?

b. What would be the maximum height of the slider?

c. How long would it take the slider to make the trip from the end of the slide, into the air, and down to the water?

4 Water Slide Business Tanya liked Mike's water slide idea, but she wondered how much they should charge customers for the experience. She asked a market research company to survey how the number of customers would depend on the admission price.

a. The market research data suggested that daily number of customers n would be related to admission price x by $n = 250 - 10x$. What function shows how predicted income depends on admission price?

b. What price gives maximum daily income? Explain how you can locate that point by estimation and by reasoning that gives an exact answer.

c. If Mike and Tanya expect operation of the water slide attraction to cost $450 per day, what function shows how predicted daily profit depends on admission price?

d. What water slide admission price leads to maximum profit?

e. What water slide admission price leads to a break-even operation of the water slide? Explain how you can locate the point(s) by estimation and by reasoning that gives an exact answer.

5 Use algebraic methods to find exact solutions for these quadratic equations. Show the steps in your reasoning and a check of each solution.

a. $2x^2 + 11x + 12 = 0$

b. $6x^2 + 10x = 0$

c. $2x^2 + 11 = 19$

UNIT 7

3 **a.** $h = -16t^2 + 20t + 12.5$ matches the given information and the scientific principles of flying objects and the height of the end of the slide.

b. The maximum height occurs at 0.625 seconds and is 18.75 feet.

c. The slider hits the water when $0 = -16t^2 + 20t + 12.5$. The solutions to this equation are $x = \dfrac{5}{8} + \dfrac{\sqrt{1{,}200}}{-32} \approx -0.46$ second and $x = \dfrac{5}{8} - \dfrac{\sqrt{1{,}200}}{-32} = 1.71$ seconds. In this situation, only the positive solution makes sense.

4 **a.** $I = x(250 - 10x)$ or $I = -10x^2 + 250x$, where x is the admission price.

b. The admission price that will lead to maximum income is $x = \$12.50$. The maximum income is $I = \$1{,}562.50$.

It can be located by tracing a graph, scanning a table, or using the general property $x = \dfrac{-b}{2a}$ relating coefficients of the standard quadratic form to the x-coordinate of the max/min point.

c. The profit function will be $P = -10x^2 + 250x - 450$, where x is the admission price.

d. Maximum profit occurs at the same point as maximum income because the costs are fixed, independent of price (and thus number of customers). A water slide admission price of $12.50 leads to maximum profit.

e. Break-even points are at $x = \dfrac{-250}{-20} + \dfrac{\sqrt{44{,}500}}{-20} \approx 1.95$ and $x = \dfrac{-250}{-20} - \dfrac{\sqrt{44{,}500}}{-20} \approx 23.05$. So, charging $1.95 or $23.05 will lead to a profit of $0. Additionally, the points could be located by estimating the x-intercepts of the function $P = -10x^2 + 250x - 450$ or by using the table to determine the x values that make the function equal to 0.

5 **a.** $x = -\dfrac{3}{2}, x = -4$

b. $x = 0, x = -\dfrac{5}{3}$

c. $x = \pm 2$

6 The graphs and tables below model quadratic, linear, and exponential growth or decay situations.

a. Without the use of technology, match each graph with its corresponding table. In each case, describe the clues that you used to match the items.

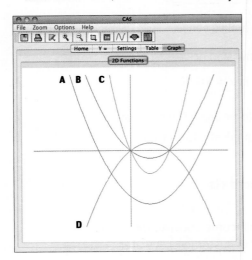

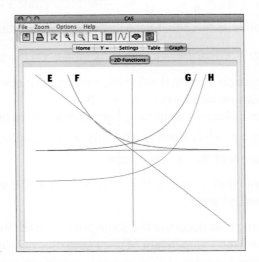

Table 1:

x	−2	−1	0	1	2
y	0.25	0.5	1	2	4

Table 2:

x	−2	−1	0	1	2
y	24	9	0	−3	0

Table 3:

x	−2	−1	0	1	2
y	8	3	0	−1	0

Table 4:

x	−2	−1	0	1	2
y	4	2	1	0.5	0.25

Table 5:

x	−2	−1	0	1	2
y	−8	−3	0	1	0

Table 6:

x	−2	−1	0	1	2
y	−3.75	−3.5	−3	−2	0

Table 7:

x	−2	−1	0	1	2
y	4	2	0	−2	−4

Table 8:

x	−2	−1	0	1	2
y	2	−3	−6	−7	−6

b. Without using technology, write "$y = \ldots$" rules for each of the graph/table pairs you matched in Part a. Then check with technology.

6 CCSS MATHEMATICAL PRACTICE You may wish to have students work in pairs on this task. The task requires students to make sense of the task and persevere in solving it, to reason abstractly and quantitatively, and to look for and make use of structure. Some students may formulate the function rules asked for in Part b while thinking about Part a. Those that do not will be asked to formulate the rules in Part b.

a.

Graph	Table	Rule
A	8	$y = x(x - 2) - 6$
B	3	$y = x(x - 2)$
C	2	$y = 3x(x - 2)$
D	5	$y = -x(x - 2)$
E	7	$y = -2x$
F	4	$y = \left(\frac{1}{2}\right)^x$
G	1	$y = 2^x$
H	6	$y = 2^x - 4$

b. See the chart above. Students should use their knowledge of patterns and symmetry in tables and graphs, x- and y-intercepts, and how coefficients of function rules affect graphs and tables to write the rules.

SUMMARIZE THE MATHEMATICS

When two variables are related by a quadratic function, that relationship can be recognized from patterns in tables and graphs of (x, y) data, from the rules that show how to calculate values of one variable from given values of the other, and from key features of the problem situations.

a Sketch two graphs illustrating the basic patterns that are modeled well by quadratic functions.

   i. For each graph, write a brief explanation of the pattern shown in the graph and describe a problem situation that involves the pattern.

   ii. Then give "y = ..." rules that would produce each given graph pattern and explain how those rules alone could be used to determine the pattern of change in the dependent variable as the independent variable increases.

b Suppose that you develop or discover a rule that shows how a variable *y* is a quadratic function of another variable *x*. Describe the different strategies you could use to complete tasks like these:

   i. Find the value of *y* associated with a specific given value of *x*.

   ii. Find the value of *x* that gives a specific target value of *y*.

   iii. Describe the way that the value of *y* changes as the value of *x* increases or decreases.

c What information about the graph of a quadratic function can be obtained easily from each of these types of rules?

   i. $y = ax^2 + c$

   ii. $y = ax^2 + bx$

   iii. $y = ax(x - m)$

d For questions that call for solving quadratic equations,

   i. How many solutions would you expect, and how is that shown by the graphs of quadratic functions? By the quadratic formula?

   ii. How would you decide on a solution strategy?

   iii. How would you find the solution(s)?

   iv. How would you check the solution(s)?

Be prepared to share your examples and descriptions with the class.

 CHECK YOUR UNDERSTANDING

Write, in outline form, a summary of the important mathematical concepts and methods developed in this unit. Organize your summary so that it can be used as a quick reference in future units and courses.

SUMMARIZE THE MATHEMATICS

a Student example graphs will vary, but they should include one in which the parabola "opens up" and one in which the parabola "opens down."

   i. **"Opens up"**—The graph decreases at a decreasing rate until it reaches a minimum, then increases at an increasing rate. A situation that could be described by the pattern is the distance from a two-tower suspension bridge wire to the bridge itself as you move from the left tower to the right.

   "Opens down"—The graph increases at a decreasing rate until it reaches a maximum, then decreases at an increasing rate. A situation that could be described by the pattern is the height above the ground of a punted football as time elapses.

  ii. **"Opens up":** $y = ax^2 + bx + c$, where $a > 0$ is a parabola that has a minimum point.

   "Opens down": $y = ax^2 + bx + c$, where $a < 0$ is a parabola that has a maximum point.

   Both rules indicate that the independent variable is squared. This calculation results in the change of direction for the graph.

b **i.** Substitute the value of x in the rule, produce a table and scan to the point where the given x value occurs, or produce a graph and trace until the given x-coordinate is located. In all three approaches, the final step is to read off the indicated y value.

  ii. To solve for x with given y, reverse the scanning of a table or tracing of a graph. Formally, this means solving an equation. Depending on the form of the equation, one could reason to a final step involving square roots (type $ax^2 + c = d$), one could factor (type $ax^2 + bx = 0$) and solve linear terms set equal to 0, or one could use the quadratic formula.

  iii. Describing the pattern of change in y as x increases or decreases is perhaps easiest by inspecting a table or a graph. However, by now students should be able to examine the rule and detect clues to what will happen (e.g., negative lead coefficient means rising to a maximum point and then falling, positive lead coefficient means falling to a minimum point and then rising, constant term tells the y-coordinate of the y-intercept, $\frac{-b}{2a}$ determines location of max/min point for a quadratic function in the form $y = ax^2 + bx + c$).

c **i.** This form easily tells which way the graph opens—up when $a > 0$ and down when $a < 0$. It also shows the max/min value, c, which occurs when $x = 0$, and that the graph is symmetric about the y-axis.

  ii. This form easily shows that the y-intercept is $(0, 0)$, and whether the graph opens up ($a > 0$) or down ($a < 0$). The graph is symmetric about $x = \frac{-b}{2a}$. More information is clear when this form is factored (see part iii).

Lesson Masters 480–481

⊙ **GO DIGITAL**

iii. The factored form easily tells the x-intercepts, $(0, 0)$ and $(m, 0)$, and whether the graph opens up ($a > 0$) or down ($a < 0$). The x-coordinate for the max/min point is halfway between 0 and m.

d

i. For quadratic equations, you would expect zero, one, or two solutions. The number of solutions is seen on the graph of the function by the number of times it crosses the x-axis. The quadratic formula gives zero real-valued solutions when $b^2 - 4ac$ is negative, one solution when $b^2 - 4ac$ is 0, and two solutions when $b^2 - 4ac$ is positive.

ii. All quadratic equations could be solved using the quadratic formula. If the equation is of the form $ax^2 + c = d$, algebraic reasoning would be a good strategy to use. If the equation is of the form $ax^2 + bx = 0$, one might decide to factor out a monomial.

iii. Exact solutions can be found for equations of the form $ax^2 + c = d$ by "undoing," for equations of the form $ax^2 + bx = 0$ by factoring, and for any quadratic equation by using the quadratic formula. Approximations (and sometimes exact values) for the solutions can be found by using a table or graph.

iv. Solution(s) can be checked by substituting the solution value(s) back into the equation.

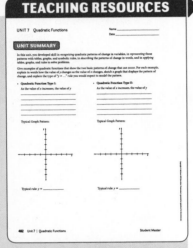
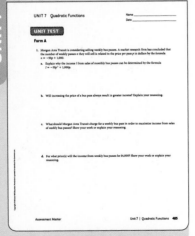
✔️ CHECK YOUR UNDERSTANDING

You may wish to have students use the Student Master, *Quadratic Functions* Unit Summary, to help them organize the information. Above all, this should be something that is useful to the individual student.

UNIT 7

Practicing for Standardized Tests

Each Practicing for Standardized Tests master presents ten questions in the multiple-choice format of test items similar to how they often appear in standardized tests. Answers are provided below.

Answers to Practice Set 7

1. (c)
2. (c)
3. (d)
4. (d)
5. (c)
6. (b)
7. (c)
8. (b)
9. (b)
10. (b)

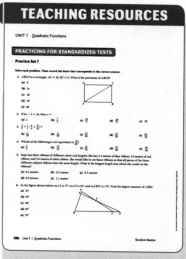

TEACHING RESOURCES

Student Masters 506–507

⓪ GO DIGITAL

UNIT 8

Patterns in Chance

Many events in life occur by chance. They cannot be predicted with certainty. For example, you cannot predict whether the next baby born will be a boy or a girl. However, in the long run, you can predict that about half of the babies born will be boys and half will be girls. Probability is the study of events that occur (or don't occur) at random from one observation to the next but that occur a fixed proportion of the time in the long run. In this unit, you will study two methods for solving problems in probability: calculating theoretical probabilities using mathematical formulas or geometric models and estimating probabilities using simulation.

Key ideas for solving problems involving chance will be developed through your work in two lessons.

LESSONS

1 Calculating Probabilities

Construct probability distributions from sample spaces of equally likely outcomes. Use the Addition Rule to solve problems involving chance.

2 Modeling Chance Situations

Use simulation to decide whether the probability model is consistent with the data. Use geometric models to solve probability problems.

McGraw-Hill Education

UNIT 8

Patterns in Chance

The *Patterns in Chance* unit introduces students to sample spaces, probability distributions, the Addition Rule, simulation, and geometric probability. Important probabilistic concepts explored include mutually exclusive events and the Law of Large Numbers.

In Lesson 1, students learn to use sample spaces and probability distributions to calculate probabilities. In Lesson 2, students learn how to use simulation to decide whether a probabilistic model is consistent with the known data. They also learn how to calculate probabilities using geometric (area) models.

Simulation is the modeling of a probabilistic situation using random devices such as coins, spinners, and random digits. Simulation is useful throughout instruction on probability. Setting up a simulation helps students clarify their assumptions about such things as whether trials are independent. Simulation helps develop students' intuition about probabilistic events. And, perhaps most importantly, students who have been introduced to simulation have a feeling of control over probability. They know that they can estimate the answer to any probability problem that arises.

Unit Objectives

- Construct sample spaces and probability distributions and use them to understand chance situations involving equally likely outcomes

- Use the Addition Rule and its special case for mutually exclusive events to compute $P(A \text{ and } B)$

- Design and carry out simulations to decide whether the probability model is consistent with the data

- Use the Law of Large Numbers to understand situations involving chance

- Use geometric diagrams to solve probability problems that involve continuous variables

Solving Probability Problems

There are four ways to estimate probabilities, although not all methods work with all problems.
(1) Use mathematical formulas or theory or a geometric model.
(2) Examine the population.
(3) Examine a sample from the population.
(4) Simulate the situation using a physically different but mathematically equivalent model; that is, a model whose outcomes have the same probabilities as the outcomes in the situation.

For example, in Investigation 1 of Lesson 2, students find the probability that a two-child family has at least one boy.

- To solve this problem using mathematical methods, you might list all possible families of two children: older boy and his younger sister, older boy and his younger brother, older girl and her younger brother, older girl and her younger sister. Two out of these four possible families have one boy and one girl. If you can make the assumption that these four possible families occur equally often, then the desired probability is $\frac{3}{4}$.

- To solve this problem by examining the population, you could call up the United States Bureau of the Census and ask if they have this information available from the last census of United States families. If so, you would have the best possible answer; in fact, it should give you the exact answer for families in the United States at the time of the last census. You do not need to make any assumptions.

- To solve this problem by examining a sample, you would take a survey of two-child families and observe the number that have one boy and one girl. If you could observe a large number of randomly-selected families, this would be a very good method of estimating the answer to your question.

- To solve this problem using simulation, you could write the word "boy" on a card and the word "girl" on another card, place the cards in a hat, and then draw one. If it says "boy," the first child in the family would be a boy. If it says "girl," the first child in the family would be a girl. Replace the card and draw a second card to represent the birth of the second child. After performing many runs of this simulation, you would have a good idea of the percentage of two-child families that have exactly one boy and one girl. This simulation assumes that boys and girls are equally likely and that this probability does not change depending on whether the first child was a boy or a girl (that is, the events are independent).

If you would like to learn how to solve many of the problems in this unit theoretically, see the book *Fifty Challenging Problems in Probability with Solutions,* by Frederick Mosteller (Dover, 1989).

CPMP-Tools

Students should learn to set up a simulation using a variety of tools, including dice, random digits, and software. Once students are confident about their ability to design a simulation using physical devices and random digits, they are ready to use the simulation software in *CPMP-Tools,* under Statistics. *CPMP-Tools* will produce a frequency table quickly for problems such as the waiting time until a boy is born (page 553), the collection of magic tricks (page 560), the number of students who have been to a movie (page 561), and homework tasks.

CCSS and CPMP Pathways

The Grade 7 CCSS standards expect students to investigate chance processes and develop, use, and evaluate probability models. This includes simulation using random digits.

If your students have been introduced to probability in middle school, you may find that some material in this unit will need fewer days to complete than is suggested in the Unit Planning Guide. Typically, the cognitive demand of the problems in *Core-Plus Mathematics* exceeds that of similar content in middle school programs. Thus, it is in students' best interests to complete the CCSS Pathway outlined in the Unit Planning Guide regardless of middle school background. If you cover the investigations and problems listed there, students will be able to complete subsequent probability units in *Core-Plus Mathematics*. The CCSS Pathway in this unit, along with the CCSS Pathways in the subsequent probability units in *Core-Plus Mathematics*, will cover all topics specified in the CCSS.

Your honors or STEM students would be well advised to complete the optional investigations in the CPMP Pathway described in the Unit Planning Guide.

UNIT 8 Planning Guide

Lesson Objectives	Pathways: Pacing and OYO Assignments*	Resources
Lesson 1 Calculating Probabilities • Construct sample spaces for chance situations involving equally likely outcomes • Construct probability distributions from sample spaces • Identify mutually exclusive (disjoint) events • Compute $P(A \text{ and } B)$ using the Addition Rule or its special case for mutually exclusive events	<u>CCSS Pathway</u> (7 days, includes assessment) **Investigation 1:** OYO—A2, A3, C7, R12, E17, Rv22–Rv26 **Investigation 2:** OYO—A4, A5, C11, R13, R15, R16, E20, Rv27–Rv30 <u>CPMP Pathway</u> (7 days, includes assessment) Use CCSS Pathway plus **Investigation 1:** OYO—C8 or C9 **Investigation 2:** OYO—R14	• Classroom set of dice (tetrahedral, octahedral, decahedral, and icosahedral dice for C10) • *Optional:* Backgammon set • Unit Resource Masters
Lesson 2 Modeling Chance Situations • Design and carry out simulations to decide whether the probability model is consistent with the data • Use the Law of Large Numbers to understand situations involving chance • Use tables of random digits to perform simulations and understand some properties of random digits • Use random numbers to perform simulations in situations that involve continuous variables • Use geometric diagrams to solve probability problems that involve continuous variables	<u>CCSS Pathway</u> (6 days, no formal assessment) See CCSS Pathway comments above. **Investigation 1:** OYO—A2, C11, R15, R17, Rv25–Rv28 **Investigation 2:** Problems 1–6 OYO—A4, A5, C12, E21, E22, Rv29–Rv33 **Investigations 3 and 4:** omit <u>CPMP Pathway</u> (8 days, no formal assessment) Use CCSS Pathway plus **Investigation 2:** Problems 7 and 8, STM Part a **Investigation 3:** all students do Problems 1 and 2, different pairs of students do Problems 3–6 OYO—A6, C13, choose one of E21–E23, Rv34 **Investigation 4:** optional	• One penny per student • Rulers • Protractor for each student for C10 • Unit Resource Masters
Lesson 3 Looking Back • Review and synthesize the major objectives of the unit	(2 days, includes unit assessment) Omit Task 5 and STM Part f.	• *Optional:* Octahedral dice • Unit Resource Masters

* When choice is indicated, it is important to leave the choice to the student.
Note: It is best if Connections tasks are discussed as a whole class after they have been assigned as homework.
Note: The Planning Guide assumes students have access to technology for homework.

Calculating Probabilities

Backgammon is the oldest game in recorded history. It originated before 3000 B.C. in the Middle East. Backgammon is a two-person board game that is popular among people of all ages. When it is your turn, you roll a pair of dice and move your checkers ahead on the board according to what the dice show. The object is to be the first to move your checkers around and then off of the board. It's generally a good thing to get doubles because then you get to use what the dice show twice instead of just once.

Comstock/SuperStock

UNIT 8

Calculating Probabilities

In the first investigation in this lesson, students will learn how to construct sample spaces for chance (random) situations involving equally likely outcomes. Students will then learn that they can construct different probability distributions from the same sample space. In Investigation 2, students will learn to use the Addition Rule to compute the probability that event *A* happens or event *B* happens.

Lesson Objectives

- Construct sample spaces for chance situations involving equally likely outcomes
- Construct probability distributions from sample spaces
- Identify mutually exclusive (disjoint) events
- Compute *P*(*A* and *B*) using the Addition Rule or its special case for mutually exclusive events

Lesson Launch

You may wish to bring in a backgammon set (which often can be found on the back of a checkers or chess board) and show students how the game is played. For an overview of the game, see en.wikipedia.org/wiki/Backgammon. For an explanation of the rules, see www.bkgm.com/rules.html. Various sites on the Web have applets where one person can play backgammon against a computer.

If your students have not studied any probability previously, they may not know how to answer some of these questions. Assure such students that they will learn probability in this unit and that the goal for this TATS is to understand the types of questions that can be asked about a chance situation.

Reducing Fractions
While students may be instructed to always reduce fractions in other situations, it can be counterproductive to do so in probability. The reason is that if you keep the common denominator that results from many sample spaces, it makes it easier to compare two probabilities. For example, it is better to say, "The probability of rolling a sum of seven with two dice is $\frac{6}{36}$, but the probability of rolling a sum of eight is only $\frac{5}{36}$," than to say, "The probability of rolling a sum of seven with two dice is $\frac{1}{6}$, but the probability of rolling a sum of eight is only $\frac{5}{36}$." Further, students should be cautioned to not automatically convert probabilities such as $\frac{5}{36}$ from exact fraction form to a rounded and inexact decimal form (0.14) unless there is some reason to do so.

Common Core State Standards CCSS

Focused on:
S-CP.1, S-CP.7,
S-MD.1, S-MD.3

Connected to:
A-CED.2, S-ID.1, S-ID.2,
S-ID.5, S-MD.2, S-MD.4

THINK ABOUT THIS SITUATION

Suppose you and a friend are playing a game of backgammon.

a Which probability should be larger?

- the probability of rolling doubles on your first turn
- the probability of rolling doubles on your first turn or on your second turn

Explain your thinking.

b What do you think is the probability of rolling doubles on your first turn? Explain your reasoning.

c What assumptions are you making about the dice in finding the probability in Part b?

d Suppose you rolled doubles on each of your first three turns. Your friend did not roll doubles on any of his first three turns. Who has the better chance of rolling doubles on their next turn? Explain.

In this lesson, you will learn to construct probability distributions from sample spaces of *equally likely outcomes* and use them to solve problems involving chance.

INVESTIGATION 1

Probability Distributions

Because of the symmetry in a fair die—each side is equally likely to end up on top when the die is rolled—it is easy to find the probabilities of various outcomes. As you work on the problems in this investigation, look for answers to this question:

How can you find and organize the probabilities associated with random situations like the outcomes from the roll of two dice?

1 Suppose a red die and a green die are rolled at the same time.

a. What does the entry "3, 2" in the chart mean?

b. Complete a copy of the chart at the right, showing all possible outcomes of a single roll of two dice.

c. How many possible outcomes are there?

d. What is the probability of rolling a (1, 2), that is, a 1 on the red die and a 2 on the green die? What is the probability of rolling a (2, 1)? A (4, 4)?

e. Would the chart be any different if both dice had been the same color?

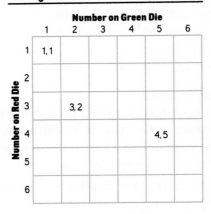

Rolling Two Dice

	Number on Green Die					
	1	2	3	4	5	6
1	1, 1					
2						
3		3, 2				
4					4, 5	
5						
6						

(Number on Red Die)

Lesson 1 | Calculating Probabilities **533**

THINK ABOUT THIS SITUATION

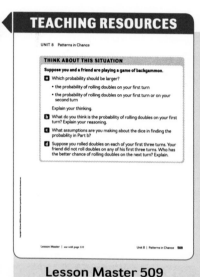

TEACHING RESOURCES

Lesson Master 509
ⓘ **GO DIGITAL**

a Students will likely correctly indicate that the probability of getting doubles on the first or second turn is larger than that of getting doubles on the first turn. They may reason that they have two chances to get doubles. (The meaning of "or" in probability will be introduced in Investigation 2. Leave the discussion until then unless your students seem to wish to pursue it now.)

b The probability of rolling doubles is $\frac{6}{36}$ or $\frac{1}{6}$. Students may explain this by using a table like that in Problem 1 of Investigation 1. There are 36 equally likely outcomes when two dice are rolled, and 6 of these are doubles. Alternatively, they may argue that the first die can show any number and the second die has 1 chance in 6 of matching it. Other valid explanations also are possible.

c There are two assumptions:

- On each die, the probability a given number comes up is $\frac{1}{6}$. (That is, each die is "fair.")

- The dice are rolled independently of each other (and not, say, stuck together).

d Some students may think that the friend has a better chance of rolling doubles even though the chance of rolling doubles remains $\frac{1}{6}$ for both students. This misconception should be addressed frequently.

(You may also want to ask the question: How can you find the probability that both you and your friend will get doubles? This probability is $\frac{1}{6} \cdot \frac{1}{6} = \frac{1}{36}$. The student responses to this question may reveal a sense of what intuitions students have regarding the distinctions among these different probabilities.)

COLLABORATION SKILL

Include every group member in discussions.

Probability Distributions

In this investigation, students learn to construct sample spaces and probability distributions. What's the difference? For example, {heads, tails} is a sample space for the chance situation of flipping a coin once. If you are counting the number of heads that you get, the probability distribution for this numerical outcome is as follows:

Probability Distribution for the Number of Heads	
Number	Probability
0	$\frac{1}{2}$
1	$\frac{1}{2}$

A probability distribution must contain numerical outcomes and must include the probability that each outcome occurs. A sample space need not have numerical outcomes (but it may), and the probabilities may not be specified.

A probability distribution gives students the complete picture of a probabilistic situation and is usually the best way to organize the analysis. When students see the complete probability distribution, they build intuition that guides the analysis of future probabilistic situations. Students who develop pictures of distributions in their heads or who are capable of generating probability distributions by simulation will have real power over probabilistic situations.

1 **a.** The entry "3, 2" means that the red die was a 3 and the green die was a 2.

b. Rolling Two Dice

	Number on Green Die					
	1	2	3	4	5	6
1	1, 1	1, 2	1, 3	1, 4	1, 5	1, 6
2	2, 1	2, 2	2, 3	2, 4	2, 5	2, 6
3	3, 1	3, 2	3, 3	3, 4	3, 5	3, 6
4	4, 1	4, 2	4, 3	4, 4	4, 5	4, 6
5	5, 1	5, 2	5, 3	5, 4	5, 5	5, 6
6	6, 1	6, 2	6, 3	6, 4	6, 5	6, 6

(Number on Red Die, row labels)

c. There are 36 possible outcomes.

d. The probability of rolling a (1, 2) is $\frac{1}{36}$. The probability of rolling a (2, 1) is $\frac{1}{36}$. The probability of rolling a (4, 4) is $\frac{1}{36}$.

e. It would not have made any difference in the chart if both dice had been the same color. (They were said to be different colors to make the point that you need to list both (1, 2) and (2, 1) in the sample space.)

ELL TIP When making assignments, be specific about what students are expected to know, to do, and to submit for a passing grade. It is particularly helpful to develop a set of guidelines or a scoring rubric. Use samples to model the expected outcome whenever possible. You may want to use an overhead projector or the chalkboard to show a sample of a proof, diagram, or other assignment. Go through it line by line or element by element and model what information should appear.

Misconceptions About Probability and the Importance of Simulation

People appear to have unreliable intuition when it comes to many probabilistic events. Many students, and adults as well, believe that a person who has rolled a pair of dice several times without getting doubles is more likely to roll doubles on the next roll. (The person is "due" to get doubles.) Such misconceptions are confronted head-on in this unit. One of the most important lessons we can teach students about probability is that they should be suspicious of their first impulse when analyzing random events.

J. Michael Shaughnessy in "Probability and Statistics" (*The Mathematics Teacher*, Volume 86, March 1993, pages 244–248) gives this "strong recommendation" for the teaching of simulation:

> "The technique of simulation is a tremendous problem-solving tool that can help change students' conceptions. It is also reassuring to be able to say, 'I don't have any idea what is going on here, but maybe we can simulate it.' Even if we have already worked out a theoretical solution to a probability problem, simulation can help us to confirm or challenge our solution. It is important to encourage students to gather data physically or with such concrete-simulation objects as spinners, dice, and random-number charts prior to engaging them in computer simulations. Students must 'get a feel' for conducting experiments and simulations themselves before they are dazzled by a computer simulation."

See the following for another good introduction to the research that documents students' misconceptions about probability and what to do about them.

Joan Garfield and Andrew Ahlgren, "Difficulties in Learning Basic Concepts in Probability and Statistics: Implications for Research," *Journal for Research in Mathematics Education* 19 (1988: 44–63).

2 The chart you completed in Problem 1 is called a sample space for the situation of rolling two dice. A **sample space** is the set of all possible outcomes for a probabilistic situation. For fair dice, all 36 outcomes in the sample space are equally likely to occur. **Equally likely** means that each outcome has the same probability. When outcomes are equally likely, the probability of an event is given by

$$P(event) = \frac{number\ of\ outcomes\ in\ the\ event}{number\ of\ possible\ outcomes}.$$

If two dice are rolled, what is the probability of getting:

a. doubles?

b. a sum of 7?

c. a sum of 11?

d. a 2 on at least one die or a sum of 2?

e. doubles and a sum of 8?

f. doubles or a sum of 8?

3 Suppose two dice are rolled.

a. What is the probability that the sum is no more than 9?

b. What is the probability that the sum is at least 9?

c. What is the probability that the sum is 2 or 3? Is greater than 3? Is at least 3? Is less than 3?

4 A **probability distribution** is a description of all possible numerical outcomes of a random situation, along with the probability that each occurs. A probability distribution differs from a sample space in that all of the outcomes must be a single number and the probabilities must be specified. For example, the probability distribution table below shows all possible sums that you could get from the roll of two dice.

Probability Distribution for the Sum of Two Dice	
Sum	**Probability**
2	
3	
4	
5	
6	
7	
8	
9	
10	
11	
12	

2 a. $\frac{6}{36}$

b. $\frac{6}{36}$

c. $\frac{2}{36}$

d. $\frac{12}{36}$

e. $\frac{1}{36}$

f. $\frac{10}{36}$

3 a. $\frac{30}{36}$

b. $\frac{10}{36}$

c. $\frac{3}{36}, \frac{33}{36}, \frac{35}{36}, \frac{1}{36}$

4 a.

Probability Distribution for the Sum of Two Dice	
Sum	**Probability**
2	$\frac{1}{36}$
3	$\frac{2}{36}$
4	$\frac{3}{36}$
5	$\frac{4}{36}$
6	$\frac{5}{36}$
7	$\frac{6}{36}$
8	$\frac{5}{36}$
9	$\frac{4}{36}$
10	$\frac{3}{36}$
11	$\frac{2}{36}$
12	$\frac{1}{36}$

b. The sum of the probabilities is $\frac{36}{36}$ or 1.

c. To find the answers you can add the probabilities specified in the question.

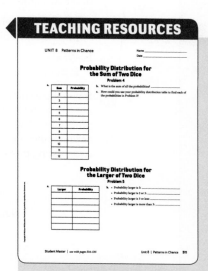
TECHNOLOGY NOTE

CPMP-Tools statistics software includes a "Simulation" tool that can simulate the distribution of the sum of two dice.

a. Complete a copy of this probability distribution by filling in the probabilities.

b. What is the sum of all of the probabilities?

c. How could you use your probability distribution table to find each of the probabilities in Problem 3?

5 Other probability distributions can be made from the sample space in Problem 1 for the roll of two dice. Suppose that you roll two dice and record the larger of the two numbers. (If the numbers are the same, record that number.)

a. Use your sample space from Problem 1 to help you complete a probability distribution table for this situation.

b. What is the probability that the larger of the two numbers is 3? Is 2 or 3? Is 3 or less? Is more than 3?

6 Now suppose you roll two dice and record the absolute value of the difference of the two numbers.

a. Use your sample space from Problem 1 to help you complete a probability distribution table for this situation.

b. What is the probability that the absolute value of the difference is 3? Is 2 or 3? Is at least 2? Is no more than 2?

7 If you flip a coin, {heads, tails} is a sample space, but not a probability distribution. However, you can make a probability distribution by recording the number of heads as your outcome, as shown in the table below. Fill in the two missing probabilities.

Probability Distribution for the Number of Heads	
Number of Heads	Probability
0	
1	

8 Now suppose that you flip a coin twice.

a. Complete a chart that shows the sample space of all possible outcomes. It should look like the chart for rolling two dice except that only heads and tails are possible for each coin rather than the six numbers that are possible for each die.

b. Make a probability distribution table that gives the probability of getting 0, 1, and 2 heads.

c. What is the probability that you get exactly one head if you flip a coin twice? What is the probability that you get at least one head?

Lesson 1 | Calculating Probabilities **535**

5 **a.**

**Probability Distribution for
the Larger of Two Dice**

Larger	Probability
1	$\frac{1}{36}$
2	$\frac{3}{36}$
3	$\frac{5}{36}$
4	$\frac{7}{36}$
5	$\frac{9}{36}$
6	$\frac{11}{36}$

b. $\frac{5}{36}, \frac{8}{36}, \frac{9}{36}, \frac{27}{36}$

NOTE The solution to Problem 4 is on page T534.

6 **a.**

**Probability Distribution for the Absolute
Value of the Difference of Two Dice**

Difference	Probability
0	$\frac{6}{36}$
1	$\frac{10}{36}$
2	$\frac{8}{36}$
3	$\frac{6}{36}$
4	$\frac{4}{36}$
5	$\frac{2}{36}$

b. $\frac{6}{36}, \frac{14}{36}, \frac{20}{36}, \frac{24}{36}$

Student Master 512
Ⓘ GO DIGITAL

7

**Probability Distribution for
the Number of Heads**

Number	Probability
0	$\frac{1}{2}$
1	$\frac{1}{2}$

8 **a.**

		Second Coin	
		Heads	**Tails**
First Coin	**Heads**	H, H	H, T
	Tails	T, H	T, T

b.

**Probability Distribution for
the Number of Heads**

Number	Probability
0	$\frac{1}{4}$
1	$\frac{2}{4}$
2	$\frac{1}{4}$

c. $\frac{2}{4}, \frac{3}{4}$

SUMMARIZE THE MATHEMATICS

In this investigation, you learned how to construct probability distributions from the sample space of equally likely outcomes from the roll of two dice and from the flip(s) of a coin.

a What is the difference between a sample space and a probability distribution?

b How would you make a probability distribution table for the product of the numbers from the roll of two dice?

c Why is it that the outcomes in the sample space for rolling two dice are equally likely?

Be prepared to share your ideas and reasoning with the class.

✔ CHECK YOUR UNDERSTANDING

Suppose that you flip a coin three times.

a. List the sample space of all 8 possible outcomes. For example, one outcome is heads, tails, tails (HTT).

b. Are the outcomes in your sample space equally likely? Explain.

c. Make a probability distribution table for the number of heads.

d. What is the probability that you will get exactly 2 heads? At most 2 heads?

INVESTIGATION 2

The Addition Rule

In the previous investigation, you constructed the probability distribution for the sum of two dice. You discovered that to find the probability that the sum is 2 or 3, you could *add* the probability that the sum is 2 to the probability that the sum is 3, $\frac{1}{36} + \frac{2}{36} = \frac{3}{36}$. As you work on the following problems, look for an answer to this question:

> *Under what conditions can you add individual probabilities to find the probability that a given event happens?*

1 Some people have shoes of many different colors, while others prefer one color and so have all their shoes in just that color. As a class, complete a copy of the following two tables on the color of your shoes.

Summary

To help students articulate the difference between a sample space and a probability distribution in Part a, it may be helpful to revisit the initial definitions of each in Problems 2 and 4. In Part b, it will be helpful for many students to allow them to actually begin creating the chart so they can think about how they would make it. This question provides an opportunity to discuss various organization techniques proposed by students.

SUMMARIZE THE MATHEMATICS

a A sample space is a description of all possible outcomes of a random situation. The outcomes may be categories (such as heads or tails) or numbers (such as 1, 2, 3, 4, 5, or 6). A probability distribution can be made only with *numerical* outcomes. It is a description of all possible numerical outcomes of a random situation and their associated probabilities.

b You could start with the chart in Problem 1 and compute the product of each pair of numbers. Then make a table of all possible products and the probability of each. Students may suggest a variety of ways to organize finding the possible products, such as writing the products in the chart cells with the two numbers or just writing down the possible products in the order that they compute them and then ordering and placing them in the first column of a probability distribution table.

c The 36 outcomes are all of the ordered pairs of numbers that can occur when you roll two dice. They are equally likely because we assume that the dice are rolled independently and are "fair"; that is, on each die any given number has a $\frac{1}{6}$ chance of coming up no matter what happens on the other die.

PROCESSING PROMPT I made sure _____ was included in our
discussions by ...   *(name)*

TEACHING RESOURCES

UNIT 8   Patterns in Chance

SUMMARIZE THE MATHEMATICS

In this investigation, you learned how to construct probability distributions from the sample space of equally likely outcomes from the roll of two dice and from the flip(s) of a coin.

a What is the difference between a sample space and a probability distribution?

b How would you make a probability distribution table for the product of the numbers from the roll of two dice?

c Why is it that the outcomes in the sample space for rolling two dice are equally likely?

Be prepared to share your ideas and reasoning with the class.

Lesson Master | use with page 534   Unit 8 | Patterns in Chance 513

Lesson Master 513
ⓘ GO DIGITAL

MATH TOOLKIT

Explain the difference between a sample space and a probability distribution and provide an example of each.

CHECK YOUR UNDERSTANDING

a. HHH, HHT, HTH, THH, HTT, THT, TTH, TTT

b. Yes. A head and a tail are equally likely on each flip. So, a head and a tail are equally likely on the first flip. On the second flip a head and a tail are again equally likely, so getting HH, HT, TH, and TT are equally likely outcomes for the first two flips. Finally, for example, if you have rolled HH, then the next flip is equally likely to be heads or tails making HHT and HHH equally likely outcomes.

c.

Probability Distribution for the Number of Heads	
Number	**Probability**
0	$\frac{1}{8}$
1	$\frac{3}{8}$
2	$\frac{3}{8}$
3	$\frac{1}{8}$

d. $\frac{3}{8}, \frac{7}{8}$

The Addition Rule

Problem 1 is a class activity that involves two situations: in the first, you can add probabilities to find the probability of event *A* or event *B* occurring; in the second, you cannot add probabilities because to do so you would count some outcomes twice. A quick way to gather the class information is to ask students to raise hands for the appropriate colors. Problems 2–5 can be completed by most students without help from the teacher. You may want to draw the class together for Problem 6 and then let students test their rule using Problem 7.

POSSIBLE MISCONCEPTION In this investigation, students learn that two events are mutually exclusive (also called "disjoint") if they cannot both happen in the same outcome. Students often want to interpret this as, "Two events are mutually exclusive if they cannot both happen at the same time." This "same time" interpretation can get them into trouble. For example, say your situation is flipping a coin until you get a head. Suppose you flip a coin seven times and record the sequence of heads and tails. Your sample space will consist of sequences like HHTTTTH. Consider these two events based on this sample space: the first flip is a head; the second flip is a head. These two events cannot both happen at exactly the same time (in the sense of time on the clock) because the second flip has to follow the first flip. They aren't mutually exclusive, however, because they both can happen in the same outcome, as with HHTTTTH.

In the first table, record the number of students in your class that today are wearing each shoe color. (If a pair of shoes is more than one color, select the color that takes up the largest area on the shoes.)

Color of Shoes You Are Wearing Today	Number of Students
Blue	
Black	
White	
Brown, Beige, or Tan	
Red	
Other	

Now complete the second table by recording the number of students in your class who own a pair of shoes of that color. For example, a student who has all shoes in the colors blue or black would identify themselves for only those two colors.

Color of Shoes You Own	Number of Students
Blue	
Black	
White	
Brown, Beige, or Tan	
Red	
Other	

In mathematics, the word "or" means "one or the other or both." So, the event that *a student owns white shoes or owns black shoes* includes all of the following outcomes:

- The student owns white shoes but doesn't own black shoes.
- The student owns black shoes but doesn't own white shoes.
- The student owns both white and black shoes.

a. Which question below can you answer using just the data in your tables? Answer that question.

   i. What is the probability that a randomly selected student from your class is wearing shoes today that are black or wearing shoes that are white?

   ii. What is the probability that a randomly selected student from your class owns shoes that are black or owns shoes that are white?

b. Why can't the other question in Part a be answered using just the information in the tables?

c. As a class, collect information that can be used to answer the other question.

1 Tables will vary. The tables from one class of 25 students follow.

Color of Shoes That You Are Wearing Today	Number of Students
Blue	4
Black	7
White	4
Brown, Beige, or Tan	6
Red	0
Other	4

Color of Shoes That You Own	Number of Students
Blue	16
Black	25
White	17
Brown, Beige, or Tan	25
Red	7
Other	18

a. You can answer question I, but not question II. Question I can be answered by adding the number of students wearing white shoes to the number of students wearing black shoes and dividing by the number of students in the class. For the class above, the probability is $\frac{7+4}{25} = \frac{11}{25}$.

b. Question II cannot be answered because it is likely that some students raised their hands twice, once for black shoes and once for white shoes. So if you add the number who own black shoes to the number who own white shoes, you may get a larger number than there are students in the class, as would happen with the class above.

c. When you ask how many own both black and white shoes, you know how many students raised their hands twice. The answer to question II may now be found by adding the number of students who own white shoes to the number of students who own black shoes, subtracting the number who own both (so raised their hands twice) and dividing by the number of students in the class.

INSTRUCTIONAL NOTE

Part b of Problem 1 is an important question. Students will need to understand that you can't just add probabilities if events are not disjoint before they can do Problem 6.

It is best to hold off introducing Venn diagrams at this point since it would undermine the thinking requested in Problem 6. This context could be revisited as a concrete example for intersecting circles in a Venn diagram as students work on Problem 6 or at the STM discussion.

2 The table below gives the percentage of ninth-grade students who say they engage in various risky behaviours.

Risky Behaviors of Ninth-Graders	
Activity	**Percentage of Ninth-Graders**
Ate fruits and vegetables less than 5 times per day	77.0
Physically active at least 60 minutes on fewer than 5 days	60.3
Watched television 3 or more hours on average school day	35.2
Drank (non-diet) soda or pop at least once a day	30.5
Used computers 3 or more hours on average school day (played video or computer games or used a computer for something that was not school work)	28.7

Source: Youth Risk Behavior Survey, U.S. Centers for Disease Control and Prevention

Use the data in the table to help answer, if possible, each of the following questions. If a question cannot be answered, explain why not.

a. What is the probability that a randomly selected ninth-grader was physically active at least 60 minutes on fewer than 5 days?

b. What is the probability that a randomly selected ninth-grader drank (non-diet) soda or pop at least once a day?

c. What is the probability that a randomly selected ninth-grader was physically active on fewer than 5 days or drank (non-diet) soda or pop at least once a day?

d. What is the probability that a randomly selected ninth-grader ate fruits and vegetables less than 5 times per day or watched television 3 or more hours on an average school day?

3 You could not answer the "or" questions in Problem 2 by adding the numbers in the table. However, you could answer the "or" questions in Problems 3, 4, 5, and 6 of the previous investigation by adding individual probabilities in the tables. What characteristic of a table makes it possible to add the probabilities to answer an "or" question?

2 **a.** 0.603

   b. 0.305

   c. This cannot be found from the table because some students are counted in both of these categories (similar to the students who own both black and white shoes in the previous problem).

   d. This cannot be found from the table because some students are counted in both of these categories here (double counting). We know this must be the case since 77.0% + 35.2% is more than 100%.

3 You can add the probabilities in a table when no person is counted in more than one category. (If the sum of the probabilities or percents is more than 1 or 100%, then there must have been double counting.)

4 The Minnesota Student Survey asks teens questions about school, activities, and health. Ninth-graders were asked, "How many students in your school are friendly?" In the frequency table below, each student is categorized by gender and by answer given.

How Many Students in Your School Are Friendly?			
Answer	Boys	Girls	Total
All	940	477	1,417
Most	13,171	13,127	26,298
Some	7,292	8,354	15,646
A few	1,882	1,909	3,791
None	235	0	235
Total	23,520	23,867	47,387

Source: Frequencies estimated from percentages in 2010 Minnesota Student Survey.

Suppose you pick one of these students at random.

a. Find the probability that the student said that all students are friendly.

b. Find the probability that the student said that most students are friendly.

c. Find the probability that the student is a girl.

d. Find the probability that the student is a girl and said that all students are friendly.

e. Think about how you would find the probability that the student said that all students are friendly or said that most students are friendly. Can you find the answer to this question using your probabilities from just Parts a and b? If so, show how. If not, why not?

f. Think about the probability that the student is a girl or said that all students are friendly.

   i. Can you find the answer to this question using just your probabilities from Parts a and c? If so, show how. If not, why not?

   ii. Can you find the answer if you also can use your probability in Part d? If so, show how. If not, why not?

5 Two events are said to be **mutually exclusive** (or **disjoint**) if it is impossible for both of them to occur on the same outcome. Which of the following pairs of events are mutually exclusive?

a. You roll a sum of 7 with a pair of dice; you get doubles on the same roll.

b. You roll a sum of 8 with a pair of dice; you get doubles on the same roll.

c. Isaac wears white shoes today to class; Isaac wears black shoes today to class.

CCSS NOTE Problem 4 is an introduction to two-way frequency tables. One of the domains in the high school-level *Common Core State Standards for Mathematics* is Interpreting Categorical and Quantitative Data S-ID. This domain includes:

Summarize, represent, and interpret data on two categorical and quantitative variables

5. Summarize categorical data for two categories in two-way frequency tables. Interpret relative frequencies in the context of the data (including joint, marginal, and conditional relative frequencies). Recognize possible associations and trends in the data.

- Part a in Problem 4 asks for a *marginal relative frequency*. Students get the answer by dividing a marginal total, 1,417 by the grand total of 47,387.
- Part b also asks for a marginal relative frequency, the marginal total of 26,298 divided by the grand total.
- Part c also asks for a marginal relative frequency, using the bottom margin this time, the marginal total of 23,867 divided by the grand total.
- Part d asks for a *joint relative frequency*, the frequency in the joint categories of *girl* and *said all students are friendly*, so the total in that cell, 477, divided by the grand total.

In Course 2 Unit 8, *Probability Distributions*, students will learn about conditional relative frequencies. An example of such a question would have been, find the probability that a boy answered "all." This conditional relative frequency would be the joint frequency of 940 divided by the number of boys, 23,520.

4 **a.** $\frac{1{,}417}{47{,}387} \approx 0.030$

b. $\frac{26{,}298}{47{,}387} \approx 0.555$

c. $\frac{23{,}867}{47{,}387} \approx 0.504$

d. $\frac{477}{47{,}387} \approx 0.010$

e. Yes, $\frac{1{,}417}{47{,}387} + \frac{26{,}298}{47{,}387} \approx 0.030 + 0.555 = 0.585$

f. **i.** No, you cannot find this probability using just Parts a and c. This is because the girls who said all students are friendly would be counted twice.

ii. If you use Part d, you can get the answer $0.030 + 0.504 - 0.010 \approx 0.524$.

5 **a.** Mutually exclusive

b. Not mutually exclusive

c. Mutually exclusive

d. Yen owns white shoes; Yen owns black shoes.

e. Pat, one of the students in the survey described in Problem 4, is a boy; Pat said most students in his school are friendly.

f. Bernardo, one of the students in the survey described in Problem 4, said all students are friendly; Bernardo said most students are friendly.

6 Suppose two events A and B are mutually exclusive.

a. Which of the *Venn diagrams* below better represents this situation?

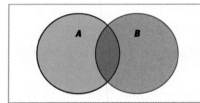 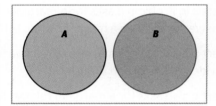

b. What does the fact that A and B are mutually exclusive mean about **$P(A$ and $B)$**—the probability that A and B both happen on the same outcome? In set language, the event A and B is called the **intersection** of event A and event B, and $P(A$ and $B)$ is written $P(A \cap B)$.

c. When A and B are mutually exclusive, how can you find the probability that A happens or B happens (or both happen)?

d. Write a symbolic rule for computing the probability that A happens or B happens, denoted **$P(A$ or $B)$**, when A and B are mutually exclusive. This rule is called the **Addition Rule for Mutually Exclusive Events**. In set language, the event A or B is called the **union** of event A and event B, and $P(A$ or $B)$ is written $P(A \cup B)$.

7 Suppose two events A and B are *not* mutually exclusive.

a. Which diagram in Problem 6 better represents this situation?

b. What does the fact that A and B are not mutually exclusive mean about $P(A$ and $B)$? Where is this probability represented on the Venn diagram you chose?

c. Review your work in Problems 1 and 4 and with the Venn diagram. Describe how you can modify your rule from Problem 6, Part d to compute $P(A$ or $B)$ when A and B are not mutually exclusive.

d. Write a symbolic rule for computing $P(A$ or $B)$. This rule is called the **Addition Rule**.

8 Test your rules on the following problems about rolling a pair of dice.

a. Find the probability that you get doubles or a sum of 5.

b. Find the probability that you get doubles or a sum of 2.

c. Find the probability that the absolute value of the difference is 3 or you get a sum of 5.

d. Find the probability that the absolute value of the difference is 2 or you get a sum of 11.

d. Not mutually exclusive

e. Not mutually exclusive

f. Mutually exclusive

6 **a.** The second diagram is better, as it shows events A and B as disjoint—not overlapping.

b. $P(A$ and $B) = 0$ or $P(A \cap B) = 0$

c. Because event A and event B are mutually exclusive, you can find the probability that A occurs or B occurs (or both occur) by adding the probability that A occurs to the probability that B occurs.

d. $P(A$ or $B) = P(A) + P(B)$ or $P(A \cup B) = P(A) + P(B)$

7 **a.** The first diagram as events A and B overlap.

b. $P(A$ and $B) \neq 0$ or $P(A \cap B) \neq 0$ (in the case of finite sample spaces). This probability is represented by the area where the interiors of circles A and B overlap, as shown in the diagram below.

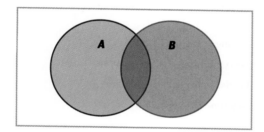

c. Add the probability that event A happens to the probability that event B happens. However, you have included the outcomes twice where event A and event B both happen, so subtract off the probability that event A and event B both happen.

d. $P(A$ or $B) = P(A) + P(B) - P(A$ and $B)$ or $P(A \cup B) = P(A) + P(B) - P(A \cap B)$
(Some students may write the rule $P(A$ or $B) = P(A$ and $\overline{B}) + P(\overline{A}$ and $B) + P(A$ and $B)$, where $\overline{A}$ means that A does not happen. This is correct, but a less useful formula.)

8 **a.** Doubles and a sum of 5 can not happen on the same roll, so $P(doubles$ or sum $is\ 5) = P(doubles) + P(sum\ is\ 5) = \frac{6}{36} + \frac{4}{36} = \frac{10}{36}$ or $\frac{5}{18}$.

b. If you roll (1, 1), both events happen on the same outcome, so $P(doubles$ or sum $is\ 2) = P(doubles) + P(sum\ is\ 2) - P(doubles$ and $sum\ is\ 2) = \frac{6}{36} + \frac{1}{36} - \frac{1}{36} = \frac{6}{36}$ or $\frac{1}{6}$.

c. If you roll (1, 4) or (4, 1), both events happen on the same outcome, so the probability that the absolute value of the difference is 3 or you get a sum of 5 is $\frac{6}{36} + \frac{4}{36} - \frac{2}{36} = \frac{8}{36}$ or $\frac{2}{9}$.

d. A difference of ± 2 and a sum of 11 cannot happen on the same roll, so the probability that the absolute value of the difference is 2 or the sum is 11 is $\frac{8}{36} + \frac{2}{36} = \frac{10}{36}$ or $\frac{5}{18}$.

SUMMARIZE THE MATHEMATICS

In this investigation, you learned how to compute the probability that event *A* happens or event *B* happens on the same outcome.

a Give an example of two mutually exclusive events different from those in the investigation.

b How do you find the probability that event *A* happens or event *B* happens if events *A* and *B* are mutually exclusive?

c How must you modify the rule in Part b if the two events are not mutually exclusive?

Be prepared to share your ideas and reasoning with the class.

 CHECK YOUR UNDERSTANDING

Use what you have learned about mutually exclusive events and the Addition Rule to complete the following tasks.

a. Which of the following pairs of events are mutually exclusive? Explain your reasoning.

   i. rolling a pair of dice: getting a sum of 6; getting one die with a 6 on it

   ii. flipping a coin 7 times: getting exactly 3 heads; getting exactly 5 heads

   iii. flipping a coin 7 times: getting at least 3 heads; getting at least 5 heads

b. Use the appropriate form of the Addition Rule to find the probability of rolling a pair of dice and

   i. getting a sum of 6 or getting one die with a 6 on it.

   ii. getting a sum of 6 or getting doubles.

c. Janet, a 50% free-throw shooter, finds herself in a two-shot foul situation. She needs to make at least one of the shots.

   i. List a sample space of all possible outcomes. Are the outcomes equally likely?

   ii. Find the probability that she will make the first shot or the second shot.

   iii. What assumptions did you make about her shooting?

SUMMARIZE THE MATHEMATICS

a Many examples are possible. Students may suggest things like:
A randomly selected student has two sisters; the student has one sister.
A randomly selected student is in school today; the student is absent.

b Add the probability that A happens to the probability that B happens.

c You must subtract off the probability that both A happens and B happens on the same outcome.

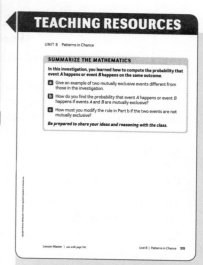
✔ CHECK YOUR UNDERSTANDING

a. **i.** These events are mutually exclusive because if you get one die with a 6 on it, the sum has to be greater than 6.

ii. These events are mutually exclusive because if you get exactly 3 heads in 7 flips, you can not also have exactly 5 heads in the same 7 flips.

iii. These events are not mutually exclusive. If you flip a coin 7 times, you might get HHTHHTH, so you have both at least 3 heads and at least 5 heads.

b. **i.** A sum of 6 and getting one die with a 6 on it cannot happen on the same roll, so $P(\text{sum is } 6 \text{ or one die is a } 6) = P(\text{sum is } 6) + P(\text{one die is a } 6) = \frac{5}{36} + \frac{11}{36} = \frac{16}{36}$.

ii. Getting a sum of 6 and getting doubles are not mutually exclusive because you might roll a (3, 3), so $P(\text{sum is } 6 \text{ or doubles}) = P(\text{sum is } 6) + P(\text{doubles}) - P(\text{sum is } 6 \text{ and doubles}) = \frac{5}{36} + \frac{6}{36} - \frac{1}{36} = \frac{10}{36}$.

c. **i.** This situation is exactly like the one of flipping a coin and counting the number of heads from Problem 8 on page 535. Thus, the sample space is make/make, make/miss, miss/make, miss/miss.

ii. The probability is $\frac{1}{2} + \frac{1}{2} - \frac{1}{4}$, or $\frac{3}{4}$.

(Students may need to be reminded that making the first shot or making the second shot includes the outcome of making both shots.)

iii. The assumptions are that the probability of making each shot is 50% and the shots are independent, meaning that what she did on the first shot does not affect the probability that she makes the second shot.

MATH TOOLKIT

Provide an example of two mutually exclusive events A and B and two events C and D that are not mutually exclusive. Then use the Addition Rule or its special form to find the probability event A or event B happens. Repeat for events C and D.

Summarize the Mathematics, *page 541*

Teacher: In this investigation, you learned how to compute the probability that event *A* happens or event *B* happens on the same outcome. Individually, think of an example of two mutually exclusive events different from those in the investigation. Once you have each thought of an example, share your examples with those in your group and decide on one to have ready to share with the class. *(Five minutes are provided for thinking and discussion.)*

Teacher: Okay, does someone have an example they would like to share? If you think any of the examples are not correct or have questions, please directly address the person reporting the example.

Phil: We decided that Stacy's example was the best in our group.

Stacy: We just studied blood types in Chemistry, so the two events that I suggested were a person having type A blood and a person having type B blood. A person cannot have two different blood types, so the two events are mutually exclusive.

Samara: Are there only two blood types? I thought there was a blood type AB? Seems like that would mean these two events are not mutually exclusive.

Stacy: It is true that there is a blood type AB, but that is another of the 4 blood types. If someone has type AB blood, they do not have type A or type B blood, so type A and type B really are mutually exclusive events.

Teacher: Thanks, Stacy. How about the group in the back? Please share one of your examples.

Jacque: We discussed drawing playing cards. Our two mutually exclusive events were drawing an ace or drawing a king.

Teacher: Using playing cards, can someone give us an example of two events that are not mutually exclusive?

Dakhil: The event of drawing a heart and the event of drawing a king would not be mutually exclusive. This is because you could draw the king of hearts.

Teacher: Let's have one more example of two mutually exclusive events.

Kwan: Since my dad just got a ticket for not wearing his seat belt, I thought of the two events wearing a seat belt and not wearing a seat belt. This is a simple example though. You could think of any example and say the event and then not the same event.

Teacher: Does that seem correct to the rest of you? *(Students indicate agreement.)* Okay. How do you find the probability of event *A* or event *B* if the two events are mutually exclusive?

Abby: You find the probability of *A* and the probability of *B* and then add the two numbers together.

Teacher: Abby, please write your explanation as a symbolic rule on the board. *(Abby writes P(A or B) = P(A) + P(B).)* Are there questions about Abby's rule? *(No questions asked.)*

Teacher: Would someone show us how to modify this rule if the two events are not mutually exclusive? Marcus, go ahead. Please explain your reasoning for the adjustment of the rule.

Marcus: The rule needs to subtract *P(A and B)*, like this. *(He writes P(A) + P(B) − P(A and B).)* That is because when the two events are not mutually exclusive, we get double part of the probability. Remember the Venn diagrams we looked at. *(Marcus draws Venn diagrams to illustrate his point.)* The overlap in the events gets counted twice when we compute *P(A) + P(B)*. The overlap can be written as *P(A and B)*, so we have to subtract that number off the total probability to eliminate the duplication.

Practice Reading the Language of Mathematics

To give students practice in reading mathematical language, they will be asked questions that include the following sets of equivalent phrases:

Math Notation	English Phrase	Math Notation	English Phrase
$x \geq 9$	x is at least 9 x is no fewer than 9 x is 9 or greater x is 9 or more x is a minimum of 9	$x \leq 9$	x is at most 9 x is no more than 9 x is 9 or less x is 9 or fewer x is a maximum of 9
$x > 9$	x is greater than 9 x is more than 9	$x < 9$	x is less than 9 x is fewer than 9

In Reflections Task 13 on page 546, students explicitly are asked to match the mathematical notation to the various English phrases.

Note that the word "fewer" is used with countable quantities: "I have fewer apples than he has," not, "I have less apples than he has."

APPLICATIONS

1 The game of Parcheesi is based on the Indian game pachisi.

In Parcheesi, two dice are rolled on each turn. A player cannot start a pawn until he or she rolls a five. The five may be on one die, or the five may be the sum of both dice. What is the probability a player can start a pawn on the first roll of the dice?

2 Suppose you roll a die and then roll it again. The die has the shape of a regular tetrahedron and the numbers 1, 2, 3, and 4 on it.

  a. Make a chart that shows the sample space of all possible outcomes.

  b. How many possible outcomes are there? Are they equally likely?

  c. Make a probability distribution table for the difference of the two rolls (*first die — second die*).

  d. What difference are you most likely to get?

  e. What is the probability that the difference is at most 2?

3 Suppose that you roll a tetrahedral die and a six-sided die at the same time.

  a. Make a chart that shows the sample space of all possible outcomes.

  b. How many possible outcomes are there? Are they equally likely?

  c. Make a table for the probability distribution of the sum of the two dice.

  d. What sum are you most likely to get?

  e. What is the probability that the sum is at most 3?

1 $\frac{15}{36}$

2 a.

		Second Roll		
	1	**2**	**3**	**4**
1	1, 1	1, 2	1, 3	1, 4
2	2, 1	2, 2	2, 3	2, 4
3	3, 1	3, 2	3, 3	3, 4
4	4, 1	4, 2	4, 3	4, 4

First Roll labels the rows (1, 2, 3, 4).

b. There are 16 equally likely outcomes.

c.

Probability Distribution for the Difference of Two Tetrahedral Dice	
Difference	**Probability**
−3	$\frac{1}{16}$
−2	$\frac{2}{16}$
−1	$\frac{3}{16}$
0	$\frac{4}{16}$
1	$\frac{3}{16}$
2	$\frac{2}{16}$
3	$\frac{1}{16}$

d. A difference of 0 is the most likely.

e. $\frac{15}{16}$

3 a.

			Six-Sided Die			
	1	**2**	**3**	**4**	**5**	**6**
1	1, 1	1, 2	1, 3	1, 4	1, 5	1, 6
2	2, 1	2, 2	2, 3	2, 4	2, 5	2, 6
3	3, 1	3, 2	3, 3	3, 4	3, 5	3, 6
4	4, 1	4, 2	4, 3	4, 4	4, 5	4, 6

Tetrahedral Die labels the rows (1, 2, 3, 4).

b. There are 24 equally likely outcomes.

TECHNOLOGY NOTE

The *CPMP-Tools* "Simulation" tool under the Statistics menu can simulate the distributions in Applications Tasks 2 and 3.

NOTE The solutions to Task 3 Parts c–e are on page T543.

4 Use your work from Applications Task 2 and the appropriate form of the Addition Rule to answer these questions about a roll of two tetrahedral dice.

   a. What is the probability that you get a difference of 3 or you get a 2 on the first die?

   b. What is the probability you get a difference of 2 or you get doubles?

   c. What is the probability you get a difference of 0 or you get doubles?

   d. What is the probability you get a difference of 0 or a sum of 6?

5 The Titanic was a British luxury ship that sank on its first voyage in 1912. It was en route from Southampton, England, to New York City. The table below gives some information about the passengers on the Titanic.

Passengers Aboard the Titanic			
	Men	**Women and Children**	**Total**
Survived	138	354	492
Died	678	154	832
Total	816	508	1,324

Source: www.titanicinquiry.org/USInq/USReport/AmInqRep03.html#a8

   a. Suppose a passenger is selected at random. Use the table above to find the probability of each of the following events.

   i. The passenger is a man.

   ii. The passenger survived.

   iii. The passenger is a man and survived.

   b. Now use your results from Part a and the appropriate form of the Addition Rule to find the probability that a randomly selected passenger is a man or a survivor. Check your answer by adding the appropriate entries in the table.

   c. Suppose a passenger is selected at random. Find the probability of each of the following events.

   i. The passenger is a woman/child.

   ii. The passenger died.

   iii. The passenger is a woman/child and died.

   iv. The passenger is a woman/child or died.

c.

Probability Distribution for the Sum of a Tetrahedral and a Six-Sided Die

Sum	Probability	Sum	Probability
2	$\frac{1}{24}$	7	$\frac{4}{24}$
3	$\frac{2}{24}$	8	$\frac{3}{24}$
4	$\frac{3}{24}$	9	$\frac{2}{24}$
5	$\frac{4}{24}$	10	$\frac{1}{24}$
6	$\frac{4}{24}$		

d. The sums of 5, 6, and 7 are the most likely, each with probability $\frac{4}{24}$.

e. $\frac{3}{24}$

4 | **INSTRUCTIONAL NOTE** Remind students that they are to practice using the Addition Rule in this task.

a. These events are mutually exclusive, so $P(\textit{difference is 3 or 2 on the first die}) = P(\textit{difference is 3}) + P(\textit{2 on the first die}) = \frac{1}{16} + \frac{4}{16} = \frac{5}{16}$.

b. These events are mutually exclusive, so $P(\textit{difference is 2 or doubles}) = P(\textit{difference is 2}) + P(\textit{doubles}) = \frac{2}{16} + \frac{4}{16} = \frac{6}{16}$ or $\frac{3}{8}$.

c. $P(\textit{difference is 0 or doubles}) = P(\textit{difference is 0}) + P(\textit{doubles}) - P(\textit{difference is 0 and doubles}) = \frac{4}{16} + \frac{4}{16} - \frac{4}{16} = \frac{4}{16}$ or $\frac{1}{4}$.

d. $P(\textit{difference is 0 or sum is 6}) = P(\textit{difference is 0}) + P(\textit{sum is 6}) - P(\textit{difference is 0 and sum is 6}) = \frac{4}{16} + \frac{3}{16} - \frac{1}{16} = \frac{6}{16}$ or $\frac{3}{8}$.

5 | **INSTRUCTIONAL NOTE** The numbers in this problem are for passengers only. In addition to the deaths here, a large percentage of the mostly male crew died.

a. **i.** $\frac{816}{1,324} \approx 0.616$

   ii. $\frac{492}{1,324} \approx 0.372$

  iii. $\frac{138}{1,324} \approx 0.104$

b. $P(\textit{man or survivor}) = P(\textit{man}) + P(\textit{survivor}) - P(\textit{man and survivor}) \approx 0.616 + 0.372 - 0.104 = 0.884$. Adding the entries in the table, you get $\frac{138 + 678 + 354}{1,324} = \frac{1,170}{1,324} \approx 0.884$, which is the same result as from the Addition Rule using the values in Part a.

c. **i.** $\frac{508}{1,324} \approx 0.384$

   ii. $\frac{832}{1,324} \approx 0.628$

  iii. $\frac{154}{1,324} \approx 0.116$

  iv. $P(\textit{woman/child or died}) = P(\textit{woman/child}) + P(\textit{died}) - P(\textit{woman/child and died}) \approx 0.384 + 0.628 - 0.116 = 0.896$

ON YOUR OWN

6 In almost all states, it is illegal to drive with a blood alcohol concentration (BAC) of 0.08 grams per deciliter (g/dL) or greater. The frequency table below gives information about the drivers involved in a crash in which someone died.

Drivers Involved in Fatal Crashes		
Age of Driver	Total Number of Drivers	Number with BAC ≥ 0.08
16–20	5,051	951
21–24	4,597	1,588
25–34	8,610	2,722
35–44	7,757	2,006
45–54	7,664	1,694
55–64	5,276	669
65–74	2,868	199
75+	2,550	85
Total	44,373	9,914

Source: National Highway Traffic Safety Administration, *Alcohol Impaired Driving Traffic Fact Sheet*, 2009

Suppose that you select a driver at random from these 44,373 drivers involved in fatal crashes.

a. Find the probability that the driver was age 16–20.

b. Find the probability that the driver was age 21–24.

c. Find the probability that the driver had a BAC of 0.08 or greater.

d. Find the probability that the driver was age 16–20 or was age 21–24.

e. Can you find the answer to Part d using just your probabilities from Parts a and b? Why or why not?

f. Find the probability that the driver was age 16–20 or had a BAC of 0.08 or greater.

g. Can you find the answer to Part f just by adding the two probabilities from Parts a and c? Why or why not?

CONNECTIONS

7 Make a histogram of the information in the probability distribution table that you created for the sum of two dice in Problem 4 (page 534) of Investigation 1. Probability will go on the *y*-axis.

a. What is the shape of this distribution?

b. What is its mean?

c. Estimate the standard deviation using the approximation that about two-thirds of the probability should be within one standard deviation of the mean. (While this distribution isn't normal, this approximation works relatively well.)

Brand X Pictures

6 **NOTE** If appropriate, you may wish to remind students that it is not a good idea to drive after having had any alcohol at all, and that it is illegal to drink if you are under age 21.

a. $\frac{5{,}051}{44{,}373} \approx 0.1138$

b. $\frac{4{,}597}{44{,}373} \approx 0.1036$

c. $\frac{9{,}914}{44{,}373} \approx 0.2234$

d. $\frac{5{,}051 + 4{,}597}{44{,}373} \approx 0.2174$

e. Yes, you can just add the probabilities from Parts a and b: $0.1138 + 0.1036 = 0.2174$. Because no driver could be both age 16–20 and 21–24, you are not counting any person twice.

f. $\frac{5{,}051}{44{,}373} + \frac{9{,}914}{44{,}373} - \frac{951}{44{,}373} = \frac{14{,}014}{44{,}373} \approx 0.3158$. Alternatively, without using the Addition Rule, $\frac{5{,}051}{44{,}373} + \frac{1{,}588}{44{,}373} + \frac{2{,}722}{44{,}373} + \frac{2{,}006}{44{,}373} + \frac{1{,}694}{44{,}373} + \frac{669}{44{,}373} + \frac{199}{44{,}373} + \frac{85}{44{,}373} = \frac{14{,}014}{44{,}373} \approx 0.3158$.

g. No, because being age 16–20 and having a BAC of 0.08 or greater are not mutually exclusive. There are 951 drivers in this study who are both. So, if you added $\frac{5{,}051}{44{,}373}$ and $\frac{9{,}914}{44{,}373}$, you would count these 951 drivers twice.

CONNECTIONS

7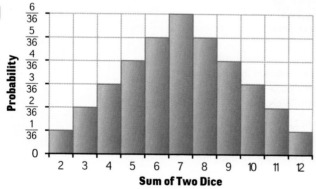

a. This distribution is triangular. It is symmetric about the middle bar. (Students will see more triangular probability distributions in Connections Tasks 8 and 9.)

b. The mean is 7.

c. The standard deviation is about 2 because $\frac{24}{36}$ or $\frac{2}{3}$ of the values are 5, 6, 7, 8, or 9. That is, $\frac{2}{3}$ of the values are within 2 of the mean of 7.

8 Graph the points that represent the information in the probability distribution table that you created for the sum of two dice in Problem 4 (page 534) of Investigation 1. For example, the first point would be $\left(2, \frac{1}{36}\right)$ and the second point would be $\left(3, \frac{2}{36}\right)$.

   a. Write a linear equation with a graph going through the points for $x = 2, 3, 4, 5, 6, 7$.

   b. Write a second linear equation with a graph going through the points for $x = 7, 8, 9, 10, 11, 12$.

   c. What are the slopes of these two lines?

9 Graph the points that represent the information in the probability distribution table that you created for the difference of two tetrahedral dice in Applications Task 2. For example, the first point would be $\left(-3, \frac{1}{16}\right)$ and the second point would be $\left(-2, \frac{2}{16}\right)$.

   a. Write a linear equation with a graph going through the points for $x = -3, -2, -1, 0$.

   b. Write a second linear equation with a graph going through the points for $x = 0, 1, 2, 3$.

   c. What are the slopes of these two lines?

10 Recall that there are five regular polyhedra: tetrahedron (4 faces), hexahedron or cube (6 faces), octahedron (8 faces), dodecahedron (12 faces), and icosahedron (20 faces).

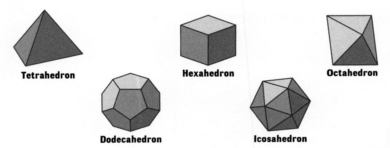

Tetrahedron   Hexahedron   Octahedron

Dodecahedron   Icosahedron

Find or imagine pairs of dice in the shape of these polyhedra. The numbers on the faces of the tetrahedron are 1, 2, 3, and 4. The hexahedron (regular die) has the numbers 1, 2, 3, 4, 5, and 6. The remaining three pairs of dice have the numbers 1 to 8, 1 to 12, and 1 to 20 on their faces, respectively.

   a. Make a sample space chart like that in Investigation 1, Problem 1 (page 533) for the octahedral dice.

   b. On which of the five pairs of dice is the probability of getting doubles the greatest? Explain why this is the case.

8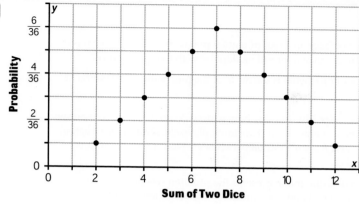

a. $y = \frac{1}{36}x - \frac{1}{36}$

b. $y = -\frac{1}{36}x + \frac{13}{36}$

c. The slopes are $\frac{1}{36}$ and $-\frac{1}{36}$.

9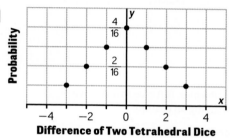

a. $y = \frac{1}{16}x + \frac{4}{16}$

b. $y = -\frac{1}{16}x + \frac{4}{16}$

c. The slopes are $\frac{1}{16}$ and $-\frac{1}{16}$.

10 a. **Octahedral Dice Sample Space**

		Second Die						
	1	**2**	**3**	**4**	**5**	**6**	**7**	**8**
1	1, 1	1, 2	1, 3	1, 4	1, 5	1, 6	1, 7	1, 8
2	2, 1	2, 2	2, 3	2, 4	2, 5	2, 6	2, 7	2, 8
3	3, 1	3, 2	3, 3	3, 4	3, 5	3, 6	3, 7	3, 8
4	4, 1	4, 2	4, 3	4, 4	4, 5	4, 6	4, 7	4, 8
5	5, 1	5, 2	5, 3	5, 4	5, 5	5, 6	5, 7	5, 8
6	6, 1	6, 2	6, 3	6, 4	6, 5	6, 6	6, 7	6, 8
7	7, 1	7, 2	7, 3	7, 4	7, 5	7, 6	7, 7	7, 8
8	8, 1	8, 2	8, 3	8, 4	8, 5	8, 6	8, 7	8, 8

(**First Die** labels the rows)

b. The probability of getting doubles is the greatest for the tetrahedral die. For n-sided dice, the probability of doubles is $\frac{1}{n}$ (see Part c). The maximum value of $\frac{1}{n}$ for regular polyhedra occurs at $n = 4$, or with a tetrahedron.

ON YOUR OWN

c. If the number of faces on a pair of regular polyhedral dice is n, what is the probability (in terms of n) of rolling doubles with that pair of dice?

d. For each type of dice, what is the mean of the probability distribution of the sum?

11 On Problem 6 on page 540, you saw how to draw Venn diagrams to represent the situation where events A and B are mutually exclusive and the situation where events A and B are *not* mutually exclusive. Now, think about three events, A, B, and C.

a. Draw a Venn diagram that represents the situation where A and B are mutually exclusive, A and C are mutually exclusive, and B and C are mutually exclusive.

b. Draw a Venn diagram that represents the situation where A and B are mutually exclusive, A and C are mutually exclusive, but B and C are not mutually exclusive.

c. Draw a Venn diagram that represents the situation where A and B are not mutually exclusive, A and C are not mutually exclusive, and B and C are not mutually exclusive.

REFLECTIONS

12 Some chance situations have exactly two outcomes. Is it true that the two outcomes must be equally likely? Explain, giving an example.

13 For each phrase below, select the corresponding symbolic phrase:

$$x \geq 9 \qquad x > 9 \qquad x \leq 9 \qquad x < 9$$

a. x is no more than 9

b. x is less than 9

c. x is 9 or greater

d. x is no less than 9

e. x is at most 9

f. x is at least 9

g. x is greater than 9

h. x is a maximum of 9

i. x is 9 or more

14 In the Think About This Situation at the beginning of this lesson, you were asked to consider the probability of rolling doubles on your first turn or on your second turn.

a. Is it true that the probability of rolling doubles on your first turn or your second turn is $\frac{1}{6} + \frac{1}{6}$? Give an explanation for your answer.

b. Is it true that the probability of rolling doubles on at least one of your first six turns is $\frac{1}{6} + \frac{1}{6} + \frac{1}{6} + \frac{1}{6} + \frac{1}{6} + \frac{1}{6}$?

Creatas/SuperStock

UNIT 8

c. Imagine rolling the first die. If each die has n sides, the probability that the second die will match the first and you get doubles is $\frac{1}{n}$. So the smaller n, the larger the probability of doubles. Thus, the tetrahedral die, which has the smallest number of sides, will have the largest probability of doubles.

Another explanation is that there is one pair of doubles for each cell along the main diagonal of the table or n doubles out of n^2 entries, so the probability is $\frac{n}{n^2}$ or $\frac{1}{n}$.

d. If there are n faces on the die, the mean roll per die is $\frac{n+1}{2}$. So the mean sum of two rolls is $n+1$, which is equal to 5 for the tetrahedral die, 7 for the six-sided die, 9 for the octahedral die, 13 for the dodecahedral die, and 21 for the icosahedral die.

 11 a.

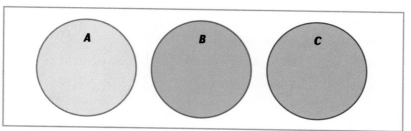

b.

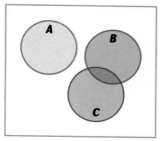

c.

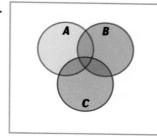

or

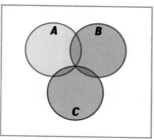

$A \cap B \cap C$ is empty.

REFLECTIONS

12 No. For example, if you buy a single lottery ticket, you will either win or you won't, but it is far more likely that you won't win. It will either snow tomorrow or it won't, but the probability of snow is unlikely to be 0.5.

13 a. $x \leq 9$ **b.** $x < 9$ **c.** $x \geq 9$

d. $x \geq 9$ **e.** $x \leq 9$ **f.** $x \geq 9$

g. $x > 9$ **h.** $x \leq 9$ **i.** $x \geq 9$

14 a. No, because you could get doubles on both turns and so you cannot use the simplified form of the Addition Rule.

b. No, this cannot be the right answer as the sum is 1 and it certainly is possible that you will roll six times and not get doubles at all. (Note that if the same reasoning were used with 12 rolls, the probability would have been an impossible 2.)

15 Refer to Applications Task 6. The age group of 21–24 had only 4,597 drivers involved in fatal accidents. This is fewer than all age groups until age 65 and up. Does this mean that a driver in this age group is less likely to get in a fatal crash? Explain your answer.

16 Draw a Venn Diagram to show the situation where event *B* is a *subset* of event *A*. That is, all outcomes in event *B* are also in event *A*. What is P(*A* or *B*) equal to?

EXTENSIONS

17 Suppose that you flip a coin four times and record head (H) or tail (T) in the order it occurs.

   a. Make a list of all 16 equally likely outcomes.

   b. Make a table of the probability distribution of the number of heads.

   c. What is the probability that you will get exactly 2 heads? At most 2 heads?

18 Flavia selects one of the special dice with faces shown below, and then Jack selects one of the remaining two.

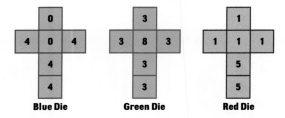

Blue Die   Green Die   Red Die

They each roll their die. The person with the larger number wins.

   a. Suppose that Flavia selects the blue die and Jack selects the green die. To see who has the best chance of winning, complete the table below by writing the color of the winning die in each cell. What is the probability that Jack wins? Determine whether the probability would be larger if he chooses the red die instead.

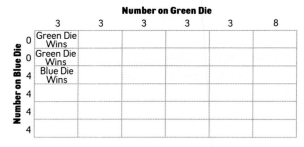

   b. If Flavia selects the green die, which die should Jack choose?

   c. If Flavia selects the red die, which die should Jack choose?

   d. What is the surprise here?

Lesson 1 | Calculating Probabilities   **547**

15 No. Notice that there are only four ages in this interval, ages 21, 22, 23, and 24. All other intervals have more ages in them, and so, presumably, more drivers. For example, the interval 25–34 has 10 ages in it: 25, 26, 27, 28, 29, 30, 31, 32, 33, and 34. This is 2.5 times as many ages as in the interval 21–24. So there probably are about 2.5 times as many drivers age 25–34 as age 21–24. At this rate, we would expect $2.5(4{,}597) = 11{,}492.5$ drivers age 25–34 to be involved in fatal accidents. But there were only 8,610. Thus, the age group 21–24 has an unusually large number of drivers involved in fatal accidents.

Further, in fatal crashes in 2009, drivers ages 21 to 24 had the highest percentage of drivers with BAC levels of 0.08 g/dL or higher (35%). The lowest percentage was for drivers age 75 or more (only 3%).

16

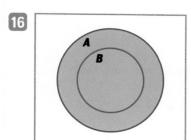

$P(A \text{ or } B) = P(A)$

EXTENSIONS

17 **a.** HHHH, HHHT, HHTH, HTHH, THHH, HHTT, HTHT, THHT, HTTH, THTH, TTHH, HTTT, THTT, TTHT, TTTH, TTTT

b.

Probability Distribution for the Number of Heads	
Number	**Probability**
0	$\frac{1}{16}$
1	$\frac{4}{16}$
2	$\frac{6}{16}$
3	$\frac{4}{16}$
4	$\frac{1}{16}$

c. $\frac{6}{16}$, $\frac{11}{16}$

NOTE The solution to Task 18 is on page T548.

19 Refer to the probability distribution table for the sum of two standard six-sided dice that you constructed in Problem 4 (page 534) of Investigation 1. Two nonstandard six-sided dice have this same probability distribution table. A net for one of those nonstandard dice is shown at the right. Using positive whole numbers, label a copy of the net for the other nonstandard die. The other die may be different from the one given, and numbers may be repeated on its faces.

20 Refer to the Venn diagrams you made in Connections Task 11. Use the appropriate one to help you write an Addition Rule that you can use to determine $P(A$ or B or $C)$ when

a. A and B are mutually exclusive, A and C are mutually exclusive, and B and C are mutually exclusive.

b. A and B are mutually exclusive, A and C are mutually exclusive, but B and C are not mutually exclusive.

c. A and B are not mutually exclusive, A and C are not mutually exclusive, and B and C are not mutually exclusive.

21 In the game of backgammon, if you "hit" your opponent's checker exactly, that checker must go back to the beginning and start again. For example, to hit a checker that is three spaces ahead of your checker, you need to move your checker three spaces. You can do this either by getting a 3 on one die or by getting a sum of 3 on the two dice. In addition, if you roll double 1s, you can also hit your opponent's checker because if you roll doubles, you get to move the numbers that show on the die twice each. So you move one space, then one space again, then one more space, hitting your opponent's checker, then move your last space. (If you roll, say, double 4s, you can't hit your opponent's checker—you must skip over it as you move your first four spaces.)

a. What is the probability of being able to hit a checker that is three spaces ahead of you?

b. What is the probability of being able to hit a checker that is five spaces ahead of you?

c. What is the probability of being able to hit a checker that is twelve spaces ahead of you?

d. If you want to have the best chance of hitting a checker ahead of you, how many spaces should it be in front of you?

18 These are Efron dice, named after Bradley Efron, the Stanford statistician who discovered them.

a.

Number on Green Die

		3	3	3	3	3	8
Number on Blue Die	0	Green Die Wins	Green Die Wins	Green Die Wins	Green Die Wins	Green Die Wins	Green Die Wins
	0	Green Die Wins	Green Die Wins	Green Die Wins	Green Die Wins	Green Die Wins	Green Die Wins
	4	Blue Die Wins	Blue Die Wins	Blue Die Wins	Blue Die Wins	Blue Die Wins	Green Die Wins
	4	Blue Die Wins	Blue Die Wins	Blue Die Wins	Blue Die Wins	Blue Die Wins	Green Die Wins
	4	Blue Die Wins	Blue Die Wins	Blue Die Wins	Blue Die Wins	Blue Die Wins	Green Die Wins
	4	Blue Die Wins	Blue Die Wins	Blue Die Wins	Blue Die Wins	Blue Die Wins	Green Die Wins

The probability that Jack wins is $\frac{16}{36}$. If Jack chooses the red die instead, the probability that he wins is $\frac{20}{36}$.

b. If Flavia selects the green die, Jack should choose the blue die. The probability of the blue die beating the green die is $\frac{20}{36}$, whereas the probability of the red die beating the green die is $\frac{10}{36}$.

c. If Flavia selects the red die, Jack should choose the green die. The probability of the green die beating the red die is $\frac{26}{36}$, whereas the probability of the blue die beating the red die is $\frac{16}{36}$.

d. The surprise is that no matter which die Flavia selects, Jack can select a different die that will give him a greater probability of winning.

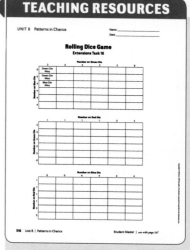

TEACHING RESOURCES

Student Master 516
GO DIGITAL

19 One of the sides of the second die must be a 1, because that is the only way to get a sum of 2. Also, the second die must have two 2s on it, as that is the only way to get two sums of 3. So far, we have the sums below.

		Second Die					
		1	2	2			
Given Die	1	2	3	3			
	3	4	5	5			
	4	5	6	6			
	5	6	7	7			
	6	7	8	8			
	8	9	10	10			

We need two more sums of 4 and the only way to get that without adding more sums of 2 or 3 is to have two 3s on the second die. Now we have the additional sums:

4, 4, 6, 6, 7, 7, 8, 8, 9, 9, 11, 11

We still need another sum of 5 and the only way to get that without adding more sums of 2, 3, or 4 is to have a 4 on the second die. This gives us the sums we need and so the second die must have 1, 2, 2, 3, 3, and 4 on its faces.

20 **a.** There is no possibility of counting anything twice because no two events overlap, so $P(A \text{ or } B \text{ or } C) = P(A) + P(B) + P(C)$.

b. Only events B and C overlap, so $P(A \text{ or } B \text{ or } C) = P(A) + P(B) + P(C) - P(B \text{ and } C)$.

c. All pairs of events overlap, so $P(A \text{ or } B \text{ or } C) = P(A) + P(B) + P(C) - P(A \text{ and } B) - P(A \text{ and } C) - P(B \text{ and } C) + P(A \text{ and } B \text{ and } C)$. The latter region has to be added back in as it was added in three times—with $P(A)$, $P(B)$, and $P(C)$—but was also subtracted off three times—with $P(A \text{ and } B)$, $P(A \text{ and } C)$, $P(B \text{ and } C)$.

21 **a.** $\frac{14}{36}$. You could roll $(1, 2)$, $(2, 1)$, $(1, 1)$, $(x, 3)$, or $(3, x)$, where x could be any number. The latter two together account for only 11 possible rolls of the dice as roll $(3, 3)$ occurs in both $(x, 3)$ and $(3, x)$.

b. $\frac{15}{36}$. You could roll $(2, 3)$, $(3, 2)$, $(4, 1)$, $(1, 4)$, $(5, x)$, or $(x, 5)$. The latter two together account for only 11 possible rolls of the dice as roll $(5, 5)$ occurs in both $(x, 5)$ and $(5, x)$.

c. $\frac{3}{36}$. You could roll $(6, 6)$, $(3, 3)$, or $(4, 4)$.

d. The best chance occurs when the checker is 6 spaces ahead of you. This table gives the probability that, on one roll of the dice, you will hit a checker that is the given number of spaces ahead of you (provided all the necessary spaces in between are legal to land on). Students may recognize that the probabilities for spaces more than 12 ahead are very small and may not bother to finish the complete table.

Spaces Ahead	Probability Will Hit	Spaces Ahead	Probability Will Hit
1	$\frac{11}{36}$	13	0
2	$\frac{12}{36}$	14	0
3	$\frac{14}{36}$	15	$\frac{1}{36}$
4	$\frac{15}{36}$	16	$\frac{1}{36}$
5	$\frac{15}{36}$	17	0
6	$\frac{17}{36}$	18	$\frac{1}{36}$
7	$\frac{6}{36}$	19	0
8	$\frac{6}{36}$	20	$\frac{1}{36}$
9	$\frac{5}{36}$	21	0
10	$\frac{3}{36}$	22	0
11	$\frac{2}{36}$	23	0
12	$\frac{3}{36}$	24	$\frac{1}{36}$

(You may want to discuss why the sum of these probabilities is greater than 1. The reason is that this is not a probability distribution table that shows all possible outcomes of some situation. The same roll, (2, 3) for example, can hit a checker 2 spaces, 3 spaces, and 5 spaces ahead. So, this single roll is included three times in the chart above.)

REVIEW

22 Determine if it is possible to draw zero, one, or more than one triangle that will fit the given description. Explain your reasoning.

   a. triangle XYZ with m$\angle X = 120°$, m$\angle Y = 30°$, and $XY = 8$ cm

   b. a triangle with two right angles

   c. an isosceles triangle with legs of length 5 cm and base of length 4 cm

   d. a triangle with sides of length 2 in., 3 in., and 5 in.

   e. a triangle with angles measuring 45°, 65°, and 70°

   f. a right triangle with sides of length 10 m, 6 m, and 7 m

23 The mean number of people who attended five high school basketball games was 468. The tickets cost $3 per person. What is the total amount received from ticket sales?

24 The height in feet of a football t seconds after a punt can be found using the equation $h = 1.8 + 50t - 16t^2$.

   a. How long was the football in the air?

   b. How high did the football go?

   c. When was the football 20 feet above the ground?

25 Solve each inequality and graph the solution on a number line. Substitute at least one number from your solution set back into the inequality to check your work.

   a. $3x + 7 \leq -59$

   b. $16 \geq 12 - 2x$

   c. $25 < 5(2x + 12)$

   d. $4x + 18 > 6x - 24$

   e. $\frac{1}{6}(5x + 12) - 8 \geq 0$

26 In the rectangle shown, is the sum of the areas of $\triangle APD$ and $\triangle BCP$ greater than, less than, or equal to the area of $\triangle DPC$? Justify your answer.

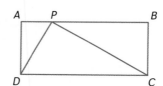

27 Find the following sums without using your calculator.

   a. $0.4 + 0.23$

   b. $0.05 + 0.24 + 0.15$

   c. $-0.62 + 0.82$

   d. $\frac{1}{6} + \frac{2}{3}$

   e. $\frac{2}{10} + \frac{1}{4} - \frac{3}{5}$

Lesson 1 | Calculating Probabilities   **549**

22 **a.** Only 1 triangle is possible because of the ASA congruence condition. (Students should recall that they tried to make two different triangles given these conditions and could not do so.)

b. It is not possible to build a triangle with two right angles. The sum of the measure of two right angles is 180°, and the sum of the measures of all three angles in a triangle is 180°. So, if there are two right angles, the third angle would have to have measure 0°. Thus, you would not have a triangle.

c. Only 1 triangle is possible because a second triangle formed with the same length sides could always be reoriented and placed on top of the first triangle—SSS congruence condition.

d. It is not possible to build a triangle with these side lengths because the sum of the lengths of the two shorter sides is not greater than the length of the third side.

e. Since the sum of the measure of the angles is 180°, a triangle can be formed. More than one triangle is possible since triangles of different sizes (but the same shape) could be formed from these three angle sizes.

f. No right triangle is possible since the side lengths will not form a right triangle because $6^2 + 7^2 \neq 10^2$.

23 The total number of people is $5(468) = 2{,}340$, so the total amount received is $\$3(2{,}340) = \$7{,}020$.

24 **a.** About 3.16 seconds

b. The maximum height of the football was about 40.86 feet.

c. At about 0.42 seconds and at about 2.7 seconds, the ball was 20 feet high.

25 **a.** $x \leq -22$

b. $x \geq -2$

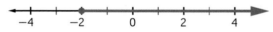

c. $x > -3.5$

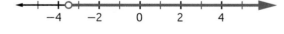

d. $x < 21$

e. $x \geq \dfrac{36}{5}$

26 The areas are equal. Students may see this more clearly by sliding $\triangle APD$ over so that point A and point B coincide (as in the diagram at the right). It may then be more obvious that the new triangle $\triangle P'PC$ and $\triangle DCP$ have equal length bases and heights, thus equal areas.

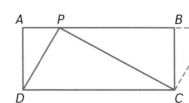

Alternatively, drop a perpendicular from point P to CD. Then it is clear that $\triangle DPC$ is composed of two triangles that are equal in area to $\triangle APD$ and $\triangle BCP$.

NOTE The solution to Task 27 is on page T550.

ON YOUR OWN

28 Find the value of x in each polygon below.

a.

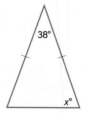

b.

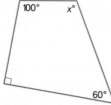

c.

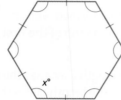

d.

29 Find two fractions on a number line that are between the two given fractions.

a. $\frac{1}{3}$ and $\frac{1}{2}$

b. $\frac{5}{6}$ and $\frac{6}{7}$

c. $\frac{a}{b}$ and $\frac{c}{d}$

30 Alia and her sister Yolanda went for a 10 mile run. Alia ran at an average speed of 6 miles per hour and Yolanda ran at an average speed of 8 miles per hour. Alia left the house 12 minutes before Yolanda did.

a. In hours and minutes, how long did it take each girl to complete the run?

b. If they ran the same course, did Yolanda catch up with Alia before the end of the 10 miles? Explain your reasoning.

c. How far must Yolanda run before she catches up with Alia? Explain your reasoning.

27 a. 0.63

b. 0.44

c. 0.20

d. $\dfrac{5}{6}$

e. $\dfrac{-3}{20}$ or -0.15

28 a. $x = 71°$

b. $x = 110°$

c. $x = \dfrac{4(180°)}{6} = 120°$

d. $x = \dfrac{360°}{5} = 72°$

29 a. Responses will vary. Three possibilities are $\dfrac{9}{24} = \dfrac{3}{8}, \dfrac{11}{24}$, and $\dfrac{2}{5}$.

b. Responses will vary.

c. Responses will vary.

30 a. Alia took 1 hour 40 minutes and Yolanda took 1 hour 15 minutes.

b. Since Yolanda starts 12 minutes after Alia, she finishes the run 1 hour 27 minutes after Alia started. Since Alia takes 1 hour 40 minutes to finish the run, Yolanda must pass Alia before the end of the run.

c. Solving the equation $6t = 8(t - 0.2)$, where t represents the number of hours Alia has been running, will give the time that Yolanda catches up to Alia. The solution is $t = 0.8$ hours. When $t = 0.8$, Yolanda has run $8(0.8 - 0.2) = 4.8$ miles.

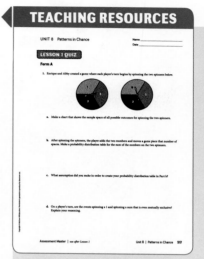

Rodrigo A. Torres/Glowimages

LESSON

2

Modeling Chance Situations

In some cultures, it is customary for a bride to live with her husband's family. As a result, couples who have no sons and whose daughters all marry will have no one to care for them in their old age.

In 2000, China had a population of over 1,200,000,000. In an effort to reduce the growth of its population, the government of China had instituted a policy to limit families to one child. The policy has been very unpopular among rural Chinese who depend on sons to carry on the family farming and care for them in their old age.

Lesson 2 | Modeling Chance Situations **551**

Modeling Chance Situations

In the first three investigations of this lesson, students will learn how to use simulation to estimate the answers to problems in probability. In the fourth investigation, they will learn that when the variables are continuous, area models sometimes can help them compute probabilities exactly.

Lesson Objectives

- Design and carry out simulations in order to estimate answers to questions about probability

- Use the Law of Large Numbers to understand situations involving chance

- Use tables of random digits to perform simulations to decide whether the probability model is consistent with the data

- Use random numbers to perform simulations in situations that involve continuous variables

- Use area models to solve probability problems that involve continuous variables

Steps in a Simulation

1. Be sure you understand the problem: State it in your own words.

2. Create a model:
   - Identify all possible outcomes and determine the probability of each. Decide whether probabilities change from one trial to the next.
   - Select a random device and describe how you will use it to conduct one run.

3. Conduct a large number of runs: Record your results in a frequency table and histogram. Stop when the shape, center, and spread of the distribution of frequencies stabilize.

4. Give your conclusion.

> **NOTE** Students love to flip coins, and they like to observe the fact that unusual events occur if you give them enough opportunities to occur. However, a simulation can get tedious and is a waste of time if students must carry out an excessive number of runs. Unfortunately, four hundred runs are needed to be at least 95% sure of estimating a probability to within 0.05.

The most important part of each problem is having students understand how to set up the simulation. Once students thoroughly understand how to model the situation, it is not important to have them do more than a few runs by hand. Consequently, in almost all simulations in this lesson, students are asked to generate only a few runs.

Common Core State Standards
Focused on:
G-MG.2, S-ID.1, S-CP.1, S-MD.1, S-MD.4
Connected to:
S-ID.6, S-CP.9

THINK ABOUT THIS SITUATION

Customs of a culture and the size of its population often lead to issues that are hard to resolve. But probability can help you understand the consequences of various policies.

a In a country where parents are allowed to have only one child, what is the probability that their one child will be a son? What is the probability they will not have a son? What assumption(s) are you making when you answer these questions?

b If each pair of Chinese parents really had only one child, do you think the population would increase, decrease, or stay the same? Explain your reasoning.

c Describe several alternative plans that the government of China might use to control population growth. For each plan, discuss how you might estimate the answers to the following questions.

    i. What is the probability that parents will have a son?

    ii. Will the total population of China grow, shrink, or stay about the same?

    iii. Will China end up with more boys than girls or with more girls than boys?

    iv. What is the mean number of children per family?

In this lesson, you will learn to estimate probabilities by designing simulations that use random devices such as coin flipping or random digits. In our complex world, simulation is often the only feasible way to deal with a problem involving chance. Simulation is an indispensable tool to scientists, business analysts, engineers, and mathematicians. In this lesson, you will also explore how geometric models can be used to solve probability problems.

INVESTIGATION 1

When It's a 50-50 Chance

Finding the answers to the questions in Part c of the Think About This Situation may be difficult for some of the plans you proposed. If that is the case, you can estimate the effects of the policies by creating a mathematical model that **simulates** the situation by copying its essential characteristics. Although slightly more than half of all births are boys, the percentage is close enough to 50% for you to use a probability of $\frac{1}{2}$ to investigate different plans. As you work on the problems of this investigation, look for answers to the following question:

How can you simulate chance situations that involve two equally likely outcomes?

A good way to begin this lesson is to present the Chinese policy of limiting families to one child, then let your students discuss the Think About This Situation questions as an entire class. For Part c, make a list of the plans proposed. At this stage, students are not expected to have the tools to fully investigate their plans.

The mathematics here is very important and rich, but the preference for boys in some cultures is a sensitive issue and must be handled with care. Different cultures have different values regarding not only the value of a boy versus a girl, but also regarding the number of children a couple should have. If you prefer, you can teach this investigation without getting into any of these issues by having students stick strictly to the mathematics involved.

The importance of students understanding the mathematics of this situation is illustrated by the misconception in a letter to the *Washington Post* on May 11, 1993. The writer suggested that China now has more boys born than girls because if the first child is a boy, then the parents tend to stop having children. The fallacious thinking here prevents understanding of the real reason that China now has more boys than girls.

As reported in a *Wall Street Journal* article on September 23, 2011, China now has almost 120 boys born for every 100 girls. In rural China, the ratio is even higher (140 boys for every 100 girls). The usual ratio is 105 boys for every 100 girls. The high ratio in China has been attributed to factors such as underreporting of girls by parents (who hide them so they can have another child). However, most reports say that the primary reason is the termination of pregnancies when the fetus is a girl. Another article about the long-term effects of this policy appeared in *The Guardian* (UK) on September 2, 2011.

The Chinese overpopulation problem has appeared as a mathematics problem in various publications. One of the first was M. Gnanadesikan *et al.*, *The Art and Techniques of Simulation*, Dale Seymour Publications, Palo Alto, CA, 1987. See also Clifford Konold, "Teaching Probability through Modeling Real Problems," *The Mathematics Teacher, 87*, April 1994, pp. 232–235.

UNIT 8   Patterns in Chance

THINK ABOUT THIS SITUATION

Customs of a culture and the size of its population often lead to issues that are hard to resolve. But probability can help you understand the consequences of various policies.

a In a country where parents are allowed to have only one child, what is the probability that their one child will be a son? What is the probability they will not have a son? What assumption(s) are you making when you answer these questions?

b If each pair of Chinese parents really had only one child, do you think the population would increase, decrease, or stay the same? Explain your reasoning.

c Describe several alternative plans that the government of China might use to control population growth. For each plan, discuss how you might estimate the answers to the following questions.

   i. What is the probability that parents will have a son?

   ii. Will the total population of China grow, shrink, or stay about the same?

   iii. Will China end up with more boys than girls or with more girls than boys?

   iv. What is the mean number of children per family?

Lesson Master | use with page 552   Unit 8 | Patterns in Chance   525

Lesson Master 525
ⓘ GO DIGITAL

COLLABORATION SKILL

Help each other challenge intuitions about probability.

THINK ABOUT THIS SITUATION

a For our purposes, 0.5 is a close enough estimate of the probability of a boy. (The actual probability is closer to 0.52.) The probability they won't have a son is also 0.5. The assumptions are that the probability of having a boy is the same for each set of parents and that the probability of having a boy is 0.5.

b If each set of two parents has only one child, the parents wouldn't replace themselves. Thus, the population would decrease rapidly, halving each generation.

c **INSTRUCTIONAL NOTE** Students may offer several different plans, varying in their complexity, to solve the problem. Except for the first plan listed below, students won't have the mathematical tools to analyze them. Tell students that the method of simulation they will learn in this unit will give a very good estimate to all of the questions. In future units, they will learn to analyze these plans using mathematical formulas. Meanwhile, have students estimate the answers to the four questions for their plans. Plans suggested by students may include:

- Limit each couple to two children so that they "replace" themselves. (Students will analyze this plan in Problem 1 of Investigation 1.) This plan has four equally likely outcomes: GG, GB, BG, or BB. So, couples have a $\frac{3}{4}$ chance of having at least one boy. The population will stay constant with this plan if everyone marries and has children. If not, the population will decrease slowly. There will be an equal number of boys and girls, and the mean number of children per family will be 2.

- Allow couples to have children until they have a boy, then no more children will be allowed. Possible families are B, GB, GGB, GGGB, and so on. There is an almost 100% chance of getting a boy. Students probably will think that this results in a population increase, as they imagine all those large families of girls. In fact, the mean family size will be 2, the number necessary to replace the population if all couples marry and follow this plan. (Students will analyze this plan using simulation in the following investigation and theoretically in the Course 2 unit, *Probability Distributions*.)

UNIT 8

When It's a 50-50 Chance

In this investigation, students will learn to simulate situations that can be modeled by flipping a coin—in each situation, there are two equally likely outcomes, each with probability $\frac{1}{2}$.

This investigation is motivated by studying the attempt in China to limit population growth. Students examine various plans that could be adopted and still give parents a reasonable expectation of having a boy.

Students learn that it is impossible to change the percentage of boys in the population by having some clever "stopping rule." For example, if every family has children until they get a boy and then stop, the proportion of boys remains 0.5. This result is contrary to most people's intuition.

At the end of this investigation, students should understand that, according to the Law of Large Numbers, a simulation with a larger number of runs has an estimated probability that tends to be closer to the true probability than a simulation with a smaller number of runs.

The Law of Large Numbers is behind the reasoning that longer championship series in sports are fairer than shorter ones. That is, the better team is more likely to win a longer series than to win a shorter one. The reason is that in a longer series, the better team's winning percentage is more likely to be closer to its true underlying winning percentage, which is greater than 0.5. (See E. Lee May, Jr.: "Are seven-game baseball playoffs fairer?" *The Mathematics Teacher, 85,* 1992, 528–531.)

It is important that students understand why they are doing each step in a simulation. Doing the actual coin flipping is deceptively mindless. But thinking out what to do, what to record, and how to use the results to answer the questions are challenging tasks. In fact, knowing what question you are trying to answer and stating it clearly is the first step. As in the rest of this unit, the important thing is for students to learn how to set up a simulation, not for them to perform a large number of runs in order to get estimates that are highly accurate.

For Problems 3 and 4, divide the number of runs among the groups in the class. Then combine the results. You may substitute a smaller number of runs if your class understands that the resulting estimated probabilities may be quite far from the theoretical probabilities.

1 Consider, first, the plan that assumes each family in China has exactly two children.

   a. Construct a sample space of the four possible families of two children.

   b. Use your sample space to answer these questions from the Think About This Situation:

      i. What is the probability that parents will have a son?

     ii. Will the total population of China grow, shrink, or stay about the same?

    iii. Will China end up with more boys than girls or with more girls than boys?

    iv. What is the mean number of children per family?

2 Your class may have discussed the following plan for reducing population growth in rural China.

> *Allow parents to continue to have children until a boy is born.*
> *Then no more children are allowed.*

Suppose that all parents continue having children until they get a boy. After the first boy, they have no other children. Write your best prediction of the answer to each of the following questions.

   a. In the long run, will the population have more boys or more girls, or will the numbers be approximately the same?

   b. What will be the mean number of children per family?

   c. If all people pair up and have children, will the population increase, decrease, or stay the same?

   d. What percentage of families will have only one child?

   e. What percentage of the children will belong to single-child families?

3 To get a good estimate of the answers to the questions in Problem 2, you could simulate the situation. To do this, you can design a **simulation model** that imitates the process of parents having children until they get a boy.

   a. Describe how to use a coin to conduct a simulation that models a family having children until they get a boy.

   b. When you flip a coin to simulate one family having children until they get the first boy, you have conducted one **run** of your simulation. What is the least number of times you could have to flip the coin on a run? The most? If it takes *n* flips to get the first "boy", how many "girls" will be in the family?

1 **NOTE** This situation is an example of a binomial distribution. A binomial distribution results when you count the number of "successes" in a fixed number of trials where trials are independent and the probability of a "success" is the same on each trial.

This problem is similar to Part c of the Check Your Understanding on page 541 in Lesson 1, Investigation 1.

a.

	Second Baby	
	Boy	**Girl**
Boy	B, B	B, G
Girl	G, B	G, G

First Baby

Each of the four outcomes is equally likely.

b. **i.** $\frac{3}{4}$

ii. If all people marry and have two children, the population of China will stay the same. If some people don't marry and have children, but all who do have two children, then the population will shrink.

iii. China will end up with the same number of boys as girls.

iv. 2

2 **NOTE** This is an example of a geometric or "waiting-time" distribution. As will be learned in Course 2, a histogram for a geometric (waiting-time) distribution has the tallest bar on the left with the height of the bars gradually decreasing.

Note that Part e is not the same question as Part d, because it is calculated from the point of view of an individual, rather than a family.

a–e. Responses will vary to all of these questions. The correct answers are given in Problem 4 of this investigation.

3 **a.** Let tails represent a boy, and toss the coin until tails appears. Count the number of tosses needed (including the final toss, which resulted in a tail). The total number of tosses is the number of children in the family.

b. You could get a tail (boy) on the very first flip. There is no "most" number of times. It is possible to flip forever without getting a tail. If you flip n times to get the first boy, there will be $n - 1$ girls in the family.

Waiting-time distributions can be simulated using *CPMP-Tools* statistics software. Select "Simulations" under the Statistics menu. In order to simulate having children until you get a boy, select the coin as the random device. Then under the Build menu, select "Count Till See" and either the H for Head or the T for Tail. Under the View menu you can choose to display the graph as was done in the screen below.

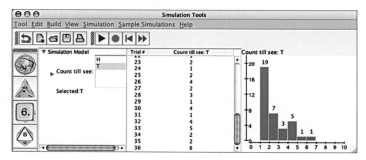

c. Carry out one run of your simulation of having children until a boy is born. Make a table like the one below. Make a tally mark (/) in the tally column opposite the number of flips it took to get a "boy."

Number of Flips to Get a "Boy"	Tally	Frequency (Number of Tallies)	Relative Frequency
1			
2			
3			
4			
5			
6			
7			
8			
9			
10			
⋮			
Total	200 runs	200 runs	1.00

d. Continue the simulation until your class has a total of 200 "families." Record your results in the frequency table. Add as many additional rows to the table as you need.

e. How many "boys" were born in your 200 "families?" How many "girls?"

f. What assumption(s) are you making in this simulation?

g. Make a relative frequency histogram on a copy of the graph shown below and describe its shape.

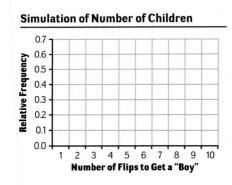

Simulation of Number of Children

h. Compare the median number of children to the mean number of children in the families.

c. Each student should flip a coin, counting the number of flips until he or she gets the first head (including this last flip in the number of flips required).

d. The table at the right is very close to the "ideal" one. For the results generated by your students, the frequencies could be quite a bit different from these.

e. In the table at the right, there were 200 boys (one for each family). There are a total of 100(1) + 50(2) + 25(3) + 12(4) + 6(5) + 3(6) + 2(7) + 1(8) + 1(9) = 402 children. So, there are 402 − 200 = 202 girls. That is, there are roughly the same number of boys as girls.

f. You are assuming that boys and girls are equally likely on each birth. That is, the probability that a child is a boy remains $\frac{1}{2}$, no matter how many girls have already been born.

> **POSSIBLE MISCONCEPTION** It is not true that boys or girls "run" in families. Many people believe that this is the case, especially when there is a run of boys or girls in their own family. However, statisticians have not found much evidence that boys or girls run in families. For example, if you look at all families that start with four boys, a fifth child is as likely to be a girl as a boy. See "Does Having Boys or Girls Run in the Family?" *Chance, 14*, 2001, pages 8–13.

Number of Flips to get a "Boy"	Frequency	Relative Frequency
1	100	0.500
2	50	0.250
3	25	0.125
4	12	0.060
5	6	0.030
6	3	0.015
7	2	0.010
8	1	0.005
9	1	0.005
10	0	0.0
⋮	0	0.0
Total	**200 runs**	**1.00**

g.

> **NOTE** A histogram gives a complete picture of the relative likelihood of the possible outcomes in a probability distribution. From the histogram, you can estimate shape, center, and spread. Thus, it is important to look at the histogram any time you have a probability distribution. As students will see in this unit, the histograms fall into families of characteristic shapes. Eventually a student's intuition will become strong enough that he or she will be able to "see" the results of some simulations before actually running the simulation.
>
> The shape is strongly skewed right, with each bar being about half the height of the bar to its left. Some students may be able to describe why this is so. (We expect half of the students to get heads on their first flip. Of the half who are left, we expect half of them to get heads on their next flip. And so on.)

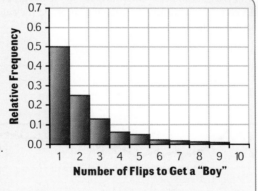

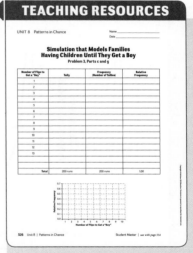

TEACHING RESOURCES

Student Master 526
🔵 GO DIGITAL

h. The mean number of children in the table above is $\frac{402}{200} = 2.01$ and the median is 1.5. (The theoretical answers are 2 and 1.5.) As is common in right-skewed distributions, the median is smaller than the mean.

4 Now reconsider the questions from Problem 2, which are reproduced below. Estimate the answers to these questions using your completed table from Problem 3.

  a. In the long run, will the population have more boys or more girls, or will the numbers be approximately the same?

  b. What will be the mean number of children per family?

  c. If all people pair up and have children, will the population increase, decrease, or stay the same?

  d. What percentage of families will have only one child?

  e. What percentage of the children will belong to single-child families?

5 Compare your estimates in Problem 4 with your original predictions in Problem 2. For which questions did your initial prediction vary the most from the estimate for the simulation? (If most of your original predictions were not accurate, you have a lot of company. Most people aren't very good at predicting the answers to probability problems. That's why simulation is such a useful tool.)

In the previous simulation, your class was asked to produce 200 runs. There is nothing special about that number except that it is about the most that it is reasonable for a class to do by hand. The **Law of Large Numbers** says that the more runs there are, the better your estimate of the probability tends to be. For example, according to the Law of Large Numbers, when you flip a coin a large number of times, eventually you should get a proportion of heads that is close to 0.5. (This assumes that the flips are independent and the probability of a head on each flip is 0.5.)

6 To illustrate the Law of Large Numbers, some students made the graph below. They flipped a coin 50 times and after each flip recorded the *cumulative* proportion of flips that were heads.

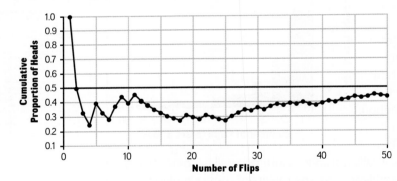

  a. Was the first flip heads or tails? How can you tell from the graph whether the next flip was a head or a tail? What were the results of each of the first 10 coin flips?

  b. To three decimal places, what was the proportion of heads at each step in the first 10 coin flips?

  c. Could the graph eventually go back above 0.5? Explain.

4 | **POSSIBLE MISCONCEPTIONS** Almost everyone originally has some misconceptions about this plan for limiting population growth. Many students will believe that there will be more boys than girls because each family must have a boy and half of the families don't have a girl. Other students will visualize the long string of girls that some families will have before they have a boy and so think that there will be more girls than boys. Almost everyone believes the mean family size is greater than 2, and so the population will increase.

The answers below are computed from the table in Problem 3, followed by the theoretical answer. The answers from your class will likely differ somewhat.

a. There were 200 boys and 202 girls, or roughly the same number of boys as girls. Theoretically, there will be the same number of boys as girls because the probability of a boy and a girl is the same on each birth. Stopping when you get a boy doesn't change that.

b. There were 402 children in the 200 families, or a mean of 2.01 or about 2 children per family. Theoretically, the mean number of children per family will be 2. (As students will learn in Course 2, the mean of a geometric distribution is $\frac{1}{p}$, where p is the probability of getting a "success" on each trial. Since the probability of a "success" is $\frac{1}{2}$, the mean number of trials needed is $\frac{1}{p} = \frac{1}{\frac{1}{2}} = 2$.)

c. Because, on average, each pair of adults has two children and so "replace" themselves, the population size will stay the same if everyone marries and has children until they get a boy. If everyone doesn't marry and have children, the population will decrease.

d. Half of the families in the table had only one child. That is the theoretical answer as well because half of the families will get a boy on the first birth.

e. Of the 402 children in the table, 100 or 0.249 of them belong to single-child families (these are the boys who were first-born). The theoretical answer is 0.25. That is, although half of the families have only one child, only 25% of the children are in single-child families.

5 Students should compare their answers in Problems 2 and 4.

6 **a.** The first flip was a head. If the graph goes up, the flip was a head. The first ten flips were H, T, T, T, H, T, T, H, H, T.

b. 1.000, 0.500, 0.333, 0.250, 0.400, 0.333, 0.286, 0.375, 0.444, 0.400

c. Yes, and this would happen, for example, if the next 7 flips were heads, so there would be 29 heads out of 57 flips.

d. Why do the lengths of the line segments between successive flips tend to get smaller as the number of flips increases?

e. At the end of 50 flips, there were 22 heads and 28 tails. Continue on from there, doing 20 more flips. As you go along, complete a copy of the following table and a copy of the graph on the previous page, extending them to 70 flips.

Number of Flips	Frequency of Heads	Proportion of Heads
10	4	0.400
20	6	0.300
30	11	0.367
40	16	0.400
50	22	0.440
60		
70		

f. Explain how your completed graph and table illustrate the Law of Large Numbers.

More flips of the coin or more runs of a simulation are better when estimating probabilities, but in practice it is helpful to know when to stop. You can stop when the distribution stabilizes; that is, you can stop when it seems like adding more runs isn't changing the proportions very much.

7 Refer to your graph showing the results of your coin flips from Problem 6. Does the proportion of heads appear to be stabilizing, or is there still a lot of fluctuation at the end of 70 flips?

8 The graph below shows the results of 200 runs of a simulation of the plan for reducing population growth in Problem 1. In that plan, each family has exactly two children. The proportion of families that had two girls is plotted. How does this graph illustrate the Law of Large Numbers?

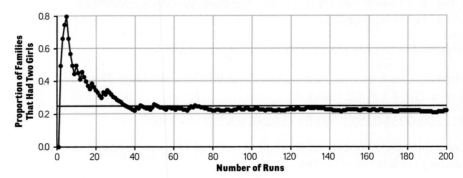

d. Students are likely to give an example. Suppose, for example, that you have 5 heads out of 10 flips, then whether you get a head or a tail on the next flip, the absolute value of the difference in proportion of heads is $\left|\frac{5}{10} - \frac{6}{10}\right| = \frac{1}{10}$. But if you have 50 heads out of 100 flips, then whether you get a head or a tail on the next flip, the absolute value of the difference in proportion of heads is the much smaller $\left|\frac{50}{100} - \frac{51}{100}\right| = \frac{1}{100}$. In each case, the horizontal distance between adjacent points is 1, so the line segment with the larger difference in proportions will be longer.

It is not always the case that a line segment is longer than the previous one, which is why the problem says that the line segments "tend to get shorter." For example, suppose that you have 16 heads out of 30 flips. If the next flip is a head and the next after that a tail, the first difference in proportions is $\frac{17}{31} - \frac{16}{30} \approx$ 0.01505 while the second difference is *larger*: $\frac{17}{32} - \frac{17}{31} \approx 0.01714$.

Notice also that the vertical differences are always larger when the graph goes towards the horizontal line at 0.5 than they would be if it went the other way. For example, after 20 flips, there were only 6 heads, so the graph is below the 0.5 line. If the next flip were a head, the graph would move towards the 0.5 line from $\frac{6}{20}$ to $\frac{7}{21}$, or from 0.30 to 0.333. If the next flip were a tail, the graph would move away from the 0.5 line from $\frac{6}{20}$ to $\frac{6}{21}$ or from 0.30 to 0.286, a smaller vertical distance. It is this phenomenon that makes the graph tend to head towards the 0.5 line.

e. Results will vary.

f. The Law of Large Numbers says that as the number of trials increases, the estimated probability tends to get closer to the theoretical probability. The graph illustrates this because as the number of flips increases, the proportion of heads tends to get closer to 0.5.

> **POSSIBLE MISCONCEPTION** Although the proportion of heads is converging to 0.5, the frequency of heads is diverging from the expected frequency. In the table in Part e, the expected number of heads in 10 flips is 5. The actual number is 4, for a difference of 1. After 50 flips, the proportion of heads is closer to 0.5 than for 10 flips, but the number of heads, 22, is 3 away from the expected number of heads, 25. Notice that while 3 is greater in magnitude than 1, it represents a smaller percentage of 50 than 1 does of 10.
>
> This is an important idea for students to learn—that as you are flipping a coin, for example, the percentage of heads tends to get closer and closer to 50% as the number of flips increases, while the number of heads tends to get further and further from half the number of tosses. If students do not understand this, they will believe that the coin must balance out the numbers of heads and tails in the future by changing the probability that it will be a head. This idea comes up again in Reflections Task 17.

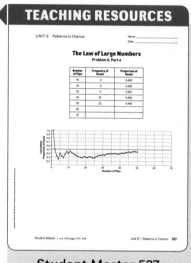

TEACHING RESOURCES

Student Master 527

⏻ GO DIGITAL

7 At the end of 70 flips, there is still quite a bit of fluctuation.

8 The proportion of two-child families that have two girls is 0.25. The estimate is off a lot at the beginning, as high as 0.80 after the first five families. As the number of families increases, the proportion of families with two girls is approaching 0.25, as it should. After 30 trials, the estimate is never off by more than 0.10. After 35 trials, it is never off by more than about 0.05, although it strays from 0.25 towards 200 trials. The Law of Large Numbers guarantees that the proportion will eventually return to a narrow band around 0.25.

SUMMARIZE THE MATHEMATICS

In this investigation, you designed and analyzed a simulation using coin flips.

a Describe what a simulation is.

b Why is it important to conduct a large number of runs in a simulation?

c Suppose one run of a simulation is to flip a coin until you get a head. After many runs, you count the total number of heads and the total number of tails in all runs. Will you tend to have a larger proportion of heads or a larger proportion of tails?

Be prepared to share your ideas and reasoning with the class.

 CHECK YOUR UNDERSTANDING

When asked in what way chance affected her life, a ninth-grader in a very large Los Angeles high school reported that students are chosen randomly to be checked for weapons. Suppose that when this policy was announced, a reporter for the school newspaper suspected that the students would not be chosen randomly, but that boys would be more likely to be chosen than girls. The reporter then observed the first search and found that all 10 students searched were boys.

a. If there are the same number of boys and girls in the high school and a student is in fact chosen randomly, what is the probability that the student will be a boy?

b. Write instructions for conducting one run of a simulation that models selecting 10 students at random and observing whether each is a boy or a girl.

c. What assumptions did you make in your model?

d. Perform five runs of your simulation and add your results to the frequency table at the right.

Number of Boys	Frequency (Before)	Frequency (After)
0	0	
1	1	
2	9	
3	20	
4	41	
5	45	
6	43	
7	23	
8	11	
9	0	
10	2	
Total	**195 runs**	**200 runs**

STR/AFP/Getty Images

SUMMARIZE THE MATHEMATICS

a A simulation involves a model of a real-life probabilistic situation that is mathematically equivalent to that situation. By using a random device to conduct a large number of runs, you can estimate the answers to probabilistic questions about the real-life situation. Information can be gathered more quickly and easily than by observing the situation itself.

b According to the Law of Large Numbers, as the number of runs increases, the estimated probability tends to get closer to the true probability. This is true as long as the runs are independent and the probability of a success remains the same.

c Neither. Since the probability of getting a head is $\frac{1}{2}$ on each flip of a coin, the proportion of heads in a large number of flips should be close to $\frac{1}{2}$ no matter how clever our scheme for starting and stopping. For example, if each person in a large group flips a coin until they get a head and then stops, the expected proportion of heads will be $\frac{1}{2}$.

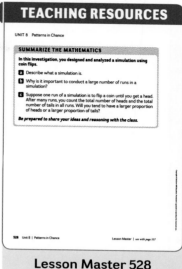
✔ CHECK YOUR UNDERSTANDING

NOTE This situation is an example of a binomial distribution.

a. The probability a randomly selected student will be a boy is 0.5.

b. Use a coin and let a head represent the event of a boy being selected and a tail represent the event of a girl being selected. Flip the coin ten times and count the number of boys (or girls) selected to be searched. (Students might choose to use a spinner or a die.)

c. The assumptions are that there is the same number of boys as girls in the school and that the choices of who is to be searched are independent of each other. For example, we assume the students are not selected in a group as they are walking together into the school. Such a group might tend to have all boys or all girls.

d. Results will vary.

e. **i.** The shape is approximately normal. Estimates will vary somewhat, but the mean is about 5 and the standard deviation is about 1.6. (Any estimate of the standard deviation between 1.5 and 2 is a good one.)

ii. Boys and girls are equally likely; so, for example, it is just as likely to get 7 boys and 3 girls as 3 boys and 7 girls.

iii. Most likely, the basic shape of the histogram would remain the same.

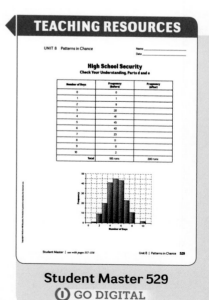

e. The histogram below displays the results in the frequency table for 195 runs.

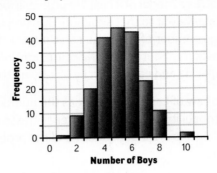

i. Describe its shape and estimate its mean and standard deviation.

ii. Why is this distribution almost symmetric?

iii. If you added your results to the histogram, would the basic shape change?

f. Using results from 200 runs of your simulation, estimate the probability that all 10 students will be boys if students are selected at random to be searched. What conclusion should the reporter make?

g. How much did adding your five runs change the probability of getting 10 boys? What can you conclude from this?

INVESTIGATION 2

Simulation Using Random Digits

In the previous investigation, the problem situations were based on two equally likely outcomes that you could simulate with a coin flip. In other situations, it is possible that there are more than two outcomes or the two outcomes aren't equally likely. In these situations, you can use random digits in designing a simulation. You can get strings of random digits from your calculator or from a random digit table produced by a computer. As you work on the following problems, look for answers to this question:

How can you use random digits when designing simulations?

1 Examine this table of random digits generated by a computer.

2 4 8 0 3	1 8 6 5 6	4 2 0 3 0	9 1 4 9 6
7 6 8 6 3	0 5 6 8 2	5 0 7 4 5	6 7 3 6 3
0 9 5 8 1	7 3 0 9 9	8 7 7 7 7	1 6 2 7 2
0 2 6 8 6	2 5 5 4 1	5 9 8 1 0	1 5 2 9 7
4 1 2 9 0	8 6 7 0 3	3 8 2 5 1	8 4 1 4 1
1 5 8 0 9	5 7 3 5 6	5 0 2 0 3	6 6 5 0 3
9 7 6 2 5	9 2 6 3 5	0 3 1 9 3	9 7 2 6 3
2 1 0 9 6	0 1 8 5 5	2 2 6 8 6	0 6 6 6 3

a. How many digits are in the table? About how many 6s would you expect to find? How many are there?

f. From the 195 runs in the table in the student text, the estimated probability of getting 10 boys is $\frac{2}{195}$ or about 0.01. (The theoretical probability is less than that: $(0.5)^{10} \approx 0.001$.) Because the probability of getting 10 boys just by chance is so small, the reporter should conclude that there is some reason, other than chance, why boys are being chosen. Possibly the person who selects the students to be searched is selecting boys deliberately. Possibly students are selected as to whether or not they are wearing a certain item that boys tend to wear. (The mathematical analysis can't tell us the reason; all it tells us is that something happened that can't reasonably be attributed to chance and so an explanation is needed.)

g. Most likely, adding more results didn't change the probability very much of getting all boys. This means that the distribution may be beginning to stabilize to its theoretical shape. (This was observed in Part e, step iii.)

NOTE The solution to Part e is on page T557.

INVESTIGATION **2** **CCSS** S-ID.1, S-MD.1, S-MD.4

Simulation Using Random Digits

In this investigation, students learn to use tables of random digits to model discrete probabilistic situations. This work is motivated by the "collector's problem" of how many boxes of cereal one might have to buy in order to get all of the different prizes offered. Students explore the nature of random digits and learn to use single random digits, and then pairs of random digits, to simulate situations. Finally, they learn to use the random integer generator on their calculator to generate random integers.

Important new vocabulary includes the terms "with replacement" and "without replacement."

Using a Table of Random Digits
When using a table of random digits, each student should start at a randomly selected spot on the table and go across or down. If students all start at the same spot, they might get identical results. After the run is finished, students should take up where they left off in the table rather than starting again at a randomly selected spot.

A table of random digits is supplied as a Teaching Master. You may need additional tables of random digits. They can be found in most introductory statistics books, or you can use the final four digits of phone numbers torn out of a phone book. (The first three digits aren't random as most localities will have only a few prefixes.)

A set of random digits has several important characteristics: (1) you cannot predict with greater than a 10% success rate what the next digit is; and (2) each digit occurs, in the long run, 10% of the time. It is these characteristics that make random digit tables so valuable for simulation.

1 **a.** There are 160 digits in the table. Because 6 should occur about $\frac{1}{10}$ of the time, you would expect to find about sixteen 6s. In this table, the digit 6 occurs 24 times.

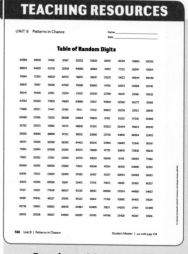

TEACHING RESOURCES

Student Master 530
① GO DIGITAL

    b. About what percentage of digits in a large table of random digits will be even?

    c. About what percentage of the 1s in a large table of random digits will be followed by a 2?

    d. About what percentage of the digits in a large table of random digits will be followed by that same digit?

2 Explain how you can use the table of random digits in Problem 1 to simulate each situation given below. (You may have to disregard certain digits.) Then perform one run of your simulation.

    a. Flip a coin and see if you get heads or tails.

    b. Observe five coin flips and record how many heads you get.

    c. Observe whether it rains or not on one day when the prediction is 80% chance of rain.

    d. Select three cars at random from a large lot where 20% of the cars are black, 40% are white, 30% are green, and 10% are silver, and record the color.

    e. Spin the spinner shown here four times and record the colors.

    f. Roll a die until you get a 6 and record the number of rolls you needed.

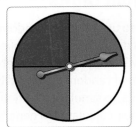

    g. Select three different students at random from a group of ten students. How is this problem different from the others you have done?

    h. Select three different students at random from a group of seven students.

3 Suppose three meteorites are predicted to hit the United States. You are interested in how many will fall on publicly owned land. About 30% of the land in the United States is owned by the public.

    a. Describe how to conduct one run that simulates this situation. What assumptions are you making in this simulation?

    b. Combine results with your class until you have 100 runs and place the results in a frequency table that shows how many of the three meteorites fell on public land.

    c. What is your estimate of the probability that all three of the meteorites will fall on public land?

    d. If all three meteorites actually do fall on public land, either a very unusual event occurred or something about your simulation model is wrong. What could be wrong?

4 In trips to a grocery store, you may have noticed that boxes of cereal often include a surprise gift such as one of a set of toy characters from a current movie or one of a collection of stickers. Cheerios, a popular breakfast cereal, once included one of seven magic tricks in each box.

    a. What is the least number of boxes you could buy and get all seven magic tricks?

Lesson 2 | Modeling Chance Situations   **559**

b. Since half of the digits from 0 through 9 are even (zero is even) and half are odd, about 50% of the digits in a large table will be even.

c. Since 10 equally likely digits could follow the 1, there is a $\frac{1}{10}$ chance that the digit will be a 2.

d. Once a digit is chosen, the probability that the following digit will be the same digit is $\frac{1}{10}$. So about 10% of the digits in a large table will be followed by the same digit.

2 | **INSTRUCTIONAL NOTE** In each part below, students should say that they will start at a random spot in the table.

a. If a digit is odd, it represents a head. If it is even, it represents a tail. (A second way would be to let the digits 0, 1, 2, 3, and 4 represent a head and the digits 5, 6, 7, 8, and 9 represent a tail. A third way would be to let the digit 0 represent a head and the digit 1 represent a tail. All other digits would be disregarded as if they weren't there.) Look at the first digit and record whether it represents a head or a tail.

b. If a digit is odd, it represents a head. If it is even, it represents a tail. (Or use one of the assignments from Part a.) Look at the first five digits and record how many are odd and so represent a head.

c. If a digit is 1 through 8, it represents rain and if it is 9 or 0 it represents not rain. (Or, assign any 8 of the 10 digits to represent rain and the remaining 2 to represent not rain.) Look at the first digit and record whether it represents rain or not rain.

d. If a digit is 1 or 2, it represents a black car. If it is 3, 4, 5, or 6, it represents a white car. If it is 7, 8, or 9, it represents a green car. If it is 0, it represents a silver car. (Many other assignments are possible, as long as a black car is assigned two digits, a white car four digits, a green car three digits, and a silver car one digit.) Look at the first three digits and record the colors of car they represent. Because it is a large lot, if a digit repeats (for example you get 3, 8, 3) use it, so then you would have two white cars and one green car.

Students may visualize the assignment of digits more clearly if they set up a table:

Assignment of Random Digits		
Color	**Probability**	**Random Digits**
Black	0.20	1, 2
White	0.40	3, 4, 5, 6
Green	0.30	7, 8, 9
Silver	0.10	0

e. If a digit is a 1 or 2, it represents red; if it is a 3 or 4, it represents blue; if it is a 5 or 6, it represents white; and if it is a 7 or 8, it represents green. If the digit is a 9 or 0, ignore it and go to the next digit. Look at the first four digits that are not a 9 or 0 and record the colors those digits represent.

f. If a digit is 1, 2, 3, 4, 5, or 6, let it represent the corresponding face on a die. If the digit is 7, 8, 9, or 0, ignore it and go on to the next digit. Keep going until a 6 appears. Count the number of digits needed (not counting any 7, 8, 9, or 0). For example, starting on the fifth line of the random digit table, 4 1 2 9 0 8 6 … , four rolls would be required to get a 6. (The 9, 0, and 8 are ignored.)

g. Assign a digit to each student. If the first digit in the table is a 4, for example, then the student who has been assigned 4 is the first student selected. Go to the second digit. If it is a 4, ignore it and go to the next digit. Keep on in this way until three different students have been selected. This problem is different from the others because you cannot use the same digit twice. You cannot select the same student twice and so must disregard a digit if it comes up a second time.

h. Assign the seven students the digits 1, 2, 3, 4, 5, 6, and 7. If the first digit is an 8, 9, or 0, go to the next digit. If the first digit is, say, a 3, then student number 3 will be selected. Go to the next digit that is not a 3, 8, 9, or 0. Continue until three students have been selected. For example, starting on the fourth line of the random digit table, 0 2 6 8 6   2 5 … , students with numbers 2, 6, and 5 would be selected.

3 **a.** Select a random digit. If it is 1, 2, or 3, the meteorite fell on public land. If the digit is 0, 4, 5, 6, 7, 8, 9, or 0, it did not fall on public land. (Other selections are possible. For example, 0, 1, and 2 could represent *fell on public land*.) Do this two more times. Count the number of meteorites that fell on public land. You are assuming that each spot in the United States is equally likely to be hit and that the meteorites fall independently (are not in a group, for example).

b. The table below gives the results of a typical simulation with 100 runs.

Number that Fall on Public Land	Frequency
0	29
1	46
2	22
3	3
Total	100

c. Estimates will vary. From the sample simulation above, the estimate is $\frac{3}{100}$ or 0.03. (The theoretical probability is 0.3^3 or 0.027.)

d. The assumption that the three meteorites were traveling independently should be checked. If they landed near each other, this assumption certainly would have been false. Also, it would be good to verify that fact given that 30% of the land in the United States is owned by the public and not a higher percentage.

4 | **INSTRUCTIONAL NOTE** This is an example of what is called "the collector's problem" or "the coupon collector's problem." You may want to continue to ask students to explain each step in their simulation.

   If you prefer, bring in a box of cereal from the grocery store that has one of a set of prizes in it and design a simulation for that set of prizes.

a. 7 boxes

b. If you buy one box of Cheerios, what is the probability that you will get a multiplying coin trick? To get your answer, what assumptions did you make about the tricks?

Collect All 7 and Put On Your Own Magic Show!

Money Clip Trick
Make two clips magically join together!

Mind-Reading Trick
Guess the color your friend secretly picked!

Vanishing Card Trick
Make a card magically disappear!

Magic Rope Trick
Make the rope magically pass through solid tube!

Disappearing Coin Trick
Make a coin magically disappear and reappear!

Surprise 4s
Turn two blank cards into two 4s!

Mulitplying Coin Trick
Turn two coins into three!

c. Suppose you want to estimate the number of boxes of Cheerios you will have to buy before you get all seven magic tricks. Describe a simulation model, including how to conduct one run using a table of random digits. (Recall that you may ignore certain digits.)

d. Compare your simulation model with that of other students. Then as a class, decide on a simulation model that all students will use.

e. Perform five runs using the agreed upon simulation. Keep track of the number of "boxes" you would have to buy. Add your numbers and those for the other students in your class to a copy of this frequency table.

Number of Boxes to Get All 7 Tricks	Frequency (Before)	Frequency (After)
7	1	
8	3	
9	4	
10	11	
11	13	
12	18	
13	22	
14	13	
15	9	
16	8	

Number of Boxes to Get All 7 Tricks	Frequency (Before)	Frequency (After)
17	10	
18	11	
19	13	
20	12	
21	4	
22	8	
23	3	
24	0	
25	0	
⋮		
Total		

560 UNIT 8 | Patterns in Chance

b. Assuming the prizes are randomly distributed amongst the boxes and that there are an equal number of each prize, the probability you will get a multiplying coin trick is $\frac{1}{7}$.

c. If a digit is a 1, it represents the money clip trick; if it is a 2, it represents the mind-reading trick; … ; if it is a 7, it represents the multiplying coin trick. If a digit is an 8, 9, or 0, ignore it and go to the next digit. To perform one run, start at a random spot in the table and keep going until all of the digits 1, 2, 3, 4, 5, 6, and 7 have appeared. Record the number of digits needed, not including any 8, 9, or 0. For example, this string of random digits would mean that 19 boxes would have to be purchased before getting all seven tricks.

64783   05320   77859   74693   63680   21

d. Models might vary in the assignment of digits to prizes, but should be equivalent to the model in Part c.

e. The numbers of boxes will vary.

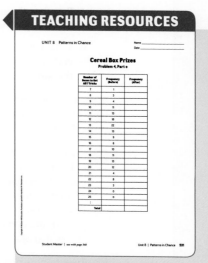

Student Master 531
🅘 **GO DIGITAL**

f. Add the runs from your class to a copy of the histogram below.

Number of Boxes to Get All 7 Tricks

   i. Describe the shape of the distribution.

   ii. Compare the shape of this distribution to others you have constructed in this unit.

g. Based on the simulation, would it be unusual to have to buy 15 or more boxes to get the 7 magic tricks? Explain.

h. What could be some possible explanations why a person would, in fact, end up buying a much larger number of boxes than you would expect from this simulation?

In the previous simulations, you have been able to use single digits from your table of random digits. In other cases, you may need to use groups of two or more consecutive random digits.

5 When playing tennis, Sheila makes 64% of her first serves. Describe how to use pairs of random digits to conduct one run of a simulation of a set where Sheila tries 35 first serves. Then conduct one run of your simulation and count the number of serves that Sheila makes.

6 Twenty-nine percent of the students at Ellett High School reported that they have been to a movie in the previous two weeks. Connie found that only 1 of her 20 (or 5%) closest friends at the school had been to a movie in the previous two weeks. Connie wants to know if this smaller-than-expected number can reasonably be attributed to chance or if she should look for another explanation.

a. Describe how to use pairs of random digits to conduct one run of a simulation to find the number of recent moviegoers in a randomly selected group of 20 students.

moodboard/Corbis

Lesson 2 | Modeling Chance Situations **561**

f. **i.** The distribution is skewed right.

   ii. This shape is different from others in this unit.

g. Students might respond by using the table or graph. Using the graph, it looks like about half of the time the number of boxes purchased was 15 or more. From the table in the student text, 15 or more boxes were required in 115 out of 200 runs, for an estimated probability of 0.575. So, having to buy 15 or more boxes would not be unusual.

h. In the real world, the assumptions listed in Part b are unlikely to be true. For example, there may be more (or fewer) of the better tricks. All of one kind of trick may go to certain regions of the country and not to others. The prizes may be introduced successively, as all money clip tricks in January and all mind-reading tricks in February, etc.

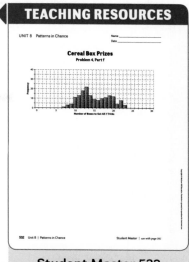
5 Look at pairs of digits in the table. If the pair is 01 through 64, Sheila makes the serve. If the pair is 65 through 99 or 00, Sheila misses. Start at a random place in the random digit table and look at 35 pairs, recording for each one whether Sheila makes the serve or does not.

   Starting, for example, on the second line of the random digit table at the beginning of this investigation, and writing *M* for makes the serve and *X* for misses the serve, you would get:

7 6 8 6 3	0 5 6 8 2	5 0 7 4 5	6 7 3 6 3
X X	M M X	M X	M X M
0 9 5 8 1	7 3 0 9 9	8 7 7 7 7	1 6 2 7 2
M M	M M X	X X	X M X
0 2 6 8 6	2 5 5 4 1	5 9 8 1 0	1 5 2 9 7
M X	M M M	M X	M M X
4 1 2 9 0	8 6 7 0 3		
M M	M X M		

In this run, Sheila made 21 out of 35 serves or 60%. (We expect her to make 64% in the long run.)

6 **a.** Look at pairs of digits in the table. If the pair is 01 through 29, the student has been to a movie in the previous two weeks. If the pair is 30 through 99 or 00, they have not. Start at a random place in the random digit table and look at 20 pairs, recording for each one whether the student has been to a movie or not.

b. The table and histogram below show the results of 195 simulations of the number of recent moviegoers in groups of 20 randomly selected students. Conduct 5 runs, adding your results to a copy of the table and histogram.

Number of Students	Frequency (Before)	Frequency (After)
0	1	
1	3	
2	8	
3	18	
4	25	
5	35	

Number of Students	Frequency (Before)	Frequency (After)
6	44	
7	30	
8	15	
9	7	
10	8	
11	1	
Total	195	200

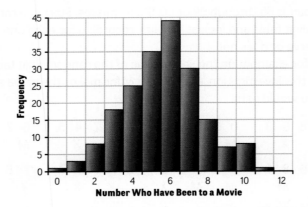

Number Who Have Been to a Movie

c. Based on your simulation, estimate the probability that no more than 1 of 20 randomly selected students have been to a movie in the previous two weeks.

d. Is the result for Connie's friends about what might be expected for a randomly selected group of 20 students? If not, what are some possible explanations?

A table of random digits is a convenient tool to use in conducting simulations. However, calculators and computer software with random number generators are more versatile tools.

7 Investigate the nature of the integers produced by the random integer generator on your calculator or computer software. You may find the command **randInt** under the probability menu. If, for example, you want six integers randomly selected from {1, 2, 3, 4, … , 19, 20}, enter **randInt(1,20,6)**.

a. If the same integer can be selected twice, the random integer generator is said to select *with replacement*. If the same integer cannot appear more than once in the same set, the random integer generator is said to select *without replacement*. Does your **randInt** command select with replacement or without replacement?

b. Results will vary.

c. From the 195 runs in the original table, the probability that no more than 1 out of 20 randomly selected students has been to a movie in the previous two weeks is $\frac{1+3}{195}$ or only about 0.0205.

d. From Part c, getting 1 or fewer students out of a randomly selected group of students is quite unlikely. Since this result cannot reasonably be attributed to chance alone, students might speculate what makes Connie's friends atypical. Perhaps Connie makes friends with students who have less money to spend, whose parents who do not approve of movies, or who simply prefer other activities themselves.

> **TECHNOLOGY NOTE** The random digits in a table generated by a calculator or computer are very close to random, while dice rolling or card drawing may not be; for example, the die may not be perfectly fair or the cards might not be shuffled thoroughly. Calculator- or computer-generated random numbers are called pseudo-random as they are generated by an algorithm. Each random number generator uses a seed value. The initial seed value for some calculators is set to the same value. This means that each machine will generate the same sequence of random numbers unless the seeds are changed. To change the seeds, students will need to enter any integer into "rand." For example "453→rand" will change the seed value for the random number generator to 453. You may wish to have students use the last four digits of their phone number as a seed number. This will reduce the likelihood of two students using the same seed number.
>
> Random number generators speed up the work of performing runs. However, students still should go through all of the steps in a simulation.
>
> If your students have more ready access to computers rather than to calculators, many of the simulations in the lesson can be done using *CPMP-Tools* software. The "Simulation" tool is located under Statistics. For example, to select six integers randomly from {1, 2, 3, ... , 19, 20}, students can "toss" the 20-sided die six times. If the six integers were selected randomly from {1, 2, 3, ... , 18, 19}, students could set up a "Custom Event" under "Build."

7 **a.** With replacement

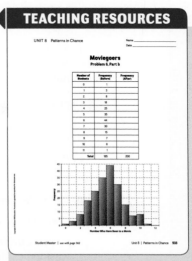

b. Your calculator probably selects integers at random with replacement. If this is the case, describe how you can get a random selection of six numbers from {1, 2, 3, 4, ... , 19, 20} without replacement.

8 Explain how to use the **randInt** command to simulate each of the following situations. Then perform one run of the simulation.

a. Roll a die five times and record the number on top.

b. Flip a coin 10 times and record whether it is heads or tails on each flip.

c. Select three different students at random from a group of seven students.

d. Roll a die until you get a 6 and count the number of rolls needed.

e. Check five boxes of Cheerios for which of seven magic tricks they contain.

f. Draw a card from a well-shuffled deck of 52 playing cards and record whether it is an ace.

SUMMARIZE THE MATHEMATICS

In this investigation, you explored the properties of random digits and learned how to use them in designing a simulation.

a What is a table of random digits? What command do you use to get random digits on your calculator?

b Give an example of when you would want to select random digits with replacement. Without replacement.

c How do you use random digits in a simulation when the probability of the event you want is 0.4? When the probability of the event is 0.394?

d As a tie-in to the opening of a baseball season, each box of Honey Bunches of Oats cereal contained one of six Major League Baseball CD-ROMs (one for each division). Suppose you want to collect all six and wonder how many boxes you can expect to have to buy. How could you simulate this situation efficiently using a table of random digits? Using your calculator? What assumptions are you making?

e Suppose that the result from the actual data lies far out in the tail of your probability distribution. What does this mean about how consistant the model is with the data? What could have gone wrong with the model?

Be prepared to share your ideas and reasoning with the class.

b. Use the command **randInt(1,20,6)**. If there is no duplication, these are your six numbers. If there is duplication, say you get two 3s, keep one of them and then use the command **randInt(1,20,1)**—or just **randInt(1,20)** until you get a digit that is different from the ones you have.

8 **a.** Use **randInt(1,6,5)**. The five digits given are the five numbers rolled on the die. It is okay if a number repeats, as a die also could repeat.

b. Use **randInt(0,1,10)**, where a 0 will represent tails and a 1 will represent heads (or vice versa). Again, it is okay if a number repeats.

c. One method is to use **randInt(1,7,3)**. If you get a repeat, which you do not want in this case, use **randInt(1,7,1)** until you get another student (or two).

d. Use **randInt(1,6,1)**—or just **randInt(1,6)**—over and over until you get a 6. Count the number of times you used the command, counting any repeats each time they occur.

e. Use **randInt(1,7,5)**, where the numbers 1 through 7 are assigned to the seven magic tricks in advance. Record which tricks you get, including any repeats.

f. Use **randInt(1,52,1)**, where, for example, the numbers 1, 2, 3, and 4 designate an ace.

SUMMARIZE THE MATHEMATICS

a A table of random digits is a list containing the digits 0 through 9 with repeats possible. These numbers have two important features: the next digit in the array cannot be predicted with probability greater than $\frac{1}{10}$, and each digit occurs approximately $\frac{1}{10}$ of the time over the long run. To get a random digit from 0 to 9, use **randInt(0,9)**.

b If you want to use random digits to simulate the situation of rolling two dice and waiting for doubles, you could let the digits 1, 2, 3, 4, and 5 represent not doubles and let 6 represent doubles. (You would disregard the other digits.) Then, you would allow repeats of the digits 1, 2, 3, 4, and 5 so that the probability of doubles would remain $\frac{1}{6}$ on each roll. For another example of sampling with replacement, see Part d on next page.

If you want to use random digits to pick 3 movies to watch out of 10 DVDs, you probably would want to select the random digits without replacement as you would not want to watch the same movie twice.

c You could let the digits 1, 2, 3, and 4 represent the event happening and the other six digits represent that it does not happen. You could let the triples of digits 001–394 represent the event happening and the triples 395–999 and 000 represent the event not happening.

✅ **CHECK YOUR UNDERSTANDING**

A teacher notices that of the last 20 single-day absences in his class, 10 were on Friday. He suspects that this did not happen just by random chance.

a. Assuming that absences are equally likely to occur on each day of the school week, describe how to use a table of random digits to simulate the days of the week that 20 single-day absences occur.

    i. Conduct 5 runs. Add your results to a copy of the frequency table and histogram at the right that show the number of absences that are on Friday for 295 runs.

    ii. Based on the simulation, what is your estimate of the probability of getting 10 or more absences out of 20 on Friday just by chance? What should the teacher conclude?

    iii. From the simulation, what is your estimate of the mean number of absences on Friday, assuming that the 20 absences are equally likely to occur on each day of the week? Does this make sense? Why or why not?

    iv. How could you get better estimates for parts ii and iii?

b. Describe how to use your calculator to conduct one run that simulates this situation.

Number of the 20 Absences that Are on Friday	Frequency (Before)	Frequency (After)
0	6	
1	13	
2	37	
3	62	
4	65	
5	47	
6	43	
7	13	
8	4	
9	5	
10	0	
Total	295	300

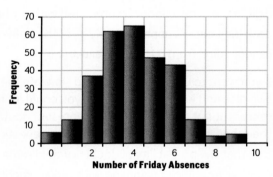

d Assign the digits 1 through 6 to the six divisions. Start at a random spot in a random digit table and count the number of digits you have to observe before you get all of the digits 1 through 6. Ignore the digits 7, 8, 9, and 0. If a digit occurs more than once, count it each time. On your calculator, keep using the command **randInt(1,6)** until you get all six different numbers. Count the number of times you used the command.

The assumptions you are making are that each of the different CD-ROMs is in $\frac{1}{6}$ of the boxes. You are also assuming that you can get a random selection from all of the boxes.

e When the result from the actual data lies far out in the tail of your probability distribution, either a very unusual event occurred or the model is inconsistent with the data. The model could be wrong in several ways: the estimate of the proportion of successes could be wrong, or the assumption that the trials are independent could be wrong.

✓ CHECK YOUR UNDERSTANDING

> **NOTE** This situation is an example of a binomial distribution.

a. One method is to assign the digits 0 and 1 to Monday, 2 and 3 to Tuesday, 4 and 5 to Wednesday, 6 and 7 to Thursday, and 8 and 9 to Friday. Begin at a random point in the table and look at the next 20 digits. The number of 8s and 9s will correspond to the number of absences that occurred on Friday.

  i. Additional results will vary.

  ii. Based on the 295 results in the student text, the probability of getting 10 or more absences on Friday just by chance is 0. (The theoretical probability is 0.0026.) The large number of absences on Friday in the teacher's class cannot reasonably be attributed to chance alone. The teacher should look for another explanation.

  iii. From the simulation, the mean number of absences on Friday is about 4. This makes sense as one-fifth of the 20 absences should be on Friday.

  iv. You could get better estimates by performing more runs.

b. One method is to use **randInt(1,5)** and assign the days of the week to the numbers 1 to 5. If the integer is a 5 (Friday), call the run a success.

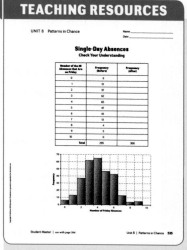

TEACHING RESOURCES

Student Master 535
Ⓘ GO DIGITAL

INVESTIGATION **3**

Using a Random Number Generator

Sometimes a simulation requires that you select numbers from a continuous interval. For example, suppose you are painting a person on the backdrop for a school play. You can't decide how tall to make the person and so decide just to select a height at random from the interval 60 inches to 72 inches. There are infinitely many heights in that interval. For example, possible heights are 60 inches, 60.1 inches, 60.11 inches, 60.111 inches, 60.1111 inches, etc. As you work on problems in this investigation, look for answers to the following question:

How can you design simulations to solve problems when numbers can come from a continuous interval?

1 Investigate the nature of the numbers produced by selecting the command **rand** in the probability menu of your calculator and then pressing ENTER repeatedly.

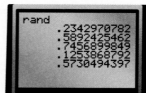

a. How many decimal places do the numbers usually have? (Some calculators leave off the last digit if it is a 0.)

b. Between what two whole numbers do all the random numbers lie?

2 Now explore how to generate random numbers in other continuous intervals.

a. Generate random numbers of the form **6rand** (or **6 × rand**). Between what two whole numbers do all the random numbers lie?

b. Between what two whole numbers do the random numbers lie when you use **10rand**? **36rand**? **rand+2**? **100rand+2**?

c. Write a **rand** command that selects a number at random from the interval between 1 and 7. Between 4 and 5. Between 60 inches and 72 inches.

d. Suppose you select two random numbers between 0 and 12 and want to estimate the probability that they are both more than 7.

   i. Use your calculator to select two numbers from this interval. Record whether both numbers are more than 7.

   ii. How can you simulate this situation using a spinner?

3 Julie wakes up at a random time each morning between 6:00 and 7:00. If she wakes up after 6:35, she won't have time for breakfast before school. Conduct one run of a simulation to estimate the probability that Julie won't have time for breakfast the next two school days. Repeat this 10 times. What is your estimate of the probability that Julie won't have time for breakfast the next two school days?

Using a Random Number Generator

In this investigation, students learn to use random numbers to model probabilistic situations where the random variable is continuous.

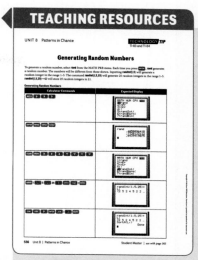

TEACHING RESOURCES

Student Master 536
(i) **GO DIGITAL**

1 **a.** Answer depends on the calculator, but typically eight to ten decimal places.

  b. The numbers lie between 0 and 1.

2 **a.** These numbers lie between 0 and 6.

  b. When "rand" is multiplied by 10, the random numbers lie between 0 and 10.
  When "rand" is multiplied by 36, the random numbers lie between 0 and 36.
  When you use **rand+2**, the random numbers lie between 2 and 3.
  When you use **100rand+2**, the random numbers lie between 2 and 102.

    In general, you can control the size of the random numbers generated by multiplying by a constant. If you want to generate numbers between 0 and n, use the command **n*rand**.

  c. **6rand+1**; **rand+4**; **12rand+60**

  d. **i.** Use the command **12rand** twice, and count the number of times that both numbers are more than 7.

    ii. Let the circumference of the circle represent 0 to 1. Make a mark where 12:00 and where 7:00 would normally fall, dividing the spinner into two parts of lengths $\frac{7}{12}$ and $\frac{5}{12}$. Spin the spinner twice. If both results are on the part of the circle representing $\frac{5}{12}$ (between 7:00 and 12:00), record the run as a success.

3 Because waking up later than 6:35 is equivalent to picking a random number greater than 7 from between 0 and 12, students could use either of the simulations in Problem 2 Part d. Estimates from the simulation will vary. (The theoretical probability is $\frac{5}{12} \cdot \frac{5}{12} = \frac{25}{144}$ or about 0.17.)

4 Recall the triangle-building experiment in the *Patterns in Shape* unit. In this problem, suppose you have a 10-inch strand of uncooked spaghetti and select two places at random along its length. You break the strand at those places and try to make a triangle out of the three pieces.

   a. What do you think the probability is that the three pieces will form a triangle? Make a conjecture.

   b. If the breaks are at 2-inch mark and 7.5-inch mark from the left end (see diagram below), how long are each of the three pieces? Can you make a triangle out of the three pieces?

   c. If the breaks are at 2.5-inch mark and at 6-inch mark from the left end, how long are each of the three pieces? Can you make a triangle out of the three pieces?

   d. Use your calculator to simulate one run of the situation of breaking a 10-inch strand of spaghetti at two randomly selected places. Can you make a triangle out of the three pieces?

   e. Carry out a simulation to estimate the probability that a triangle can be formed by the three pieces of a strand of spaghetti broken at two places at random along its length. Compare your estimated probability to your conjecture in Part a.

5 The square region pictured below is 250 feet by 250 feet. It consists of a field and a pond, which lies below the graph of $y = 0.004x^2$. Imagine a totally inept skydiver parachuting to the ground and trying to avoid falling into the pond. The skydiver can be sure of landing somewhere inside the region, but the spot within it is random.

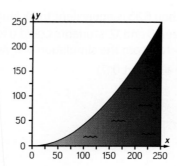

   a. Describe how to use the **rand** function of your calculator to simulate the point where the skydiver will land. (You will need an x-coordinate between 0 and 250 and a y-coordinate between 0 and 250.)

   b. How can you tell from the coordinates (x, y) of the simulated landing whether the skydiver landed in the pond?

4 **a.** Student estimates will vary.

   b. The pieces are 2", 5.5", and 2.5". According to the Triangle Inequality, you cannot make a triangle because the sum of the two shortest pieces is less than the longest piece: $2" + 2.5" < 5.5"$.

   c. The pieces are 2.5", 3.5", and 4". You can make a triangle because the sum of the two shortest pieces is larger than the longest piece: $2.5" + 3.5" > 4"$.

   d. Use the command **10rand** to pick the number of inches from the left side for one break and then the same command to pick the number of inches from the left side for the other break. To decide whether or not a triangle can be formed, find the length of the three pieces, find the sum of the two smaller pieces, and check to see if that sum is larger than the third length.

   e. The theoretical probability is 0.25. (See Extensions Task 24 on page 583.)

5 **a.** Use the command **250rand** twice to create an ordered pair (x, y).

   b. Find the value of y given by $y = 0.004x^2$ for the value of x in your ordered pair. If this is larger than the y in your ordered pair, then the skydiver fell in the pond. If it is smaller, the skydiver missed the pond. For example, if the ordered pair is (156.9, 201.7), then the skydiver did not land in the pond because this point is above the graph of the function: $201.7 > 0.004(156.9)^2 \approx 98.5$.

c. Simulate one landing and tell whether the skydiver landed in the pond or not.

d. Simulate a second landing and tell whether the skydiver landed in the pond or not.

6 Al and Alice work at the counter of an ice cream store. Al takes a 10-minute break at a random time between 12:00 and 1:00. Alice does the same thing, independently of Al.

a. Suppose that Al takes his break at 12:27. If Alice goes on her break at 12:35, would there be an overlap in the two breaks? What times for Alice to go on her break would result in an overlap of the two breaks?

b. Use the **rand** command to simulate this situation. Did the two breaks overlap?

SUMMARIZE THE MATHEMATICS

In this investigation, you explored further how to generate random numbers on your calculator and use them to estimate probabilities.

a In what situations would you use a calculator command such as **rand** rather than a command such as **randInt**?

b How would you use simulation to estimate the probability that two numbers randomly selected between 0 and 5 are both less than 3?

Be prepared to share your ideas and examples with the class.

✔ CHECK YOUR UNDERSTANDING

Jerome arrives at school at a random time between 7:00 and 7:30. Nadie leaves independently of Jerome and arrives at a random time between 6:45 and 7:15. Suppose you want to estimate the probability that Nadie arrives at school before Jerome.

a. Describe how to use a calculator command to simulate the time that Jerome arrives at school. To simulate the time that Nadie arrives at school.

b. Perform one run of a simulation. Did Jerome or Nadie get to school first?

c. Continue until you have a total of 10 runs. What is your estimate of the probability that Nadie gets to school before Jerome?

ROB & SAS/Corbis

c–d. Results will vary.

6 **a.** Yes, the breaks would overlap. They would both be on break between 12:35 and 12:37. The breaks will overlap if Alice leaves any time between 12:17 and 12:37.

b. If students think about the time between 12:00 and 1:00 as 60 minutes, then the command **60rand** can be used to simulate the time Al or Alice left for their break. Using the **60rand** command twice simulates the time when Al left for his break and then when Alice left for her break. If the absolute value of the differences between the two numbers is less than 10, then the breaks overlap.

SUMMARIZE THE MATHEMATICS

a You would use **rand** when you want any number selected at random from between 0 and 1. You would use **randint** when you want only integers.

b Use the command **5rand**; record the number. Then use the same command again and record the number. If both numbers are less than 3, call this run a success. Repeat for many runs and compute the proportion of runs that were successes.

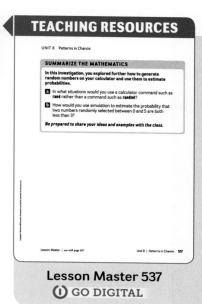

TEACHING RESOURCES

UNIT 8 Patterns in Chance

SUMMARIZE THE MATHEMATICS

In this investigation, you explored further how to generate random numbers on your calculator and use them to estimate probabilities.

a In what situations would you use a calculator command such as **rand** rather than a command such as **randint**?

b How would you use simulation to estimate the probability that two numbers randomly selected between 0 and 5 are both less than 3?

Be prepared to share your ideas and examples with the class.

Lesson Master | *use with page 567*   Unit 8 | Patterns in Chance   **537**

Lesson Master 537
(i) **GO DIGITAL**

✓ CHECK YOUR UNDERSTANDING

a. **30rand** will give a time between 0 and 30. Use this command once for Jerome, The result represents the number of minutes that Jerome arrives after 7:00. Use the command again for Nadie. The result represents the number of minutes that Nadie arrives after 6:45.

b. Simulations will vary. Suppose that **30rand** gives 9.93 for Jerome. Then Jerome arrived at 7:00 plus 9.93 minutes or at 7:09.93. Suppose that **30rand** gives 21.52 for Nadie. Then Nadie arrived at 6:45 plus 21.52 minutes or at 7:06.52. Nadie got to school first.

   Note that the random numbers were rounded to two decimal places. If the two students get to school at the same time, students should include more decimal places to break the tie.

c. Simulations will vary. (The theoretical probability that Nadie arrives first is $\frac{7}{8}$ or 0.875.)

INVESTIGATION **4**

Geometric Probability

You can solve some problems similar to those in the previous investigation without a simulation. The method involves drawing a geometric diagram and reasoning with areas. As you work on the problems in this investigation, look for answers to the following question:

*How can you use area models to solve probability problems
when numbers can come from a continuous interval?*

1 Suppose you select two random numbers that are both between 0 and 1.

   a. You want to find the probability that both numbers are more than 0.5. Explain how this problem can be solved using the diagram below.

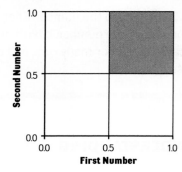

   b. Now suppose that you want to find the probability that both numbers are less than 0.2. Draw a square with sides of length 1 and shade in the area that represents the event that both numbers are less than 0.2. What is the probability that they are both less than 0.2?

   c. Use an area model to find the probability that both numbers are less than 0.85.

2 Suppose you select two random numbers between 0 and 12 and want to find the probability that they both are greater than 7. Use an area model to represent this situation and find the probability.

3 The National Sleep Association estimates that teens generally require 8.5 to 9.25 hours of sleep each night. However only 15% of teens report that they sleep 8.5 hours or more on school nights. (**Source:** www.sleepfoundation.org/article/sleep-topics/teens-and-sleep) Suppose you pick two teens at random and ask them if they sleep 8.5 hours or more on school nights.

   a. Draw a square with sides of length 1 and shade in the area that represents the probability that at least one teen says that they sleep 8.5 hours or more on school nights.

   b. Use your diagram from Part a to find the probability that at least one teen says they sleep 8.5 hours or more on school nights.

Ingram Publishing

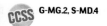
Geometric Probability

In this investigation, students learn to use area models to model chance situations where the numbers are selected at random from a continuous interval. The diagrams will enable students to compute a probability exactly. The work that they do here will prepare them for the Multiplication Rule that they will learn in Course 2 Unit 8, *Probability Distributions*: If events A and B are independent, then $P(A \text{ and } B) = P(A) \cdot P(B)$. For example, in Course 2, students will learn that they can solve Problem 1 Part c using this formula: $P(\text{first number is less than 0.85 and second number is less than 0.85}) = P(\text{first number is less than 0.85}) \cdot P(\text{second number is less than 0.85}) = (0.85)(0.85) = 0.7225$.

1 **a.** The entire square represents all possible pairs of random numbers between 0 and 1. The shaded area represents the event that both random numbers are between 0.5 and 1. The shaded area is $\left(\frac{1}{2}\right)\left(\frac{1}{2}\right) = 0.25$ (or $\frac{1}{4}$ of the entire area), so the probability is 0.25.

b. The shaded area in the diagram below represents the probability that both random numbers are between 0 and 0.2. This area is $\left(\frac{2}{10}\right)\left(\frac{2}{10}\right) = \frac{4}{100}$ of the entire square so the probability is 0.04.

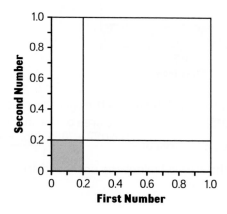

c. The probability that both numbers are less than 0.85 is the ratio of the area of the shaded portion of the diagram below to the entire area or $\frac{(0.85)(0.85)}{1} \approx 0.7225$.

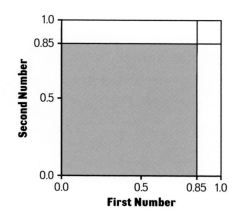

2 The probability that both numbers are greater than 7 is the ratio of the area of the shaded portion of the diagram below to the entire area or $\frac{5 \cdot 5}{144} \approx 0.174$.

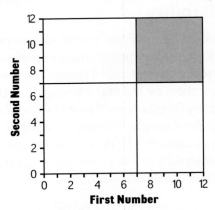

3 **a.**

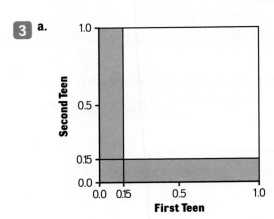

b. The probability that both teens say they get this much sleep (both numbers are less than 0.15) is the ratio of the area of the shaded portion of the diagram in Part a to the entire area or $\frac{(0.15)(0.15) + (0.85)(0.15) + (0.15)(0.85)}{1} = 0.2775$.

Alternatively, the area is 1 minus the unshaded area, or $1 - (0.85)(0.85) = 0.2775$.

Teacher Notes

4 Suppose you select two random numbers between 0 and 1.

   a. Draw a square with sides of length 1 and shade in the area that represents the event that the sum of the two numbers is between 0 and 1.

      i. What is the probability that their sum is less than 1?

      ii. What is the equation of the line that divides the shaded and unshaded regions in your area model?

   b. Draw a square with sides of length 1 and shade in the area that represents the event that the sum of the two numbers is less than 0.6.

      i. What is the probability that their sum is less than 0.6?

      ii. What is the equation of the line that divides the shaded and unshaded regions in this area model?

5 In Investigation 3 Problem 6 (page 567), you used simulation methods to estimate the probability that the breaks of two employees would overlap. The problem conditions were that Al takes a 10-minute break at a random time between 12:00 and 1:00 and Alice does the same thing, independently of Al. Now consider how you could calculate the exact probability using an area model.

   a. On a copy of the diagram below, identify points that correspond to identical start times for breaks by Al and Alice.

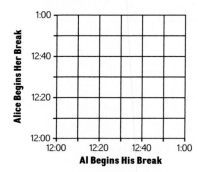

   b. For any given start time for a break by Al, what start times for a break by Alice would overlap with Al's break?

   c. On your diagram, shade in the beginning times of the two breaks that would result in overlap in their breaks.

   d. What is the probability that their two breaks overlap?

6 Imagine an archer shooting at the target shown. The square board has a side length of 6 feet. The archer can always hit the board, but the spot on the board is random. Use geometric reasoning to find the probability that an arrow lands in the circle.

4 **a.** The shaded area in the diagram at the right represents the probability that the sum of the two numbers is less than 1.

    i. The area is $\frac{1}{2}$ of the square, so the probability is $\frac{1}{2}$.

    ii. The equation of the line that divides the regions is $y = -x + 1$.

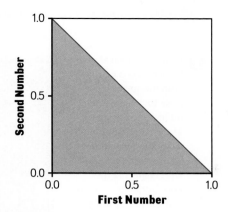

b. The shaded area in the diagram at the right represents the probability that the sum of the two numbers is less than 0.6.

    i. The area is $\frac{1}{2}(0.6)(0.6) = \frac{18}{100}$ of the square, so the probability is 0.18.

    ii. The equation of the line that divides the regions is $y = -x + 0.6$.

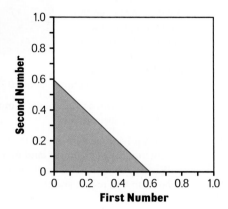

5 **a.** All points along the diagonal represent points where they began their breaks at the same time.

b. For example if Al takes his break at 12:30, his break will overlap with Alice's break if Alice takes her break within 10 minutes of 12:30. These points are represented by a vertical segment between 12:20 and 12:40 above Al's time of 12:30.

c. The shaded region represents any breaks begun by Alice within 10 minutes of the time Al begins his break.

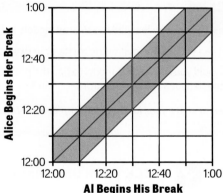

d. The shaded area is 11 of the 36 small squares or $\frac{11}{36}$ of the square, so the probability the breaks overlap is $\frac{11}{36}$. Some students may find the area of the unshaded region and subtract from the whole area to determine this probability. Each unshaded triangle has area $\frac{1}{2}\left(\frac{5}{6} \cdot \frac{5}{6}\right)$. Therefore, the probability that the breaks overlap is $1 - \frac{25}{36}$ or $\frac{11}{36}$.

6 The probability is the area of the circle divided by the area of the square or $\frac{\pi r^2}{s^2} = \frac{\pi \cdot 3^2}{6^2} = \frac{\pi}{4} \approx 0.785$

7 In an old carnival game, players toss a penny onto the surface of a table that is marked off in 1-inch squares. The table is far enough away that it is random where the penny lands with respect to the grid, but large enough that the penny always lands on the table. If the penny lies entirely within a square, the player wins a prize. If the penny touches a line, the player loses his or her penny. A penny is about 0.75 inch in diameter.

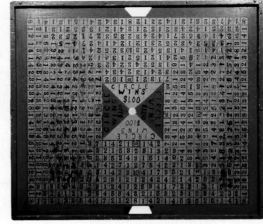

a. In order to win a prize, how far must the center of the penny be from any side of a 1-inch square?

b. Draw a 1-inch square. Shade the region where the center of the penny must land in order to win a prize. What is the probability that the center of the penny lands in that region and the player wins the prize?

SUMMARIZE THE MATHEMATICS

In this investigation, you learned to use area models to find probabilities exactly.

a When can you use the geometric methods in this investigation to find probabilities?

b How would you use an area model to find the probability that two numbers randomly selected between 0 and 5 are both less than 3?

Be prepared to share your ideas and examples with the class.

✅ CHECK YOUR UNDERSTANDING

The midpoint *M* of a 10-inch piece of spaghetti is marked as shown below. Suppose you break the spaghetti at a randomly selected point.

A   M   B

a. What is the probability that the break point is closer to point *M* than to point *A*?

b. What is the probability that the break point is closer to point *A* or point *B* than to point *M*?

Courtesy The Splendid Peasant, Ltd.

7 a. The center of the penny must land $\frac{0.75}{2}$ or 0.375 inches away from any edge.

b. See the diagram at the right. For the center of the penny to be 0.375 inches away from any side, the center must land within a square that is $1 - 2(0.375) = 0.25$ in. on each side. The area of the square where the center of the penny may land is $(0.25)(0.25) = 0.0625$ in^2. Because the bigger square has area 1 in^2, the probability is 0.0625.

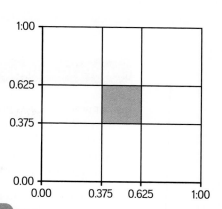

SUMMARIZE THE MATHEMATICS

a The numbers must be selected from a continuous interval for the area models to apply.

b The shaded square on the diagram below represents the probability that both numbers are less than 3. The area of the shaded square is $\left(\frac{3}{5}\right)\left(\frac{3}{5}\right) = \frac{9}{25}$ of the area of the entire square, so the probability is $\frac{9}{25}$ or 0.36.

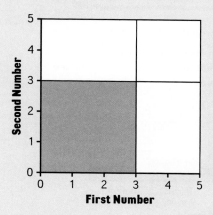

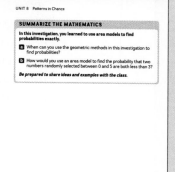
MATH TOOLKIT

Write and answer a probability problem that can be answered using a geometric diagram.

✅ CHECK YOUR UNDERSTANDING

This is an example of geometric probability in one dimension. Let point P be the point midway between points A and M and point P' be the point midway between points M and B. The darker lines below represent the break points that represent a "success."

PROCESSING PROMPT

We worked together to clearly state the following question:

_____

Part a: A ——— P ——— M ——— P' ——— B

Part b: A ——— P ——— M ——— P' ——— B

a. $\frac{3}{4}$

b. $\frac{1}{2}$

APPLICATIONS

1 Suppose that a new plan to control population growth in China is proposed. Parents will be allowed to have at most three children and must stop having children as soon as they have a boy.

a. Describe how to use a coin to conduct one run that models one family that follows this plan.

b. Conduct 5 runs. Copy the following frequency table, which gives the results of 195 runs. Add your results to the frequency table so that there is a total of 200 runs.

Type of Family	Frequency (Before)	Frequency (After)	Relative Frequency
First Child is a Boy	97		
Second Child is a Boy	50		
Third Child is a Boy	26		
Three Girls and No Boy	22		
Total	195	200	1.0

c. Estimate the percentage of families that would not have a son.

d. A histogram of the 195 results in the frequency table is given below. Describe its shape. If you added your results to the histogram, would the basic shape change? Explain your reasoning.

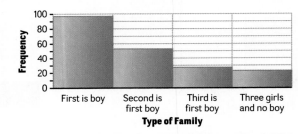

e. How does the shape of the histogram based on 200 runs differ from that of the have-children-until-you-have-a-boy plan from Problem 3 of Investigation 1 on page 553? Explain why that makes sense.

f. What is the mean number of children per family? Will the total population increase or decrease under this plan, or will it stay the same?

g. In the long run, will this population have more boys or more girls, or will the numbers be about equal? Explain your reasoning.

1 **a.** For each birth, flip a coin letting heads represent a boy and tails represent a girl. Flip the coin until a head appears, but no more than three times. Record the number of flips. Repeat many times.

b. Results will vary.

c. From the frequency table in the student text, the estimate of the percentage is $\frac{22}{195}$ or about 11%. (The theoretical answer is $(0.5)(0.5)(0.5) = 12.5\%$.)

d. The shape is skewed right. If you add five runs, it won't change the basic shape.

e. The shape differs only in the right tail. The first three bars should be about the same height as in the other plan, because those bars represent families who first got a boy with the first, second, and third child. The "three girls and no boy" relative frequency should be about the same as the sum of the rest of the relative frequencies in the have-children-until-you-get-a-boy simulation. In both cases, those represent the families who had three girls in a row for the first three children. That is, all bars in the right tail of the histogram from Problem 3 of Investigation 1 are combined into the final bar in this histogram (starting with three girls).

f. From the frequency table in the student text, the estimate of the mean number of children per family is 1.75. (The theoretical mean is also 1.75.) The population will decrease as, on average, two parents won't quite replace themselves.

g. In the frequency table in the student text, there were 173 boys out of the 341 children, or 50.7%. (The theoretical percentage is 50%.) The number of boys and girls should be about equal because they are equally likely on each birth.

ON YOUR OWN

2 Jeffrey is taking a 10-question true-false test. He didn't study and doesn't even have a reasonable guess on any of the questions. He answers "True" or "False" at random.

a. Decide how to use a coin to conduct one run that models the results of this true-false test.

b. Conduct 5 runs. Copy the following frequency table, which gives the results of 495 runs. Add your results to the frequency table so that there is a total of 500 runs.

Number Correct	Frequency (Before)	Frequency (After)
0	1	
1	6	
2	24	
3	57	
4	98	
5	127	
6	100	
7	61	
8	17	
9	3	
10	1	
Total Number of Runs	495	500

c. A histogram of the 495 results in the frequency table is given below. Add your results to a copy of the histogram. Describe its shape and estimate its mean and standard deviation.

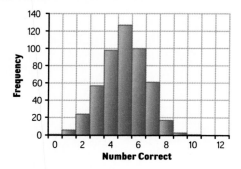

d. On average, how many questions should Jeffrey expect to get correct using his random guessing method? How does this compare to the mean from the simulation?

e. If 70% is required to pass the test, what is your estimate of the probability that Jeffrey will pass the test?

f. Considering the Law of Large Numbers, should Jeffrey prefer a true-false test with many questions or with few questions?

2

a. For each question Jeffrey answers, flip a coin. If the coin is a head, he guessed the right answer. If the coin is a tail, he guessed the wrong answer. Flip the coin 10 times and count the number of heads, which represents the number of answers Jeffrey got right.

b. Results will vary.

c. The shape is approximately normal, the mean is about 5, and the standard deviation is about 1. Recall that because the distribution is approximately normal, one standard deviation either side of the mean captures about $\frac{2}{3}$ of the 495 cases or 330 cases. (The theoretical standard deviation is 1.1.) Adding five more results to the histogram will not change its basic shape.

d. He should expect to get half, or 5 questions, correct. The estimate of the mean from the frequency table in the student text is 4.95 or about 5.

e. A score of 70% or better would be the same as 7 or more correct. Using the results from the frequency table in the text, Jeffrey passed the test only 82 times out of the 495 runs, for an estimated probability of 0.166. Theoretically, the probability he gets 70% or more correct is about 0.17.

f. Jeffrey should prefer a true-false test with few questions. In fact, his best chance of passing the test occurs if there is only one question. Then he has a 50% chance of passing the test (with a score of 100%).

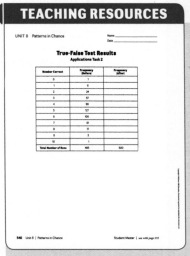

TEACHING RESOURCES

Student Master 540
ⓘ GO DIGITAL

3 The winner of baseball's World Series is the first of the two teams to win four games.

a. What is the fewest number of games that can be played in the World Series? What is the greatest number of games that can be played in the World Series? Explain.

b. Suppose that the two teams in the World Series are evenly matched. Describe how to use a table of random digits to conduct one run simulating the number of games needed in a World Series.

c. Conduct 5 runs. Construct a frequency table similar to the one shown below and add your 5 results so that there is a total of 100 runs.

Number of Games Needed in the Series	Frequency (Before)	Frequency (After)
4	11	
5	21	
6	30	
7	33	
Total Number of Runs	95	100

d. What is your estimate of the probability that the series will go seven games?

e. By how much did your 5 results change the probability that the series will go seven games? What can you conclude from this?

f. A histogram of the 95 results in the frequency table is given below. If you added your results to the histogram, how, if at all, would the basic shape change? Explain your reasoning.

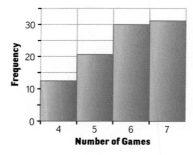

Lesson 2 | Modeling Chance Situations **573**

3 **a.** If one team wins the first four games, the series is over in four games. The greatest number of games is seven, because, if there are seven games, one of the two teams must have won at least four of them.

b. For example, let the digits 0 through 4 represent the first team winning the game, and let the digits 5 through 9 represent the second team winning the game. Count the number of digits needed until one team has won four games. (Don't ignore a digit because it has been used before.)

c. Results will vary.

d. From the frequency table in the text, the estimate is $\frac{33}{95}$ or about 0.347. (The theoretical answer is 0.3125.)

e. Adding five results is unlikely to change the probability very much. You can conclude that 100 runs is enough to get a rough estimate of the probability.

f. The basic shape probably won't change. (Because, theoretically, a 6-game series and a 7-game series are equally likely, the bars for 6 games and for 7 games eventually will be about the same height.)

ON YOUR OWN

Lesson 2 | Modeling Chance Situations   **T573**

g. The following frequency table and histogram give the actual number of games played in each World Series from 1940 through 2011. (There was no series in 1994.) Compare the results of the simulation with that of the actual World Series. What conclusions can you draw?

(**Source:** www.baseball-reference.com)

Number of Games Played in the Series	Frequency
4	12
5	15
6	15
7	29

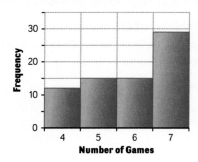

4 For some rock concerts, audience members are chosen at random to have their bags checked for cameras, food, and other restricted items. Suppose that you observe the first 25 males and 25 females entering a concert. Ten of them are chosen to be searched. All 10 are male. You will simulate the probability of getting 10 males if you randomly select 10 people from a group of 25 males and 25 females.

a. When simulating the rock concert situation, why can't you use a flip of a coin like you did in the high school weapons search problem in the Check Your Understanding on page 557 of Investigation 1?

b. Describe a simulation using slips of paper drawn from a bag. How are your assumptions different from those in the Check Your Understanding in Investigation 1 on page 557?

c. How would you conduct this simulation using a table of random digits? Would you select with or without replacement?

Chris O'Meara/AP Images

UNIT 8

g. The shapes are somewhat similar. In both the real World Series and the simulation, a 4-game series is the least likely outcome and a 7-game series the most likely. The mean number of games played, 5.9, is about the same for both the real World Series and the simulation.

However, it looks like the World Series is more likely to go 7 games (0.41) than you would expect from evenly matched teams (estimate of 0.347, theoretical probability 0.3125). We may be tempted to look for an explanation. (If one team is a lot better than the other, we expect the series to last fewer than 7 games. One reason that there are so many 7-game World Series may be the home field advantage, which tends to alternate the team that is more likely to win.) However, students should realize that even if the teams are equally matched on each game, the results from the real World Series will not exactly match that of the simulation. In fact, the World Series data are close enough to the theoretical (when the teams are equally matched) that it is reasonable to attribute the difference to chance alone.

4 a. The sample of 10 people is being chosen from a small group of only 50 people rather than from a large group. This means that the probability of choosing a male does not remain approximately the same as the people are chosen. The number of people observed here is small, so the probability of getting a male changes depending on who has been selected before. With the first draw, the chance of a male being selected is $\frac{25}{50}$ or $\frac{1}{2}$. But if the first student is a male, the probability that the next student selected is a male is only $\frac{24}{49}$ because one of the males has been removed from the group of possible students. Consequently you cannot flip a coin to model the situation except on the first selection.

b. One model is to take 25 cards with the word "female" written on them (or 25 red cards) and 25 cards with the word "male" written on them (or 25 black cards). Shuffle the cards. Deal out the top 10 to represent the people chosen to be searched. Count the number of "male" cards out of the 10.

In both situations, you must assume that the people are selected independently of one another. That is, the people are not selected in groups which might consist of all males or all females. In the simulation in the high school weapons search, the population was so large that you were able to make the assumption that the probability was 0.5 that each student selected to be searched was a male. However, this time you cannot make the assumption that the probability that a male is chosen is $\frac{1}{2}$ on each selection.

c. You could use the pairs of digits 01 to 25 to represent the males and the pairs 26 to 50 to represent the females. Then you would read 10 different pairs of digits to represent those being searched and count the run a success only if all pairs were between 01 and 25. You would select without replacement; that is, you would skip over any pair of digits that had been selected previously in that run.

NOTE This situation is an example of a hypergeometric distribution.

TEACHING RESOURCES

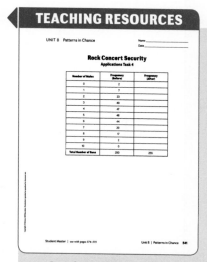

Student Master 541
Ⓘ **GO DIGITAL**

d. Conduct 5 runs of your simulation using the method of your choice. Record the results in a copy of the frequency table below, which shows the number of males selected.

Number of Males	Frequency (Before)	Frequency (After)
0	2	
1	7	
2	23	
3	40	
4	47	
5	48	
6	44	
7	20	
8	17	
9	2	
10	0	
Total Number of Runs	250	255

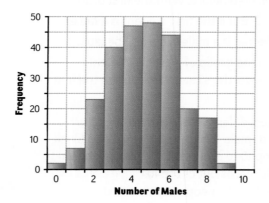

e. What is your conclusion about the probability that all 10 concert attendees chosen to be searched would be male? Is your conclusion different from your conclusion in the high school weapons search problem? Explain.

5 According to the U.S. Department of Education report, *The Condition of Education 2011*, about 70% of high school graduates enroll in college immediately after high school graduation.

a. Describe how to use your random digit generator to simulate the situation of picking a randomly selected high school graduate and finding out if he or she enrolls in college immediately after graduation.

Lesson 2 | Modeling Chance Situations **575**

d. Results will vary.

e. The estimated probability that all ten are male is 0. It is very unlikely that all of the people chosen would be male if selections were made by chance alone. The screeners must be using some criterion that makes males much more likely to be chosen than female. The probability that all ten people chosen to be searched are male is less in this situation than in the case of the large high school.

To see why this is the case, suppose that you already have 9 males and one selection to go. In a large high school, the probability of getting a male for the final selection is 0.5. However, in this situation, the probability is only $\frac{16}{41}$ or about 0.39.

5 | **NOTE** This situation is an example of a binomial distribution.

a. Group the digits by pairs. Let 01 through 70 represent a graduate who immediately enrolls in college. The pairs 71 through 99 and 00 represent a graduate who does not immediately enroll in college. The calculator random number generator command is **randInt(1,100)**.

Alternatively, students could use single digits, letting 1 through 7 represent a graduate who immediately enrolls in college and 0, 8, 9 represent a graduate who does not.

TEACHING RESOURCES

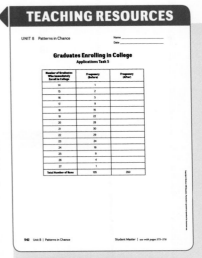

Student Master 542
GO DIGITAL

b. Describe how to conduct one run of a simulation of the situation of selecting 30 high school graduates at random and counting the number who enroll in college immediately after graduation.

c. Conduct 5 runs of your simulation. Copy the frequency table below that shows the results of 195 runs. Add your results to the table.

Number of Graduates Who Immediately Enroll in College	Frequency (Before)	Frequency (After)
14	1	
15	2	
16	5	
17	9	
18	15	
19	22	
20	28	

Number of Graduates Who Immediately Enroll in College	Frequency (Before)	Frequency (After)
21	30	
22	29	
23	24	
24	16	
25	9	
26	4	
27	1	
Total Number of Runs	**195**	**200**

d. Use your results to estimate answers to these questions.

    i. What is the probability that 18 or fewer of a randomly selected group of 30 high school graduates immediately enroll in college?

    ii. Would it be unusual to find that 26 or more of 30 randomly selected graduates immediately enroll in college?

e. Suppose you select a classroom of seniors at random in your school. You find that all 30 of the seniors in the class plan to enroll immediately in college. List as many reasons as you can why this could occur.

6 About 41.8% of violent crimes in the United States are committed by someone who is a stranger to the victim. (**Source:** *Statistical Abstract of the United States,* 2012, page 202, Table 317; www.census.gov/prod/compendia/statab) Suppose that you select four violent crimes at random and count the number committed by strangers.

a. Describe how to use the **randInt** function of your calculator to conduct one run that simulates this situation.

b. Describe how to use the **rand** function of your calculator to conduct one run that simulates this situation.

c. Conduct 10 runs using the calculator function of your choice and place the results in a frequency table that shows how many of the four violent crimes were committed by strangers.

d. What is your estimate of the probability that at least half of the four violent crimes were committed by strangers?

b. Look at 30 pairs of random digits (using a pair again even if it has appeared before) and count the number of pairs that are 01 through 70. **randInt(1,100,30)** would generate 30 random numbers.

c. Results will vary.

d. **i.** From the results given in the frequency table in the text, the estimate of the probability that 18 or fewer of 30 randomly selected graduates immediately enroll in college is $\frac{32}{195}$ or about 0.16.

　 ii. The estimate of the probability that 26 or more of 30 randomly selected graduates immediately enroll in college is $\frac{5}{195}$ or about 0.026. So, yes, this would be quite unusual.

e. Students may give reasons such as you picked an AP or honors class or they may reason that students in your school are more likely to go to college than the national average. Taking all of the students in one class rather than a random sample of all seniors is a bad idea as it is unlikely to give a representative sample.

6 **a.** **randInt(1,1000,4)** will select four integers from 1 to 1,000, inclusive. If the integer is 1 through 418, count that crime as having been committed by a stranger. For example, if the integers are 943, 730, 133, and 378, then two of the four crimes were committed by a stranger.

b. Using the command **1000rand** four times will select four numbers from between 0 and 1,000. Count the number that are less than 418. For example, if the numbers are 567.108, 583.368, 338.072, and 222.775, then two of the four crimes were committed by a stranger.

c. Simulations will vary. A typical table appears below.

Number of Violent Crimes Committed by Strangers	Frequency
0	1
1	3
2	4
3	2
4	0

d. Estimates will vary, but should be based on the simulation in Part c. (The theoretical probability is 0.556.)

7 Suppose that you select two numbers at random from between 0 and 2. Draw a geometric diagram to help find the following probabilities.

 a. What is the probability that both are less than 1.2?

 b. What is the probability that their sum is less than 1?

8 Jerome arrives at school at a random time between 7:00 and 7:30. Nadie leaves independently of Jerome and arrives at a random time between 6:45 and 7:15.

 a. Draw a geometric diagram to help find the probability that Nadie arrives at school before Jerome.

 b. Compare your answers to that obtained in the Check Your Understanding on page 567.

CONNECTIONS

9 You can use random devices other than coins to simulate situations with two equally likely outcomes.

 a. Is rolling the die below equivalent to flipping a coin? Explain.

 One View   **Another View**

 b. How could a regular, six-sided die marked with the numbers 1 through 6 be used to simulate whether a child is a boy or a girl?

 c. How could a tetrahedral die marked with the numbers 1 through 4 be used to simulate whether a child is a boy or a girl?

 d. Identify other geometric shapes of dice that could be used to simulate a birth.

10 Make an accurate drawing of a spinner that simulates rolling a die. Describe the characteristics of this spinner.

11 Refer to your frequency table from Problem 3 from Investigation 1 (page 553).

 a. Make a scatterplot of the ordered pairs (*number of flips to get a "boy", relative frequency*).

 b. What function is a reasonable model of the relationship between *number of flips to get a "boy"* and *relative frequency*?

12 Explain how you can use each of the devices in the situation described.

 a. How could you use an icosahedral die to simulate picking random digits?

7 | **INSTRUCTIONAL NOTE** In this task some students may find the probabilities by computing the areas. Others may use part/whole reasoning considering the 2 by 2 square as the "whole." For example, in Part b rather than computing the area of the triangle and the square, some students may recognize that the square can be subdivided into 8 congruent triangles, one of which is shaded. It would be valuable to discuss these two ways to think about computing the probability. This discussion will help students recognize that sometimes one approach is more efficient than another and also that this type of reflection on solution methods can be helpful when they do other probability problems.

a. The shaded square on the diagram below represents the probability that both numbers are less than 1.2. The area of the shaded square is $(1.2)(1.2) = 1.44$ square units. The area of the full diagram is 4 square units. The probability is $\frac{1.44}{4} = 0.36$. Alternatively, some students might recognize that the area of the shaded square is $(0.6)(0.6) = 0.36$ of the area of the entire square.

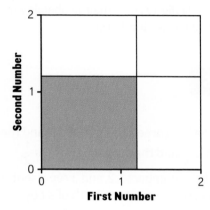

b. The shaded area on the diagram below represents the probability that the sum of both numbers is less than 1. The area shaded is $\frac{1}{8}$ of the area of the entire square, so the probability is $\frac{1}{8}$.

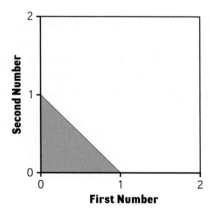

8 **a.** The shaded area on the diagram below represents the probability that Nadie arrives at school before Jerome. The area of the shaded region is $\frac{7}{8}$ of the area of the entire square, so the probability is $\frac{7}{8}$ or 0.875.

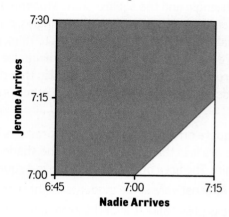

b. Since students only did 10 runs, their probability may be somewhat different than 0.875 (Law of Large Numbers).

CONNECTIONS

9 **a.** Yes. Since the die has three sides marked H and three sides marked T, the probability of H is $\frac{1}{2}$, and the probability of T is $\frac{1}{2}$.

b. For example, let the numbers 1, 2, and 3 represent the birth of a girl and the numbers 4, 5, and 6 represent the birth of a boy.

c. For example, let the numbers 1 and 2 represent the birth of a girl and the numbers 3 and 4 represent the birth of a boy.

d. You could use any of the other dice shaped like platonic solids. Assign half of the sides to represent a girl and half to represent a boy.

10 Draw a circle using a compass or by tracing around a circular object. Through the center of the circle, draw a diameter. On each half of the diameter, measure off three 60° angles. Label the resulting six congruent sections with the numbers 1, 2, 3, 4, 5, and 6. The spinner should have six regions.

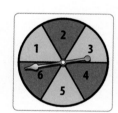

11 **a.** Scatterplots should resemble the plot below.

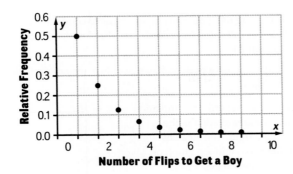

b. A function that models this situation is $y = \left(\frac{1}{2}\right)^x$, where x is the total number of flips and y is the relative frequency.

12 **a.** Label two sides each with the digits 0 through 9. Roll the die repeatedly to generate the list of random digits. If the die is already labeled with the numbers 1 through 20, let the sides 1 and 2 represent the digit 0, the sides 3 and 4 represent the digit 1, and so on.

b. How could you use a deck of playing cards to conduct one run in a simulation of collecting Cheerios tricks? (See Problem 4 on page 559 of Investigation 2.)

c. How could you use a deck of playing cards to generate a table of random digits?

13 Describe how you could use simulation to estimate the area shaded in the diagram to the right. The area lies between the x-axis and the graph of $y = x^2$ on the interval $0 \leq x \leq 1$.

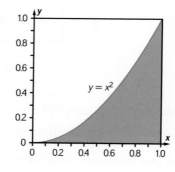

14 In Investigation 4, Problem 3 (page 568), you used geometric probability to find the probability that at least one of the two randomly selected teens says they sleep 8.5 hours or more on school nights. Dana suggested that since the probability for each teen reporting 8.5 or more hours of sleep is 15%, the probability that at least one teen says they sleep 8.5 hours or more is 30%, or 0.3. Use a geometric diagram and what you learned about the Addition Rule in Lesson 1 to explain why Dana's thinking is incorrect.

REFLECTIONS

15 A school is selling magazine subscriptions to raise money. A group of students wants to simulate the situation of asking 10 people if they will buy a magazine and counting the number who will say yes. Jason proposes that the group flip a coin 10 times and count the number of heads since a person either says "yes" (heads) or says "no" (tails). Is Jason's simulation model a reasonable one? Explain your position.

16 Suppose you want to estimate the probability that a family of two children will have at least one girl. You will count the number of heads in two flips of a coin. Does it matter if you flip one coin twice or flip two coins at the same time? Explain your reasoning.

17 The Law of Large Numbers tells you that if you flip a coin repeatedly, the percentage of heads tends to get closer to 50%. This is something that most people intuitively understand:

the more "trials," the closer $\dfrac{number\ of\ heads}{number\ of\ flips}$ should be to $\dfrac{1}{2}$.

a. Jack flips a coin 300 times and gets 157 heads. What is his estimate of the probability that a coin will land heads?

b. Take out seven cards numbered ace, 2, 3, 4, 5, 6, and 7 to represent the seven different tricks. Shuffle them and draw one out. Record the "trick" that you got. Replace that card. Repeat until you have gotten all seven different tricks. Record the number of draws needed.

c. Take out ten cards numbered ace, 2, 3, 4, 5, 6, 7, 8, 9, and 10. These represent the 10 different digits, with the ace representing 1 and the 10 representing 0. Shuffle and draw a card. Record the number you got. Replace that card. Repeat until you get a list of random digits that is as long as you need.

13 Pick two random numbers from between 0 and 1 by using the **rand** command twice. This establishes a point (*first number, second number*) that lies in the square. If it is the case that (*second number*) < (*first number*)^2, then the point falls below the graph of $y = x^2$. Record this as a success. Repeat many times. The proportion of successes out of the total number of runs gives an estimate of the probability a randomly selected point is below $y = x^2$. This is also an estimate of the area below the curve. (The theoretical answer, found using calculus, is $\frac{1}{3}$.)

14 Dana seems to be thinking that the probability at least one of the two teens reports 8.5 or more hours of sleep is the sum P(*first teen reports 8.5 hours or more*) + P(*second teen reports 8.5 hours or more*). This is incorrect because the two events are not mutually exclusive. You must subtract P(*both teens report 8.5 hours or more*) from the above sum. The diagram at the right shows the duplication of probability that occurs.

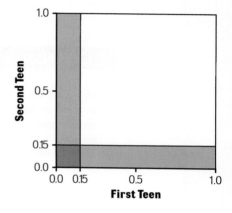

REFLECTIONS

15 Jason's simulation model is not a reasonable one. The probability that a person will buy a magazine is not likely to be exactly $\frac{1}{2}$. Just because there are only two outcomes does not mean they are equally likely.

16 In this particular problem, which amounts to counting the number of heads and tails in two flips of a fair coin, the order of the heads and tails is not important. It does not matter if you flip one coin twice or flip two coins once. In the first method, the student would flip a coin, note whether it was heads or tails, and then flip the coin again and note whether it was heads or tails. At the end, all the student records is the number of heads and the number of tails in the two flips. In the second method, the student flips two coins at the same time and records the number of heads and the number of tails in the two flips.

(Students may convince themselves that the two methods are equivalent by imagining that in the two-coin situation, one coin has a big "1" written on it and the other has a big "2" written on it. Coin "1" corresponds to the first flip of a single coin, and coin "2" corresponds to the second flip of a single coin.)

17 **a.** $\frac{157}{300}$ or about 0.523

> **NOTE** The Law of Large Numbers depends on independence of the trials and on the probability of a success staying constant over all trials. This is true of coin flips.

b. Julie flips a coin 30 times and uses her results to estimate the probability a coin will land heads. Would you expect Jack or Julie to have an estimate closer to the true probability of getting a head?

c. Find the missing numbers in the table below. Do the results illustrate the Law of Large Numbers? Why or why not?

Number of Flips	Number of Heads	Percentage of Heads	Expected Number of Heads	Excess Heads
10	6	60	5	1
100	56	56	50	6
1,000	524			
10,000	5,140			

d. What surprising result do you see in the completed table?

18 When presented with a problem involving chance, how would you decide whether to calculate the probability using a formula, using a geometric probability model, or by conducting a simulation?

EXTENSIONS

19 Suppose a cereal company is thinking about how many different prizes to use in its boxes. It wants children to keep buying boxes, but not get too discouraged. The company conducted very large simulations where all prizes are equally likely to be in each box. It could then estimate quite accurately the mean number of boxes that must be purchased to get all of the prizes. The company's estimates are given in the table below.

Number of Possible Prizes	Mean Number of Boxes Purchased
1	1
2	3
3	5.5
4	8.3
5	11.4
6	14.7
7	18.1

b. Jack, because he flipped more times.

c.

Number of Flips	Number of Heads	Percentage of Heads	Expected Number of Heads	Excess Heads
10	6	60.0	5	1
100	56	56.0	50	6
1,000	524	52.4	500	24
10,000	5,140	51.4	5,000	140

Yes, as the number of flips increases, the percentage of heads is approaching 50%.

d. Even though the percentage of heads in the flips is getting closer to the expected probability of 0.5, the number of heads in the flips gets farther from the expected number of heads.

18 When you have enough information from the problem to either complete a probability distribution table or determine how many outcomes of the total possible outcomes fit the problem conditions, you can calculate the probability using the appropriate ratio $\frac{number\ of\ successful\ outcomes}{number\ of\ possible\ outcomes}$ or the Addition Rule.

When the problem context asks for continuous numerical intervals that can be represented on a number line or a grid, the probability ratio can be calculated as a ratio of length or area measures (that meet the problem conditions) to the length or area of the total geometric diagram.

When the situation is complex and the other methods above are not feasible, simulation should be considered. When the outcomes can be categorized into events and assigned to random numbers produced by dice, coins, random number generators, or spinners, simulation can be used to estimate probabilities.

ON YOUR OWN

a. Examine this scatterplot of (*number of prizes, mean number of boxes purchased*). Find a model that fits these data reasonably well.

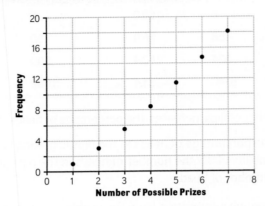

b. Below is an exact formula that can be used to find the mean number of boxes that must be purchased when there are *n* equally likely prizes:

$$M(n) = n\left(1 + \frac{1}{2} + \frac{1}{3} + \ldots + \frac{1}{n}\right)$$

  i. Check the values in the table using this formula.

  ii. What is the mean number of boxes you would have to buy to get all of 20 possible prizes?

20 The card below shows a scratch-off game. There are ten asteroids. Two say "Zap," two say "$1," and the other six name six larger cash prize amounts. All of the asteroids were originally covered. The instructions say:

> *Start anywhere. Rub off silver asteroids one at a time. Match 2 identical prizes BEFORE a "ZAP" appears and win that prize. There is only one winning match per card.*

a. Describe how to conduct one run of a simulation to estimate the probability of winning a prize with this card. Conduct 10 runs of your simulation and estimate the probability.

b. Would the estimated probability be different if the prizes with no match were not on the card?

UNIT 8

19 **a.** Although a line will come close to the points, a line isn't a good model. The points curve up, as can be seen once you draw the regression line on the plot.

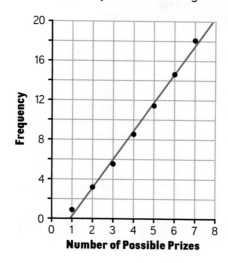

b.

> **NOTE** This formula is based on the observation that if the probability of an event is p, the mean or expected number of trials before it occurs is $\frac{1}{p}$. For example, suppose we have 3 of the 7 magic tricks already. The probability of getting a new trick in the next box purchased is $\frac{4}{7}$. So, on average, we would have to purchase $\frac{1}{\frac{4}{7}} = \frac{7}{4}$ additional boxes to get a new magic trick.)

    i. The numbers in the table are the same as those given by the formula.

   ii. About 72

20 **a.** One easy way to do the simulation is to number the ten asteroids from 1 to 10. Shuffle ten playing cards, the ace through 10, and turn them over one at a time to represent scratching off the asteroids.

  b. No. These prizes don't help you win or lose. There are only four asteroids that matter, the two Zaps and the two matching $1. (Students will learn in the Course 2 *Probability Distributions* unit that the probability of scratching off the two $1 before either Zap is $P(scratch\ off\ \$1\ from\ the\ 4\ asteroids) \cdot P(scratch\ off\ \$1\ from\ the\ remaining\ 3\ asteroids) = \frac{2}{4} \times \frac{1}{3} = \frac{1}{6}$.)

21 Toni does not have a key ring and so she just drops her keys into the bottom of her backpack. Her four keys—a house key, a car key, a locker key, and a key to her bicycle lock—are all about the same size.

a. If she reaches into her backpack and grabs the first key she touches, what is the probability it is her car key?

b. If the key drawn is not her car key, she holds onto it. Then, without looking, she reaches into her backpack for a second key. If that key is not her car key, she holds on to both keys drawn and reaches in for a third key. Do the chances that Toni will grab her car key increase, decrease, or remain the same as she continues? Explain your reasoning.

c. The frequency table below gives the results of 1,000 simulations of this situation. From the frequency table, it appears that the numbers of keys needed are equally likely. Explain why this is the case.

Number of Grabs Toni Needs to Get Her Car Key	Frequency
1	255
2	252
3	236
4	257
Total Number of Runs	1,000

d. Estimate the probability that all four keys have to be drawn before Toni gets her car key.

22 Toni's key selection problem in Extensions Task 21 is one that depends on *order*—the order in which she chooses the keys. One way to model the problem would be to list all the possible orders in which the keys could be selected. An ordering of a set of objects is called a **permutation** of the objects. For example, the six permutations of the letters A, B, and C are:

ABC   ACB   BAC   BCA   CAB   CBA

a. List all of the permutations of the letters A and B. How many are there?

b. List all of the permutations of the letters A, B, C, and D. How many are there?

c. Look for a pattern relating the number of permutations to the number of different letters.

UNIT 8

21 a. The probability that the first key she touches is her car key is $\frac{1}{4}$.

   b. The chance that Toni will grab her car key increases on each grab. For example, if she grabs her house key first, then the chance she will get her car key on the next (second) draw is $\frac{1}{3}$.

   c. Theoretically, all of these outcomes are equally likely. For example, there is no reason why Toni's car key should appear first more often than fourth.

   (If you would like to have students practice simulating this situation, here are the instructions: Let the digit 1 represent the house key, the digit 2 represent the car key, the digit 3 represent the locker key, and the digit 4 represent the bicycle key. Ignore all other digits. Start at a random spot in the random digit table and count the number of digits required until "2" appears. This time, do not count repeats of the digits 1, 3, and 4. For example, starting on the third line of the random digit table,

   51584   712 ...
   Toni gets her car key on the third draw.

   Alternatively, with a calculator use the instruction **randInt(1,4)** and count the number of digits until a 2 appears, ignoring repetitions of the digits 1, 3, and 4.)

   d. $\frac{257}{1,000}$

22 a. AB; BA
   There are two permutations.

   b.
   ABCD   BACD   CABD   DABC
   ABDC   BADC   CADB   DACB
   ACBD   BCAD   CBAD   DBAC
   ACDB   BCDA   CBDA   DBCA
   ADBC   BDAC   CDAB   DCAB
   ADCB   BDCA   CDBA   DCBA
   There are 24 permutations.

   c. The number of permutations of n different letters is $n \cdot (n-1) \cdot (n-2) \cdot \cdots \cdot 3 \cdot 2 \cdot 1$, or $n!$.

d. How many permutations are there of Toni's four keys? What is the probability that all four keys have to be drawn before Toni gets her car key? Compare your answer with that for Extensions Task 21 Part d.

e. How many permutations do you think there are of the letters A, B, C, D, and E? Check your conjecture by using the permutations option on your calculator or computer software. (For most calculators, you need to enter "5 nPr 5". This means the number of permutations of 5 objects taken 5 at a time.)

23 In the history of National Basketball Association finals, the home team has won about 71% of the games. Suppose that the Los Angeles Lakers are playing the Philadelphia 76ers in the NBA finals. The two teams are equally good, except for this home team advantage. The finals are a best-of-seven series. The first two games will be played in Philadelphia, the next three (if needed) in Los Angeles, and the final two (if needed) in Philadelphia.

a. What is the probability that the 76ers will win a game if it is at home? What is the probability that the 76ers will win a game if it is played in Los Angeles? What is the probability the 76ers will win the first game of the series? The second game? The third game? The fourth game? The fifth game? The sixth game? The seventh game?

b. Describe how to conduct one run to simulate this series.

c. Conduct 5 runs and add your results to a copy of the frequency table below to make a total of 200 runs.

Number of Games Won by the 76ers	Frequency (Before)	Frequency (After)
0	9	
1	33	
2	21	
3	20	
4	112	
Total Number of Runs	195	200

d. What is your estimate of the probability that the 76ers win the finals?

e. Suppose that, to cut travel costs, the NBA schedules three games in Los Angeles followed by four in Philadelphia.

    i. Design a simulation to estimate the probability that the 76ers win the finals in this situation.

d. There are 24 orders for Toni's four keys. (Label the keys A, B, C, and D. As figured in Part b above, there are 24 ways of permuting the 4 letters.) The probability that the car key is the last one drawn is $\frac{6}{24} = \frac{1}{4}$. This is close to the simulated probability in Extensions Task 21.

e. There are $6 \cdot 5 \cdot 4 \cdot 3 \cdot 2 \cdot 1 = 120$ permutations.

23 a. The probability the 76ers will win a home game is 0.71 and an away game is 0.29. The probabilities that the 76ers will win each game are 0.71, 0.71, 0.29, 0.29, 0.29, 0.71, and 0.71.

b. For example, randomly generate integers 1 to 100, inclusive, using **randInt(1,100)**. For the games played in Philadelphia (the first, second, and sixth and seventh if needed), let the numbers 1 through 71 represent a win by the 76ers. For the games played in Los Angeles, let the numbers 72 through 100 represent a win by the 76ers. These different representations account for the home court advantage. Alternatively, students could use the **rand** command where a number less than or equal to 0.71 is a win in the first game for the 76ers, etc. Select integers, with replacement, until the 76ers have either 4 wins or 4 losses.

c. Results will vary.

d. Students should look at the ratio of the number of times the 76ers won four games to the total number of games played. The estimate from the table in the text is $\frac{112}{195}$ or about 0.574. (The theoretical probability is about 0.575.)

e. **i.** Students could use **randInt(1,100)** to generate the integers 1 to 100, inclusive. This time, for the games played in Los Angeles (games 1 through 3), let the integers 72 through 100 represent a 76ers' win. For the games in Philadelphia, let the integers 1 through 71 represent a 76ers' win.

ii. Conduct 5 runs, adding your results to those in a copy of the frequency table below.

Number of Games Won by the 76ers	Frequency (Before)	Frequency (After)
0	21	
1	21	
2	22	
3	19	
4	112	
Total Number of Runs	195	200

iii. What is your estimate of the probability that the 76ers win this series?

f. Compare the estimated probability that the 76ers win the series in Parts d and e. Does it matter which way the series is scheduled?

24 Suppose that you break a 10-inch strand of spaghetti at two random places.

a. On a copy of the diagram below, shade in the region that includes the points where a triangle can be formed from the three pieces.

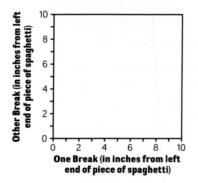

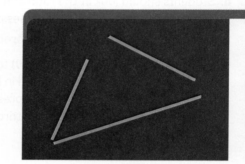

b. Find the probability that a triangle can be formed from the three pieces.

REVIEW

25 Find the number that lies halfway between the two given numbers on a number line.

a. 0.005 and 0.006

b. 0.12345 and 0.123451

c. 0.52 and 0.520001

ii. The frequencies in the table below are close to the theoretical values.

Number of Games Won by 76ers	Theoretical Frequency	Probability
0	21	0.104
1	22	0.110
2	22	0.109
3	20	0.102
4	115	0.575
Total Number of Runs	200	

iii. Using the table above, $\frac{115}{200} = 0.575$. Students' probabilities here and in Part d should be almost the same.

f. The theoretical probability that the 76ers win either series is 0.575, which will surprise most students.

It doesn't matter in what order the four Philadelphia and three Los Angeles games are scheduled, which is a counterintuitive result. Both proposed schemes would give the 76ers the same chance of winning. (The scheme described in Part e might be perceived as unfair by fans and may contribute to the league decision to switch locations after two games.)

24 **a.** Points in the interior of these triangles (not points on the sides) represent breaks that will form triangles. So, the shaded areas in the diagram at the right show places where a triangle can be formed.

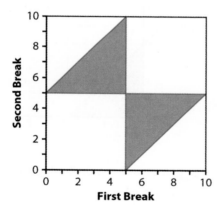

b. The square is formed by 8 triangles of the same size. The probability a triangle can be formed from the three pieces is $\frac{2}{8}$ or $\frac{1}{4}$.

REVIEW

25 **a.** 0.0055

b. 0.1234505

c. 0.5200005

ON YOUR OWN

26 In reporting health statistics like births, deaths, and illnesses, rates are often expressed in phrases like "26 per 1,000" or "266 per 100,000." Express each of the following in equivalent percent language.

  a. Infant mortalities occur in about 7 of every 1,000 live births in the United States.

  b. Each year about 266 out of every 100,000 Americans die from heart disease.

  c. Twins, triplets, or other multiple births occur in about 255 out of every 10,000 births in the United States.

27 Find the area of the shaded portion on each graph below.

  a.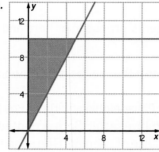

  b.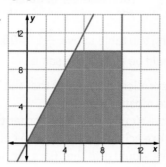

  c.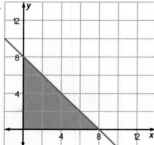

  d.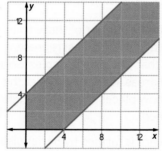

28 Graph each of the following lines on a separate coordinate system.

  a. $y = -2$

  b. $y = 8 - \frac{5}{3}x$

  c. $x + y = 4$

  d. $x = 3$

  e. $y = 2x - 3$

29 John could take any of four different routes to get from his home to school and then take any one of five different routes to get to after-school soccer practice. How many different ways are there for him to travel from home to school to soccer practice? Illustrate your answer using a geometric diagram.

26 **a.** $\frac{7}{1,000} = 0.7\%$ **b.** $\frac{266}{100,000} = 0.266\%$ **c.** $\frac{255}{10,000} = 2.55\%$

27 **a.** $A = \frac{1}{2}(10)(5) = 25$ square units

b. The area is 75 square units.

c. $A = \frac{1}{2}(8)(8) = 32$ square units

d.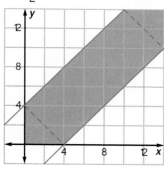

$A = 2(\text{area of triangles at each end})$
$\quad + (\text{area of rectangle in middle})$
$= 2\left(\frac{1}{2}(4)(4)\right) + (\sqrt{32})(\sqrt{200})$
$= 16 + 80$
$= 96$ square units

Alternatively, students might count 24 shaded squares of area 4 square units each to get 96 square units, or they might find the shaded region by subtracting the area of the unshaded triangles from the area of the larger square with side 14 units.

28 **a.**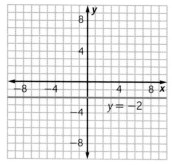

b.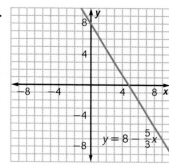

c.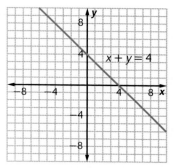

d.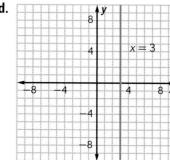

e.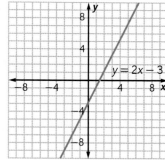

29 John has 4 · 5 or 20 possible routes, as shown in the diagram below. (Students also may illustrate the 20 possible routes using a 4 by 5 rectangle with 20 cells.)

30 For each of the tables of values below:

   i. Decide if the relationship between x and y can be represented by a linear, exponential, or quadratic function.

   ii. Find an appropriate function rule for the relationship.

   iii. Use your rule to find the y value that corresponds to an x value of 10.

a.

x	−2	−1	0	1	2	3	4	5
y	12	5	0	−3	−4	−3	0	5

b.

x	−2	−1	0	1	2	3	4	5
y	1	2.5	4	5.5	7	8.5	10	11.5

c.

x	−2	−1	0	1	2	3	4	5
y	1	2	4	8	16	32	64	128

31 Draw and label two right triangles PQR and WXY for which: $\angle Q$ and $\angle X$ are right angles, $\overline{PR} \cong \overline{WY}$, and $\angle R \cong \angle Y$. Explain as precisely as you can whether or not $\triangle PQR \cong \triangle WXY$.

32 Rewrite each expression in equivalent standard quadratic form, $ax^2 + bx + c$.

   a. $4x(6 - x)$

   b. $(x + 5)(x + 10)$

   c. $x - 2x(x + 3)$

   d. $(7x - 2)^2$

   e. $(3x + 6)(3x - 6)$

   f. $(3x + 5)(x - 9)$

33 Write each exponential expression in simplest possible equivalent form using only positive exponents.

   a. $\dfrac{(2x)^3}{x^5}$

   b. $(-4a^3bc^4)^3$

   c. $(4x^3y)(-6x^4y)$

   d. $3x^{-2}$

   e. $(4n)^{-1}$

   f. $\left(\dfrac{6xy^2}{2y}\right)^3$

   g. $a^{-1}\left(a^3\right)^{\frac{1}{3}}$

   h. $\left(x^4y^8\right)^{\frac{1}{4}}$

34 Rhombus $ABCD$ has sides of length 11 cm.

   a. Could the length of diagonal $\overline{AC}$ be 6 cm? What about 24 cm? Explain your reasoning.

   b. If $m\angle A = 50°$, find the measures of the other three angles.

   c. If rhombus $ABCD$ is a square, find the length of diagonal $\overline{BD}$.

30 a. i. Quadratic function

    ii. $y = x(x - 4) = x^2 - 4x$

    iii. When $x = 10$, $y = 60$.

  b. i. Linear function

    ii. $y = 1.5x + 4$

    iii. When $x = 10$, $y = 19$.

  c. i. Exponential function

    ii. $y = 4(2^x)$

    iii. When $x = 10$, $y = 4{,}096$.

 31 Yes, $\triangle PQR \cong \triangle WXY$.

Since two pairs of angles in the triangles are congruent, the third pair of angles $\angle P$ and $\angle W$ must also be congruent. So, the two triangles are congruent by the ASA congruence condition.

32 a. $-4x^2 + 24x$ **b.** $x^2 + 15x + 50$

  c. $-2x^2 - 5x$ **d.** $49x^2 - 28x + 4$

  e. $9x^2 - 36$ **f.** $3x^2 - 22x + 45$

33 a. $\dfrac{8}{x^2}$ **b.** $-64a^9b^3c^{12}$

  c. $-24x^7y^2$ **d.** $\dfrac{3}{x^2}$

  e. $\dfrac{1}{4n}$ **f.** $27x^3y^3$

  g. 1 **h.** xy^2

34 a. Yes, the diagonal $\overline{AC}$ could have length 6 cm. No, the diagonal could not be 24 cm. By the Triangle Inequality the diagonal must be less than 22 cm.

  b. $m\angle C = 50°$; $m\angle B = m\angle D = 130°$

  c. $BD = \sqrt{11^2 + 11^2} = 11\sqrt{2} \approx 15.56$ cm^2

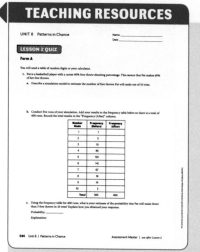

LESSON 3

Looking Back

When outcomes are equally likely, such as those from the roll of a die, you often can calculate probabilities exactly. In this unit, you learned how to write out sample spaces for such situations and to make probability distributions based on them. For more complex situations, you used geometric models to find probabilities or simulation to estimate probabilities. An important feature of your simulation models was the use of coins, dice, spinners, or random numbers to produce random outcomes. Each simulation had the same mathematical characteristics as those of the original problem.

The tasks in this final lesson will help you review and apply key ideas for constructing probability distributions and using simulation and geometric models to solve problems involving chance.

1 Suppose that you roll two octahedral dice, which have the numbers 1 through 8 on each one.

  a. Make a sample space that shows all possible outcomes.

  b. Make a probability distribution table for the sum of the two dice.

  c. What is the probability that the sum is 8? At least 8?

  d. Make a probability distribution table for the absolute value of the difference of the two dice.

  e. What is the probability that the difference is 6? At most 6?

2 Show how to use the appropriate form of the Addition Rule to answer these questions about rolling two octahedral dice.

  a. What is the probability you get doubles or a sum of 7?

  b. What is the probability you get doubles or a sum of 8?

  c. What is the probability you get a sum of 7 or a sum of 8?

Looking Back

1 | **INSTRUCTIONAL NOTE** If students completed Connections Task 10 (page 545), they will have the sample space for a pair of octahedral dice in their notes.

a.

	Second Die							
First Die	**1**	**2**	**3**	**4**	**5**	**6**	**7**	**8**
1	1, 1	1, 2	1, 3	1, 4	1, 5	1, 6	1, 7	1, 8
2	2, 1	2, 2	2, 3	2, 4	2, 5	2, 6	2, 7	2, 8
3	3, 1	3, 2	3, 3	3, 4	3, 5	3, 6	3, 7	3, 8
4	4, 1	4, 2	4, 3	4, 4	4, 5	4, 6	4, 7	4, 8
5	5, 1	5, 2	5, 3	5, 4	5, 5	5, 6	5, 7	5, 8
6	6, 1	6, 2	6, 3	6, 4	6, 5	6, 6	6, 7	6, 8
7	7, 1	7, 2	7, 3	7, 4	7, 5	7, 6	7, 7	7, 8
8	8, 1	8, 2	8, 3	8, 4	8, 5	8, 6	8, 7	8, 8

b.

Probability Distribution for the Sum of Two Octahedral Dice

Sum	Probability	Sum	Probability
2	$\frac{1}{64}$	10	$\frac{7}{64}$
3	$\frac{2}{64}$	11	$\frac{6}{64}$
4	$\frac{3}{64}$	12	$\frac{5}{64}$
5	$\frac{4}{64}$	13	$\frac{4}{64}$
6	$\frac{5}{64}$	14	$\frac{3}{64}$
7	$\frac{6}{64}$	15	$\frac{2}{64}$
8	$\frac{7}{64}$	16	$\frac{1}{64}$
9	$\frac{8}{64}$		

c. $\frac{7}{64}, \frac{43}{64}$

Common Core State Standards

This unit focused on the CCSS domains:

Modeling with Geometry★, G-MG

Interpreting Categorical and Quantitative Data★, S-ID

Conditional Probability and the Rules of Probability★, S-CP

Using Probability to Make Decisions★, S-MD

Plus the Modeling Conceptual Category

NOTE The solutions to Task 1 Parts d and e and Task 2 are on page T587.

3 According to the 2010 Census, about 10% of the adults in New York City are age 20–24.

a. Juries have 12 members. Design a simulation model to determine the probability that a jury randomly selected from the adults of New York would have no members age 20–24.

b. Conduct 5 runs. Add your results to a copy of the frequency table below so that there is a total of 200 runs.

Number on the Jury Age 20–24	Frequency (Before)	Frequency (After)
0	56	
1	73	
2	45	
3	16	
4	4	
5	1	
⋮	⋮	⋮
Total Number of Runs	195	200

c. Add your results to a copy of the histogram below. Describe its shape and estimate the mean.

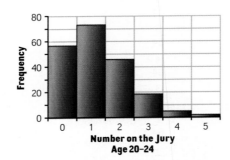

d. What is your estimate of the probability that a randomly selected jury of 12 people would have no members age 20–24?

e. Suppose that a randomly selected jury of 12 people had *no* members age 20–24. Is this evidence that your model, which assumed a probability of 0.10 that a juror is age 20–24, is wrong? Explain your reasoning.

d.

Probability Distribution for the Absolute Value of the Difference of Two Octahedral Dice

Difference	Probability
0	$\frac{8}{64}$
1	$\frac{14}{64}$
2	$\frac{12}{64}$
3	$\frac{10}{64}$
4	$\frac{8}{64}$
5	$\frac{6}{64}$
6	$\frac{4}{64}$
7	$\frac{2}{64}$

e. $\frac{4}{64}, \frac{62}{64}$

2 **a.** $P(doubles \text{ or } sum\ 7) = P(doubles) + P(sum\ 7) = \frac{8}{64} + \frac{6}{64} = \frac{14}{64}$

b. $P(doubles \text{ or } sum\ 8) = P(doubles) + P(sum\ 8) - P(doubles \text{ and } sum\ 8) =$
$\frac{8}{64} + \frac{7}{64} - \frac{1}{64} = \frac{14}{64}$

c. $P(sum\ 7 \text{ or } sum\ 8) = P(sum\ 7) + P(sum\ 8) = \frac{6}{64} + \frac{7}{64} = \frac{13}{64}$

3 **a.** Responses may vary. For example, let the digit 4 represent a juror age 20–24. Let the other nine digits represent a juror who is not age 20–24. Look at the first twelve digits in a randomly selected place in the random digit table or use **randInt(1,10,12)**. Count the number of 4s.

> **NOTE** This situation is an example of a binomial distribution.

b. Responses will depend on the results of each simulation. The frequencies in the table below are close to the theoretical ones.

Number on the Jury Age 20–24	Frequency	Theoretical Probability
0	57	0.282
1	75	0.3765
2	46	0.230
3	17	0.0852
4	4	0.0213
5	1	0.0038
Total Number of Runs	**200**	

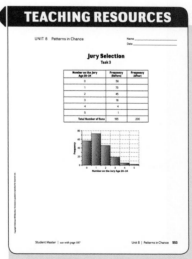

c. The shape is skewed to the right. The mean is at about 1.2. The shape should not change much if 5 results are added.

d. From the frequency table in the text, $P(no\ one\ on\ the\ jury\ age\ 20{-}24) \approx$
$\frac{56}{195} \approx 0.287$. (The theoretical probability is $(0.9)^{12} \approx 0.28$.)

e. No, there is no reason to suspect the model. The chance of getting no members age 20–24 is pretty high, 0.287.

f. A *grand jury* decides whether there is enough evidence against a person to bring him or her to trial. A grand jury generally consists of 24 people. Do you think the probability that a randomly selected grand jury in New York would have no members age 20–24 is more, less, or the same as your answer to Part e? Why?

4 This roller coaster has 7 cars. Ranjana stands in a long line to get on the ride. When she gets to the front, the attendant directs her to the next empty car. No one has any choice of cars, but must take the next empty one in the coaster. Ranjana goes through the line 10 times, each time hoping she gets to sit in the front car.

a. Each time she goes through the line, what is the probability that Ranjana will sit in the front car? Do you think Ranjana has a good chance of sitting in the front car at least once in her 10 rides? Explain your reasoning.

b. Describe how to use random digits to conduct one run simulating this situation.

c. Perform 15 runs. Place the results in a frequency table that lists the number of times out of the 10 rides that Ranjana sits in the front car.

d. From your simulation, what is your estimate of the probability that Ranjana will sit in the front car at least once?

e. How could you get a better estimate of the probability that Ranjana will sit in the front car at least once?

5 Mark arrives at the gym at a random time between 7:00 and 7:30. Susan arrives at a random time between 7:10 and 7:40.

a. Shade in the region on the following diagram that represents the event that Mark gets to the gym before Susan.

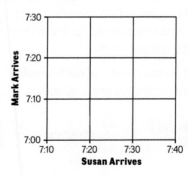

b. What is the probability that Mark gets to the gym before Susan?

c. What is the probability that Susan gets to the gym before Mark?

©Royalty-Free/Corbis

f. The probability is much less because there are twice as many people on a grand jury. Therefore there is a greater chance that a person age 20–24 will be on the jury. (The theoretical probability of no one this age is only $(0.9)^{24} \approx 0.08$.)

4 **a.** Each time, the probability is $\frac{1}{7}$. Yes, because she has 10 chances at something that happens 1 time out of 7. (The theoretical probability she sits in the front seat at least once is $1 - \left(\frac{6}{7}\right)^{10}$ or approximately 0.79.)

NOTE This situation is an example of a binomial distribution.

b. For example, choose 1 to mean that Ranjana sits in the front car, 2 to mean she sits in the second car, and so on. Since the roller coaster has only seven cars, disregard the digits 8, 9, and 0. For each trial, look at the first 10 digits that are not 8, 9, or 0 to see how many 1s appear. The number of 1s represents the number of times she sits in the front car.

c. One simulation resulted in the following table.

Number of Times in the Front Car	Frequency
0	5
1	7
2	2
3	1

d. In the example simulation from Part c, Ranjana sat in the front car at least once in 10 of the 15 trials, so the estimated probability is $\frac{10}{15}$ or approximately 0.67.

e. For a better estimate, perform more runs.

5 **a.** The area shaded below represents the times when Mark gets to the gym before Susan.

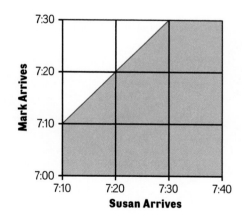

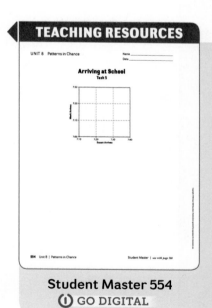

TEACHING RESOURCES

Student Master 554
Ⓘ GO DIGITAL

b. The shaded area makes up $\frac{7}{9}$ of the entire area of the square, so the probability that Mark gets to school before Susan is $\frac{7}{9}$.

c. The probability Susan gets to the gym before Mark is $1 - \frac{7}{9} = \frac{2}{9}$.

SUMMARIZE THE MATHEMATICS

In this unit, you learned how to find exact probabilities using a sample space of equally likely outcomes. You also learned how to use simulation and geometric diagrams to model more complex situations.

a What is a probability distribution?

b What are mutually exclusive events? Give an example of two mutually exclusive events. Give an example of two events that are not mutually exclusive.

c How can you find $P(A \text{ or } B)$ when A and B are mutually exclusive? When they aren't?

d Summarize the steps involved in using simulation to model a problem involving chance.

e Why does simulation not give you an "exact" probability? What does the Law of Large Numbers tell you about how to get a more precise answer?

f Summarize the main ideas involved in using geometric probability models to solve problems involving chance.

Be prepared to share your ideas and reasoning with the class.

 CHECK YOUR UNDERSTANDING

Write, in outline form, a summary of the important mathematical concepts and methods developed in this unit. Organize your summary so that it can be used as a quick reference in future units and courses.

SUMMARIZE THE MATHEMATICS

a A probability distribution is a description of all possible numerical outcomes of a probabilistic situation, along with the probability that each occurs. A probability distribution may be defined by a table or a histogram. (Probability distributions defined by formulas will be studied in Course 2.)

b Mutually exclusive events are events that cannot happen on the same outcome. Being a registered Republican and being a registered Democrat are mutually exclusive events. Being a registered Republican and voting Democratic are not mutually exclusive.

c If *A* and *B* are mutually exclusive, you can just add their individual probabilities. If they are not mutually exclusive, you add their individual probabilities and then subtract off the probability that they both happen on the same outcome.

d 1. Be sure you understand the problem: State it in your own words.

2. Create a model:

- Identify all possible outcomes and determine the probability of each. Decide whether probabilities change from one trial to the next.

- Select a random device and describe how you will use it to conduct one run.

3. Conduct a large number of runs: Record your results in a frequency table and/or histogram. Stop when the shape, center, and spread of the distribution of frequencies stabilize.

4. Give your conclusion.

e A simulation usually will not give an exact answer because probability experiments do not always come out exactly like you expect them to. For example, if you flip a coin 10 times you do not always get exactly 5 heads. However, according to the Law of Large Numbers, the more runs that are performed, the closer you can expect the estimated probability to be to the theoretical probability.

f The main idea in using geometric probability is to represent continuous intervals on a geometric diagram and then identify the region on the diagram that represents "successful" events. The area of the region that represents successful events divided by the total area gives the probability that a successful event will occur.

TEACHING RESOURCES

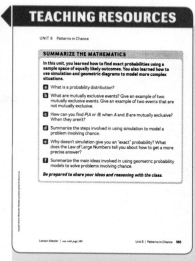

Lesson Master 555
GO DIGITAL

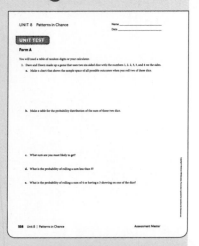

Student Masters 556–557
⟳ GO DIGITAL

Assessment Masters 558–578
⟳ GO DIGITAL

✓ CHECK YOUR UNDERSTANDING

You may wish to have students use the Teaching Master, *Patterns in Chance* Unit Summary, to help them organize the information. Above all, this should be something that is useful to the individual student.

Practicing for Standardized Tests

Each Practicing for Standardized Tests master presents 10 questions in the multiple-choice format of test items similar to how they often appear in standardized tests. Answers are provided below.

Answers to Practice Set 8

1. (d)　　　**2.** (e)　　　**3.** (d)　　　**4.** (c)　　　**5.** (a)

6. (b)　　　**7.** (a)　　　**8.** (e)　　　**9.** (b)　　　**10.** (e)

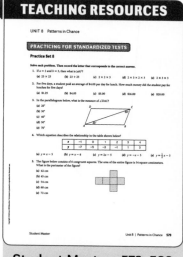

Student Masters 579–580
① GO DIGITAL

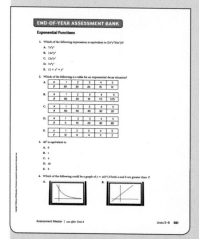

Assessment Masters 581–637
① GO DIGITAL

English	Español

Acute triangle (p. 68) A triangle with three *acute angles* (angles whose measures are less than 90°).

Adjacency matrix (p. 248) A matrix representation of a vertex-edge graph in which each entry of the matrix is the number of edges between the corresponding pair of vertices.

Adjacent vertices (p. 248) Two vertices are adjacent if there is an edge between them.

Algorithm (p. 246) A list of step-by-step instructions or a systematic step-by-step procedure.

Altitude In a triangle, the perpendicular segment from a side to the opposite vertex (p. 389). In a parallelogram, a perpendicular segment from the line containing the base to the opposite side (p. 389). In a prism, a segment that is perpendicular to the planes of both bases (p. 428). In a pyramid, the perpendicular segment from the plane of the base to the apex (p. 428). In a cone, the perpendicular segment from the plane of the base to the vertex. In a cylinder, a perpendicular from the plane of one base to the plane of the other base.

Apex *see* **pyramid**

Approximately normal distribution (mound-shaped) (p. 77) A data or probability distribution that has one peak and tapers off on both sides. Normal distributions are **symmetric**—the two halves look like mirror images of each other.

Triángulo acutángulo (pág. 68) Triángulo con tres *ángulos agudos* (ángulos cuyas medidas son menos de 90°).

Matriz de adyacencia (pág. 248) Representación matricial de un grafo en que cada entrada de la matriz es el número de aristas entre pares correspondientes de vértices.

Vértices adyacentes (pág. 248) Dos vértices son adyacentes si hay una arista entre ellos.

Algoritmo (pág. 246) Lista de instrucciones detalladas o procedimiento detallado.

Altura En un triángulo, el segmento perpendicular de un lado al vértice opuesto (pág. 389). En un paralelogramo, un segmento perpendicular de la recta que contiene la base al lado opuesto (pág. 389). En un prisma, segmento perpendicular a ambas bases (pág. 428). En una pirámide, el segmento perpendicular del plano de la base al vértice (pág. 428). En un cono, el segmento perpendicular del plano de la base al vértice. En un cilindro, la perpendicular del plano de una de las bases al plano de la otra.

Ápice *véase* **pirámide**

Distribución aproximadamente normal (campaniforme) (pág. 77) Datos o distribución probabilística que tiene un pico y que disminuye en ambos lados. Las distribuciones normales son **simétricas**: las dos mitades son imágenes especulares mutuas.

Back-to-back stemplot (p. 98) A stemplot used to compare two sets of data. The center column contains the stem of the data, while the right leaf contains one data set and the left leaf the other.

Base *see* **exponential expression**, **parallelogram**, **prism**, **pyramid**, and **triangle**

Base angles of a triangle (p. 372) Angles opposite the congruent sides of an isosceles triangle. These angles are congruent.

Esquema de tallos consecutivo (pág. 98) Un esquema de tallos que se usa para comparar dos conjuntos de datos. La columna central lleva los tallos de los datos, la hoja derecha lleva uno de los conjuntos de datos y la izquierda el otro.

Base *véase* **expresión exponencial**, **paralelogramo**, **prisma**, **pirámide** y **triángulo**

Ángulos basales de un triángulo (pág. 372) Ángulos opuestos a los lados congruentes de un triángulo isósceles. Dichos ángulos son congruentes.

English

Bimodal distribution (p. 96) A distribution with two well-defined peaks.

Bisector of an angle (p. 385) A ray that begins at the vertex of an angle and divides the angle into two angles of equal measure.

Box plot (box-and-whiskers plot) (p. 109) A statistical graphic in which only the minimum, lower quartile, median, upper quartile, maximum, and outliers are displayed.

C

Categorical data (p. 94) Data that fall into categories such as male/female or freshman/sophomore/junior/senior.

Central angle of a regular polygon (p. 401) An angle whose vertex is at the center of the polygon and whose sides (rays) extend through the endpoints of a side of the polygon.

Chromatic number (p. 275) The smallest number of colors needed to color all the vertices of a graph. (*see* **color a graph**)

Coefficient (p. 157) A number in front of a variable. For example, in the expression $x^2 - 10x + 25$, the coefficient of x^2 is 1 and the coefficient of x is -10.

Color a graph (p. 269) Assign a color to each vertex of a graph so that adjacent vertices have different colors. This may also be referred to as *graph coloring* or *vertex coloring.*

Coloring the edges (p. 282) Assign a color to each edge of a graph so that edges that share a vertex have different colors.

Computer Algebra System (CAS) (p. 54) Software that directs a calculator or computer to perform numeric, graphic, and symbolic mathematical operations required in arithmetic, algebra, calculus, and beyond.

Cone (p. 430) A figure formed by a circular region (the *base*), a point (the *vertex*) not in the plane of the base, and all of the segments joining the vertex to the base.

Español

Distribución bimodal (pág. 96) Distribución con dos picos bien definidos.

Bisectriz de un ángulo (pág. 385) Rayo que parte del vértice de un ángulo y que lo divide en dos ángulos congruentes.

Diagrama de caja (diagrama de caja y patillas) (pág. 109) Gráfica estadística en que sólo se muestran el mínimo, el cuartil inferior, la mediana, el cuartil superior, el máximo y los valores atípicos.

Datos categóricos (pág. 94) Datos que caen en categorías como masculino/femenino o primer año/segundo año/tercer año/cuarto año.

Ángulo central de un polígono regular (pág. 401) Ángulo cuyo vértice está en el centro del polígono y cuyos lados (rayos) se extienden por los extremos de un lado del polígono.

Número cromático (pág. 275) Mínimo de colores que se requieren para pintar todos los vértices de un grafo. (*véase* **coloración de un grafo**)

Coeficiente (pág. 157) Número delante de una variable. Por ejemplo, en la expresión $x^2 - 10x + 25$, el coeficiente de x^2 es 1 y el de x es -10.

Colorear un grafo (pág. 269) Asignación de un color a cada vértice de un grafo de modo que vértices adyacentes tengan colores distintos. Esto se llama también *coloración de un grafo* o *coloración de vértices.*

Coloración de aristas (pág. 282) Asignación de un color a cada arista de un grafo de modo que las aristas con vértices comunes tengan colores distintos.

Sistema algebraico computacional (SAC) (pág. 54) Programas que hacen que una computadora ejecute operaciones matemáticas numéricas, gráficas o simbólicas que se requieren en aritmética, álgebra, cálculo y otros.

Cono (pág. 430) Figura formada por una región circular (la *base*), un punto (el *vértice*) fuera del plano de la base y todos los segmentos que unen el vértice a la base.

English

Congruent figures (p. 370) Figures that have the same shape and size, regardless of position or orientation.

Connected graph (p. 243) A graph that is all in one piece. That is, from each vertex there is at least one path to every other vertex.

Consecutive angles (p. 387) In a polygon, two angles whose vertices are adjacent.

Constant term (p. 157) The term in an algebraic expression in which a variable does not appear. For example, in the expression $x^2 - 10x + 25$, the 25 is the constant term.

Counterexample (p. 451) A statement or diagram that shows that a given statement is not always true.

Converse (p. 380) A statement formed by interchanging the "if"-clause and the "then"-clause of a given "if-then" statement.

Convex polygon (p. 404) A polygon in which no segment connecting any two vertices of the polygon contains points in the exterior of the polygon. Otherwise the polygon is called *nonconvex*.

Convex polyhedron (p. 426) A polyhedron in which no segment connecting any two vertices of the polyhedron contains points in the exterior of the polyhedron. Otherwise the polyhedron is called *nonconvex*.

Cube (regular hexahedron) (p. 427) A regular polyhedron with six congruent, square faces.

Cycle graph (p. 279) A vertex-edge graph consisting of a single cycle—a route that uses each edge and vertex exactly once and ends where it started.

Cylinder (p. 430) A figure formed by two congruent circular regions (the *bases*) contained in parallel planes along with all segments having an endpoint on each base and parallel to the line joining the centers of the bases.

Español

Figuras congruentes (pág. 370) Figuras de la misma forma y tamaño, sea cual sea su posición u orientación.

Grafo conexo (pág. 243) Un grafo que es de una sola pieza, o sea, de cada vértice hay por lo menos un camino a cada uno de los otros vértices.

Ángulos consecutivos (pág. 387) En un polígono, dos ángulos cuyos vértices son adyacentes.

Término constante (pág. 157) Término de una expresión algebraica sin variables. Por ejemplo, en la expresión $x^2 - 10x + 25$, 25 es un término constante.

Contraejemplo (pág. 451) Enunciado o diagrama que prueba que un enunciado dado no es verdadero.

Recíproco (pág. 380) Enunciado que resulta al intercambiar las cláusulas "si" y "entonces" de un enunciado "si-entonces."

Polígono convexo (pág. 404) Polígono en que no hay segmento que una dos de sus vértices y que contenga puntos fuera del mismo. De lo contrario, el polígono se llama *no convexo*.

Poliedro convexo (pág. 426) Poliedro en que no hay segmento que una dos de sus vértices y que contenga puntos fuera del mismo. De lo contrario, el poliedro se llama *no convexo*.

Cubo (hexaedro regular) (pág. 427) Poliedro regular con seis caras cuadradas congruentes.

Grafo cíclico (pág. 279) Grafo que consta de un solo ciclo: un camino que pasa por cada arista y cada vértice solo una vez y que termina donde empezó.

Cilindro (pág. 430) Figura formada por dos regiones circulares congruentes (las *bases*) contenidas en planos paralelos, junto con todos los segmentos que tienen un extremo en cada base y que son paralelos a la recta que une los centros de las bases.

D

Dart (p. 422) A nonconvex quadrilateral with two distinct pairs of consecutive sides the same length.

Data distribution (pp. 75–82) The collection of data values, typically summarized in a table or plotted so that the number or proportion of times that each value occurs can be observed.

Dardo (pág. 422) Cuadrilátero no convexo con dos pares de lados consecutivos que tienen la misma longitud.

Distribución de datos (págs. 75–82) Conjunto de datos típicamente tabulados o graficados de modo que pueda observarse el número o proporción de veces que ocurre cada valor.

GLOSSARY/GLOSARIO

English

Data transformation (p. 124) A change in each value in a set of data such as adding the same constant to each value, taking the square root of each value, or dividing each value by the same constant; often used to change units of measure.

Degree of a vertex (p. 245) The number of edges touching a vertex. If an edge loops back to the same vertex, that counts as two edge-touchings.

Dependent variable (p. 6) A dependent variable is one whose value changes in response to change in one or more related independent variables.

Deviation from the mean (p. 118) The difference between a data value and the mean of its distribution.

Directed edge (p. 262) An edge in a vertex-edge graph with a direction indicated.

Directed graph (digraph) (p. 262) A vertex-edge graph in which all the edges are directed.

Dot plot (number line plot) (p. 76) A statistical graphic where dots that represent data values are plotted above a number line.

Doubling time (p. 314) For a quantity growing exponentially, the time it takes for the quantity to double.

Dual of a tessellation (p. 418) A tessellation obtained by connecting the centers of regular polygons that share a common edge in a given tessellation of regular polygons.

E

Edge (of a vertex-edge graph) (p. 241) Segment or arc joining two vertices in a vertex-edge graph.

Equally-likely outcomes (p. 534) Outcomes that all have the same probability of occurring.

Equation A statement using symbols indicating that two expressions are equivalent.

Equilateral polygon (p. 419) A polygon in which all sides have equal length.

Equivalent expressions (p. 215) Expressions that produce equal output values from all possible equal input values.

Español

Transformación de datos (pág. 124) Cambio de cada valor en un conjunto de datos, como la adición de la misma constante a cada valor, la extracción de la raíz cuadrada de cada valor o la división de cada valor entre la misma constante; se usan a menudo para convertir unidades de medida.

Grado de un vértice (pág. 245) Número de aristas que concurren en un vértice. Los lazos se cuentan dos veces.

Variable dependiente (pág. 6) Variable cuyos valores cambian en respuesta a cambios en una o más variables independientes relacionadas.

Desviación de la media (pág. 118) Diferencia entre un dato y la media de su distribución.

Arista dirigida (pág. 262) Arista de un grafo en que se indica la dirección de la misma.

Grafo dirigido (digrafo) (pág. 262) Grafo en que todas las aristas poseen dirección.

Esquema de puntos (esquema lineal numérico) (pág. 76) Gráfica estadística en que puntos que corresponden a los datos se grafican encima de una recta numérica.

Tiempo de duplicación (pág. 314) Tiempo que tarda en duplicarse una cantidad que crece exponencialmente.

Dual de un teselado (pág. 418) En un teselado dado de polígonos regulares, teselado que se obtiene al unir los centros de los polígonos regulares que tienen una arista común.

Arista (de un grafo) (pág. 241) Segmento o arco que une dos vértices de un grafo.

Resultados equiprobables (pág. 534) Resultados que tienen la misma probabilidad de ocurrir.

Ecuación Enunciado que usa símbolos y que indica que dos expresiones son iguales.

Polígono equilátero (pág. 419) Polígono cuyos lados tienen todos la misma longitud.

Expresiones equivalentes (pág. 215) Expresiones que producen los mismos valores de salida para todos los valores de entrada posibles iguales.

English

Euler circuit (p. 243) A route through a connected graph such that (1) each edge is used exactly once, and (2) the route starts and ends at the same vertex.

Euler path (p. 256) A route through a connected graph that traces each edge of the graph exactly once.

Expanding (p. 221) Rewriting an algebraic expression with parentheses as an equivalent expression that does not contain parentheses.

Exponent (power) *see* **exponential expression**

Exponential decay (p. 323) Process in which change of the dependent variable can be modeled by an exponential function with rule in the form $y = a(b^x)$ where $a > 0$ and $0 < b < 1$.

Exponential expression (p. 304) An algebraic expression in the form b^n, where b and n are real numbers or variables. The number b is called the *base* of the exponential expression, and n is called the **exponent** or the **power**.

Exponential function (pp. 296, 328) A function of the form $y = a(b^x)$ where $a \neq 0$ and $0 < b < 1$ or $b > 1$.

Exponential growth (p. 291) Process in which change of the dependent variable can be modeled by an exponential function with rule in the form $y = a(b^x)$ where $a > 0$ and $b > 1$.

Expression A symbolic representation of a calculation procedure.

Exterior angle of a convex polygon (p. 405) An angle formed at a vertex of the polygon by one side and the extension of the adjacent side.

F

Factoring (p. 221) Rewriting an algebraic expression in an equivalent form as a product of several expressions.

Fibonacci sequence (p. 35) The sequence of numbers 1, 1, 2, 3, 5, 8, 13, 21, 34, ...

Five-number summary (p. 108) The minimum, lower quartile (Q_1), median (Q_2), upper quartile (Q_3), and maximum of a data set.

Español

Circuito de Euler (pág. 243) Camino en un grafo conexo de modo que (1) cada arista se recorre sólo una vez y (2) el camino empieza y termina en el mismo vértice.

Camino de Euler (pág. 256) Camino en un grafo conexo que traza cada arista sólo una vez.

Desarrollo (pág. 221) Volver a escribir una expresión algebraica con paréntesis como una expresión equivalente sin paréntesis.

Exponente (potencia) *véase* **expresión exponencial**

Desintegración exponencial (pág. 323) Proceso en que el cambio de la variable dependiente viene dado por una función exponencial de la forma $y = a(b^x)$, con $a > 0$ y $0 < b < 1$.

Expresión exponencial (pág. 304) Expresión algebraica de la forma b^n, con b y n números reales o variables. El número b es la base de la expresión exponencial y n es su **exponente** o **potencia**.

Función exponencial (págs. 296, 328) Función de la forma $y = a(b^x)$, con $a \neq 0$ y $0 < b < 1$ ó $b > 1$.

Crecimiento exponencial (pág. 291) Proceso en que el cambio de la variable dependiente viene dado por una función exponencial de la forma $y = a(b^x)$, con $a > 0$ y $b > 1$.

Expresión Representación simbólica de un procedimiento de cálculo.

Ángulo exterior de un polígono convexo (pág. 405) Ángulo formado en un vértice del polígono por un lado y la extensión del lado adyacente.

Factorización (pág. 221) Replanteamiento de una expresión algebraica en una equivalente que sea un producto de varias expresiones.

Sucesión de Fibonacci (pág. 35) La sucesión de números 1, 1, 2, 3, 5, 8, 13, 21, 34, ...

Resumen de cinco números (pág. 108) El mínimo, el cuartil inferior (Q_1), la mediana (Q_2), el cuartil superior (Q_3) y el máximo de un conjunto de datos.

English

Frequency table (p. 87) A summary table for numerical data, where typically the column on the left gives the different data values and the column on the right gives the number of times each value occurs.

Function (in one variable) (p. 69) A relationship between two variables in which each value of the independent variable corresponds to exactly one value of the dependent variable.

Function graph The set of points (x, y) on a coordinate grid whose coordinates are related by a function.

Español

Tabla de frecuencias (pág. 87) Una tabla sumarial de datos numéricos, donde la columna de la izquierda lleva típicamente los diversos valores de los datos y la columna de la derecha lleva el número de veces que aparece cada valor.

Función (de una variable) (pág. 69) Relación entre dos variables en que a cada valor de la variable independiente corresponde un solo valor de la variable dependiente.

Gráfica de una función El conjunto de puntos (x, y) en un cuadriculado cuyas coordenadas están relacionadas por una función.

G

Graph *see* **vertex-edge graph, function graph**

Graph coloring *see* **color a graph**

Gráfica *véase* **grafo, gráfica de función**

Coloración de un grafo *véase* **colorear un grafo**

H

Half-life (p. 327) For a quantity decaying exponentially, the amount of time it takes for the quantity to diminish by half.

Height of a figure (p. 389) The length of the figure's altitude. (*see* **altitude**)

Histogram (p. 78) A statistical graphic for numerical data, where the height of a bar shows the *frequency* or count of the values that lie within the interval covered by the bar.

Media vida (pág. 327) Tiempo que tarda en reducirse a la mitad una cantidad que decrece exponencialmente.

Altura de una figura (pág. 389) Longitud de la altura de una figura. (*véase* **altura**)

Histograma (pág. 78) Gráfica estadística para datos numéricos en que la altura de una barra muestra la *frecuencia* o cuenta de los valores que yacen en el intervalo cubierto por la barra.

I

Independent variable (p. 6) Variables whose values are free to be changed in ways that are restricted by the context of the problem or by mathematical restrictions on allowed values. These variables influence the values of other variables called *dependent variables*.

Interquartile range (IQR) (p. 108) A measure of spread; the distance between the first and third quartiles.

Variable independiente (pág. 6) Variable cuyos valores cambian libremente según las restricciones de un problema o por restricciones matemáticas sobre los valores permisibles. Estas variables influyen en los valores de otras variables, las llamadas *variables dependientes*.

Rango intercuartílico (RI) (pág. 108) Medida de dispersión; distancia entre los cuartiles primero y tercero.

English	**Español**
Isosceles triangle (p. 68) A triangle with at least two sides the same length. A side that joins two congruent sides is called a *base*, and the angles that lie opposite the congruent sides are called the *base angles*.	**Triángulo isósceles** (pág. 68) Triángulo con por lo menos dos lados de la misma longitud. Un lado que une dos lados congruentes se llama *base* y los ángulos opuestos a los lados congruentes se llaman *ángulos basales*.

K

Kite (p. 366) A convex quadrilateral with two distinct pairs of consecutive sides the same length.	**Deltoide** (pág. 366) Cuadrilátero convexo con dos pares distintos de lados consecutivos de la misma longitud.

L

Lateral face *see* **prism, pyramid**	**Cara lateral** *véase* **prisma, pirámide**
Linear equation (p. 189) An equation in which expressions on both sides of the equal sign are either numbers or linear expressions.	**Ecuación lineal** (pág. 189) Ecuación en que las expresiones en ambos lados del signo de igualdad son números o expresiones lineales.
Linear expression (p. 216) An expression that defines a linear function.	**Expresión lineal** (pág. 216) Expresión que define una función lineal.
Linear function (p. 150) A function of the form $y = a + bx$ where a and b are real numbers.	**Función lineal** (pág. 150) Función de la forma $y = a + bx$, donde a y b números reales.
Linear inequality (p. 189) An inequality in which expressions on both sides of the inequality sign are either numbers or linear expressions.	**Desigualdad lineal** (pág. 189) Desigualdad en que las expresiones en ambos lados del signo de desigualdad son o números o expresiones lineales.
Linear regression (p. 166) A systematic method of finding linear mathematical models for patterns in (x, y) data sets.	**Regresión lineal** (pág. 166) Método sistemático para hallar modelos matemáticos lineales de patrones en conjuntos de datos de la forma (x, y).
Loop (p. 262) An edge in a graph connecting a vertex to itself.	**Lazo** (pág. 262) Arista de un grafo que une un vértice a sí mismo.

M

Main diagonal of a matrix (p. 248) The entries in a square matrix running from the top-left corner of the matrix to the bottom-right corner.	**Diagonal principal de una matriz** (pág. 248) Las entradas de una matriz que van de la esquina superior izquierda de la matriz a la esquina inferior derecha.
Mathematical model (pp. 162; 240) A symbolic or pictorial representation including only the essential features of a problem situation.	**Modelo matemático** (págs. 162; 240) Representación simbólica o pictórica de un problema que sólo incluye sus características esenciales.
Matrix (plural: matrices) (p. 248) A rectangular array of numbers.	**Matriz (plural: Matrices)** (pág. 248) Arreglo rectangular de números.
Mean (arithmetic average) (p. 84) The sum of the values in a data set divided by how many values there are; the balance point of the distribution.	**Media (promedio aritmético)** (pág. 84) Suma de los valores de un conjunto de datos dividida entre el número de valores; punto de equilibrio de la distribución.

English	Español

Mean absolute deviation (MAD) (p. 140) A measure of variability in a data set found by computing the mean of the absolute values of the deviations from the mean of the distribution.

Desviación absoluta media (DAM) (pág. 140) Medida de variabilidad de un conjunto de datos que se halla calculando la media de los valores absolutos de las desviaciones de la media de la distribución.

Measure of center (p. 83) Numerical summary of the center of a distribution, such as the mean or median.

Medida central (pág. 83) Resumen numérico del centro de una distribución, como la media o la mediana.

Measure of position (p. 104) A number that tells the position of a data value in its distribution, such as a percentile or a deviation from the mean.

Medida de posición (pág. 104) Número que indica la posición de un dato en su distribución, como el percentil o la desviación de la media.

Measure of spread (measure of variability) Numerical summary of the variability of the values in a distribution, such as the range, interquartile range, or standard deviation.

Medida de dispersión (medida de variabilidad) Resumen numérico de la variabilidad de los valores de una distribución, como el rango, el rango intercuartílico o la desviación estándar.

Median (second quartile, Q_2) (p. 84) The value in the middle of an ordered list of data; the 50th percentile. If there are an even number of values, the mean of the two values in the middle.

Mediana (segundo cuartil, Q_2) (pág. 84) Valor central de una lista ordenada de datos; percentil quincuagésimo. Si hay un número par de valores, la mediana es la media de los dos valores centrales.

Median of a triangle (p. 95) The line segment joining a vertex to the midpoint of the opposite side.

Mediana de un triángulo (pág. 95) Segmento de recta que une un vértice al punto medio del lado opuesto.

Mode (p. 94) The most frequent value in a set of numerical data; the category with the highest frequency in a set of categorical data is called the modal category.

Moda (pág. 94) Valor más frecuente de un conjunto de datos numéricos; en un conjunto de datos categóricos, la categoría de mayor frecuencia, la llamada categoría modal.

Mutually-exclusive events (disjoint) (p. 539) Events that cannot occur on the same outcome of a probability experiment.

Eventos mutuamente excluyentes (disjuntos) (pág. 539) Eventos que no pueden ocurrir en el mismo resultado de un experimento probabilístico.

N

Net (p. 426) A two-dimensional pattern consisting of polygons that can be folded along edges to form a polyhedron.

Red (pág. 426) Patrón bidimensional que consta de polígonos que forman un poliedro al plegarse a lo largo de sus aristas.

Nonconvex *see* **convex**

No convexo *véase* **convexo**

Nonperiodic tessellation *see* **periodic tessellation**

Teselado aperiódico *véase* **teselado periódico**

Normal distribution *see* **approximately normal**

Distribución normal *véase* **aproximadamente normal**

***NOW-NEXT* rule** (p. 29) An equation that shows how to calculate the value of the next term in a sequence from the value of the current term.

Regla de recurrencia (pág. 29) Ecuación que muestra cómo hallar el valor del término siguiente a partir del valor del término actual.

English

Español

O

Oblique drawing (p. 433) A way to depict three-dimensional objects that maintains parallelism of lines.

Proyección oblicua (pág. 433) Forma de presentar sólidos, que mantiene el paralelismo de rectas.

Oblique prism (p. 428) A prism in which some lateral faces are parallelograms that are not rectangles.

Prisma oblicuo (pág. 428) Prisma en que algunas caras laterales son paralelogramos que no son rectángulos.

Obtuse triangle (p. 68) A triangle with an *obtuse angle* (an angle with measure greater than 90°).

Triángulo obtusángulo (pág. 68) Triángulo con un ángulo obtuso (uno que mide más de 90°).

Opposite angles (p. 375) In a triangle $\triangle ABC$, $\angle A$ is opposite $\overline{BC}$, $\angle B$ is opposite $\overline{AC}$, and $\angle C$ is opposite $\overline{AB}$. In a quadrilateral $ABCD$, $\angle A$ is opposite $\angle C$ and $\angle B$ is opposite $\angle D$.

Ángulos opuestos (pág. 375) En un triángulo $\triangle ABC$, $\angle A$ se opone a $\overline{BC}$, $\angle B$ se opone a $\overline{AC}$, y $\angle C$ se opone a $\overline{AB}$. En un cuadrilátero $ABCD$, $\angle A$ se opone a $\angle C$ y $\angle B$ se opone a $\angle D$.

Orthographic drawing (p. 432) A way to depict three-dimensional objects by sketching several two-dimensional face-views such as a top view, a front view, and a right-side view.

Proyección ortogonal (pág. 432) Forma de presentar sólidos mediante el bosquejo de varias vistas fisonómicas bidimensionales, como las vistas superior, frontal o derecha.

Outlier (p. 77) A data value that lies far away from the bulk of the other values; for single-variable data, an unusually large or an unusually small value.

Valor atípico (pág. 77) Dato que está muy alejado del grueso de los otros valores; para datos de una variable, un valor inusualmente grande o inusualmente pequeño.

P

P(A and B) (p. 540) The probability that A and B both happen on the same outcome.

P(A y B) (pág. 540) Probabilidad que A y B ocurran ambos en el mismo resultado.

P(A or B) (p. 540) The probability that A or B occurs.

P(A o B) (pág. 540) Probabilidad de que ocurra A o B.

Parabola (p. 470) The shape of the graph of a quadratic function.

Parábola (pág. 470) La forma de la gráfica de una función cuadrática.

Parallel lines (p. 177) Lines that are coplanar and do not intersect.

Rectas paralelas (pág. 177) Rectas coplanarias que no se intersecan.

Parallel planes Planes that do not intersect.

Planos paralelos Planos que no se intersecan.

Parallelogram (pp. 365, 389) A quadrilateral with opposite sides the same length. Any side may be designated the *base*, and an *altitude* to that base is a perpendicular segment from the line containing the base to the opposite side.

Paralelogramo (págs. 365, 389) Cuadrilátero con lados opuestos de la misma longitud. Cualquier lado puede designarse como la *base* y la *altura* correspondiente es el segmento perpendicular trazado de la recta que contiene la base al lado opuesto.

Percentile (p. 104) A way of describing the position of a value in a distribution. The 60th percentile, for example, is the value that separates the smallest 60% of the data values from the largest 40%.

Percentil (pág. 104) Forma de describir la posición de un valor en una distribución. El percentil sexagésimo, por ejemplo, es el valor que separa el 60% inferior de los datos del 40% superior de los mismos.

English

Periodic tessellation (p. 421) A tessellation that fits exactly on itself when translated in different directions. Such a tessellation has translation symmetry. A tessellation that does not have any translation symmetry is called *nonperiodic*.

Permutation (p. 581) A rearrangement of a finite set of objects.

Perpendicular bisector of a segment (p. 374) A line or a line segment that is perpendicular to a segment and contains its midpoint.

Perpendicular lines (p. 396) Lines that intersect to form a right angle (an angle with measure of 90°).

Planar graph (p. 278) A vertex-edge graph that can be drawn in the plane so that edges intersect only at the vertices.

Polygon (p. 398) A closed figure in a plane, formed by connecting line segments (sides) endpoint-to-endpoint (vertices) with each segment meeting exactly two other segments. Polygons with four, five, six, seven, and eights sides are called quadrilaterals, pentagons, hexagons, septagons, and octagons respectively. An *n*-gon is a polygon with *n* sides.

Polyhedron (*plural:* **polyhedra**) (p. 426) A three-dimensional counterpart of a polygon, made up of a set of polygons that encloses a single region of space. Exactly two polygons (faces) meet at each edge and three or more edges meet at each vertex.

Prism (p. 428) A polyhedron with two congruent polygonal faces, called *bases*, contained in parallel planes, and joined by parallelogram faces called *lateral faces*.

Probability distribution (p. 534) A description of all possible numerical outcomes of a random situation, along with the probability that each occurs; may be in table, formula, or graphical form.

Pyramid (p. 428) A polyhedron in which all but one of the faces must be triangular and share a common vertex. The triangular faces are called *lateral faces*, and the *apex* is the vertex that is common to the lateral faces. The *base* is the face that does not contain the apex.

Español

Teselado periódico (pág. 421) Teselado que encaja perfectamente en sí mismo cuando se traslada en diversas direcciones. Tal teselado posee simetría de traslación. Un teselado que carece de tal simetría se llama *aperiódico*.

Permutación (pág. 581) Una reordenación de un conjunto finito de objetos.

Mediatriz de un segmento (pág. 374) Recta o segmento de recta perpendicular a un segmento y que contiene su punto medio.

Rectas perpendiculares (pág. 396) Rectas que se intersecan en ángulo recto (uno que mide 90°).

Grafo planar (pág. 278) Grafo que puede trazarse en el plano de modo que sus aristas se intersequen sólo en los vértices.

Polígono (pág. 398) Figura cerrada planar, que consta de segmentos de recta (los lados), unidos extremo a extremo (los vértices) y cada segmento sólo interseca a otros dos segmentos. Los polígonos de cuatro, cinco, seis, siete y ocho lados se llaman cuadriláteros, pentágonos, hexágonos, heptágonos y octágonos, respectivamente. Un *n*ágono es un polígono de *n* lados.

Poliedro (pág. 426) Homólogo tridimensional de un polígono, compuesto por un conjunto de polígonos que encierran una sola región del espacio. Sólo se intersecan dos polígonos (caras) en cada arista y tres o más aristas concurren en cada vértice.

Prisma (pág. 428) Poliedro con dos caras poligonales congruentes llamadas *bases*, contenidas en planos paralelos y unidas por caras que son paralelogramos llamadas *caras laterales*.

Distribución probabilística (pág. 534) Descripción de todos los resultados numéricos posibles de una situación aleatoria, junto con la probabilidad de cada uno; puede darse en una tabla, fórmula o gráfica.

Pirámide (pág. 428) Poliedro en que todas las caras, salvo una, son triangulares y tienen un vértice común. Las caras triangulares se llaman *caras laterales* y el *ápice* es el vértice común a todas ellas. La *base* es la cara que no contiene el ápice.

English	Español

Q

Quadratic equation (p. 511) An equation in which expressions on both sides of the equal sign are either numbers, linear expressions, or quadratic expressions and at least one of those expressions is quadratic.

Quadratic expression (p. 494) An expression that defines a quadratic function.

Quadratic function (p. 470) A function of the form $y = ax^2 + bx + c$ where a, b, and c are real numbers and $a \neq 0$.

Quartile, lower (first quartile, Q_1) (p. 108) The value that divides the ordered list of data into the smallest one-fourth and the largest three-fourths; the median of the smaller half of the values; the 25th percentile.

Quartile, upper (third quartile, Q_3) (p. 108) The value that divides the ordered list of data into the smallest three-fourths and the largest one-fourth; the median of the larger half of the values; the 75th percentile.

Ecuación cuadrática (pág. 511) Ecuación con por lo menos una expresión cuadrática y en la cual las expresiones en ambos lados del signo de igualdad son números, expresiones lineales o expresiones cuadráticas.

Expresión cuadrática (pág. 494) Expresión que define una función cuadrática.

Función cuadrática (pág. 470) Función de la forma $y = ax^2 + bx + c$, donde a, b, c son números reales y $a \neq 0$.

Cuartil inferior (primer cuartil, Q_1) (pág. 108) Valor que divide una lista ordenada de datos en el cuarto inferior y los tres cuartos superiores; mediana de la mitad inferior de los valores; percentil vigésimo quinto.

Cuartil superior (tercer cuartil, Q_3) (pág. 108) Valor que divide una lista ordenada de datos en los tres cuartos inferiores y el cuarto superior; mediana de la mitad superior de los valores; percentil septuagésimo quinto.

R

Random digit (p. 558) A digit selected from 0, 1, 2, 3, 4, 5, 6, 7, 8, 9 in a way that makes each of the digits equally likely to be chosen (has probability $\frac{1}{10}$); successive random digits should be independent, which means that if you know what random digits have already been selected, each digit from 0 through 9 still has probability $\frac{1}{10}$ of being the next digit.

Range (p. 77) A measure of spread; the difference between the largest value and the smallest value in a data set.

Rate of change (p. 155) The ratio of change in value of a dependent variable to change in value of a corresponding independent variable.

Rectangle A parallelogram with one right angle.

Rectangular distribution (uniform) (p. 96) A distribution where all values in intervals of equal length are equally likely to occur.

Dígito aleatorio (pág. 558) Dígito escogido de 0, 1, 2, 3, 4, 5, 6, 7, 8, 9, de modo que cada uno tenga la misma probabilidad de elegirse que cualquier otro (tiene probabilidad $\frac{1}{10}$); los dígitos aleatorios consecutivos deben ser independientes, o sea, si conoces los dígitos aleatorios ya escogidos, cada dígito de 0 a 9 aún tiene $\frac{1}{10}$ de probabilidad de escogerse como el dígito siguiente.

Rango (pág. 77) Medida de dispersión; diferencia entre los valores máximo y mínimo de un conjunto de datos.

Tasa de cambio (pág. 155) La razón de cambio en valor de una variable dependiente al cambio en valor de la variable independiente correspondiente.

Rectángule Un paralelogramo con un ángulo recto.

Distribución rectangular (uniforme) (pág. 96) Distribución en que todos los valores en intervalos de la misma longitud son equiprobables.

English

Reflection symmetry (p. 401) In two dimensions, a figure has reflection symmetry if there is a line (called the *line of symmetry*) that divides the figure into mirror-image halves. Also called *mirror symmetry*. In three dimensions, a figure has reflection symmetry if there is a plane (called the *symmetry plane*) that divides the figure into mirror-image halves. Also called *plane symmetry*.

Regular dodecahedron (p. 441) A regular polyhedron with twelve congruent, regular pentagonal faces.

Regular hexahedron *see* **cube**

Regular icosahedron (p. 441) A regular polyhedron with twenty congruent, equilateral triangular faces.

Regular octahedron (p. 441) A regular polyhedron with eight congruent, equilateral triangular faces.

Regular polygon (p. 400) A polygon in which all sides are congruent and all angles are congruent.

Regular polyhedron (platonic solid) (p. 439) A polyhedron in which all faces are congruent, regular polygons, and the arrangement of faces and edges is the same at each vertex.

Regular tessellation (p. 409) A tessellation that consists of repeated copies of a single regular polygon.

Regular tetrahedron (equilateral triangular pyramid) (p. 441) A regular polyhedron with four congruent, equilateral triangular faces.

Relative frequency histogram (p. 79) A histogram that shows the proportion or percentage that fall into the interval covered by each bar, rather than the frequency or count.

Relative frequency table (p. 100) A summary table for numerical data, where typically the column on the left gives the different data values and the column on the right gives the proportion (*relative frequency*) of measurements that have that value.

Resistant to outliers (less sensitive to outliers) (p. 86) Condition where a summary statistic does not change much when an outlier is removed from a set of data.

Español

Simetría de reflexión (pág. 401) En dos dimensiones, una figura posee simetría de reflexión si hay una recta (el *eje de simetría*) que la divide en mitades especulares. También llamada *simetría especular*. En tres dimensiones, una figura posee simetría de reflexión si hay un plano (el *plano de simetría*) que la divide en mitades especulares. También llamada *simetría con respecto a un plano*.

Dodecaedro regular (pág. 441) Poliedro regular con doce caras pentagonales regulares congruentes.

Hexaedro regular *véase* **cubo**

Icosaedro regular (pág. 441) Poliedro regular con veinte caras triangulares equiláteras congruentes.

Octaedro regular (pág. 441) Poliedro regular con ocho caras triangulares equiláteras congruentes.

Polígono regular (pág. 400) Polígono cuyos lados son todos congruentes y cuyos ángulos son todos congruentes.

Poliedro regular (sólido platónico) (pág. 439) Poliedro cuyas caras son todas polígonos regulares congruentes y la disposición de caras y aristas en cada vértice es la misma.

Teselado regular (pág. 409) Teselado que consta de copias de un solo polígono regular.

Tetraedro regular (pirámide triangular equilátera) (pág. 441) Poliedro regular con cuatro caras triangulares equiláteras congruentes.

Histograma de frecuencias relativas (pág. 79) Histograma que muestra la proporción o porcentaje que cae en el intervalo cubierto por cada barra, en vez de la frecuencia o cuenta.

Tabla de frecuencias relativas (pág. 100) Tabla sumarial de datos numéricos, donde la columna de la izquierda lleva típicamente los diversos valores de los datos y la columna de la derecha lleva la proporción (*frecuencia relativa*) de las medidas que tienen dicho valor.

Resistencia a los valores atípicos (menos susceptible a los valores atípicos) (pág. 86) Condición en que una estadística sumarial no cambia mucho cuando se elimina un valor atípico de un conjunto de datos.

English	Español
Rhombus (p. 366) A quadrilateral with all four sides of equal length.	**Rombo** (pág. 366) Cuadrilátero con cuatro lados que son de longitudes iguales.
Right triangle (p. 45) A triangle with a *right angle* (an angle with measure of 90°). The side opposite the right angle is the *hypotenuse*. The other two sides are the *legs*.	**Triángulo rectángulo** (pág. 45) Triángulo con un *ángulo recto* (ángulo que mide 90°). El lado opuesto al ángulo recto se llama *hipotenusa* y los otros dos lados son los *catetos*.
Rigid shapes (p. 366) Shapes that cannot flex when pressure is applied.	**Formas rígidas** (pág. 366) Formas que no se pueden doblar al aplicárseles presión.
Rotational symmetry (p. 401) In two dimensions, a figure has rotational symmetry if there is a point (called the *center of rotation*) about which the figure can be turned less than 360° in such a way that the rotated figure appears in exactly the same position as the original figure. In three dimensions, a figure has rotational symmetry if there is a line (called the *axis of symmetry*) about which the figure can be turned less than 360° in such a way that the rotated figure appears in exactly the same position as the original figure.	**Simetría de rotación** (pág. 401) En dos dimensiones, una figura posee simetría de rotación si hay un punto (el *centro de la rotación*) alrededor del cual la figura puede girar en menos de 360° de modo que la figura girada aparece en la misma posición que la figura original. En tres dimensiones, una figura posee simetría de rotación si hay una recta (el *eje de simetría*) alrededor de la cual la figura puede girar en menos de 360° de modo que la figura girada aparece en la misma posición que la figura original.
Row sum of a matrix (p. 249) The sum of the numbers in a row of a matrix.	**Suma de fila de una matriz** (pág. 249) Suma de las entradas de la fila de una matriz.
Run (trial) (p. 553) One repetition of a simulation.	**Prueba** (pág. 553) Una repetición de un simulacro.

S

English	Español
Sample space (p. 534) The set of all possible outcomes of a chance situation.	**Espacio muestral** (pág. 534) Conjunto de todos los resultados posibles de una situación probabilística.
Scalene triangle (p. 68) A triangle with no two sides of equal length.	**Triángulo escaleno** (pág. 68) Triángulo sin ningún par de lados de la misma longitud.
Scatterplot (p. 5) A plot on a coordinate grid of the points whose (x, y) coordinates correspond to related data values of two variables.	**Gráfica de dispersión** (pág. 5) Gráfica en un cuadriculado de los puntos (x, y) cuyas coordenadas corresponden a datos relacionados de dos variables.
Schlegel diagram (p. 449) A vertex-edge graph resulting from "compressing" a three-dimensional object down into two dimensions.	**Diagrama de Schlegel** (pág. 449) Grafo que resulta de "comprimir" a dos dimensiones un objeto tridimensional.
Semiregular polyhedron (p. 442) A polyhedron whose faces are congruent copies of two or more different regular polygons and whose faces and edges have the same arrangement at each vertex.	**Poliedro semirregular** (pág. 442) Poliedro cuyas caras son copias congruentes de dos o más polígonos regulares distintos y cuyas caras y aristas poseen la misma disposición en cada vértice.
Semiregular tessellation (p. 410) A tessellation of two or more regular polygons that has the same arrangement of polygons at each vertex.	**Teselado semirregular** (pág. 410) Teselado de dos o más polígonos regulares que posee la misma disposición de polígonos en cada vértice.

GLOSSARY/GLOSARIO

English

Sensitive to outliers (p. 86) Condition where a summary statistic changes quite a bit when an outlier is removed from a set of data.

Simulation (p. 553) Creating a mathematical model that copies (simulates) a real-life situation's essential characteristics.

Single-variable data (p. 75) Data where a single measurement or count is taken on each object of study, such as height of each person or age of each person.

Skewed distribution (p. 77) A distribution that has a tail stretched either towards the larger values (*skewed right*) or towards the smaller values (*skewed left*).

Slope-intercept form (p. 160) A linear function with rule in the form $y = mx + b$ is said to be written in slope-intercept form because the value of m indicates the slope of the graph and the value of b indicates the y-intercept of the graph.

Slope of a line (p. 155) Ratio of change in y-coordinates to change in x-coordinates between any two points on the line; $\frac{\text{change in } y}{\text{change in } x}$ or $\frac{\Delta y}{\Delta x}$; indicates the direction and steepness of a line.

Solve (an equation, inequality, or system of equations) (p. 189) To find values of the variable(s) that make the statement(s) true.

Speed (p. 11) When a person or object moves a distance d in a time t, the quotient $\frac{d}{t}$ gives the average speed of the motion. The units of speed are given as "distance per unit of time."

Spreadsheet (p. 32) A spreadsheet is a two-dimensional grid of cells in which numerical data or words can be stored. Numerical values in the cells of a spreadsheet can be related by formulas, so that the entry in one cell can be calculated from values in other cells.

Square A rhombus with one right angle.

Square root (p. 335) If r is a number for which $r^2 = n$, then r is called a square root of n. Every positive number n has two square roots, denoted with the radical forms $\sqrt{n}$ and $-\sqrt{n}$.

Español

Susceptible a los valores atípicos (pág. 86) Condición en que una estadística sumarial cambia bastante cuando se elimina un valor atípico de un conjunto de datos.

Simulacro (pág. 553) Modelo matemático que copia (simula) las características esenciales de una situación concreta.

Datos de una sola variable (pág. 75) Datos en que se ejecuta una sola medida o cuenta en cada objeto de estudio, como la estatura o la edad de una persona.

Distribución asimétrica (pág. 77) Distribución que posee una *cola* extendida ya sea hacia los valores más grandes (*asimétrica derecha*) o hacia los valores más pequeños (*asimétrica izquierda*).

Forma pendiente-intersección (pág. 160) Una función lineal de la forma $y = mx + b$ se dice que está escrita en la forma pendiente-intersección porque m es la pendiente de la gráfica y b es la intersección y de la misma.

Pendiente de una recta (pág. 155) Razón del cambio en las coordenadas y al cambio en las coordenadas x entre dos puntos de una recta; $\frac{\text{cambio en } y}{\text{cambio en } x}$ o $\frac{\Delta y}{\Delta x}$; indica la dirección e inclinación de la recta.

Solución (de una ecuación, desigualdad o sistema de ecuaciones) (pág. 189) Calcular valores de la variable o variables que las satisfagan.

Rapidez (pág. 11) Cuando una persona o un cuerpo se desplaza una distancia d en un tiempo t, el cociente $\frac{d}{t}$ da la rapidez media del movimiento. Las unidades de rapidez son "distancia por unidad de tiempo."

Hojas de cálculos (pág. 32) Cuadriculado bidimensional de celdas en que pueden almacenarse datos numéricos o palabras. Los valores numéricos en una hoja de cálculos pueden estar relacionados por fórmulas, de modo que la entrada en una celda puede calcularse de los valores en otras celdas.

Cuadrado Un rombo con un ángulo recto.

Raíz cuadrada (pág. 335) Si r es un número que cumple $r^2 = n$, r se llama una raíz cuadrada de n. Todo número positivo r posee dos raíces cuadradas, designadas por los radicales $\sqrt{n}$ y $-\sqrt{n}$.

English

Standard deviation (*s*) (p. 116) A useful measure of spread; based on the sum of the squared deviations from the mean; in a normal distribution about 68% of the values lie no more than one standard deviation from the mean.

Stemplot (stem-and-leaf plot) (p. 97) A statistical display using certain digits (such as the tens place) as the "stem" and the remaining digit or digits (such as the ones place) as "leaves."

Summary statistic (p. 77) A numerical summary of the values in a distribution. For example, the mean, median, or range.

Symmetry plane (mirror plane) *see* **reflection symmetry**

System of equations (p. 199) Two or more equations. The *solution of a system* is the set of solutions that satisfy each equation in the system.

T

Tessellation (tiling) (p. 408) Repeated copies of one or more shapes so as to completely cover a planar region without overlaps or gaps.

Translation symmetry (p. 408) A pattern has translation symmetry if it coincides with itself under some translation (slide).

Triangle (p. 389) A polygon with three sides. A *base* of a triangle is the side of the triangle that is perpendicular to an altitude.

Triangulate (p. 366) To divide a polygon into a set of nonoverlapping triangles where the vertices of the triangles are the vertices of the polygon.

V

Variability (p. 103) The spread in the values in a distribution. (*see* **measure of spread**)

Variable A quantity that changes. Variables are commonly represented by letters like *x, y, z, s,* or *t*. (*see* **dependent variable** and **independent variable**)

Español

Desviación estándar (pág. 116) Medida útil de dispersión; se basa en la suma de las desviaciones al cuadrado de la media; en una distribución normal, cerca del 68% de los valores yacen a no más de una desviación estándar de la media.

Diagrama de tallos (diagrama de tallo y hojas) (pág. 97) Presentación estadística en que se usan ciertos dígitos (las decenas, por ejemplo) como los "tallos" y el dígito o dígitos restantes (las unidades, por ejemplo) como "las hojas."

Estadística sumarial (pág. 77) Resumen numérico de los valores de una distribución. Por ejemplo, la media, la mediana o el rango.

Plano de simetría (plano especular) *véase* **simetría de reflexión**

Sistema de ecuaciones (pág. 199) Dos o más ecuaciones. La *solución de un sistema* es el conjunto de soluciones que satisfacen cada ecuación del sistema.

Teselado (embaldosado) (pág. 408) Copias repetidas de una o más formas que cubren una región plana completamente sin traslapos o espacios.

Simetría de traslación (pág. 408) Un patrón posee simetría de traslación si coincide consigo mismo bajo alguna traslación (deslizamiento).

Triángulo (pág. 389) Polígono con tres lados. Una *base* de un triángulo es un lado del mismo el cual es perpendicular a una altura.

Triangulación (pág. 366) División de un polígono en un conjunto de triángulos que no se traslapan y en que los vértices de los triángulos son los del polígono.

Variabilidad (pág. 103) Dispersión de los valores de una distribución. (*véase* **medida de dispersión**)

Variable Cantidad que cambia. Se representan en general por letras como *x, y, z, s* o *t*. (*véanse* **variable dependiente** y **variable independiente**)

English	Español

Vertex (*plural:* **vertices**) (p. 241) A point where edges of a vertex-edge graph meet. Also, a point where two sides of a polygon meet.

Vértice (pág. 241) Punto al que concurren aristas de un grafo. También, punto al que concurren dos lados de un polígono.

Vertex angle defect (p. 437) In a convex polyhedron, the vertex angle defect is the positive difference between the sum of the measures of the *face angles* (the angle formed by two edges of a polyhedral angle) at that vertex and 360°.

Defecto del ángulo de un vértice (pág. 437) En un polígono convexo, la diferencia positiva entre la suma de las medidas de los *ángulos de cara* (el ángulo formado por dos aristas de un ángulo poliedro) en ese vértice y 360°.

Vertex coloring *see* **color a graph**

Coloración de vértices *véase* **colorear un grafo**

Vertex-edge graph (graph) (p. 241) A diagram consisting of a set of points (called *vertices*) along with segments or arcs (called *edges*) joining some of the points.

Grafo (pág. 241) Diagrama que consta de un conjunto de puntos (los vértices) junto con segmentos o arcos (las aristas) que unen algunos de los puntos.

Vertical angles (p. 376) Two angles whose sides form two pairs of opposite rays.

Ángulos opuestos por el vértice (pág. 376) Dos ángulos cuyos lados forman dos pares de rayos opuestos.

Venn diagram (p. 540) A diagram involving circles that depicts collections of objects and the relationships between them.

Diagrama de Venn (pág. 540) Diagrama que consta de círculos que exhiben colecciones de objetos y las relaciones entre ellos.

W

With replacement (p. 562) Selecting a sample from a set so that each selection is replaced before selecting the next; thus, each member of the set can be selected more than once.

Con devolución (pág. 562) Selección de una muestra de un conjunto de modo que cada selección se devuelve antes de elegir la siguiente; así, cada miembro del conjunto puede escogerse más de una vez.

Without replacement (p. 562) Selecting a sample from a set so that each selection is not replaced before selecting the next; each member of the set cannot be selected more than once.

Sin devolución (pág. 562) Selección de una muestra de un conjunto de modo que cada selección no se devuelve antes de elegir la siguiente; así, cada miembro del conjunto no puede escogerse más de una vez.

X

x-intercept of a graph (p. 477) The point(s) where the graph intersects the x-axis.

Intersección x de una gráfica (pág. 477) El punto o los puntos en que una gráfica interseca el eje x.

Y

y-intercept of a graph (p. 155) The point(s) where the graph intersects the y-axis.

Intersección y de una gráfica (pág. 155) El punto o los puntos en que una gráfica interseca el eje y.

Math Online A mathematics multilingual glossary is available at www.glencoe.com/apps/eGlossary612/grade.php. The Glossary includes the following languages:

Arabic	English	Korean	Tagalog
Bengali	Haitian Creole	Russian	Urdu
Cantonese	Hmong	Spanish	Vietnamese

INDEX OF MATHEMATICAL TOPICS

INDEX OF MATHEMATICAL TOPICS